D1281402

CHEMICAL KINETICS

CHEMICAL KINETICS

KEITH J. LAIDLER

Chairman of the Department of Chemistry,
Vice-Dean of the Faculty of Science,
The University of Ottawa

Second Edition

NEW YORK ST. LOUIS SAN FRANCISCO TORONTO LONDON SYDNEY

McGraw-Hill Book Company

CHEMICAL KINETICS

Library of Congress Catalog Card Number 64-66203

35831

5 6 7 8 9 - MP - 9

To HENRY EYRING
CYRIL NORMAN HINSHELWOOD
and to the memory of
EDGAR WILLIAM RICHARD STEACIE
with respect and gratitude

PREFACE

THE OBJECT of this book is the presentation, within a reasonably small compass, of the more important facts and theories relating to the rates with which chemical reactions occur. The book is aimed at university students who have already studied physical chemistry and who are familiar with the basic principles of thermodynamics and kinetics.

The first edition of the book was written with the assumption that the reader would have had no previous knowledge of kinetics. Experience has shown, however, that practically all the users of the book had already studied the basic principles of that subject. As a result in the present edition, which has been completely rewritten, I have omitted elementary derivations, such as those of the kinetic laws, and merely presented the results in summary form; this has had the result of keeping the book at a reasonably small size. Readers who desire additional background material can readily find it in the various textbooks of physical chemistry.

A word about the problems included at the end of some of the chapters is in order. They have been designed in such a manner as to cover the main points made in the various chapters, and a student who works all or many of the problems will achieve a sound understanding of most of the fundamental principles of chemical kinetics. Some of the problems require a considerable amount of time for their solution, and these have been marked with a star.

I wish to thank Dr. S. Glasstone, who made valuable suggestions about the general arrangement of the first edition of the book and read and commented on early drafts of much of the material. Dr. E. K. Gill has also helped greatly in connection with Chap. 6, particularly in preparing an outline of the section on reactions in the solid state; also Dr. J. T. Edward has provided valuable advice regarding hydrolytic reactions. I am also grateful to Drs. Margaret H. Back and Eileen Ramsden who have read the manuscript of the present edition and have contributed to its improvement by their constructive suggestions; they have helped considerably with the correcting of proof, as have Mr. J. S. Muirhead-Gould and Mr. Leon Loucks. Professor Peter E. Yankwich made many valuable comments on the manuscript; these led to a number of changes, one of which was the addition of the section on the more advanced theoretical treatments (pages 98 to 110). I am indebted to Mrs. Claire Goodchild, Mrs. Vivianne Brazeau, and Miss Judith M. Pyne for typing the manuscript and preparing the name index.

It is a pleasure to dedicate this book to three leading kineticists, in three different countries, with whom I had the privilege of working and who inspired my interest in the subject: Professor Sir Cyril Hinshelwood, Dean Henry Eyring, and the late Dr. E. W. R. Steacie.

KEITH J. LAIDLER

CONTENTS

PREFACE vii

1. *The Analysis of Kinetic Results* 1
2. *The Measurement of Reaction Rates* 31
3. *The Mechanisms of Elementary Processes* 49
4. *Elementary Gas-phase Reactions* 115
5. *Elementary Reactions in Solution* 198
6. *Reactions on Surfaces and in the Solid State* 256
7. *Complex Reactions* 321
8. *Some Complex Reactions in the Gas Phase* 356
9. *Homogeneous Catalysis* 434
10. *Some Reaction Mechanisms in Solution* 488

Appendix **A** *Determination of Rate Constants by Numerical Methods* 538

Appendix **B** *Numerical Values* 541

BIBLIOGRAPHY 542

NAME INDEX 549

SUBJECT INDEX 561

chapter

The Analysis of Kinetic Results 1

THE SUBJECT OF chemical kinetics is concerned with the quantitative study of the rates of chemical reactions and of the factors upon which they depend. Not much work was done in this field until comparatively recently. In a few investigations carried out at the beginning of the last century rates of reactions were determined, but little attempt was made to interpret them in terms of exact laws. Among these early studies may be mentioned the experiments of Kirchhoff[1] on the hydrolysis of starch by dilute acids, and Thénard's investigation[2] of the rate of decomposition of hydrogen peroxide in the presence of alkalis.

The first kinetic measurements, however, may be said to have been those of Wilhelmy,[3] who in 1850 measured the rate of inversion of sucrose and investigated the influence of concentration upon the rate. The important result at which he arrived was that the rate of reaction at any instant was proportional to the concentration of sucrose remaining

[1] J. Kirchhoff, *Schweigger's J.*, **4**, 108 (1912).

[2] J. Thénard, *Ann. chim. et phys.*, (2) **9**, 314 (1818).

[3] L. Wilhelmy, *Pogg. Ann.*, **81**, 413, 499 (1850).

at that time. A similar conclusion was reached in 1862 by Berthelot and St. Gilles;[1] their investigations concerned mainly the equilibrium between ethanol, acetic acid, ethyl acetate, and water, but they obtained some data on the rate of combination of the acid and alcohol and concluded that the rate in this case was proportional to the product of the two concentrations.

In the years 1865 to 1867 Harcourt and Esson[2] published the results of their investigations on the reaction between potassium permanganate and oxalic acid. Very detailed experimental studies of the rate of this reaction and of its variation with the concentrations of the reacting substances were carried out by Harcourt, and the results were analyzed mathematically by Esson in the manner in which this is still frequently done today. Expressions for the amount of reaction as a function of time were worked out for a "first-order" reaction, in which the rate is proportional to the concentration of only one reacting substance, and for a "second-order" reaction, in which the rate is proportional to the product of two concentrations. The theory of successive first-order reactions, in which the product of one reaction undergoes a second reaction, was also developed.

At about the same time it was pointed out by Guldberg and Waage[3] that the laws of chemical equilibrium can be derived from the kinetic laws by assuming that at equilibrium the rates of forward and reverse reactions are the same. This concept has been of great value, although it should be noted that the kinetic laws employed in the derivations of the equilibrium laws frequently do not correspond to reality; for a rigorous treatment of equilibrium it is necessary to avoid the use of kinetic laws and to use thermodynamics or statistical mechanics.

In 1889 an important advance was made by Arrhenius,[4] who explained the large increases in velocity that are very often brought about by a rise in temperature. This development will be discussed in some detail in Chap. 3; most of the remainder of the present chapter will be devoted to the laws expressing the influence of concentration on the rate, and to showing how reaction rates are obtained from experimental data.

THE SCOPE OF CHEMICAL KINETICS

The subject of chemical kinetics covers a very wide range. It includes empirical studies of the effects of concentration, temperature,

[1] M. Berthelot and L. P. St. Gilles, *Ann. chim. et phys.*, (3) **63**, 385 (1862); Berthelot, *ibid.*, **66**, 110 (1862), and several later papers.

[2] A. V. Harcourt and W. Esson, *Proc. Roy. Soc.* (*London*), **14**, 470 (1865); *Phil. Trans.*, **156**, 193 (1866); **157**, 117 (1867).

[3] C. M. Guldberg and P. Waage, "Études sur les affinités chimiques," Brøgger and Christie, Christiania (Oslo), 1867.

[4] S. Arrhenius, *Z. Physik. Chem.*, **4**, 226 (1889).

and hydrostatic pressure on reactions of various types; such studies may be of practical value in connection with technical processes. Of more fundamental interest are those kinetic studies of chemical reactions in which the objective is to arrive at a reaction mechanism. Of even more basic significance are studies whose object is to throw light on the general principles of reactivity.

There are many different types of chemical reactions, and a wide variety of experimental techniques may be used to investigate them. A considerable amount of effort, for example, has been devoted to the study of the kinetics and mechanisms of reactions in the gas phase; in many ways these investigations provide the most satisfactory way of testing the basic theories of reactions. Perhaps the greatest volume of kinetic work has been done on reactions in the liquid phase, especially since it is these that are of greatest interest to the organic and inorganic chemist. A limited amount of work has also been done on reactions in the solid phase. Reactions at gas-solid interfaces have received more attention.

It is natural that the majority of kinetic investigations should have been concerned with reactions whose rates can be measured easily, without the use of special methods. During recent years, partly as a result of the development of new electronic techniques, a good deal of effort has been devoted to the study of reactions that are difficult to study by conventional methods. Examples are reactions occurring at very high hydrostatic pressures or temperatures, and reactions occurring at very high velocities. Some of the investigations of these types are considered later in this book.

In general, there are two kinds of problems that arise in any kinetic investigation. The first is the establishment of the relationships between the velocity and various factors, such as concentration, temperature, and pressure. When this has been done, one can consider the second problem, which is to arrive at an interpretation of the empirical laws in terms of a reaction mechanism. In doing so, one frequently obtains valuable help from studies of a nonkinetic nature.

The remainder of this chapter is concerned mainly with some of the empirical kinetic laws, and with the interpretation of rate data in the light of these laws. Only a brief account is given here, since it is assumed that the reader has already studied something of this subject in the textbooks of physical chemistry.[1]

KINETIC LAWS

Rate of Reaction. The rate of a reaction, which may also be called its velocity or speed, may be expressed in terms of the concentration of

[1] See, for example, W. J. Moore, "Physical Chemistry," 3d ed., chap. 8, Prentice-Hall, Inc., Englewood Cliffs, N.J., 1962; K. J. Laidler, "Reaction Kinetics," vol. 1, "Homogeneous Gas Reactions," chap. 1, Pergamon Press, Oxford, 1963.

any reactant or of any product of the reaction. It may be expressed as the rate of decrease of the concentration of a reactant, or as the rate of increase of a product of the reaction. Thus if the substance chosen is a reactant which has a concentration c at any time t, the rate is $-dc/dt$, while the rate with reference to a product having a concentration x at time t is dx/dt. According to this formulation the rate must have the units of concentration divided by time. The time is almost invariably expressed in seconds, while concentrations are frequently given as moles per liter or as moles per cubic centimeter; in such a case the units for the rate are moles liter^{-1} sec^{-1} or moles cc^{-1} sec^{-1}. For gas reactions, pressure units are sometimes used in place of concentrations, so that the rate could be expressed in atmospheres per second.

Order of Reaction. The manner in which the rate of a reaction varies with the concentrations of the reacting substances can sometimes be indicated by stating the order of the reaction. In general, if it is found experimentally that the rate of a reaction is proportional to the αth power of the concentration of one of the reactants A, to the βth power of the concentration of B, etc.,

$$\text{Rate} = kc_A^{\alpha}\, c_B^{\beta} \cdots \tag{1}$$

the overall order of the reaction is simply

$$n = \alpha + \beta + \cdots \tag{2}$$

Such a reaction would be said to be of the αth order with respect to A, the βth order with respect to B, etc.

It is important to realize that by no means all reactions can be spoken of as having an order. In many cases the relationship between the rate and the concentrations is much more complicated than that represented by Eq. (1); frequently, for example, concentrations appear also in the denominator of the rate expression. Such complex rate equations arise as a result of the fact that the reaction occurs by a complex mechanism, involving a number of steps.

There is not necessarily a simple relationship between the stoichiometric coefficient in a reaction and the order; a reaction whose stoichiometric equation is, for example, of the form

$$A + 2B = 3C$$

is not necessarily first order in A and second order in B. If a reaction occurs in a single step, there is generally such a relationship, but a complex mechanism may lead to a completely different type of kinetic law. The order of a reaction is strictly an experimental quantity, and merely provides information about the way in which the rate depends on concentration. The term "order" should not be used to mean the same as "molecularity," which represents a conclusion concerning the number of molecules entering into an elementary reaction.

Rate Constant. The rate constant, which is also known as the specific rate and as the rate coefficient, is the value of the constant k appearing in the above equations; it is numerically equal to the reaction rate when the reactants are present at unit concentrations. In general, its units depend upon those employed for the concentration; thus, if moles per liter are used, the rate constant has the units (moles per liter)/(sec) (moles per liter)^n, where n, equal to $\alpha + \beta + \cdots$, is the overall order; this reduces to moles^{1-n} liters^{n-1} sec^{-1}. For a second-order reaction ($n = 2$) this becomes liters mole^{-1} sec^{-1}, whereas for a reaction of the first order ($n = 1$) the units are sec^{-1}; i.e., the concentration units are irrelevant. For a reaction of the three-halves order the units are liters$^{1/2}$ mole$^{-1/2}$ sec^{-1}.

The rate of a reaction and the rate constant both depend in general on the way they are defined. Suppose, for example, that a reaction obeys a stoichiometric equation of the type

$$A + 2B = 3C$$

The rate of formation of C, in moles per liter per second, is clearly three times the rate of disappearance of A, which is one-half the rate of disappearance of B:

$$\frac{d[C]}{dt} = -3\frac{d[A]}{dt} = -\frac{3}{2}\frac{d[B]}{dt} \tag{3}$$

If the reaction is first order in A, the rate constant for the appearance of C, defined by

$$\frac{d[C]}{dt} = k_C[A] \tag{4}$$

is similarly three times the rate constant for the disappearance of A, which is defined by

$$-\frac{d[A]}{dt} = k_A[A] \tag{5}$$

In stating a rate or a rate constant it is therefore sometimes necessary to express not only the concentration units but also the substance to which the rate refers.

THE METHOD OF INTEGRATION

Change of Concentration with Time. In a kinetic study of a reaction there is no way of measuring the rate directly in a simple manner; normally the concentration of a reactant or product is determined at various times. If this concentration is plotted against the time, a

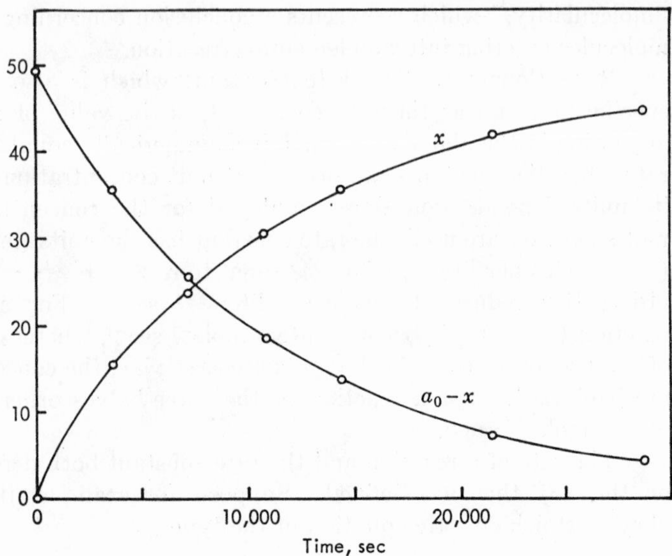

Fig. 1. Plots of the concentrations of product x and of reactant $a_0 - x$ against time, for the conversion of N-chloroacetanilide into p-chloroacetanilide. [*Data of J. J. Blanksma, Rec. Trav. Chim.*, **21**, 366 (1902); **22**, 290 (1903).]

smooth curve should be obtained, as is seen in the example given in Fig. 1, and the slope of the curve at any time, $-dc/dt$ or dx/dt, is the rate of the reaction at that time. In particular, the initial slope, at $t = 0$, gives the rate of the reaction corresponding to the concentrations with which the experiment was started. This method of determining the initial slope, known as the differential method, has in fact been employed in certain investigations and is sometimes the only reliable procedure (cf. p. 18). Another method which is very commonly employed involves using expressions relating the concentration to the time for reactions of various orders, and fitting the appropriate expression to the experimental data; this is known as the *method of integration*. Suppose, for example, that a reaction is of the nth order and involves substances that initially have a concentration a_0; such a reaction may be represented schematically as

$$nA \rightarrow P$$

If x is the amount of A per unit volume that has disappeared in time t, the amount of A remaining is $a_0 - x$; the rate of disappearance of A is thus

$$-\frac{d(a_0 - x)}{dt} = \frac{dx}{dt} = k(a_0 - x)^n \tag{6}$$

This must be integrated subject to the boundary condition that $x = 0$ when $t = 0$. If n is other than unity, the solution is

$$k = \frac{1}{t(n-1)}\left[\frac{1}{(a_0 - x)^{n-1}} - \frac{1}{a_0^{n-1}}\right] \tag{7}$$

If n is unity, the solution is

$$k = \frac{1}{t}\ln\frac{a_0}{a_0 - x} \tag{8}$$

The integrated rate equations for various values of n are given in Table 1.

Table 1 SUMMARY OF RATE EQUATIONS

Order	Rate equation: Differential form	Rate equation: Integrated form	Units of the rate constant
0	$\frac{dx}{dt} = k$	$k = \frac{x}{t}$	Moles liter^{-1} sec^{-1}
½	$\frac{dx}{dt} = k(a_0 - x)^{1/2}$	$k = \frac{2}{t}[a_0^{1/2} - (a_0 - x)^{1/2}]$	Moles$^{1/2}$ liter$^{-1/2}$ sec^{-1}
1	$\frac{dx}{dt} = k(a_0 - x)$	$k = \frac{1}{t}\ln\frac{a_0}{a_0 - x}$	Sec^{-1}
3/2	$\frac{dx}{dt} = k(a_0 - x)^{3/2}$	$k = \frac{2}{t}\left[\frac{1}{(a_0 - x)^{1/2}} - \frac{1}{a_0^{1/2}}\right]$	Liters$^{1/2}$ mole$^{-1/2}$ sec^{-1}
2	$\frac{dx}{dt} = k(a_0 - x)^2$	$k = \frac{1}{t}\frac{x}{a_0(a_0 - x)}$	Liters mole^{-1} sec^{-1}
3	$\frac{dx}{dt} = k(a_0 - x)^3$	$k = \frac{1}{2t}\frac{2a_0x - x^2}{a_0^2(a_0 - x)^2}$	Liters^2 mole^{-2} sec^{-1}

In each case the rate constant k refers to the disappearance of reactant.

In the last column is given an appropriate set of units for the rate constant.

Other situations are also possible. Suppose, for example, that the stoichiometry of a reaction is such that one molecule of A reacts with one molecule of B, and that the reaction is first order in both A and B. Then if a_0 and b_0 are the initial concentrations of A and B, and if x is the amount of A that has disappeared per unit volume in time t (and is therefore also the amount of B that has disappeared in time t), the amounts of A and B remaining at time t are $a_0 - x$ and $b_0 - x$, respectively. The rate of disappearance of A, equal to the rate of disappearance of B, is therefore given by

$$\frac{dx}{dt} = k(a_0 - x)(b_0 - x) \tag{9}$$

If a_0 and b_0 are different, the solution of this is

$$k = \frac{1}{t(a_0 - b_0)} \ln \frac{b_0(a_0 - x)}{a_0(b_0 - x)} \tag{10}$$

If a_0 and b_0 are identical, Eq. (6) can be written as

$$\frac{dx}{dt} = k(a_0 - x)^2 \tag{11}$$

the solution of which is given in Table 1.

Another possibility is that the stoichiometric equation is of the type

$$A + 2B = \text{products}$$

but that the reaction is nevertheless first order in both A and B. If a_0 and b_0 are the initial amounts of A and B (per unit volume), and x is the amount of A that has disappeared in time t, the equation for the rate of disappearance of A is

$$\frac{dx}{dt} = k(a_0 - x)(b_0 - 2x) \tag{12}$$

The solution of this is

$$k = \frac{1}{t(b_0 - 2a_0)} \ln \frac{a_0(b_0 - 2x)}{b_0(a_0 - 2x)} \tag{13}$$

Other cases of the same kind can easily be worked out; some of the solutions are given in Table 2.

In some cases a reaction proceeds simultaneously in two or more ways. Some examples are given in Table 3.

The general procedures that have just been described constitute the basis of the method of integration, which is probably the most widely used method of analyzing kinetic data. In using this method one starts with a differential rate equation that is believed to apply to the reaction under consideration. The integrated equation is then applied to the kinetic data, by graphical means or otherwise. If there is a good fit, one concludes that the equation chosen is applicable, and one can obtain the rate constant. If the fit is not good, the procedure is repeated with another equation until the fit is satisfactory. The method evidently involves a certain amount of trial and error, but is nevertheless very valuable, especially when there is previous evidence as to the reaction order, and when there are no complications in the mechanism.

Table 2 RATE EQUATIONS

For these cases the initial concentrations are not equal, and the rate equation does not necessarily agree with the stoichiometry. Initial concentrations are written as a_0, b_0, c_0, and x_0 and concentrations at time t as x, a, b, and c.

Stoichiometric equation	Rate equation	Integrated equation
$A = X + \cdots$	$\frac{dx}{dt} = kax = k(a_0 - x)(x + x_0)$ (autocatalysis)	$\frac{1}{a_0 - x_0} \ln \frac{a_0(x_0 + x)}{x_0(a_0 - x)} = kt$
$A + B = X + \cdots$	$\frac{dx}{dt} = kab = k(a_0 - x)(b_0 - x)$	$\frac{1}{b_0 - a_0} \ln \frac{a_0(b_0 - x)}{b_0(a_0 - x)} = kt$
$A + 2B = X + \cdots$	$\frac{dx}{dt} = kab = k(a_0 - x)(b_0 - 2x)$	$\frac{1}{b_0 - 2a_0} \ln \frac{a_0(b_0 - 2x)}{b_0(a_0 - 2x)} = kt$
$A + B + C = X + \cdots$	$\frac{dx}{dt} = kabc = k(a_0 - x)(b_0 - x)(c_0 - x)$	$\frac{1}{(a_0 - b_0)(b_0 - c_0)(c_0 - a_0)} \ln \left(\frac{a}{a_0}\right)^{b_0 - c_0} \left(\frac{b}{b_0}\right)^{c_0 - a_0} \left(\frac{c}{c_0}\right)^{a_0 - b_0} = kt$
$2A + B = X + \cdots$	$\frac{dx}{dt} = ka^2b = k(a_0 - 2x)^2(b_0 - x)$	$\frac{1}{2b_0 + a_0} \left(\frac{1}{a} - \frac{1}{a_0}\right) + \frac{1}{(2b_0 - a_0)^2} \ln \frac{b_0 a}{a_0 b} = kt$

Table 3 SOLUTIONS FOR SIMULTANEOUS REACTION

System	Rate equation	Integrated equation
$A \rightarrow X$	$\frac{dx}{dt} = k_1(a_0 - x) + k_2(a_0 - x)^2$ (simultaneous first- and second-order reaction)	$\ln \frac{k_1a_0 + k_2a_0(a_0 - x)}{(k_1 + k_2a_0)(a_0 - x)} = kt$
$\left.\begin{matrix} A \rightarrow X_1 \\ A \rightarrow X_2 \\ A \rightarrow X_3 \end{matrix}\right\}$	$\begin{Bmatrix} \frac{dx_1}{dt} = k_1(a_0 - x_1 - x_2 - x_3) \\ \frac{dx_2}{dt} = k_2(a_0 - x_1 - x_2 - x_3) \\ \frac{dx_3}{dt} = k_3(a_0 - x_1 - x_2 - x_3) \end{Bmatrix}$	$x_1 = \frac{k_1a_0}{k_1 + k_2 + k_3}[1 - e^{-(k_1+k_2+k_3)t}]$ etc.
$\left.\begin{matrix} A \rightarrow X + \cdots \\ A + B \rightarrow X + \cdots \end{matrix}\right\}$	$\frac{dx}{dt} = k_1(a_0 - x) + k_2(a_0 - x)(b_0 - x)$	$\frac{1}{(k_1/k_2) + b_0 - a_0} \ln \frac{a_0[(k_1/k_2) + b_0 - x]}{[(k_1/k_2) + b_0 - x][a_0 - x]} = k_2t$

Some of the procedures that may be used for applying the integrated equations to the experimental data[1] may now be considered very briefly.

Tabular Method. A very simple procedure is to calculate the rate constant, using expressions such as those listed in Tables 1 and 2, at various stages of the reaction. An example of the use of this method, for a second-order reaction, is shown in Table 4. The fact that the figures in the right-hand column of this table are reasonably constant, and show no detectable drift, is an indication that the reaction is indeed of the second order.

Table 4 ALKALINE HYDROLYSIS OF ETHYL NITROBENZOATE

$a_0 = 0.05$ mole per liter

t, sec	Percentage change	$k \times 10^2$, liters mole^{-1} sec^{-1}
120	32.95	8.19
180	41.75	7.96
240	48.8	7.94
330	58.05	8.39
530	69.0	8.40
600	70.35	7.92

A disadvantage of the method is that drifts may escape detection. It is essential that the reaction be studied over a wide time interval; if all the measurements are made, for example, when the reaction is between 20 and 25 percent complete, drifts will probably not be observed, even if the wrong order has been assumed.

Graphical Methods. A somewhat more satisfactory procedure consists in putting the integrated rate equation into such a form that a linear plot can be obtained. In a first-order reaction, for example, for which the integrated equation is given in Table 1, a plot of $\ln [a_0/(a_0 - x)]$ against t will give a straight line which passes through the origin and has a slope of k. A deviation from linearity indicates that the reaction is not of the first order. Alternatively one can plot $\ln (a_0 - x)$ against t, in which case the slope is $-k$.

Similar linear plots can readily be obtained for reactions of other orders. For a second-order reaction, for example, $x/a_0(a_0 - x)$, or more simply $x/(a_0 - x)$, can be plotted against t.

[1] For a review see W. E. Roseveare, *J. Am. Chem. Soc.*, **53**, 1651 (1931).

In using any of these procedures the method of least squares may be used for obtaining the best value of the slope.

A special type of graphical procedure, involving the use of dimensionless parameters, has been proposed by Powell.[1] If a_0 is the initial concentration of a reactant, and a the concentration after time t, a relative reactant concentration may be defined as

$$\alpha = \frac{a}{a_0} \tag{14}$$

For a reaction of the nth order, involving equal initial concentrations,

$$\frac{1}{n-1}\left[\frac{1}{a^{n-1}} - \frac{1}{a_0^{n-1}}\right] = kt \tag{15}$$

Elimination of a between (14) and (15) gives

$$\frac{1}{(n-1)a_0^{n-1}}\left[\frac{1}{\alpha^{n-1}} - 1\right] = kt \tag{16}$$

If a dimensionless time is defined as

$$\tau = ka_0^{n-1}t \tag{17}$$

Eq. (16) becomes

$$\alpha^{1-n} - 1 = (n-1)\tau \tag{18}$$

This equation is valid for any value of n except unity; for the special case of a first-order reaction the corresponding equation is

$$\ln \alpha = -\tau \tag{19}$$

Equations (18) and (19) do not involve c_0 or k, so that for a reaction of a given order there is a unique relation between α and τ. Plots of α against $\log \tau$ are given in Fig. 2 for various values of n, and such plots may be used to determine the order and the rate constant. The procedure is to plot experimental values of α against $\log t$; $\log \tau$ cannot at first be determined since n and k are unknown. If the reaction has one of the orders shown in Fig. 2, the experimental plot will match one of the theoretical curves as far as shape is concerned, but will be shifted along the $\log t$ axis. The amount of the shift is seen from the definition of τ to be $-\log ka_0^{n-1}$, and since n is now known, k can be determined.

Other graphical methods, applicable to more complex reactions also, will be referred to later.

Half-life Method. In some early investigations orders and rate constants were obtained by determining the half life of the reaction, and finding how it changes with concentration. The half life, or half period, of a reaction is the time that it takes for one-half of the original substance

[1] R. E. Powell, quoted by A. A. Frost and R. G. Pearson, "Kinetics and Mechanism," 2d ed., pp. 14–15, John Wiley & Sons, Inc., New York, 1961.

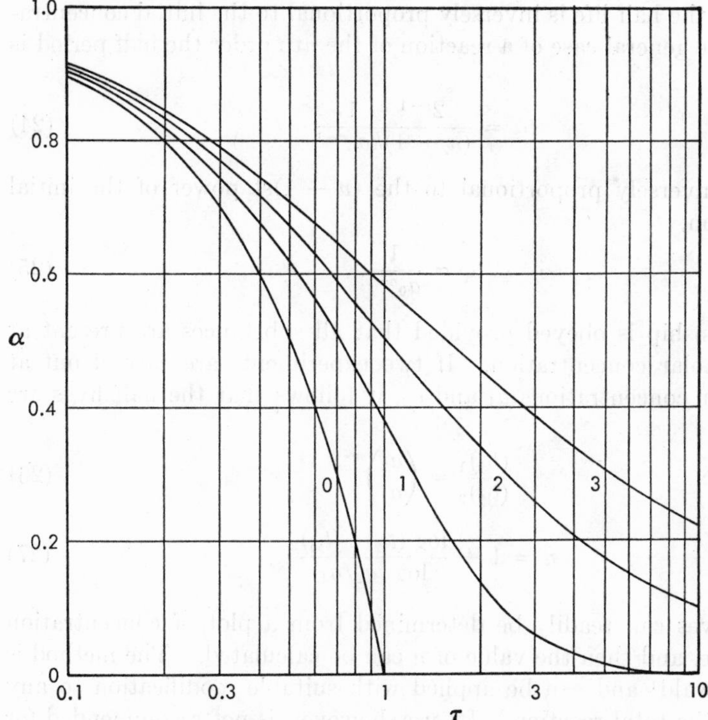

Fig. 2. Plots of α against log τ for reactions of various orders. (*Powell's method, which uses dimensionless parameters.*)

to disappear. Its value is readily calculated for a reaction of a given order in terms of the rate constant k and the initial concentration a_0 by setting x, the amount of substance reacted, equal to $a_0/2$ in the appropriate rate expression. Thus for a first-order reaction the half life is given by

$$k = \frac{1}{t_{1/2}} \ln \frac{a_0}{a_0 - a_0/2} \tag{20}$$

whence

$$t_{1/2} = \frac{1}{k} \ln 2 \tag{21}$$

In this case the half life is seen to be independent of the initial concentration.

For a second-order reaction the half life is given by

$$k = \frac{a_0/2}{t_{1/2} a_0 (a_0 - a_0/2)} \tag{22}$$

whence

$$t_{1/2} = \frac{1}{a_0 k} \tag{23}$$

In this case the half life is inversely proportional to the initial concentration. In the general case of a reaction of the nth order the half period is found to be

$$t_{1/2} = \frac{2^{n-1} - 1}{(n - 1)ka_0^{n-1}} \tag{24}$$

It is thus inversely proportional to the $(n - 1)$st power of the initial concentration,

$$t_{1/2} \propto \frac{1}{a_0^{n-1}} \tag{25}$$

This relationship is obeyed provided that all substances are present at the same molar concentration. If two experiments are carried out at initial molar concentrations a_1 and a_2, it follows that the half lives are related by

$$\frac{(t_{1/2})_1}{(t_{1/2})_2} = \left(\frac{a_2}{a_1}\right)^{n-1} \tag{26}$$

whence

$$n = 1 + \frac{\log (t_{1/2})_1/(t_{1/2})_2}{\log (a_2/a_1)} \tag{27}$$

The half lives can readily be determined from a plot of concentration against time, and then the value of n can be calculated. The method is due to Ostwald[1] and can be applied with suitable modification to any fraction of the total reaction. Its use, however, is not recommended for the accurate determination of rate constants, and may even lead to serious error when complexities arise.

Guggenheim's Method for First-order Reactions. A special method was suggested by Guggenheim[2] for obtaining the rate constant of a first-order reaction in the case that the initial amount of reactant cannot be determined; this situation sometimes arises when a physical method is employed for following the reaction. The procedure is to take a series of readings of the concentration of product x at times t that are spread over an interval which is two or three times the half life of the reaction. A second series of readings x' is also made, each at time $t + t'$, where t' is an exactly constant interval after the time of the corresponding reading x; the period t' must be at least two or three times the half life of the reaction. If a_0 is the (unknown) value of x at infinite time, it follows from the first-order rate equation that, for a given reading,

$$a_0 - x_1 = a_0 \exp [-kt_1] \tag{28}$$

For a reading after the interval t',

$$a_0 - x_1' = a_0 \exp [-k(t_1 + t')] \tag{29}$$

[1] W. Ostwald, *Z. Physik. Chem.*, **2**, 127 (1888).
[2] E. A. Guggenheim, *Phil. Mag.*, **1**, 538 (1926).

Similar equations are true at t_2 and $t_2 + t'$. Subtraction of (29) from (28) gives

$$x_1' - x_1 = a_0 e^{-kt_1}(1 - e^{-kt'}) \tag{30}$$

whence

$$kt_1 + \ln (x_1' - x_1) = \ln [a_0(1 - e^{-kt'})] \tag{31}$$

The right-hand side of this equation is constant, since t' has been chosen as constant; it therefore follows that for each of the corresponding readings (that is, x_1' and x_1, x_2' and x_2, etc.),

$$kt + \ln (x' - x) = \text{const} \tag{32}$$

A plot of $\ln (x' - x)$ against t will therefore give a straight line of slope equal to $-k$.

Extensions of the method to other cases have been suggested by Roseveare[1] and by Sturtevant.[2]

THE DIFFERENTIAL METHOD

In the differential method, which was suggested by van't Hoff,[3] one deals with the actual rates of reactions as determined by measuring the slopes of concentration-time curves. The rate of a reaction may be related to the concentration of a reactant by the equation

$$v = kc^n \tag{33}$$

Taking either common or natural logarithms,

$$\log v = \log k + n \log c \tag{34}$$

If, therefore, the velocity is measured at various values of the reactant concentration, a double-logarithmic plot of the velocity against the concentration may give a straight line. If so, the slope is the order of the reaction with respect to the substance whose concentration is being varied, and the intercept on the $\log v$ axis is equal to $\log k$.

Two different procedures may be employed. In one of them initial rates are measured at various initial concentrations, as shown schematically in Fig. 3. Figure 3*a* shows runs made at various initial concentrations, and tangents drawn at the beginning of each reaction. The negative of the slope of each of these represents the initial rate, corresponding to a particular initial concentration. In Fig. 3*b* the logarithms of these rates are plotted against the logarithms of the corresponding initial con-

[1] Roseveare, *loc. cit.*

[2] J. M. Sturtevant, *J. Am. Chem. Soc.*, **59**, 699 (1937).

[3] J. H. van't Hoff, "Études de dynamique chimique," p. 87, F. Muller and Company, Amsterdam, 1884.

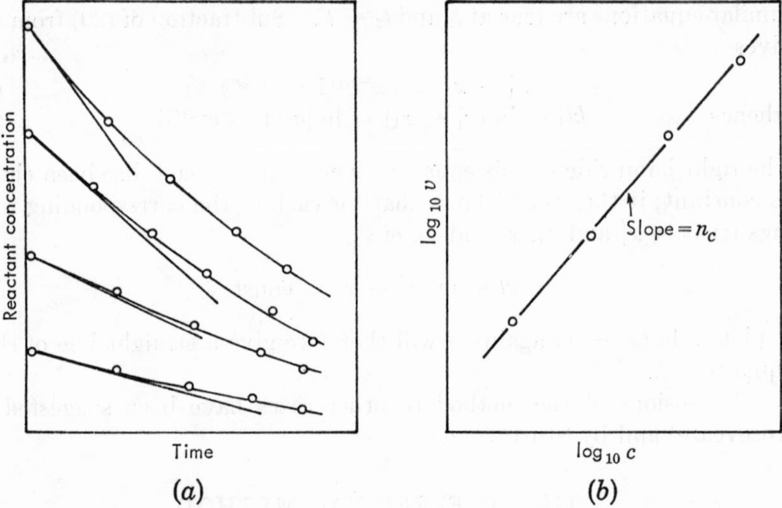

Fig. 3. In the left-hand graph (*a*) concentration is plotted against time for various initial concentrations, and initial slopes are measured. In (*b*) the logarithms of the initial rates are plotted against the logarithms of the corresponding initial concentrations.

centrations. The slope represents the order of reaction n. This procedure of dealing with initial rates avoids possible complications due to interference by products, and leads to an order which corresponds to the simplest type of situation. In view of this Letort[1] has referred to the order determined in this way as the *order with respect to concentration*, or the *true order*. The symbol n_c will be used to denote this order.

The second procedure involves considering a single run, and measuring slopes at various times, corresponding to a number of values of the reactant concentration. This method is illustrated schematically in Fig. 4, and again the logarithms of the rates are plotted against the logarithms of the corresponding reactant concentrations (Fig. 4*b*). The slope is the order; since time is now varying, Letort referred to this order as the *order with respect to time* n_t.

The two orders are not always found to be the same for a given reaction. In the thermal decomposition of acetaldehyde, for example, Letort found that the order with respect to concentration (the true order) is $3/2$, and that the order with respect to time is 2. The fact that the order with respect to time is greater than the order with respect to concentration means that, as the reaction proceeds, the rate falls off more rapidly than it would do if the true order applied to the time course of

[1] M. Letort, Thesis, University of Paris, 1937; *J. Chim. Phys.*, **34**, 206 (1937); *Bull. Soc. Chim. France*, **9**, 1 (1942).

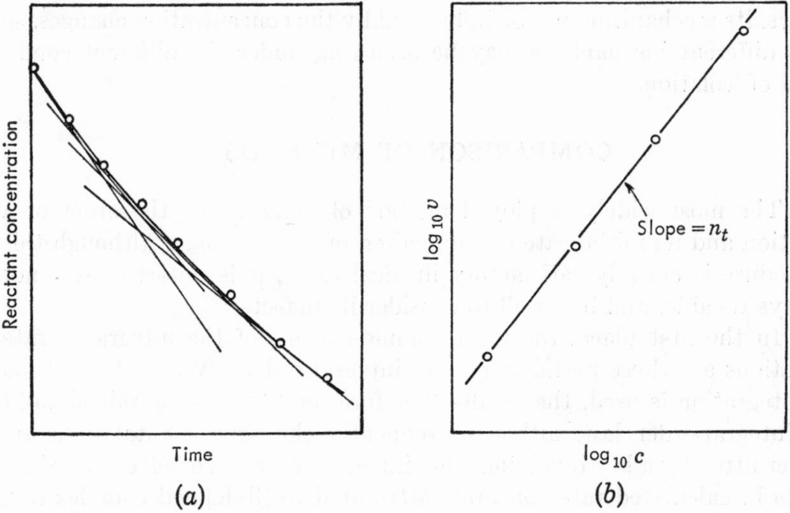

Fig. 4. The left-hand graph (*a*) shows the results of a single run, with slopes indicated at various reactant concentrations. In (*b*) a double logarithmic plot is made of rate against concentration.

the reaction. This abnormally large falling off can only mean that some intermediate in the reaction is acting as an inhibitor. Conversely, if n_t is less than n_c, the rate is falling off less rapidly with time than expected on the basis of the true order. There is therefore some activation by the products of reaction; the reaction is then said to be *autocatalytic.*

THE ISOLATION METHOD

It was pointed out by Harcourt and Esson that if all the reactants except one are present in excess, the apparent order will be the order with respect to the one reactant "isolated," since the concentrations of those in excess will not change very much during the course of reaction. This method was generalized by Ostwald[1] as follows: If a reaction is of the αth order with respect to A, of the βth order with respect to B, and of the γth order with respect to C, and if B and C are in excess of A, the apparent order, determined by any of the methods described above, will correspond to α; β and γ can be determined in a similar way. The method should always be employed in conjunction with other methods of determining the order, however, as in many cases it does not yield reliable results; thus if the reaction under investigation is complex, involving a number of

[1] W. Ostwald, "Lehrbuch der allgemeinen Chemie," vol. 2, part 2, p. 238, Akademische Verlagsgesellschaft, Leipzig, 1902.

stages, its mechanism may be influenced by the concentration changes, so that different mechanisms may be occurring under the different conditions of isolation.

COMPARISON OF METHODS

The most widely employed method of determining the order of a reaction and its initial rate is the method of integration. Although this procedure is entirely satisfactory in ideal cases, it is unfortunately not always reliable, and it is well to consider its defects.

In the first place, the most common forms of the integrated rate equations are those pertaining to an integral order. When the method of integration is used, the results therefore tend to be constrained to fit an integral-order law, although frequently the experimental data are better fitted by a law involving a nonintegral order. Too often are slight drifts in calculated rate constants attributed to ill-defined complexities.

A second and more fundamental objection to the method is that it characterizes a reaction according to the way in which the concentration of a product or a reactant varies with the time, and this may give rise to misleading deductions about the way in which the rate varies with the concentration of reactants.

The most important quantities to be measured are the true order and the initial rate; from them the rate constant can be obtained. Since these quantities are given by the differential method, particularly when the graphical procedure is employed, this must be considered the most reliable method. Its disadvantage is that it involves the measurements of tangents to the concentration-time curves. At first the method of integration and the half-period method should be used only in a subsidiary manner for obtaining information concerning the influence of the products on the rate; however, if it is established that the two orders are the same, it is satisfactory to employ these methods for determining rate constants.

The isolation method of Ostwald has been seen to be applicable in conjunction with any of the other three methods; it is clearly best used with the differential method.

REACTIONS HAVING NO SIMPLE ORDER

There are many reactions which do not admit of the assignment of an order; i.e., their rates are not simple power functions of the concentrations. Such reactions cannot be treated satisfactorily by the method of integration, which may indeed yield quite misleading conclusions. Application of the graphical differential method to such a reaction generally gives a curve instead of a straight line, and the variation of the slope gives an indication of the type of complication that is occurring. The elucidation of the exact kinetic law then requires carefully planned experiments in which the influences of products and reactants are studied systematically.

OPPOSING REACTIONS

One complication that frequently exists, and for which due allowance must be made, is that a reaction may proceed to a state of equilibrium which differs appreciably from completion. The simplest case of this occurs when both forward and reverse reactions are of the first order, so that the situation can be represented as

$$\mathrm{A} \underset{k_{-1}}{\overset{k_1}{\rightleftharpoons}} \mathrm{X}$$

k_1 and k_{-1} being the rate constants in the forward and reverse directions. If the experiment is started using pure A, of concentration a_0, and if after the time t the concentration of X is x, then that of A is $a_0 - x$. The net rate of production of X is then given by

$$\frac{dx}{dt} = k_1(a_0 - x) - k_{-1}x \tag{35}$$

since X is being produced by the forward reaction (first term) and removed by the reverse reaction (second term). If x_e is the concentration of X at equilibrium, when the net rate of reaction is zero,

$$k_1(a_0 - x_e) - k_{-1}x_e = 0 \tag{36}$$

which rearranges to

$$k_{-1} = \frac{k_1(a_0 - x_e)}{x_e} \tag{37}$$

Substitution of this expression in Eq. (35) gives rise to

$$\frac{dx}{dt} = \frac{k_1 a_0}{x_e}(x_e - x) \tag{38}$$

Integration of this equation, using the fact that $x = 0$ when $t = 0$, gives

$$k_1 = \frac{x_e}{a_0 t} \ln \frac{x_e}{x_e - x} \tag{39}$$

If x_e is known, it is therefore possible to calculate k_1 from measurements of x as a function of the time.

For certain purposes it is convenient to have this equation in a different form. Equation (36) rearranges to

$$x_e(k_1 + k_{-1}) = k_1 a_0 \tag{40}$$

whence

$$\frac{x_e}{a_0} = \frac{k_1}{k_1 + k_{-1}} \tag{41}$$

Equation (39) may therefore be written as

$$k_1 = \frac{k_1}{k_1 + k_{-1}} \frac{1}{t} \ln \frac{x_e}{x_e - x} \tag{42}$$

or

$$k_1 + k_{-1} = \frac{1}{t} \ln \frac{x_e}{x_e - x} \tag{43}$$

Comparison of this equation with that for a simple first-order reaction (Table 1) shows that the two are formally analogous, x_e replacing a_0, and $k_1 + k_{-1}$ replacing k.

In the foregoing derivation it has been assumed that the initial concentration of the product X is zero. If this is not the case, and the initial concentrations of A and X are a_0 and x_0, the net rate at time t is given by

$$\frac{dx}{dt} = k_1(a_0 - x) - k_{-1}(x + x_0) \tag{44}$$

By methods similar to those used earlier it can be shown that this equation integrates to

$$k_1 + k_{-1} = \frac{1}{t} \ln \frac{k_1 a_0 - k_{-1} x_0}{k_1 a_0 - k_{-1} x_0 - (k_1 + k_{-1})x} \tag{45}$$

The concentration x_e, at equilibrium, is defined by

$$x_e = \frac{k_1 a_0 - k_{-1} x_0}{k_1 + k_{-1}} \tag{46}$$

Equation (45) reduces to

$$k_1 + k_{-1} = \frac{1}{t} \ln \frac{x_e}{x_e - x} \tag{47}$$

which is the same as Eq. (43).

The application of Eq. (43) may be illustrated with reference to some early data[1] on the conversion of γ-hydroxybutyric acid into its lactone, the initial concentration of the lactone being zero. At equilibrium it was found that $x_e = 13.28$, and values of $k_1 + k_{-1}$ at various times, calculated using Eq. (43), are shown in Table 5; the constancy of the values in the last column indicates that the law is obeyed. Since k_1/k_{-1} can be calculated from the values of a_0 and x_e, the individual constants k_1 and k_{-1} can

[1] P. Henry, *Z. Physik. Chem.*, **10**, 98 (1892).

Table 5 CONVERSION OF γ-HYDROXYBUTYRIC ACID INTO ITS LACTONE

t, sec	x	$x_e - x$	$(k_1 + k_{-1}) \times 10^{-4}$, sec^{-1}
1,260	2.41	10.87	1.59
3,000	4.96	8.32	1.56
6,000	8.11	5.17	1.58
7,200	8.90	4.38	1.56
9,600	10.35	2.93	1.58
13,200	11.55	1.73	1.55

Table 6 RATE EQUATIONS FOR OPPOSING REACTIONS

Stoichiometric equation	Rate equation	Integrated rate equation
$A \rightleftharpoons X$	$\frac{dx}{dt} = k_1(a_0 - x) - k_{-1}x$	$\frac{x_e}{a_0} \ln \frac{x_e}{x_e - x} = k_1 t$
$A \rightleftharpoons X$	$\frac{dx}{dt} = k_1(a_0 - x) - k_{-1}(x + x_0)$	
$2A \rightleftharpoons X$	$\frac{dx}{dt} = k_1(a_0 - x) - k_{-1}\frac{x}{2}$	
$A \rightleftharpoons 2X$	$\frac{dx}{dt} = k_1\left(a_0 - \frac{x}{2}\right) - k_{-1}x$	
$A \rightleftharpoons X + Y$	$\frac{dx}{dt} = k_1(a_0 - x) - k_{-1}x^2$	$\frac{x_e}{(2a_0 - x_e)} \ln \frac{a_0 x_e + x(a_0 - x_e)}{a_0(x_e - x)} = k_1 t$
$A + B \rightleftharpoons X$	$\frac{dx}{dt} = k_1(a_0 - x)^2 - k_{-1}x$	$\frac{x_e}{(a_0^2 - x_e^2)} \ln \frac{x_e(a_0^2 - x x_e)}{a_0^2(x_e - x)} = k_1 t$
$A + B \rightleftharpoons X + Y$	$\frac{dx}{dt} = k_1(a_0 - x)^2 - k_{-1}x^2$	$\frac{x_e}{2a_0(a_0 - x_e)} \ln \frac{x(a_0 - 2x_e) + a_0 x_e}{a_0(x_e - x)} = k_1 t$
$2A \rightleftharpoons X + Y$	$\frac{dx}{dt} = k_1(a_0 - x)^2 - k_{-1}\left(\frac{x}{2}\right)^2$	

be found. Since the procedure involves the method of integration, it is applicable only to reactions proceeding without complexity.

The solutions for this and other cases are given in Table 6. Graphical procedures for analyzing data using these equations can readily be devised.

KINETIC EQUATIONS FOR FLOW SYSTEMS

In kinetic investigations, particularly those concerned with obtaining fundamental information, it is usual to employ a static system; the reactants are introduced into a reaction vessel, and the concentration changes are followed. The equations developed so far in this chapter relate particularly to such static systems. In some cases, however, it is more convenient to allow the reaction mixture to flow through a reaction vessel, which in such cases is usually known as a *reactor*. Such a flow system may be useful, for example, when it is desired to study a reaction at extremely low pressures or concentrations; to obtain enough product it may then be necessary to pass a stream of reactants through the reactor for a considerable time. Flow systems are also useful in studies of very rapid reactions; a convenient technique is then the "stopped-flow" method, in which a rapid flow is suddenly stopped and an analysis immediately made of the change of concentration with time. Some of the experimental procedures for flow systems are described in the next chapter.

Flow systems are of two general types. In the first, there is no stirring in the reactor, and the flow through it is sometimes spoken of as *plug flow*. In the second there is stirring which is sufficiently vigorous to effect complete mixing within the reactor. Intermediate situations are also possible, but are difficult to analyze.

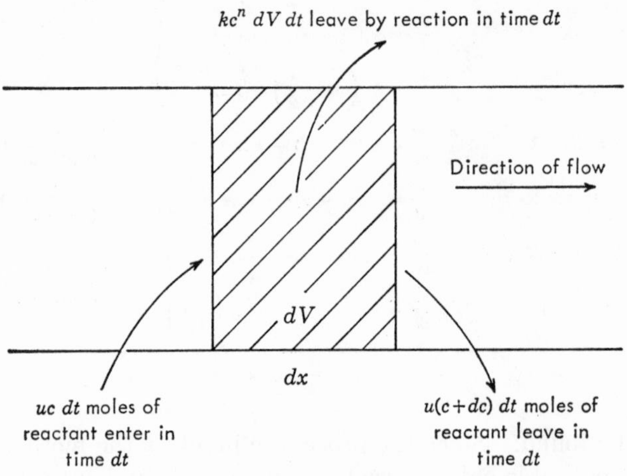

Fig. 5. Schematic diagram showing the processes occurring in plug flow through a reaction vessel.

Plug flow is illustrated schematically in Fig. 5. The reaction mixture is passed through the reactor at a volume rate of flow (expressed, for example, in liters per second) equal to u. Consider an element of volume dV in the reactor, and suppose for simplicity that the reaction rate depends upon the concentration c of a single reactant. For a reaction of the nth order the rate of disappearance of the substance is given by

$$v = -\frac{dc}{dt} = kc^n \tag{48}$$

The rate of disappearance of reactant in a volume dV is therefore $kc^n\,dV$.

After the system has been operating for a sufficient period of time, a steady state is established; this means that there is no change, with time, in the concentration of reactant in the volume element. Three processes contribute to the steady state, as follows:

1. Molecules of reactant enter the slab through the left face, the number of moles entering in time dt being $uc\,dt$.
2. Molecules leave the slab by the right face, the number of moles leaving in time dt being $u(c + dc)\,dt$.
3. Molecules disappear by chemical reaction; for a reaction of the nth order the number of moles $(-dn)$ disappearing in time dt is $kc^n\,dV\,dt$.

The steady-state equation is obtained by equating the rate of entry of reactant into the slab (by process 1) to the sum of the rates of removal (by processes 2 and 3). The result is

$$uc\,dt = u(c + dc)\,dt + kc^n\,dV\,dt \tag{49}$$

or

$$-\frac{dc}{c^n} = \frac{k}{u}\,dV \tag{50}$$

This equation must be integrated over the volume V_0 of the reactor; at the entrance to the reactor $V = 0$ and $c = c_i$ (the initial concentration), while at the exit $V = V_0$ and $c = c_f$ (the final concentration of reactant). Therefore

$$-\int_{c_i}^{c_f}\frac{dc}{c^n} = \frac{k}{u}\int_0^{V_0} dV \tag{51}$$

For the particular case in which $n = 1$, integration gives

$$\ln\frac{c_f}{c_i} = \frac{kV_0}{u} \tag{52}$$

or

$$c_f = c_i e^{-kV_0/u} \tag{53}$$

This equation may be compared with Eq. (8) for a static system, and it is to be noted that the two are equivalent if V_0/u is replaced by t. This quantity V_0/u is known as the *contact time* for the reaction; it is the average time that a molecule takes to pass through the reactor. Equation (53) may be tested by varying V_0/u (by varying either the volume of reactor or the flow rate), just as in a static system the time is varied. Reactions that are too rapid for convenient study in a static system may frequently be studied in a flow system, the contact time being reduced by using a high flow rate and small volume.

The solution of Eq. (51) when n is other than unity is

$$\frac{1}{n-1}\left[\frac{1}{c_f^{n-1}} - \frac{1}{c_i^{n-1}}\right] = \frac{kV_0}{u} \tag{54}$$

This equation is to be compared with Eq. (7) on page 7, with V_0/u equal to t.

In the above derivation the assumption is tacitly made that there is no volume change during the course of reaction; any such change will cause the volume flow rate to vary through the reactor. The inclusion of such volume changes considerably complicates the handling of the rate equations, and will not be considered here; reference may be made to a treatment by Hougen and Watson.[1]

In a stirred-flow reactor, in which the concentrations are maintained constant within the reactor, it is no longer necessary to consider a thin slab, but rather the reactor as a whole. The rate of flow of reactants into the reactor is uc_i, and the rate of flow out is uc_f; the difference between these is the rate of reaction in the reactor, which is vV, where v is the rate per unit volume. Thus

$$uc_i - uc_f = vV \tag{55}$$

or

$$v = \frac{u(c_i - c_f)}{V} \tag{56}$$

The measurement of c_i and c_f at a given flow rate thus allows the reaction rate to be calculated. The order of reaction, and the rate constant, can then be determined by working at different initial concentrations and rates of flow. The theory of stirred-flow reactions has been treated by Denbigh.[2]

RELAXATION THEORY

It will be seen in the next chapter that for the study of fast reactions there have recently been developed methods of an entirely different character from those referred to earlier. These methods are known as *relaxation methods*, since they involve measuring the *relaxation time* of the reaction: this is the time that it takes for a reaction to cover a certain fraction of its path toward equilibrium The methods differ from the conventional static and flow methods, in both of which the technique involves mixing the reactants or bringing them to a suitable temperature. When a relaxation method is used, the reaction is first allowed to go to equilibrium. It is then disturbed in some way, so that it is no longer at

[1] O. A. Hougen and K. M. Watson, "Chemical Process Principles," part 3, p. 834, John Wiley & Sons, Inc., New York, 1947.

[2] K. G. Denbigh, *Trans. Faraday Soc.*, **40**, 352 (1944); *Discussions Faraday Soc.*, **2**, 263 (1947).

equilibrium. The speed with which the system approaches its new equilibrium is then followed, usually using special e'ectronic techniques, and from an analysis of the behavior, rate constants can be determined.

The simplest situation to which this technique could be applied is that of an equilibrium of the type

$$\mathrm{A} \underset{k_{-1}}{\overset{k_1}{\rightleftharpoons}} \mathrm{X}$$

the reactions in both directions being of the first order. Suppose that such a system is allowed to come to equilibrium, and that its temperature is then suddenly altered so that it is no longer at equilibrium. As before, let a_0 be the total concentration of A and X, and x be the concentration of X; that of A is $a_0 - x$. The kinetic equation is thus

$$\frac{dx}{dt} = k_1(a_0 - x) - k_{-1}x \tag{57}$$

At equilibrium

$$k_1(a_0 - x_e) = k_{-1}x_e \tag{58}$$

where x_e is the concentration of X at equilibrium. The deviation from equilibrium, Δx, may be defined as $x - x_e$, and its derivative with time is thus

$$\frac{d\,\Delta x}{dt} = \frac{dx}{dt} = k_1(a_0 - x) - k_{-1}x \tag{59}$$

$$= k_1a_0 - (k_1 + k_{-1})x \tag{60}$$

$$= k_1a_0 - (k_1 + k_{-1})(x_e + \Delta x) \tag{61}$$

From (58) and (61) it follows that

$$\frac{d\,\Delta x}{dt} = -(k_1 + k_{-1})\,\Delta x \tag{62}$$

The quantity Δx thus varies with time in the same manner as does the concentration of a reactant in a first-order reaction. Integration of Eq. (62), subject to the boundary condition that $\Delta x = (\Delta x)_0$ when $t = 0$, leads to

$$\ln\frac{(\Delta x)_0}{\Delta x} = (k_1 + k_{-1})t \tag{63}$$

It is convenient to define the relaxation time t^* as the time corresponding to

$$\frac{(\Delta x)_0}{\Delta x} = e \tag{64}$$

or to

$$\ln\frac{(\Delta x)_0}{\Delta x} = 1 \tag{65}$$

The relaxation time is thus the time at which the distance from equilibrium is $1/e$ of the initial distance. From Eq. (63) it is seen that

$$t^* = \frac{1}{k_1 + k_{-1}} \tag{66}$$

If, therefore, t^* is determined experimentally for such a system, $k_1 + k_{-1}$ is known. However the ratio k_1/k_{-1} can also be determined, and hence the individual rate constants k_1 and k_{-1} can be calculated.

The theoretical treatment varies slightly with the reaction orders. Consider, for example, the case of a reaction of the type

$$\mathrm{A} + \mathrm{B} \underset{k_{-1}}{\overset{k_1}{\rightleftharpoons}} \mathrm{X}$$

which is second order from left to right and first order from right to left. If the concentrations of A, B, and X at any time are $a_0 - x$, $b_0 - x$, and x,

$$\frac{dx}{dt} = k_1(a_0 - x)(b_0 - x) - k_{-1}x \tag{67}$$

As before, Δx is defined as $x - x_e$, and

$$\frac{d\,\Delta x}{dt} = \frac{dx}{dt} = k_1a_0b_0 - (k_1a_0 + k_1b_0 + k_{-1})x + k_1x^2 \tag{68}$$

At equilibrium

$$k_1(a_0 - x_e)(b_0 - x_e) = k_{-1}x_e \tag{69}$$

or

$$k_1a_0b_0 - (k_1a_0 + k_1b_0 + k_{-1})x_e + k_1x_e^2 = 0 \tag{70}$$

Subtraction of (70) from (68) gives

$$\frac{d\,\Delta x}{dt} = -(k_1a_0 + k_1b_0 + k_{-1})(x - x_e) + k_1(x^2 - x_e^2) \tag{71}$$

$$= -(k_1a_0 + k_1b_0 + k_{-1})\Delta x + k_1(x + x_e)\,\Delta x \tag{72}$$

If the displacement from equilibrium is only slight, $x \approx x_e$, so that $x + x_e$ may be written as $2x_e$; Eq. (72) thus becomes

$$\frac{d\,\Delta x}{dt} = -(k_1a_0 + k_1b_0 + k_{-1} - 2k_1x_e)\,\Delta x \tag{73}$$

Table 7 Relaxation times for simple equilibria

System	Rate equation	Relaxation time
$A \underset{k_{-1}}{\overset{k_1}{\rightleftharpoons}} X$	$\frac{dx}{dt} = k_1(a_0 - x) - k_{-1}x$	$\frac{1}{k_1 + k_{-1}}$
$2A \underset{k_{-1}}{\overset{k_1}{\rightleftharpoons}} X$	$\frac{dx}{dt} = k_1(a - 2x)^2 - k_{-1}x$	$\frac{1}{4k_1a_e + k_{-1}}$
$A + B \underset{k_{-1}}{\overset{k_1}{\rightleftharpoons}} X$	$\frac{dx}{dt} = k_1(a_0 - x)(b_0 - x) - k_1x$	$\frac{1}{k_1(a_e + b_e) + k_{-1}}$
$A \underset{k_{-1}}{\overset{k_1}{\rightleftharpoons}} X + Y$	$\frac{dx}{dt} = k_1(a_0 - x) - k_{-1}(x_0 + x)(y_0 + x)$	$\frac{1}{k_1 + k_{-1}(x_e + y_e)}$
$A \underset{k_{-1}}{\overset{k_1}{\rightleftharpoons}} 2X$	$\frac{dx}{dt} = k_1\left(a - \frac{x}{2}\right) - k_{-1}x^2$	$\frac{1}{\frac{1}{2}k_1 + 2k_{-1}x_e}$
$A + B \underset{k_{-1}}{\overset{k_1}{\rightleftharpoons}} X + Y$	$\frac{dx}{dt} = k_1(a_0 - x)(b_0 - x) - k_{-1}(x_0 + x)(y_0 + x)$	$\frac{1}{k_1(a_e + b_e) + k_{-1}(x_e + y_e)}$

In each case the rate constants k_1 and k_{-1} refer to the rate of increase or decrease of the concentration of a substance on the right-hand side of the equation.

Integration gives

$$\ln \frac{(\Delta x)_0}{\Delta x} = (k_1 a_0 + k_1 b_0 + k_{-1} - 2k_1 x_e)t \tag{74}$$

and the relaxation time, defined as before, is

$$t^* = \frac{1}{k_1 a_0 + k_1 b_0 + k_{-1} - 2k_1 x_e} \tag{75}$$

$$= \frac{1}{k_1(a_e + b_e) + k_{-1}} \tag{76}$$

where a_e and b_e, equal to $a_0 - x_e$ and $b_0 - x_e$, are the equilibrium concentrations of A and B. The constants k_1 and k_{-1} can now be separated by measuring t^* at various values of $a_e + b_e$; in addition one may make use of the fact that k_1/k_{-1} is the equilibrium constant.

These two examples will serve to explain the procedure used to obtain an expression for the relaxation time for a given reaction type. Some expressions for relaxation times are given in Table 7.

PROBLEMS

1. (a) The rate constant of a first-order reaction is 2.5×10^{-6} sec^{-1}, and the initial concentration is 0.1 mole per liter. What is the initial rate in moles liter^{-1} sec^{-1}, in moles cc^{-1} sec^{-1}, and in moles cc^{-1} min^{-1}?
(b) The initial rate of a second-order reaction is 5.0×10^{-7} mole liter^{-1} sec^{-1}, and the initial concentrations of the two reacting substances are 0.2 mole per liter. What is the rate constant in liters mole^{-1} sec^{-1}, in cc mole^{-1} min^{-1}, and in cc molecule^{-1} sec^{-1}?

2. A first-order reaction is 40 percent complete at the end of 50 min; what is the value of the rate constant in sec^{-1}? In how many minutes will the reaction be 80 percent complete?

3. The three-halves-order decomposition of a gas, initially present at 1 atm pressure, is 60 percent complete in one hour; what is the value of the rate constant?

4. The half period for the decomposition of radium is 1,590 years; calculate the rate constant in sec^{-1}. In how many years will three-quarters of a given amount of radium have disappeared?

5. Obtain an expression for the average life period for an aggregate of molecules undergoing first-order decomposition, in terms of the rate constant k.

6. A second-order reaction involving reactants initially present at 0.1 mole per liter is found to be 20 percent complete in 40 min. Calculate (**a**) the rate constant, (**b**) the half period, and (**c**) the time it would take for the reaction to be 20 percent complete if the initial concentrations were 0.01 mole per liter.

7. The following values were given by Letort[1] for the rate of decomposition of acetaldehyde corresponding to various degrees of decomposition:

Percent decomposed	*Rate of decomposition, mm Hg per min*
0	8.53
5	7.49
10	6.74
15	5.90
20	5.14
25	4.69
30	4.31
35	3.75
40	3.11
45	2.67
50	2.29

Plot log v against log (percent acetaldehyde present), and thus determine the order of the reaction with respect to time. This is an illustration of the use of van't Hoff's differential method.

8. The following results have been obtained for the reaction between triethylamine and methyl iodide in nitrobenzene solution, both substances being present in initial concentrations of 0.02 mole per liter:

Time, sec	*Percent reacted*
325	31.4
1,295	64.9
1,530	68.8
1,975	73.7

Calculate the second-order rate constant, using the method of integration.

9. The following results were obtained in a study of the enzymatic oxidation of lactic acid, of initial concentration a_0 equal to 0.320 mole per liter:

[1] Letort, thesis, University of Paris, 1937.

Time, min	$x \times 10^3$ *moles per liter*
5	2.55
8	4.12
10	5.11
13	6.71
16	8.16

Calculate the first-order rate constant corresponding to each time.

Plot log $(a_0 - x)$ against t, and determine k from the slope of the line.

10. Surface-catalyzed reactions that are inhibited by products sometimes obey the rate equation

$$\frac{dx}{dt} = \frac{k(a_0 - x)}{1 + bx}$$

where a_0 is the initial concentration of reactant and $a_0 - x$ the amount after time t; k and b are constants. Integrate the equation and suggest a graphical method of testing it.

chapter

The Measurement of Reaction Rates 2

IN THIS CHAPTER some of the experimental procedures used in the study of reaction kinetics will be described. No attempt at completeness is made; only a brief account will be given of the main methods.

REACTIONS IN SOLUTION

Reactions in solution will be considered first, since the methods of measuring their rates are frequently more straightforward than those used in the investigation of gas-phase reactions. The rate of a reaction is defined as the rate of disappearance of a reactant or the rate of appearance of a product, and in the investigation of reactions in solution the most common procedure involves chemical analysis for one of these species at various stages during the course of reaction, the time corresponding to each analysis being determined accurately.

Since the rates of reactions are very sensitive to the temperature, it is necessary for the reaction to be carried out in a system that is carefully maintained at constant temperature. For work between 0 and 60°C water baths may be used; for temperatures above the temperature of the room, electric heat is usually employed, the heat being automatically cut off when the temperature reaches the desired degree, by means of a mercury thermoregulator and a relay system. For lower temperatures the bath may be cooled by a refrigeration coil, thermostatic control being effected in the same way as above. At temperatures above 60°C evaporation of the water may be prevented by placing a layer of oil on the surface, or alternatively a bath of pure oil may be used. For temperatures above the boiling point of water a convenient method of achieving a constant-temperature system involves the use of a liquid which boils at the desired temperature; this can be continuously refluxed in a suitably constructed vessel to which is attached a manostat to maintain a constant pressure, and hence a constant boiling temperature.

If the reaction occurs very slowly at room temperature, it is satisfactory to use tubes containing aliquot amounts of the reacting substances present in the solvent; the tubes are then sealed (to prevent evaporation of the solvent and the reactants and products) and placed in the bath, the time of insertion being noted. A correction to this time should be made to allow for the fact that the system takes an appreciable time to attain the temperature of the bath; this correction may be determined directly by measuring the rate of heating of the system. A number of tubes are placed in each bath, and after various intervals of time are removed rapidly and cooled in order to inhibit the progress of the reaction, and the contents are analyzed for a reactant, a product, or both. In some cases the reaction can also be stopped by chemical means; if, for example, the reaction involves hydrogen ions, but does not occur in alkaline solution, the addition of alkali is an effective means of "quenching" the reaction.

If the reaction occurs at an appreciable rate at room temperature, the method is a little different and may be illustrated with reference to a reaction involving two substances. Solutions of each are prepared, and a sample of each solution is placed in the thermostat. After the solutions have attained the temperature of the bath, an aliquot portion of one is placed in a flask or tube, and an aliquot portion of the other solution added rapidly, the time corresponding to one-half addition being noted. This mixture can be prepared in such an amount that quantities may be removed after various times and analyzed, or alternatively a number of equivalent mixtures can be made and analyzed after various times. For reactions of this type "quenching" may be effected by cooling to a lower temperature; alternatively, chemical methods of stopping the reaction may be employed.

In addition to methods involving chemical analysis after various times, physical methods of following a chemical change may be used in certain cases. If the reaction involves a change in the total volume of the solution, the progress of the reaction may be followed by a dilatometric method; such a procedure has been used to study the mutarotation of glucose.[1] Since this reaction involves a change in optical rotation, polarimetric methods have also been used in studying it.

The reaction between an alkyl iodide and a tertiary amine will be taken to illustrate the kinetic study of a reaction by chemical methods. This type of reaction was the subject of some classical investigations by Menschutkin[2] in 1890. One of the reactions studied was that between triethylamine and ethyl iodide, tetraethylammonium iodide being formed,

$$N(C_2H_5)_3 + C_2H_5I \rightarrow N(C_2H_5)_4I$$

This reaction was studied by Menschutkin in a large number of different solvents, but at one temperature only, 100°C.

The experimental procedure was extremely simple. A solution was prepared containing the base and the iodide in equimolecular proportions (reaction being very slow at ordinary temperatures), and aliquot portions of the solution were introduced into small glass tubes, which were then sealed. The tubes were placed in a temperature-controlled bath at 100°, and the time was noted. After various intervals of time the tubes were removed and cooled in ice water so as to reduce rapidly the rate of reaction to a negligible figure, and the contents were analyzed. The analytical method employed depended on the fact that the product of the reaction contains iodine in the ionized form, so that it can be estimated by titration. The tubes were broken and the contents introduced into a flask containing a small amount of water, under which conditions the iodide ions pass almost completely into the aqueous phase; the free base was then neutralized with dilute nitric acid, and the solution titrated with silver nitrate solution in the presence of a few drops of potassium chromate solution (Volhard's method).

GAS REACTIONS[3]

A common method for investigating the rate of a reaction involving gases is to introduce the reactants into a bulb maintained at the desired temperature, and to make determinations of the composition after various intervals of time; this is known as the static method. The determination of the composition of the gas may be carried out either directly, i.e., by chemical analysis, or indirectly. The most widely used indirect method of measuring the rate of a reaction involves the measurement of the pressure of the system. It is applicable to reactions in which the total

[1] J. N. Brønsted and E. A. Guggenheim, *J. Am. Chem. Soc.*, **49**, 2554 (1927).

[2] N. Menschutkin, *Z. Physik. Chem.*, **5**, 589 (1890); **6**, 41 (1890).

[3] For a detailed account see H. W. Melville and B. G. Gowenlock, "Experimental Methods in Gas Reactions," Macmillan & Co., Ltd., London, 1964.

number of molecules, and hence the total pressure, changes; it can also be used for reactions not involving such a change but in which one of the products can be removed by condensation or absorption, so effecting a decrease in total pressure. The pressure measurements can be made while the reaction is in progress by having a pressure-measuring device connected to the reaction vessel; liquid manometers containing mercury, oil, water, or other liquids can be used in certain cases, as can gauges of the mechanical type. A device for obtaining a continuous pressure-time record is shown in Fig. 6. Certain modifications of this general scheme

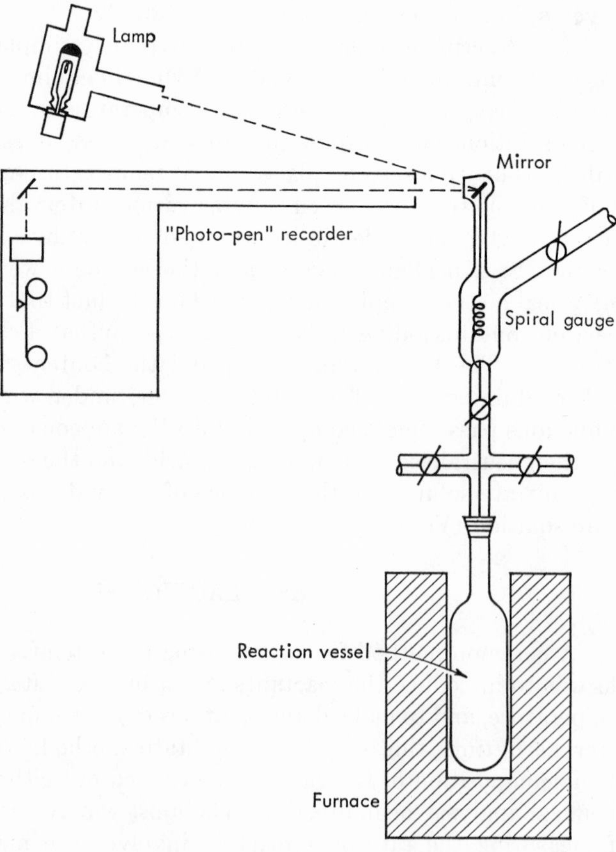

Fig. 6. Apparatus for obtaining a continuous pressure-time record. [*K. J. Laidler and B. W. Wojciechowski, Proc. Roy. Soc.* (*London*), **A259,** 257 (1960).] A quartz spiral gauge is used to measure pressure, and a small mirror is attached to the gauge. The reflected light from a lamp passes into a "photo-pen" recorder, which gives a record of displacement against time.

have been used; e.g., the reaction may be stopped after various intervals of time by cooling the reaction system with liquid air (which may also condense out certain products), and the total pressure may be measured, after which the system may be heated to the required temperature and the reaction allowed to continue.

In a number of reactions, particularly those in which complicated changes take place, the total pressure does not provide reliable information about the course of the change, and conclusions drawn on the basis of such measurements are consequently in error. In many cases intermediate products are formed in measurable amounts and disappear. In all such cases extensive analyses are necessary in addition to manometric measurements.

Other Methods of Following Reactions. The rate of a reaction can also be determined by removing samples at various times and carrying out a chemical analysis. Such a procedure is a good deal more laborious than the manometric method, but some analyses should always be carried out in order for the course of the reaction to be properly established. Frequently one carries out a group of analyses in order to relate the concentration changes to the pressure changes, after using a manometric technique.

The classical methods of chemical analysis are seldom used today, being much more tedious than gas-chromatographic or mass-spectrometric techniques. In the study of a hydrocarbon decomposition, for example, it is very difficult to distinguish between various hydrocarbons by chemical analysis, but this is readily done by gas chromatography. Mass spectrometry is used in particular when it is desired to distinguish between isotopic species, but is also frequently used for ordinary chemical analysis.

Gas reactions are sometimes followed by observing the light absorption, at a suitable wavelength, of some reactant or product. Sometimes this is done in the reaction vessel itself; otherwise samples are withdrawn at various times. Occasionally gas reactions have been studied by following, using an interferometer, the refractive index. If radiation is emitted in a reaction, the measurement of its wavelength and intensity may be used for following the rate.

The Reaction Vessel. The vessel in which a chemical reaction in the gas phase is investigated is most frequently constructed of glass; for low-temperature work Pyrex glass may be satisfactory, but at higher temperatures quartz must be used. One advantage of glass is that it is not attacked by most of the common gases, hydrogen fluoride being an important exception. A further advantage is that most substances other than glass allow reactions to occur on their surfaces, i.e., exert a catalytic effect, so that the observed rate does not correspond to reaction in the gas phase; this behavior is also shown with glass but not quite so extensively as with other substances. Glass is also suitable for certain investigations in which it is desired to irradiate the reactants, as it is transparent over a considerable range of wavelength. It absorbs light of wavelength below about 3,500 A, however, and so for work in the ultraviolet, quartz is usually used.

Surface Catalysis. A reaction involving a gas or a mixture of gases may occur homogeneously, i.e., entirely in the gas phase, or heterogeneously, i.e., on a surface, and in a number of instances a reaction may occur partly in the gas phase and partly on the surface. Whether it is desired to measure the rate of the homogeneous or the heterogeneous change, it is clearly necessary to know what fraction of the reaction goes by each mechanism. If the homogeneous reaction is under investigation, the greatest accuracy in its measurement will be achieved if the proportion of the reaction occurring on the surface is negligible, in which case the overall rate can be identified with that of the homogeneous change; this condition is most often realized, as has been seen, with glass vessels.

The best way to determine the fraction of the reaction that is taking place on the surface is to vary the surface-volume ratio of the vessel. The rate and the rate constant of a homogeneous reaction are independent of the volume of the vessel and of the area and nature of the surface; the rate of a surface reaction, on the other hand, is proportional to the area of the surface and depends upon its nature. If a reaction is proceeding partly in the gas phase, the proportion of the surface reaction is increased by increasing the surface-volume ratio, and the overall rate will increase. The ratio can be varied by changing the size or shape of the vessel, but the extent of the alteration that can conveniently be effected in this way is limited to a factor of 10 or so. A more effective method is to pack the reaction vessel with tubes or irregular pieces of material made of the same material as the vessel; in this way the surface is increased considerably and by an amount that can be determined accurately. If there is a change in rate, the amount of reaction occurring on the surface of the unpacked vessel can readily be calculated.

In some cases packing the reaction vessel brings about a decrease in the reaction rate. When this occurs, it can be concluded that the reaction is complex in character and that recombination of atoms or free radicals is occurring at the surface. The influence of the surface on reactions of this type is discussed in more detail later.

If it is desired to investigate the rate of a reaction on a surface, it is preferable to employ a reaction vessel which does not catalyze the reaction, and to introduce the catalyst into it. If the reaction does not occur in the absence of the catalyst, the rate in its presence is clearly that of the surface-catalyzed reaction; otherwise allowance has to be made for the homogeneous reaction. Since the rate of a surface-catalyzed reaction is usually proportional to the surface area of the catalyst, it is important, in a fundamental investigation of the kinetics, for the surface area to be known accurately.

Photochemical Reactions.[1] Special techniques are required for the study of reactions which depend upon the absorption of radiation. Various sources of light are employed, of which mercury lamps are used most frequently; these emit a number of intense lines between 1,860 and 5,688 A. A number of different types of lamp are in use, some operating at low and others at high pressures. For work in the ultraviolet the lamp must be constructed of quartz, and the reaction vessel must be of quartz or at least contain a quartz window. It is necessary to use radiation within a very narrow range of wavelengths, and for this purpose monochromators or suitable filters must be used.

The general arrangement of the apparatus in a photochemical investigation is illustrated in Fig. 7. The light from a suitable source is

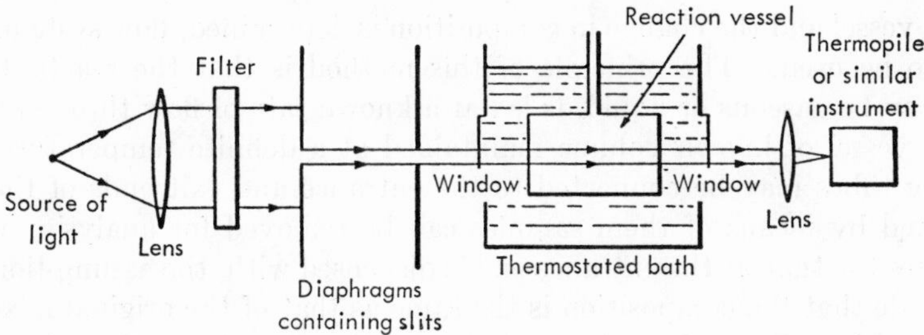

Fig. 7. General arrangement of apparatus in a photochemical investigation.

made monochromatic by passage through a filter. By means of slits it is passed as a parallel beam through the reaction vessel, which must be suitably thermostated, and then passes through a lens which focuses it upon an actinometer, which may be a thermopile, a photoelectric cell, or a chemical actinometer, for measurement of its final intensity. Many modifications of this arrangement are possible; sometimes the lamp is specially constructed so as to surround the reaction vessel. The progress of a photochemical reaction may be followed by any of the methods used for thermal reactions.

Since the rate of a photochemical reaction depends upon the intensity of the light absorbed, it is necessary to measure the intensity of the light passing through the reaction system in the absence of the reacting substances, and that passing through when the reaction is actually occurring; the difference is the intensity absorbed by the reaction system. Various

[1] Cf. W. A. Noyes and P. A. Leighton, "The Photochemistry of Gases," Reinhold Publishing Corporation, New York, 1941.

methods of measuring the radiation intensity are available, of which the most common are chemical actinometers, which depend on the measurement of the amount of the chemical reaction brought about by the light passing into them. The uranyl oxalate actinometer is an example of this type: a weighed quantity of a solution of uranyl oxalate is placed in a suitable cell and exposed to the radiation for a known period of time. Radiation of wavelengths between 2,000 and 4,500 A induces decomposition to carbon monoxide, carbon dioxide, and formic acid, and the amount of oxalate remaining at the end of the period is determined by titration with acid permanganate. Chemical actinometers of this type ultimately have to be calibrated against more absolute standards, such as a thermopile.

REACTIONS IN FLOW SYSTEMS[1]

In addition to the static method, in which the gases are confined in a reaction vessel and the change in composition is determined, flow systems may also be used. The principle of this method is that the reactant, which may be gaseous or liquid, is led at a known rate of flow through a reaction vessel of known volume maintained at a definite temperature. Sampling tubes may be connected to the entrance and exit ends of the vessel, and by means of them samples can be removed for analysis; in some cases the tube at the entrance end is dispensed with, the assumption being made that the composition is the same as that of the original mixture passed in. From the volume of the reaction vessel and the rate of flow, it is possible to calculate the mean time spent by the reaction mixture in the vessel, and the difference between the compositions at the entrance and the exit represents the amount of reaction that has occurred in this time; this divided by the time of contact is therefore the rate. The order of the reaction can be determined by varying the rate of flow through the chamber and the concentrations of the entering gases or solutions. The elementary theory of flow systems has been given in Chap. 1.

One source of error in this method arises from the fact that it is impossible to define exactly the effective chamber volume; at each end of the vessel the temperature varies from the furnace temperature to room temperature, and some kind of mean volume has to be estimated. This error is sometimes reduced by the use of a preheater through which the reactants are passed immediately before entering the reaction chamber and which brings them to the temperature of the chamber. In this case it is necessary for the initial sampling tube to be inserted between the preheater and the reaction chamber, since some reaction occurs in the

[1] Cf. O. A. Hougen and K. M. Watson, "Chemical Process Principles," John Wiley & Sons, Inc., New York, 1947.

preheater. The error at the exit end of the chamber can be reduced by connecting the sampling tube to the chamber inside the furnace. If these modifications are employed, the effective volume of the chamber is clearly that between the two sampling tubes.

For accurate work other refinements of the flow method must be applied; these will be mentioned only briefly. If a gas reaction is accompanied by a volume change, the mean rate of flow through the reaction system will differ somewhat from its value before the gas is admitted to the vessel, and the time of contact must be corrected to take account of this. This correction is particularly important if an appreciable fraction of the total reaction takes place in the reaction system, but it may be neglected if the amount of reaction is only slight. In certain systems the gas does not flow smoothly through the vessel, and an allowance has to be made for the amount of diffusion that is occurring.

THE STUDY OF FAST REACTIONS[1]

The experimental techniques that have been considered are directly applicable to reactions that are not too rapid, and that have half lives of at least several minutes. Some reactions occur much more rapidly, and for them special techniques must be employed. There are two main reasons why conventional techniques are not directly applicable to very rapid reactions:

1. Reaction cannot be initiated within a period of time that is negligible compared with the half life. Reactions must be started either by mixing two or more reactants, or by raising the temperature of the reaction system. When the usual techniques are employed, there may be a considerable uncertainty (usually of at least a few seconds) in the time at which the reaction starts. If the reaction is rapid, this uncertainty cannot be neglected in comparison with the times measured in the kinetic experiment, and a serious error is therefore introduced.
2. The time that it takes to make a measurement during the kinetic investigation may not be negligible in comparison with the duration of the experiment; this clearly introduces an error into the rate constant.

Even if half lives are a matter of several minutes, the error when conventional methods are used is quite considerable. If a reaction has a half life of a few seconds or less, such methods are completely useless.

Flow Systems. The first difficulty referred to above is often overcome by studying the reaction in a flow system rather than in a static system. Such techniques have been employed for both gas reactions and reactions in the liquid phase. The first use of a flow technique in a

[1] See *Discussions Faraday Soc.*, **17** (1954); F. J. W. Roughton and B. Chance, in "Rates and Mechanisms of Reactions," chap. 10 (Eds. S. L. Friess and A. Weissberger), Interscience Publishers, New York, 1953; *Z. Elektrochem.*, **64** (1960).

kinetic investigation appears to have been that of Raschig,[1] who in 1905 studied the rapid reaction between nitric oxide and oxygen by forcing the two gases through a mixing chamber into a reaction vessel. A number of such vessels were used, of different volumes, and the reaction mixture was passed into a solution which stopped the reaction. The extent of reaction was determined by chemical analysis of this solution. By varying flow rates and the volume of the reaction vessel, the residence time could be varied from 0.025 to 25 sec.

In 1923 Hartridge and Roughton[2] developed a valuable technique for the study of rapid reactions in solution, and applied it in particular to biological processes. Their method allowed them to study reactions with half lives ranging from 10 down to 0.001 sec. A more recent piece of apparatus of the same kind, built by Caldin and Trowse,[3] is shown schematically in Fig 8. The principle of the method is that the two

[1] F. Raschig, *Z. Angew. Chem.*, **18**, 281 (1905).

[2] H. Hartridge and F. J. W. Roughton, *Proc. Roy. Soc.* (*London*), **A104**, 376 (1923); cf. F. J. W. Roughton and B. Chance, *Z. Elektrochem.*, **64**, 3 (1960).

[3] E. F. Caldin and F. W. Trowse, *Discussions Faraday Soc.*, **17**, 133 (1954).

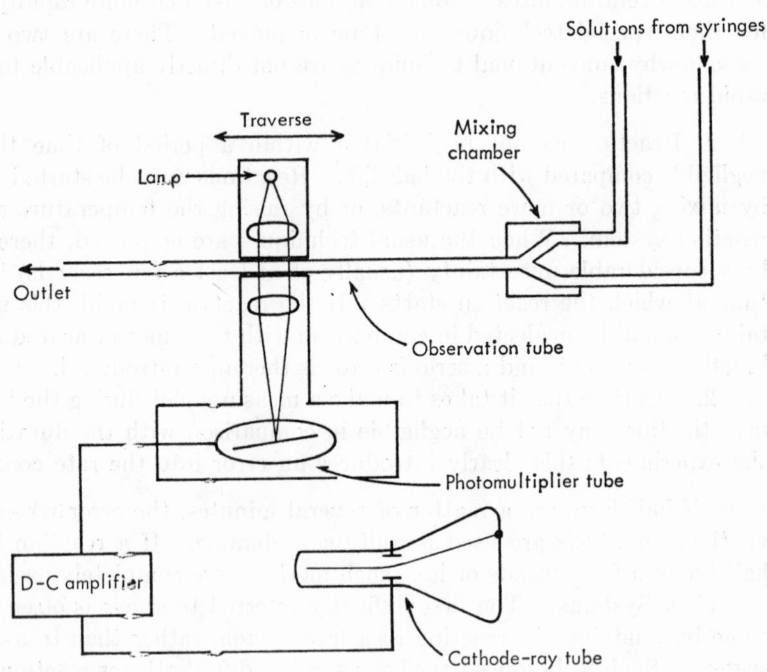

Fig. 8. Schematic diagram of apparatus for the study of fast reactions in solution, using a flow system. [*After Caldin and Trowse, Discussions Faraday Soc.*, **17**, 133 (1954).]

solutions that are to react together are placed in separate containers and driven through a special mixing chamber into an observation tube. At various points along the observation tube the composition of the solution is determined by optical, thermal, or other methods. The average time during which reaction has proceeded before an element of volume has reached a distance d along the reaction tube is $d/\dot{x}$, where $\dot{x}$ is the linear velocity; by the making of measurements at various distances a concentration-time curve can be obtained, and from this the rate constant can be determined. Alternatively, the measurements can be made at a fixed distance, and the velocity of flow varied. A technique for varying the flow velocity by discrete steps was developed by Milliken,[1] while Chance[2] employed a procedure by which the flow was accelerated (the *accelerated-flow* method), and the concentration at a given position recorded continuously. With all these techniques much slower reactions can be studied by interposing dead spaces between the mixing chamber and the observation point; in this way it is possible to bridge the gap between the high-speed techniques, which are normally concerned with half lives of up to a second, and the conventional techniques which deal with half lives of several minutes and more.

One valuable procedure that embodies some of the best features of both the static and the flow systems is the *stopped-flow* technique, which was first used for reactions in solution by Chance.[2] The type of apparatus employed is shown schematically in Fig. 9. Two solutions are forced through jets into a mixing chamber, which is so designed that mixing is extremely rapid; chambers have been designed in such a way that mixing occurs within 10^{-3} sec. From the mixing chamber the solution passes at once into the reaction vessel; sometimes the mixing chamber and reaction vessel are one and the same. The flow is stopped suddenly, and measurements are made, usually spectrophotometrically, of concentration as a function of time; since the reactions are rapid, the spectrophotometric reading must be recorded continuously, using either a high-speed recorder or an oscilloscope, the trace of which is photographed.

The main advantages of the stopped-flow technique over continuous-flow methods are:

1. The method is not affected by the rate and character of the flow, provided that the mixing is satisfactory.

2. A permanent record can be obtained of the progress of the reaction, covering as wide a range as is desired.

3. The volumes of reagents used are smaller; this is particularly important when it is desired to work with substance such as enzymes that are difficult to obtain in large quantities.

[1] G. A. Milliken, *Proc. Roy. Soc.* (*London*), **A155**, 277 (1936).

[2] B. Chance, *J. Franklin Inst.*, **229**, 455, 613, 737 (1940).

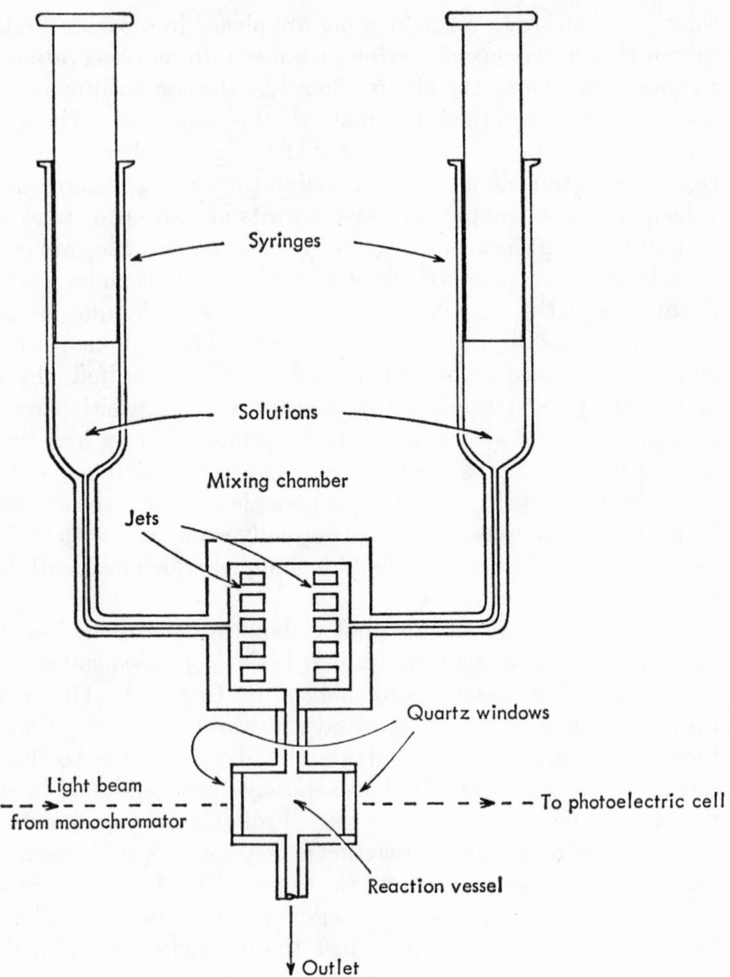

Fig. 9. The stopped-flow technique.

The disadvantages of the method are that it is less sensitive than the continuous-flow method, and that there are fewer convenient methods of observation.

Following Chance's early work, the stopped-flow technique has been used by a number of workers on reaction in solution,[1] particularly for enzyme reactions. The method has also occasionally been used for gas

[1] See, for example, H. Dalziel, *Biochem. J.*, **55**, 79, 90 (1953); *Discussions Faraday Soc.*, **17**, 128 (1954); Q. H. Gibson, *J. Physiol.* (*London*), **117**, 49P (1952); *Discussions Faraday Soc.*, **17**, 137 (1954); Q. H. Gibson and F. J. W. Roughton, *Proc. Roy. Soc.* (*London*), **B143**, 310 (1955); H. Gutfreund, *Discussions Faraday Soc.*, **20**, 167 (1955); C. R. Allen, A. J. W. Brook, and E. F. Caldin, *Trans. Faraday Soc.*, **56**, 788 (1960).

reactions. In 1923 Stewart and Edlund[1] used what is essentially the stopped-flow technique to study the reaction between ethylene and bromine vapor. More modern gas-phase techniques of a similar type have been described by Johnston.[2]

Methods of Following Rapid Reactions. The second difficulty referred to above, that measurements of concentration cannot be made sufficiently rapidly, may be overcome by employing techniques that allow certain properties to be measured instantaneously. Such methods must be used in collaboration with methods of rapid recording; pen-and-ink recorders may be employed for moderately rapid reactions, oscilloscopes (the trace being photographed) for more rapid reactions. Probably the most widely used method for following rapid reactions when the stopped-flow technique is used is spectrophotometry. If the products of a reaction absorb differently from the reactants at a particular wavelength, one may pass monochromatic light of this wavelength through the reaction vessel; using a photoelectric device with suitable electronic apparatus, the output can be led to a pen-and-ink recorder on an oscilloscope. Chance[3] has, in numerous publications, described the application of spectrophotometry to the study of enzyme reactions in both continuous-flow and stopped-flow systems; Johnston[4] has developed what is essentially a stopped-flow spectrophotometric apparatus for gas reactions.

Other techniques for following rapid reactions will be mentioned only briefly. Most reactions involve either the liberation or absorption of heat, and may be followed by measuring the temperature rise in the system.[5] When a continuous-flow technique is employed, the products may be passed into a medium (usually a solution) that "quenches" the reaction;[6] chemical procedures, such as titrations, can then be used to determine the extent of reaction. This may be carried out at different residence times, thus allowing the rate constant to be obtained. Interferometry has also been employed in a few instances,[7] as have measurements of conductivity and pH.[8] The method of electron-spin resonance

[1] T. D. Stewart and K. R. Edlund, *J. Am. Chem. Soc.*, **48**, 1014 (1923).

[2] H. S. Johnston, *Discussions Faraday Soc.*, **17**, 14 (1954).

[3] See, for example, Chance, *op. cit.;* Roughton and Chance, in Friess and Weissberger (eds.), *op. cit.*, p. 690; Roughton and Chance, *Z. Elektrochem.*, **64**, 8 (1960).

[4] Johnston, *loc. cit.*

[5] J. B. Bateman and F. J. W. Roughton, *Biochem. J.*, **29**, 2622, 2630 (1935); L. Pearson, B. R. W. Pinsent, and F. J. W. Roughton, *Discussions Faraday Soc.*, **17**, 141 (1954); R. P. Bell and J. C. Clunie, *Proc. Roy. Soc.* (*London*), **A212**, 16 (1952); R. P. Bell, V. Gold, J. Hilton, and M. H. Rand, *Discussions Faraday Soc.*, **17**, 151 (1954); A. Lifshitz and B. Perlmutter-Hayman, *J. Phys. Chem.*, **64**, 1663 (1960).

[6] See, for example, B. R. W. Pinsent, *Discussions Faraday Soc.*, **17**, 140 (1954).

[7] G. M. Burnett, *ibid.*, **17**, 173 (1954).

[8] J. A. Sirs, *Trans. Faraday Soc.*, **54**, 201, 207 (1958); R. H. Prince, *Trans. Faraday Soc.*, **54**, 838 (1958); *J. Chem. Soc.*, 1783 (1959); *Z. Elektrochem.*, **64**, 13 (1960).

has also been applied to reactions occurring in flow systems and involving free radicals as intermediates.[1]

Relaxation Methods. Owing to problems of mixing, flow techniques are not suitable for the study of reactions whose half lives are smaller than about 1 msec. Many reactions of considerable interest occur with higher rates than this, and they must be studied using techniques that avoid the difficulty arising from mixing. One approach to this problem involves the use of what are known as *competition methods;*[2] the reaction is allowed to compete with a physical process (such as diffusion), the rate of which is known. More widely employed are the so-called *relaxation methods;* these involve measuring the relaxation time for a reaction, a quantity that was defined and considered briefly in the last chapter (p. 24). When these methods are used, the reaction is not started by initially mixing the reactants or raising their temperature. Instead, the reaction is first allowed to go to equilibrium, and is then disturbed in some way; its approach to a new equilibrium is then followed using high-speed techniques, and from these measurements the relaxation time of the process can be calculated. The relationship between the relaxation time and the rate constants was considered for simple processes in the last chapter.

In order for the relaxation methods to be used, the perturbation from equilibrium must be accomplished in a time that is much less than the relaxation time; for the fastest reactions that occur it is usually possible to arrange the reaction conditions in such a way that it is satisfactory for the perturbation to take place over a period of 10^{-6} or 10^{-7} sec. A number of experimental techniques have been employed.[3] These include the *pressure-jump* and *temperature-jump* methods, in which pressure and temperature changes are brought about rapidly; the latter may be done using very large currents. These methods are particularly suitable for times that are greater than 10^{-5} sec. For shorter times high electric fields may be used to bring about the perturbation, and ultrasonic vibrations can be used to produce oscillating temperatures. Perturbations may be in the form of step functions, highly damped oscillations, and continuous oscillations. Various techniques may be used for following the response of the system to the perturbation and so obtaining the relaxation time; spectrophotometric methods have frequently been employed.

[1] B. Venkataraman and G. K. Fraenkel, *J. Am. Chem. Soc.*, **77**, 2707 (1955); I. Yamazaki and H. S. Mason, *Biophys. Res. Comm.*, **1**, 336 (1959).

[2] For a review of recent applications of competition methods see M. Eigen and J. S. Johnson, *Ann. Rev. Phys. Chem.*, **11**, 307 (1960).

[3] For reviews see M. Eigen, *Discussions Faraday Soc.*, **24**, 25 (1957); L. de Maeyer, *Z. Elektrochem.*, **64**, 65 (1960); K. Tamm, *Z. Elektrochem.*, **64**, 73 (1960); M. Eigen and K. Kustin, *ICSU Rev.*, **5**, 97 (1963).

Shock Tubes.[1] During recent years a number of investigations of fast gas reactions have been carried out using shock tubes. The principle of the method is that the reaction system is contained in a long metal tube, through which a shock wave is caused to pass. As the shock wave traverses an element of gas, it raises it to a high temperature, and reaction occurs in and behind the shock front. The course of reaction and the temperature are determined by various methods, and in this way knowledge of the kinetics can be obtained. The method has something in common with relaxation techniques, but the system is not usually at equilibrium when the shock wave passes (although it is in certain applica-

[1] For reviews see H. O. Pritchard, *Quart. Rev. (London)*, **14,** 46 (1960); C. J. S. M. Simpson, *Ann. Rept. Chem. Soc.*, **43,** 46 (1961). J. N. Bradley, "Shock Waves in Chemistry and Physics," Methuen, London, 1962; A. G. Gaydon and I. R. Hurle, "The Shock Tube in High-temperature Chemical Physics," Reinhold Publishing Corporation, New York, 1963.

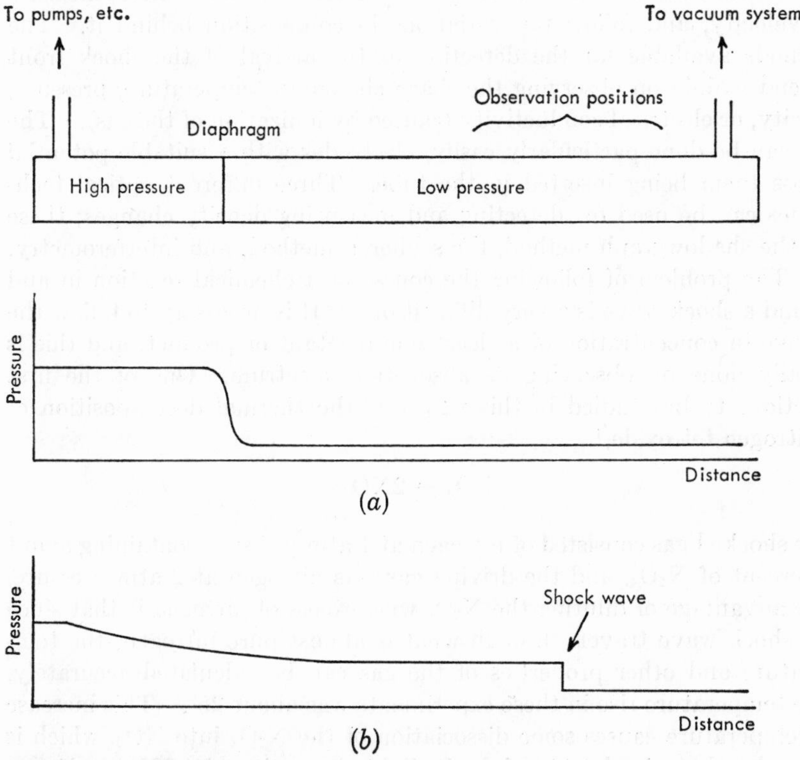

Fig. 10. Schematic diagram of a shock tube, showing the pressure along the tube. In (*a*) the diaphragm has just been ruptured, and no shock wave has developed; in (*b*) a longer time has elapsed, and there is a sharp pressure change.

tions), and the perturbation caused by the shock wave is a much larger one than is usually employed in relaxation methods.

Various designs of shock tubes have been employed. A typical system is shown schematically in Fig. 10; the metal tube might, for example, be 6 in. in diameter and 20 ft long. A thin diaphragm, of metal foil or other material, divides the tube into a high-pressure and a low-pressure end. The reaction system is in the low-pressure compartment, and a gas at high pressure is at the other side of the diaphragm. The diaphragm may be burst either by mechanical means or by increasing the pressure, and a plane shock wave then moves along the tube. At first the boundary at the wave is not a sharp one, because of initial turbulence, but after the wave travels a short distance, it becomes a true shock wave in which there is a very sharp boundary between the high- and low-pressure regions. As the wave passes, the gas is rapidly raised to a very high temperature, and the reaction can be studied by making high-speed observations at various points along the tube.

Various methods have been used to detect the shock wave, measure its velocity, and follow the variations in composition behind it. The methods available for the detection of the arrival of the shock front depend mainly on observing the sharp change in temperature, pressure, density, or electrical conductivity (caused by ionization of the gas). The last can be done particularly easily, electrodes with a suitable potential across them being inserted in the tube. Three different optical techniques can be used for detecting and measuring density changes; these are the shadowgraph method, the schlieren method, and interferometry.

The problem of following the course of a chemical reaction in and behind a shock wave is a very difficult one. It is necessary to follow the change in concentration of at least one reactant or product, and this is usually done by observing its absorption spectrum. One of the first reactions to be studied in this way was the thermal decomposition of dinitrogen tetroxide,[1]

$$N_2O_4 \rightarrow 2NO_2$$

The shocked gas consisted of nitrogen at 1 atm pressure containing about 1 percent of N_2O_4, and the driving gas was nitrogen at 2 atm pressure. The advantage of diluting the N_2O_4 with excess of nitrogen is that since the shock wave travels through what is almost pure nitrogen, the temperature and other properties of the gas can be calculated accurately. The temperature rise in these experiments was about 25°. This increase in temperature causes some dissociation of the N_2O_4 into NO_2, which is colored and can be detected from its light absorption at 4,000 A. It was found necessary to use a beam of 1 mm width, and this limits the resolu-

[1] T. Carrington and N. Davidson, *J. Phys. Chem.*, **57**, 418 (1953).

tion attainable; the shock passes through a 1-mm beam in about 3 μsec, so that anything occurring within this period cannot be measured. In order to reduce the rate of the dissociation, the whole tube was cooled to $-35°C$ before the beginning of each experiment. A considerable number of atom-combination reactions have been studied using similar techniques; some of the results are described in Chap. 4.

An alternative technique for following reactions in a shock tube has been developed by Bradley and Kistiakowsky.[1] This method involves the use of a time-of-flight mass spectrometer to follow concentrations of species produced by the shock wave. This mass spectrometer has a time resolution of about 50 μsec, which is not as good as using optical absorption. The great advantage of the method, however, is that it can follow the concentrations of species such as oxygen atoms, which cannot be followed easily by other means. The method can be used to follow the concentrations of several species simultaneously.

Besides being used to study chemical reactions, the shock-wave technique has been applied to the study of vibrational and rotational energy transfers between gaseous molecules. Some of the results of this type of study are considered later.

Flash Photolysis.[2] Another very important method for studying very fast reactions, both in the gas and the liquid phase, is flash photolysis. This technique as applied in particular to kinetic problems has been largely developed by Norrish and Porter. The procedure is to produce a light flash of very high intensity and very short duration ($\sim 10^{-6}$ sec) in the neighborhood of a reaction vessel. Under suitable conditions this will produce atoms, free radicals, and excited species in the system, and these will undergo further reactions which can be followed by spectroscopic means. The method is very often referred to as *kinetic spectroscopy*.

REACTIONS IN MOLECULAR BEAMS[3]

During recent years several groups of workers have developed techniques for producing monoenergetic beams of molecules. The object of this work is to study chemical reactions under conditions in which there is no maxwellian distribution of velocity; the results of such experiments are in principle easier to interpret in terms of theoretical treatments of reaction rates.

[1] J. N. Bradley and G. B. Kistiakowsky, *J. Chem. Phys.*, **35**, 256 (1961).

[2] For reviews see R. G. W. Norrish and B. A. Thrush, *Quart. Rev.* (*London*), **10**, 149 (1956); R. G. W. Norrish, *Proc. Chem. Soc.*, 247 (1958); *Advancement of Sci.*, **74**, 1 (1961); *Am. Scientist*, **56**, 131 (1962).

[3] For reviews see D. R. Herschbach, *Vortex*, **22**, No. 8 (1961); *Discussions Faraday Soc.*, **33**, 149 (1962).

By allowing two molecular beams to impinge on each other, it has been possible to study the kinetics of bimolecular reactions. Herschbach, Kwei, and Norris,[1] for example, have investigated the reaction

$$K + CH_3I \rightarrow CH_3 + KI$$

while Beck, Greene, and Ross[2] have studied

$$K + HBr \rightarrow KBr + H$$

Some results obtained using this important new technique are considered in Chap. 4.

SUMMARY OF EXPERIMENTAL PROCEDURES

In Table 8 are listed the most important different types of methods that are used in the study of the kinetics of reactions, with an indication of the range of half lives to which each method applies.

Table 8 SUMMARY OF EXPERIMENTAL METHODS

Method	*Range of half lives, sec*
Conventional	10^{2}–10^{8}†
Flow	10^{-3}–10^{2}
Relaxation	10^{-10}–1
Pressure jump	10^{-6}–1
Temperature jump	10^{-7}–1
Field pulse	10^{-10}–10^{-4}
Shock tubes	10^{-9}–10^{-3}
Kinetic spectroscopy	10^{-15}–10^{-10}

† The upper limit is the order of magnitude of the half life of a research student.

[1] D. R. Herschbach, G. H. Kwei, and J. A. Norris, *J. Chem. Phys.*, **34**, 1842 (1961).
[2] D. Beck, E. F. Greene, and J. Ross, *ibid.*, **37**, 2895 (1962).

chapter

The Mechanisms of Elementary Processes 3

As KNOWLEDGE OF the mechanisms of chemical reactions has advanced, it has become increasingly clear that the formation of the final products from the initial reactants always takes place by one or more relatively simple steps, in each of which the amount of atomic rearrangement is at a minimum. As a result, the number of overall processes that take place in a single stage is quite small. A large fraction of the work now being carried out in the field of chemical kinetics consists of the elucidation of the individual reaction steps by which chemical changes occur, a matter which will be treated in the latter part of this book. The individual steps that take place are generally spoken of as *elementary* processes, and some consideration will be given first to the characteristics and mechanisms of elementary processes. The theoretical work that has been done on these processes will be treated in this chapter. The three chapters following this one are devoted largely to a study of the special features of reactions occurring in the gas phase, in solution, on surfaces, and in the solid state.

MOLECULARITY OF AN ELEMENTARY REACTION

In considering the mechanisms of elementary reactions, an important question concerns the number of reactant molecules which come together in the course of reaction, forming a complex which directly gives rise to the products of reaction; this number is known as the *molecularity* of the reaction. Whereas the order of a reaction is deduced directly from the experimental results, the molecularity can be determined only on the basis of additional arguments, about which there is sometimes some uncertainty.

At first sight it might appear that it would be possible to identify the molecularity of an elementary reaction with its overall order, i.e., the order which is obtained after due regard has been paid to the influence of substances in excess, and of catalysts. Such identification is correct except for unimolecular gas reactions, which are not necessarily of the first order: it will be seen later that they become of the second order at low pressures. If a gas reaction is found to be of the first overall order under any pressure conditions, it may be inferred that it is unimolecular; if it is second order and becomes first order at higher pressures, it is also unimolecular. There is always some doubt about the molecularity of second-order gas reactions which involve only one reacting gas and which remain of the second order at all pressures, as it is always possible that at higher pressures than those investigated they would become of the first order and hence reveal themselves as unimolecular.

In all other cases the molecularity of an elementary reaction may safely be identified with the overall order, the assumption being made that in establishing the overall order the influence of every possible reactant has been investigated.

THE ARRHENIUS LAW

That increasing the temperature frequently causes a marked increase in the rate of reactions has been known for many years; for reactions in solution a useful rough generalization is that the rate is doubled by a rise in temperature of 10°C. It was first found empirically by Hood[1] that the rate constant k of a reaction varies with the absolute temperature T according to a law of the form

$$\log k = B - \frac{A'}{T} \tag{1}$$

where A' and B are constants. In 1884 some theoretical significance to this law was given by van't Hoff,[2] who argued on the basis of the effect of

[1] J. J. Hood, *Phil. Mag.*, **6**, 371 (1878); **20**, 323 (1885).

[2] J. H. van't Hoff, "Etudes de dynamique chimique," F. Muller and Company, Amsterdam, 1884.

temperature on equilibrium constants. This idea was extended by Arrhenius[1] and was successfully applied by him to the data for a number of reactions; on account of his work the law is usually referred to as the *Arrhenius law*.

The arguments of van't Hoff and Arrhenius proceeded as follows. The variation of the equilibrium constant obeys the law

$$\frac{d \ln K_c}{dT} = \frac{\Delta E}{RT^2} \tag{2}$$

where K_c is the equilibrium constant expressed in terms of concentrations, and ΔE is the energy change. On the hypothesis that equilibrium is dynamic, the equilibrium conditions for a reaction $A + B \rightleftharpoons C + D$ can be formulated by equating the rates of the two opposing reactions,

$$k_1[A][B] = k_{-1}[C][D] \tag{3}$$

where k_1 and k_{-1} are the second-order rate constants for the reactions. The equilibrium constant is therefore equal to k_1/k_{-1}:

$$\frac{[C][D]}{[A][B]} = \frac{k_1}{k_{-1}} = K_c \tag{4}$$

The reaction isochore [Eq. (2)] may therefore be written as

$$\frac{d \ln k_1}{dT} - \frac{d \ln k_{-1}}{dT} = \frac{\Delta E}{RT^2} \tag{5}$$

which may be split into the two equations

$$\frac{d \ln k_1}{dT} = \frac{E_1}{RT^2} + I \tag{6}$$

and

$$\frac{d \ln k_{-1}}{dT} = \frac{E_{-1}}{RT^2} + I \tag{7}$$

where $E_1 - E_{-1} = \Delta E$. Experimentally it was found that I can be set equal to zero, the rate constant therefore being related to the temperature by an equation of the form

$$\frac{d \ln k}{dT} = \frac{E}{RT^2} \tag{8}$$

There is therefore a close analogy between the equation for an equilibrium constant [Eq. (2)] and that for a rate constant [Eq. (8)].

The fact that the constant of integration I turned out to be zero has a particular significance. If I had not been zero, it would be necessary to conclude that the temperature dependencies of the rates in the forward and reverse directions were affected by some common factor. The result that I is actually zero makes it possible for one to assume that the

[1] S. Arrhenius, *Z. Physik. Chem.*, **4**, 226 (1889).

reaction path from A + B to C + D may be divided into two parts, one of which is concerned with the rate from left to right, the other from right to left. As far as energy is concerned, one can say that between the initial and final states there is an intermediate state that has energy E_1 greater than that of A + B; this situation is represented in Fig. 11.

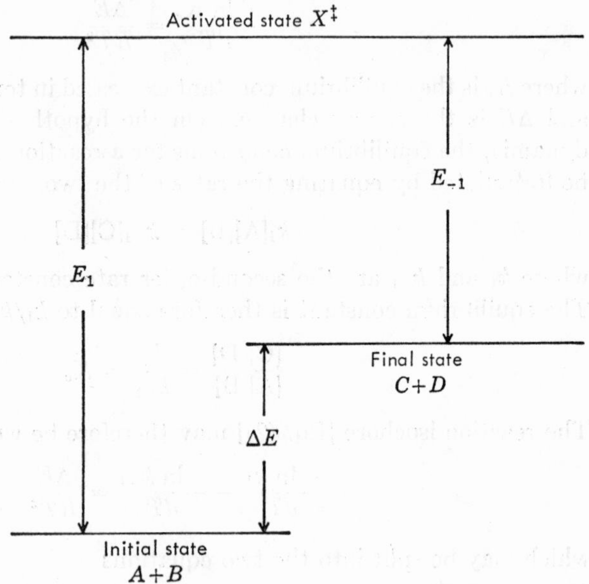

Fig. 11. Schematic energy diagram, showing the relative energies of the initial state, the final state, and the activated state.

The results suggest that the rate of the reaction between A and B is determined solely by the difference between the energy of A + B and that of the intermediate state, and in no way by factors related to what occurs after the intermediate state has been reached. Similarly the rate from right to left is controlled solely by the energy E_{-1}.

This argument can be expressed in a slightly different way by saying that when reaction occurs between A and B, there exists an equilibrium between A + B on the one hand and a particular collision complex on the other. This complex represents a special type of collision complex, and is now generally known as an *activated complex*.[1] The energy E_1, the energy required for the system to pass from the state A + B to the

[1] The term *transition state* is also employed, but its use will be avoided in this book since it is also frequently applied to other kinds of reaction intermediate.

activated state $AB^‡$, is known as the *energy of activation*, or the *activation energy*. There may be many collision complexes in existence at a given time in the reaction system, but only those with the energy E_1 are capable of forming products directly, and it is only these that are referred to as activated complexes.

The rate equation (8) integrates to

$$\ln k = -\frac{E}{RT} + \text{const} \tag{9}$$

provided that E is independent of temperature. This equation may be written as

$$k = Ae^{-E/RT} \tag{10}$$

where A is a constant which is usually known as the *frequency factor*[1] for the reaction. The factor $e^{-E/RT}$ is recognized as the Boltzmann expression for the fraction of systems having energy in excess of the value E, so that it may be identified with the fraction of the reactant molecules (undergoing collision at a given instant) that are activated complexes.

The Arrhenius law can be tested by plotting $\ln k$ (or $\log_{10} k$) against the reciprocal of the absolute temperature; according to Eq. (9) a straight line should be obtained. Its slope is $-E/R$ (or $-E/2.303R = -E/4.57$ if common logarithms are used), so that the activation energy E can be calculated. The law has been found to be obeyed with high accuracy for all types of chemical reactions. Figure 12 shows a plot of $\log_{10} k$ against $1/T$ for the thermal decomposition of hydrogen iodide, a reaction that was studied very carefully by Bodenstein.[2]

From the standpoint of the Arrhenius law, a complete understanding of the factors determining the rate constant of a reaction involves an understanding of the activation energy and the frequency factor. A considerable amount of effort has been devoted to both these problems. The activation energy must be interpreted using the methods of quantum mechanics. Although the quantum-mechanical theories of molecular structure have been formulated in detail, it is still not possible to obtain accurate numerical results, even for the simplest molecular structures. Some of the procedures that have been used to calculate activation energies are considered in the next section.

The problem of calculating frequency factors on the basis of fundamental principles has been attacked in two different ways. The problem is essentially one of calculating frequencies of particular kinds of collisions, and originally this was done by using the kinetic theory of collisions, in which the molecules are treated as hard spheres. It has become appar-

[1] The frequency factor has the same units as the rate constant, and is therefore only a frequency in the case of a first-order reaction.

[2] M. Bodenstein, *Z. Physik. Chem.*, **13**, 56 (1894); **22**, 1 (1897); **29**, 295 (1899).

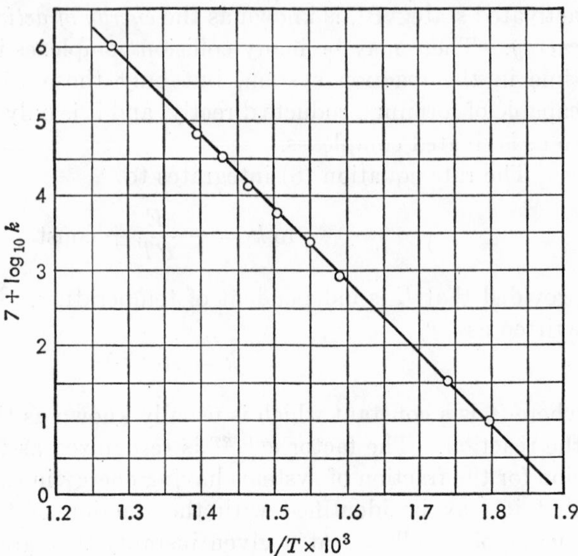

Fig. 12. A plot of $\log_{10} k$ against $1/T$ for the thermal decomposition of hydrogen iodide. (*Data of Bodenstein.*) The slope is equal to $-E/2.303R$, and leads to $E = 44.0$ kcal.

ent, however, that this procedure is not satisfactory, and leads to very large errors in a number of cases. A more accurate theory of collisions has therefore been developed, on the basis of statistical mechanics. The theory of hard-sphere collisions is treated briefly in a later section, after which a more detailed account will be given of the more reliable statistical-mechanical formulation.

THE SIGNIFICANCE OF ACTIVATION ENERGIES

Potential-energy Surfaces. The activation energies of chemical reactions are most conveniently considered using the method of potential-energy surfaces. The application of this method involves making a plot of energy as a function of the various interatomic distances in the complex that is formed when the reacting species come together. If the reaction is between two atoms, only one distance, that between the nuclei, is involved, and one could plot potential energy against this distance; the result would be a two-dimensional diagram, and would be a potential-energy curve for the diatomic molecule. If three atoms are involved, as in a reaction of the type

$$A + B—C \rightarrow A—B + C$$

the complex A—B—C must be described in terms of three parameters; these might be the A—B, B—C, and A—C distances or the A—B and B—C distances and the angle between the bonds. In order to plot energy against these three distances a four-dimensional diagram would be necessary. If only linear A—B—C complexes are considered, only two distances are involved, and a three-dimensional diagram is then adequate to describe the situation.

The method of potential-energy surfaces is conveniently described with reference to one of the simplest chemical reactions, the reaction between a hydrogen atom and a hydrogen molecule. Experimentally it has been found that the activation energy of this reaction is 8.8 kcal per mole.[1] The energy levels of the reactants and the products are the same, but the fact that there is an activation energy of 8.8 kcal means that an energy barrier of this height must be crossed during the passage of the system from the initial to the final state. This is shown schematically in Fig. 13, in which the energy of the system is plotted against a reaction coordinate that represents the extent to which the individual reaction process has occurred.

A discussion of chemical reactions from the standpoint of molecular structure was first given in 1928 by London,[2] who suggested that the properties of an activated complex can be calculated by quantum mechanics, using the same methods that are used for calculating the energies of stable molecules. One may consider a series of complexes, with H^α at various distances from the H^β—H^γ molecules. The atom H^α and the molecule H^β—H^γ are imagined to possess sufficient energy so that they come close together and give rise to an activated complex, in which there will be an extension of the H^β—H^γ bond. During the approach of the atom and the molecule there will be an electronic interaction between them, and during this process the potential energy of the system will first increase, and later decrease. Since this particular system is a symmetrical one, it is expected that the maximum energy will correspond to a symmetrical complex in which the distance between H^α and H^β is equal to the distance between H^β and H^γ. After this activated complex has been formed, the energy will gradually decrease as the system approaches the state corresponding to the molecule H^α—H^β and the separated atom H^γ.

This problem is treated in terms of quantum mechanics as follows. The permissible energy levels in which a molecule can exist are obtained by solving the appropriate Schrödinger wave equation. This is a differential equation involving the various coordinates of the electrons in the molecule, and its form depends upon the general expressions for the

[1] R. E. Weston, *J. Chem. Phys.*, **31**, 892 (1959).

[2] F. London, "Probleme der modernen Physik," p. 104, Sommerfeld Festschrift, 1928.

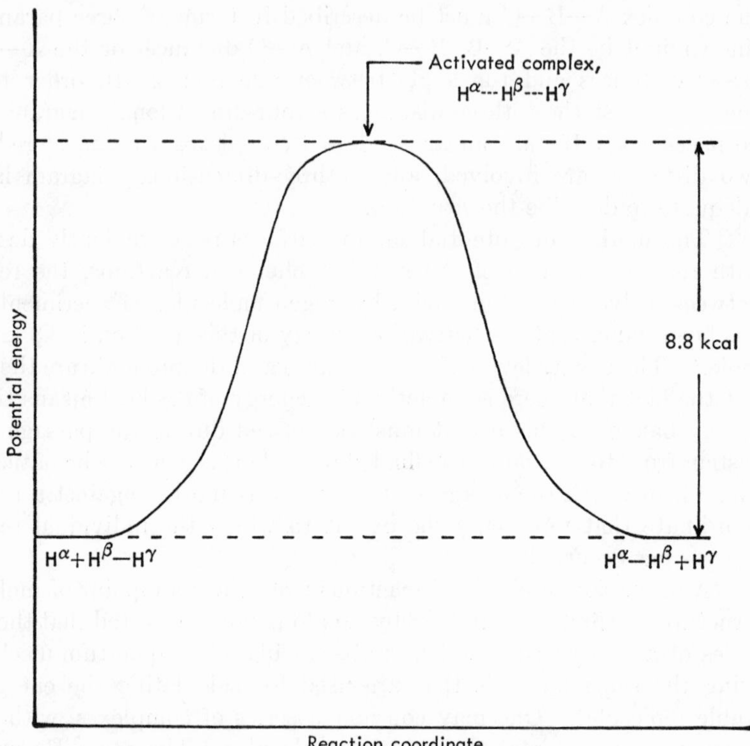

Fig. 13. The energy barrier for the reaction between a hydrogen atom and a hydrogen molecule.

potential energies of the electrons with respect to their coordinates. This wave equation has a solution only for certain definite values of the total energy of the system, and the function ψ corresponding to these values is known as an eigenfunction. The significance of the eigenfunction is that it is related to the electron density as a function of the coordinates.

The hydrogen molecule itself may be considered first; a simple solution for this was first given by Heitler and London.[1] The important result that comes out of their quantum-mechanical treatment of the hydrogen molecule is that two of the allowed energy levels are the sum and difference of two integrals that have the dimensions of an energy; that is, the energy may be expressed approximately as

$$E = A \pm \alpha \tag{11}$$

where A and α are energies. The integral A is known as a *coulombic*

[1] W. Heitler and F. London, *Z. Physik,* **44,** 455 (1927).

energy and is roughly equivalent to the energy that arises from the classical electrostatic interaction between the protons and electrons. The energy α, known as the *exchange* energy, has no counterpart in classical theory, but arises in quantum mechanics as a result of the fact that the electrons cannot be regarded as localized with respect to any particular nucleus. The energies A and α are usually both negative in numerical value, and the energy E in the above equations is the energy relative to the separated atoms; the lowest energy, corresponding to the most stable state, is therefore obtained when the positive sign is taken, i.e., is equal to $A + \alpha$.

The integrals A and α are both functions of the distance between the nuclei, and approach zero as the nuclei are separated from each other. When the nuclei are moved close to each other, the values of A and α both become positive, corresponding to repulsion. Values of $A + \alpha$ and $A - \alpha$ are plotted in Fig. 14 as functions of the interatomic separation.

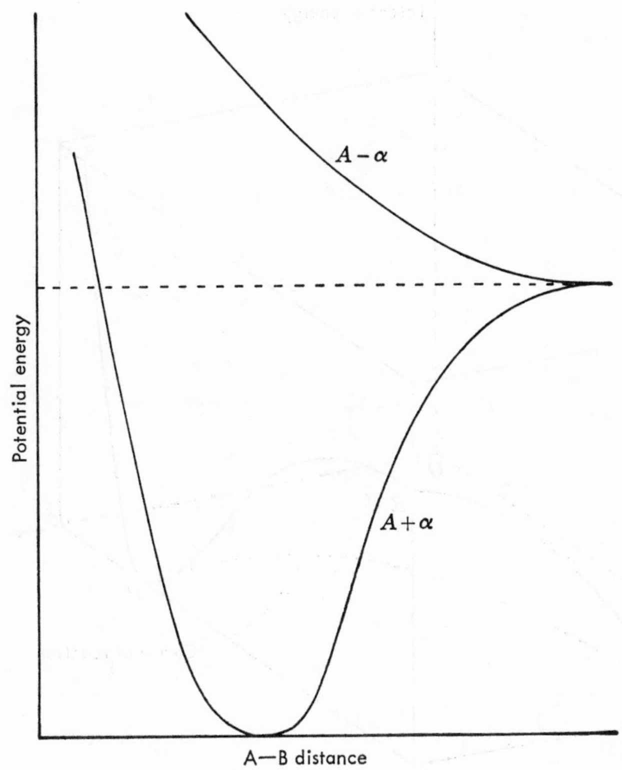

Fig. 14. Potential-energy curves for a diatomic molecule A—B.

The function $A + \alpha$ has a minimum value at some particular separation, and this corresponds to the most stable configuration of the molecule. The function $A - \alpha$ always corresponds to repulsion between the atoms, the molecule not being a stable one. It will be shown later that the most stable complex formed by the interaction between the hydrogen atom and a hydrogen molecule is linear, and the way in which the energy of such a linear complex varies with the distances between the atoms may be considered from the following point of view. The distance between H^α and H^β is designated as r_1, and the distance between H^β and H^γ as r_2; since the complex is assumed to be linear, the distance between H^α and H^γ is $r_1 + r_2$. The energy of such a linear system of atoms can be represented in a three-dimensional diagram in which the energy is plotted against r_1 and r_2, and such a diagram is shown schematically in Fig. 15. On the left-hand face of this diagram the distance r_2 may be considered to be sufficiently great so that one is dealing simply with the diatomic molecule

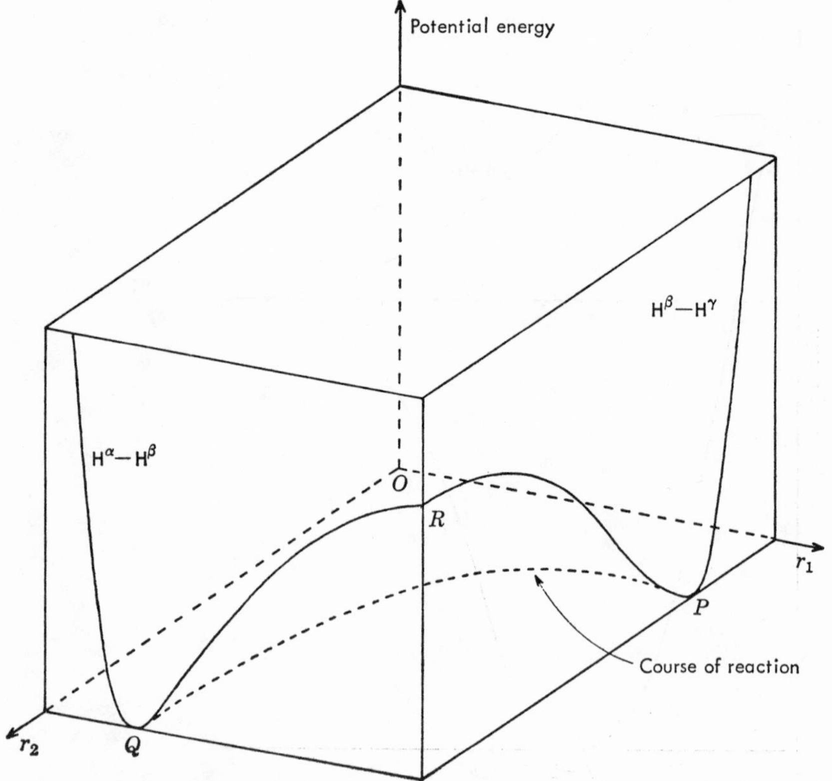

Fig. 15. The variation of potential energy E with r_1 and r_2, for a linear triatomic molecule such as H—H—H.

H^α—H^β; similarly, on the right-hand face of the diagram there is a curve for the diatomic molecule H^β—H^γ, the distance r_1 now being sufficiently great so that H^α is far away. The course of reaction may be considered to be the transition on the potential-energy surface from the point P to the point Q, the point R corresponding to the system $H^\alpha + H^\beta + H^\gamma$.

To trace the course of such a reaction it is necessary to make quantum-mechanical calculations corresponding to a number of points in the interior of the diagram, i.e., to a number of values of r_1 and r_2. Such calculations were first made by Eyring and Polanyi,[1] and were based on the theoretical treatment of London. These calculations have shown that starting from the points P and Q on the diagram there are two valleys, which meet in the interior of the diagram at a col, or saddle point. This result may be shown in a different type of diagram, as in Fig. 16, in

[1] H. Eyring and M. Polanyi, *Z. Physik. Chem.*, **B12**, 279 (1931); cf. also H. Eyring, *J. Am. Chem. Soc.*, **53**, 2537 (1931); *Chem. Rev.*, **10**, 103 (1932).

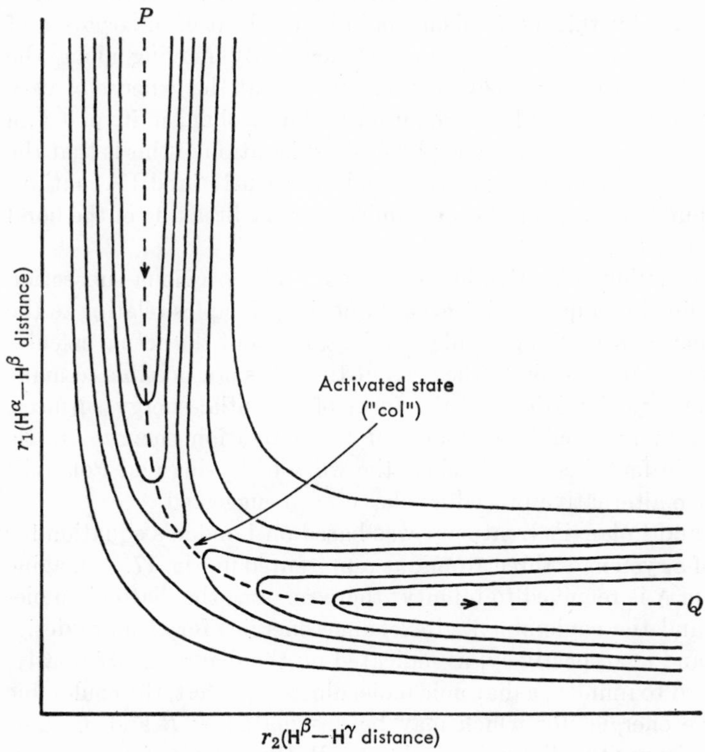

Fig. 16. A contour diagram, showing in a different form the same relationships shown in Fig. 15.

which the energy levels are indicated by means of contour lines. In order for the system to pass from the point P to the point Q, using the minimum amount of energy, it will travel along the first valley, over the col, and down into the second valley. This reaction path is represented in the contour diagram by a dashed line, and for energetic reasons the majority of the reaction systems will follow this path. The energy corresponding to the col is, from one point of view, a maximum energy, and from another point of view a minimum energy. It is a minimum energy in that the system cannot pass from P to Q by using less energy, and it is a maximum energy in the sense that as the system travels along its most economical path, the col represents the highest point in the path. The height of this col represents the activation energy of the system.

If a reaction is not a symmetrical one, but involves three atoms that are not identical, the results are similar, but the potential-energy surfaces are no longer symmetrical with respect to the two axes.

It is important to note that the mechanism of this reaction is very different from one corresponding to an initial complete dissociation of the molecule H^β—H^γ and then a combination of H^α with H^β. The activation energy necessary for this mechanism would be the heat of dissociation of the hydrogen atom, which is about 103 kcal. By moving along the valleys the system can obviously achieve reaction at the expense of very much less energy than would be required if the mechanism involved an initial complete dissociation. The physical explanation of this is that the energy released by the making of the bond between H^α and H^β continuously contributes toward the energy required for the breaking of the bond between H^β and H^γ.

The Calculation of Activation Energies. The previous subsection has been confined to a qualitative account of the principles relating to the activation energy; something should now be said about the actual calculations. Unfortunately, even at the present time it is not possible to make very satisfactory calculations of the form of potential-energy surfaces, and hence to make reliable estimates of the activation energy. Little advance has, in fact, been made since the work of Eyring and Polanyi,[1] although some alternative procedures have been suggested.

Eyring and Polanyi's treatment was based on London's equation for the energy of a system of three atoms, as represented in Fig. 17. Imagine that the atom A is removed to infinity; there remains the diatomic molecule B—C, and the coulombic and exchange energies for this are designated as A and α, respectively, as indicated on the diagram. Similarly, if B is removed to infinity, a diatomic molecule A—C is left, the coulombic and exchange energies for which may be designated as B and β. The removal of C leaves the diatomic species A—B, the energies for which are

[1] *Ibid.*

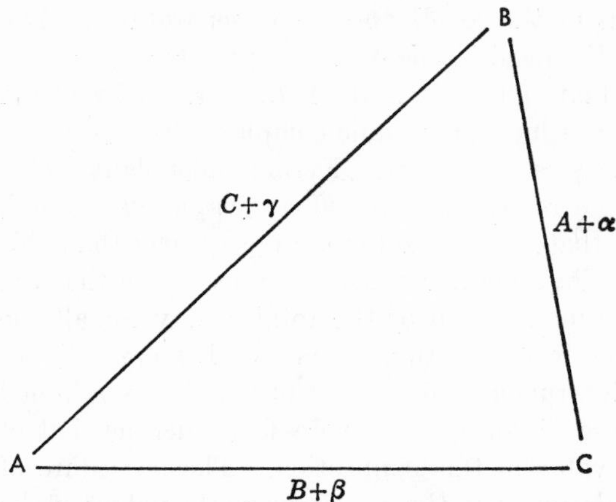

Fig. 17. A triatomic system; A, B, and C represent the coulombic energies of the individual diatomic species (e.g., A—B) and α, β, and γ the corresponding exchange energies.

called C and γ. According to London's treatment the energy of the general triatomic complex shown in Fig. 17 can be given in terms of these six energies, A, B, C, α, β, and γ. London's equation is in fact

$$E = \frac{1}{1 + S^2} [A + B + C \pm \{\tfrac{1}{2}[(\alpha - \beta)^2 + (\beta - \gamma)^2 + (\gamma - \alpha)^2]\}^{1/2}] \tag{12}$$

where S is an "overlap" integral. Eyring and Polanyi neglected the overlap integral and used the equation in the form

$$E = A + B + C \pm \{\tfrac{1}{2}[(\alpha - \beta)^2 + (\beta - \gamma)^2 + (\gamma - \alpha)^2]\}^{1/2} \tag{13}$$

It is readily seen that this equation does reduce to the correct forms when one of the atoms is removed to infinity. For example, if A is removed to infinity the energies B, C, β, and γ all become zero, and Eq. (13) reduces to Eq. (11) for the diatomic molecule B—C. The equation of London given above is only applicable to complexes in which the electrons are in s states; other equations were worked out for p orbitals, which are directional in character.

It follows from Eq. (13) that the most stable configuration of three atoms, with the electrons in s states, is the linear one. Examination of the equation reveals that for given values of α and γ the energy will be smaller (i.e., the molecule will be more stable), the smaller the value of β. This will be true when the distance between the atoms A and C is as great as possible for given values of the A—B and B—C separations. The linear configuration is thus the most stable one.

The actual work of evaluating the integrals A, B, C, α, β, and γ from first principles, for a variety of linear triatomic complexes having different A—B and B—C distances, is very great. Eyring and Polanyi actually employed what has been referred to as the *semiempirical* method, although it is often argued that the method is more empirical than this expression would suggest. Their method consisted in assuming that the coulombic energy is a constant fraction of the total energy for all the internuclear distances under consideration. The total energy E per molecule, as a function of internuclear distance, can readily be obtained from an analysis of spectroscopic data, and expressions such as that of Morse have been of great value in this connection. The procedure of Eyring and Polanyi was to derive from the Morse curve the values of the total energy, and then to split these into coulombic and exchange contributions by assuming the coulombic energy to be 14 percent of the total, and the exchange energy to be 86 percent of the total. In this way they were able to obtain A, B, C, α, β, and γ as functions of the two distances in the linear complex, and hence to calculate the energy for each pair of distances using the London equation. Their calculations were made for the $H + H_2$ reaction, and the principle can readily be extended to other reactions provided that the relevant spectroscopic data are available. Later workers have tried using different percentages of coulombic and exchange energy, and sometimes the procedure has been to use the percentage as an empirical parameter in order to obtain satisfactory agreement for one particular reaction.

This method of Eyring and Polanyi has proved useful in making rough estimates of energies of activation, but is not capable of high accuracy. It is probably in most cases sufficiently accurate for calculating the vibrational frequencies of activated complexes, quantities that are required for calculations of absolute rates. Serious difficulties arise with the method, however, when one attempts to interpret small differences in rates, such as may arise from isotopic substitution.

An alternative method has been suggested by Sato,[1] and has been employed in several recent calculations.[2] In Sato's method the overlap integral S is not neglected but is used as an empirical parameter in order to obtain good agreement with experiment for a standard reaction such as $H + H_2$. The relative contributions of coulombic and exchange energy are obtained on the basis of an application of the Heitler-London

[1] S. Sato, *J. Chem. Phys.*, **23**, 592, 2465 (1955); *Bull. Chem. Soc. Japan*, **28**, 450 (1955).

[2] E.g., J. Bigeleisen, F. S. Klein, R. E. Weston, and M. Wolfsberg, *J. Chem. Phys.*, **30**, 1340 (1959); Weston, *ibid.*, **31**, 892 (1959); T. E. Sharp and H. S. Johnston, *ibid.*, **37**, 1541 (1962).

theory to the attractive and repulsive states of a diatomic molecule; the latter, however, have to be obtained in an empirical manner. The method is just as arbitrary and empirical as that of Eyring and Polanyi, and in a recent comparison of the methods Weston[1] has concluded that there is not much to choose between them. A slight point in favor of Sato's method is that the Eyring-Polanyi method frequently leads to the result that the potential-energy surface has a slight basin at the col, so that there are really two maxima, either of which could be identified with the activated complex. More exact calculations[2] do not show such a basin, and it is not found when the Sato method is employed.

It will be evident from what has been said that the present state of the theoretical calculation of activation energies is a very unsatisfactory one. It is, of course, no worse than the state of the calculation of energies of stable molecules.

THE KINETIC THEORY OF COLLISIONS

It now remains to consider the theories relating to the frequency factor, a matter that initially presented some difficulty. The first reasonably satisfactory quantitative theory of the frequency factor was formulated in 1918 by W. C. McC. Lewis,[3] who identified the frequency factor with the "collision number," and calculated its value using a simple version of the kinetic theory of gases in which the molecules are treated as hard spheres. This treatment is a basically correct one, and all theories regard the frequency factor as the collision number. The calculation of the frequency of collisions on the assumption that molecules are hard spheres is, however, undoubtedly too crude, and the Lewis theory gives satisfactory agreement with experiment only for species (such as atoms) that do behave approximately as hard spheres. For reactions between more complicated molecules it is necessary to treat collisions in a more accurate and detailed manner. Such a treatment was first given in 1935 by Eyring, and is considered later in this chapter.

Lewis was concerned with bimolecular reactions, and for a reaction between two identical gaseous molecules he suggested that the rate in molecular units is

$$v = z_{AA}e^{-E/RT} \qquad \text{molecules cc}^{-1}\text{ sec}^{-1} \tag{14}$$

where z_{AA} is the number of collisions per second between two molecules of A in 1 cc of gas. Application of simple kinetic theory to this problem leads to the result that the total number of collisions per second of all of

[1] Weston, *loc. cit.*

[2] See, for example, I. Shavitt, *J. Chem. Phys.*, **31**, 1359 (1959).

[3] W. C. McC. Lewis, *J. Chem. Soc.*, **113**, 471 (1918); a similar, but somewhat less explicit, treatment was given earlier by M. Trautz, *Z. Anorg. Chem.*, **96**, 1 (1916).

the n molecules that are contained in 1 cc of gas is

$$z_{AA} = \tfrac{1}{2}\sqrt{2}\,\pi d^2 \bar{c} n^2 \tag{15}$$

where d is the distance between the centers of the spheres when the collision occurs, and $\bar{c}$ is the average velocity of each molecule. This average speed $\bar{c}$ is given by kinetic theory as

$$\bar{c} = \sqrt{\frac{8\mathbf{k}T}{\pi m}} \tag{16}$$

where m is the mass of each molecule and $\mathbf{k}$ is the Boltzmann constant. The collision frequency z_{AA} is therefore

$$z_{AA} = \frac{1}{2}\sqrt{2}\,\pi n^2 d^2 \sqrt{\frac{8\mathbf{k}T}{\pi m}} \tag{17}$$

$$= 2n^2 d^2 \sqrt{\frac{\pi \mathbf{k}T}{m}} \tag{18}$$

The corresponding expression for the frequency z_{AB} between two unlike molecules A and B, of masses m_A and m_B, the concentrations (numbers of molecules per cubic centimeter) being n_A and n_B, is

$$z_{AB} = n_A n_B d_{AB}{}^2 \left[8\pi \mathbf{k}T \frac{m_A + m_B}{m_A m_B} \right]^{1/2} \tag{19}$$

Here d_{AB} is the average of the diameters, or the sum of the radii. The quantity $d_{AB}{}^2$ is known as the *collision cross section.*

The rate of reaction between molecules A and B, with an activation energy of E, is given by

$$v = n_A n_B d_{AB}{}^2 \left[8\pi \mathbf{k}T \frac{m_A + m_B}{m_A m_B} \right]^{1/2} e^{-E/RT} \tag{20}$$

This equation implies that the rate is the number of molecules colliding per second and having a joint energy E in excess of the mean energy. If the concentrations are set equal to unity, the resulting expression is

$$k' = d_{AB}{}^2 \left[8\pi \mathbf{k}T \frac{m_A + m_B}{m_A m_B} \right]^{1/2} e^{-E/RT} \tag{21}$$

This constant k', equal to $v/n_A n_B$, is a rate constant for the reaction in the molecular units, namely, cc molecule^{-1} sec^{-1}. It can be put into the units of cc mole^{-1} sec^{-1} by multiplication by N, the Avogadro number,

$$k = N d_{AB}{}^2 \left[8\pi \mathbf{k}T \frac{m_A + m_B}{m_A m_B} \right]^{1/2} e^{-E/RT} \quad \text{cc mole}^{-1}\text{ sec}^{-1} \tag{22}$$

Comparison with Eq. (10) shows that according to this theory the frequency factor A is given by

$$A = N d_{AB}^2 \left[8\pi \mathbf{k} T \frac{m_A + m_B}{m_A m_B} \right]^{1/2} \qquad \text{cc mole}^{-1} \text{ sec}^{-1} \tag{23}$$

The expression on the right-hand side (or the corresponding expression in the units liters mole^{-1} sec^{-1}) is known as the *collision number*, and is usually written as Z. The frequency factor of the reaction is therefore identified with the collision number. In the case of a reaction between two like molecules the expression for the frequency factor is

$$A = 2N d_{AA}^2 \sqrt{\frac{\pi \mathbf{k} T}{m}} \tag{24}$$

The collision number can readily be calculated using molecular diameters derived from viscosity data, or in other ways, and since E can be determined from the experimental variation of the rate with the temperature, it is easy to test the theory. Calculation shows that Z usually has a value lying between 4×10^{13} and 4×10^{14} cc mole^{-1} sec^{-1}, depending upon the molecular radii. In many instances the agreement with experiment is satisfactory,[1] within a factor of 10 or so. This is true for gas reactions involving relatively simple molecules and for many reactions in solution, particularly those in which at least one of the reactants is a simple molecule or ion. However, a number of reactions, especially those involving more complex molecules, take place at rates which are markedly different from those calculated on the basis of the collision theory. For example, certain gas-phase reactions between radicals and molecules (p. 129) take place much more slowly than expected, whereas the addition of tertiary amines to alkyl iodides in solution frequently proceeds at rates which are 10^{-5} to 10^{-8} of the calculated values.[2] At one time the anomalies in solution were thought to be due to solvent effects, but in some instances the rates were shown to be low in the gas phase also (see Chap. 5). Certain reactions were found to proceed more rapidly than calculated.

In order to account for deviations from the simple collision theory, it has been postulated that the number of effective collisions may be less than that given by kinetic theory, since for reaction to take place a critical orientation of the molecules on collision may be necessary. The rate constant was therefore written as

$$k = PZe^{-E/RT} \tag{25}$$

where P is referred to as a probability, or steric, factor.

[1] Cf. E. A. Moelwyn-Hughes, "Kinetics of Reactions in Solution," p. 71, Oxford University Press, Fair Lawn, N.J., 1947.

[2] C. A. Winkler and C. N. Hinshelwood, *J. Chem. Soc.*, 1147 (1935).

Several weaknesses of the collision treatment have become apparent in recent years. In the first place, attempts to correlate the value of P with the structures and properties of the reacting molecules have not been very successful. Secondly, it is hardly possible to interpret on this basis the abnormally *high* rates that are sometimes observed. Furthermore a logical weakness of the collision treatment becomes apparent when reversible reactions are considered;[1] thus for the reaction

$$A_2 + B_2 = 2AB$$

the rate constant for the forward reaction would be given as

$$k_1 = P_1 Z_1 e^{-E_1/RT} \tag{26}$$

while that for the reverse reaction is

$$k_{-1} = P_{-1} Z_{-1} e^{-E_1/RT} \tag{27}$$

The equilibrium constant K, equal to k_1/k_{-1}, is therefore given by

$$K = \frac{k_1}{k_{-1}} = \frac{P_1 Z_1}{P_{-1} Z_{-1}} e^{-(E_1 - E_{-1})/RT} \tag{28}$$

However, from thermodynamics the equilibrium constant is equal to

$$K = e^{-\Delta G/RT} \tag{29}$$

$$= e^{\Delta S/R} e^{-\Delta H/RT} \tag{30}$$

where ΔG, ΔS, and ΔH are the increases in free energy, entropy, and heat content (enthalpy). If these expressions for K are compared, it is clear that the terms $e^{-(E_1-E_{-1})/RT}$ and $e^{-\Delta H/RT}$ correspond; consequently the ratio $P_1Z_1/P_{-1}Z_{-1}$ must be equal to $e^{\Delta S/R}$. If the molecules A_2, B_2, and AB are of comparable dimensions, Z_1 will be practically equal to Z_{-1} so that the entropy term $e^{\Delta S/RT}$ must be approximately equal to the ratio of the probability factors. It is therefore not sufficient to correlate the probability factors with the probability that certain reacting groups come together on collision: they should be interpreted in terms of entropy factors in a precise manner.

The way in which this can be done is indicated by the following argument. The equilibrium constant for a reaction may be expressed as

$$K = e^{-\Delta G/RT} \tag{31}$$

where ΔG is the standard Gibbs free-energy change in the reaction. Since K is equal to k_1/k_{-1}, one may write

$$\ln k_1 - \ln k_{-1} = -\frac{\Delta G}{RT} \tag{32}$$

[1] A. E. Stearn and H. Eyring, *J. Chem. Phys.*, **3**, 113 (1937).

By analogy with the argument of van't Hoff, considered above, this equation may be split as follows:[1]

$$\ln k_1 = -\frac{\Delta G_1^\ddagger}{RT} + \text{const} \tag{33}$$

$$\ln k_{-1} = -\frac{\Delta G_{-1}^\ddagger}{RT} + \text{const} \tag{34}$$

This splitting of Eq. (32) into (33) and (34) involves the assumption that the rate constant of the reaction from left to right depends only on the

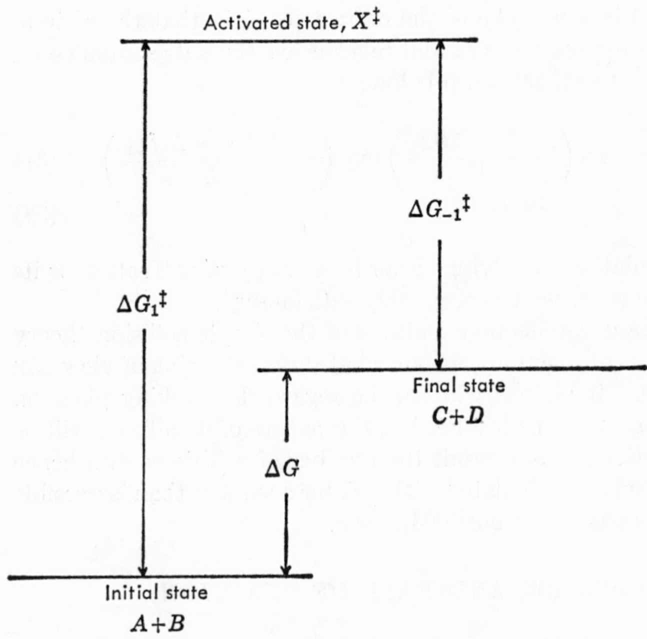

Fig. 18. Schematic free-energy diagram (compare with Fig. 11).

increase $\Delta G_1^\ddagger$ in free energy in going from the initial state to some intermediate state, and not on any free-energy changes occurring after the attainment of that intermediate state, which is the activated state. The relationships between the free-energy changes are shown in Fig. 18. Equations (33) and (34) may be written as

$$k = \nu e^{-\Delta G^\ddagger/RT} \tag{35}$$

[1] Eyring introduced the symbol ‡ to indicate an activated complex, and to denote a quantity which is the difference between a value (e.g., an energy) for the reactants and the activated complex.

where ν is a constant. The free-energy term $\Delta G^{\ddagger}$ may be split into its heat and entropy terms, $\Delta H^{\ddagger} - T\,\Delta S^{\ddagger}$, giving rise to the rate equation

$$k = \nu \exp\left(\frac{\Delta S^{\ddagger}}{R} - \frac{\Delta H^{\ddagger}}{RT}\right) \tag{36}$$

This is actually the form of the rate equation that has been given by Wynne-Jones and Eyring.[1] It will be seen later that Eyring's theory of absolute reaction rates gives a magnitude for the constant ν, and shows that it is equal to $\mathbf{k}T/\mathbf{h}$, where $\mathbf{k}$ is the Boltzmann constant and $\mathbf{h}$ is Planck's constant.

Equation (36) is seen to be of the correct form, in that the ratio of the rate constants for the forward and reverse reactions does involve an entropy and a heat term, as shown below:

$$K = \frac{k_1}{k_{-1}} = \exp\left(\frac{\Delta S_1{}^{\ddagger} - \Delta S_{-1}{}^{\ddagger}}{R}\right) \exp\left(-\frac{\Delta H_1{}^{\ddagger} - \Delta H_{-1}{}^{\ddagger}}{RT}\right) \tag{37}$$

$$= e^{\Delta S/R} e^{-\Delta H/RT} \tag{38}$$

Only such a formulation, involving either an entropy of activation or its equivalent, can be regarded as completely satisfactory.

In view of the unsatisfactory features of the simple collision theory as applied to chemical reactions, a somewhat different point of view will be presented here. Reactions will still be regarded as taking place on collision between reacting molecules, but the nature of a collision will be defined more precisely. As a result the number of collisions, and hence the rate constant, will be calculated with greater accuracy than is possible on the basis of the treatment outlined above.

EQUILIBRIUM AND RATE OF REACTION

In considering chemical reactions it is important to distinguish clearly between two aspects of the problem: one is concerned with the direction and extent of chemical change, the other with the rate with which it takes place. There is no simple connection between these two problems. Two chemical substances, A and B, may react together to give C and D; if A and B are brought together under constant external

[1] W. F. K. Wynne-Jones and H. Eyring, *J. Chem. Phys.*, **3**, 492 (1935). Prior to their work, equations of the same form as (36) had been arrived at, on the basis of arguments similar to the above, by a number of workers, including P. Kohnstamm and F. E. C. Scheffer, *Proc. Koninkl. Ned. Akad. Wetenschap.*, **13**, 789 (1911); F. E. C. Scheffer and W. F. Brandsma, *Rec. Trav. Chim.*, **45**, 522 (1926); Brandsma, *ibid.*, **47**, 94 (1928); **48**, 1205 (1929); V. K. LaMer, *J. Chem. Phys.*, **1**, 289 (1933); V. K. LaMer and M. L. Miller, *J. Am. Chem. Soc.*, **57**, 2674 (1935); cf. also E. A. Moelwyn-Hughes, *Proc. Roy. Soc. (London)*, **A164**, 295 (1938).

conditions, they will react at a rate that is a function of their concentrations, and which will become less and less as reaction proceeds. Theoretically, equilibrium between A, B, C, and D will be reached only after an infinite time, but in practice after a certain lapse of time (which in some cases may be extremely long) no further change in the system can be detected. The concentrations will then obey the relationship

$$\frac{[\mathrm{C}]^c[\mathrm{D}]^d}{[\mathrm{A}]^a[\mathrm{B}]^b} = K_c \tag{39}$$

where a, b, c, and d are the numbers of molecules of A, B, C, and D which react according to the stoichiometric equation, and K_c is a constant which does not depend on the concentrations but which does depend on the temperature.

If at a given temperature the equilibrium constant K_c has a high value, it is clear that at equilibrium the concentrations of C and D are higher than those of A and B; A and B have therefore reacted to a considerable extent. If on the other hand the constant K_c is a small fraction, there will be little of C and D at equilibrium.

The tendency of chemical substances to combine, as determined by the equilibrium constant, is not related in any simple way to the velocity with which the chemical change takes place. The reaction between two substances may occur almost to completion, but the time for even a very small fraction of the molecules to react may be extremely long. The equilibrium constant for the reaction $2H_2 + O_2 = 2H_2O$ is well over on the side of the water, but a mixture of hydrogen and oxygen may be kept for an indefinite period without a measurable amount of reaction taking place.

It is only with the second aspect, the rates of chemical reactions, that this book is primarily concerned; the theory of equilibrium is treated in works on thermodynamics and statistical mechanics. There is, however, a close relationship between the *theory* of rates and the theory of equilibria, in spite of there being no general connection between equilibrium and rate constants. This is so because molecules undergoing reaction pass through activated states which to a good approximation can be regarded as in equilibrium with the molecules in their normal states. The concentration of activated molecules can therefore be calculated by ordinary equilibrium theory, so that if the probability of the decomposition of activated molecules is known, the rate of reaction can be calculated. The problem of calculating rates therefore resolves itself into two parts: the first is the calculation of the concentrations of activated molecules, the second the calculation of the rates of reaction of the activated molecules. In the following section a brief outline of the statistical-thermodynamical theory of equilibrium will be presented.

STATISTICAL MECHANICS OF CHEMICAL EQUILIBRIUM[1]

According to statistical mechanics, the equilibrium constant for a reaction

$$aA + bB = cC + dD$$

with the concentrations expressed in molecules per cubic centimeter, is equal to

$$K_c = \frac{F_C{}^c F_D{}^d}{F_A{}^a F_B{}^b} e^{-E_0/RT} \tag{40}$$

The F's are the partition functions per unit volume (1 cc) of the molecules A, B, C, and D; and E_0 is the energy increase at the absolute zero when a moles of A react with b moles of B to form c moles of C and d moles of D, all substances being in their standard states. The manner of evaluating the partition functions will now be described briefly.

The partition function F for a molecule is defined by

$$F = \sum_i g_i e^{-\epsilon_i/\mathbf{k}T} \tag{41}$$

where ϵ_i is the energy, with respect to the zero-point energy, for a given energy level of the molecule, and g_i is the number of states corresponding to that level; the summation is taken over all states, i.e., electronic, translational, rotational, and vibrational. Since these various types of energy are to a good approximation independent of one another, the total energy corresponding to a given energy level may be written as

$$\epsilon_i = e_i + t_i + r_i + v_i \tag{42}$$

where the four terms on the right-hand side represent the four types of energy corresponding to the ith state. The partition function therefore becomes

$$F = \sum_i g_{ei} e^{-e_i/\mathbf{k}T} g_{ti} e^{-t_i/\mathbf{k}T} g_{ri} e^{-r_i/\mathbf{k}T} g_{vi} e^{-v_i/\mathbf{k}T} \tag{43}$$

the g_i having factorized as well as the exponential terms. This equation may be written as

$$F = f_e f_t f_r f_v \tag{44}$$

where f_e, f_t, f_r, and f_v are separate partition functions, each referring to one type of energy. The partition function has thus been factorized, so that each term may be evaluated separately.

[1] For reviews see R. H. Fowler, "Statistical Mechanics," Cambridge University Press, New York, 1936; R. H. Fowler and E. A. Guggenheim, "Statistical Thermodynamics," Cambridge University Press, New York, 1939; S. Glasstone, "Theoretical Chemistry," D. Van Nostrand Company, Inc., Princeton, N.J., 1946; G. S. Rushbrooke, "Introduction to Statistical Mechanics," Oxford University Press, Fair Lawn, N.J., 1949.

The partition function for electronic energy is calculated directly, from the observed electronic levels of the atom or molecule, using the relationship

$$f_e = \sum_i g_{ei} e^{-e_i/\mathbf{k}T} \tag{45}$$

At ordinary temperatures the excited energy levels of an atom or molecule are usually too high to make a significant contribution to the partition function. If the lowest state is a singlet state, the statistical weight g_e is unity, so that if the lowest state is taken as the zero level and all other levels are sufficiently high, the partition function is approximately unity; as a rough guide it may be assumed that excited electronic levels may be neglected if their energy is more than $4\mathbf{k}T$. For nitric oxide, oxygen, and one or two other molecules, the lowest level is not a singlet, so that the partition function is no longer unity.

The partition function per unit volume (1 cc) for the translational motion of a molecule of mass m having three degrees of translational motion can be shown to be

$$f_t = \frac{(2\pi m\mathbf{k}T)^{3/2}}{\mathbf{h}^3} \tag{46}$$

where $\mathbf{h}$ is Planck's constant. The rotational partition function for a linear molecule, which has only two degrees of rotational freedom, is given by

$$f_r = \frac{8\pi^2 I\mathbf{k}T}{\mathbf{h}^2} \tag{47}$$

where I is the moment of inertia of the molecule; for a homonuclear molecule this function must be divided by 2. For a polyatomic molecule having no axis of symmetry the rotational partition function is given by

$$r = \frac{8\pi^2(8\pi^3 ABC)^{1/2}(\mathbf{k}T)^{3/2}}{\mathbf{h}^3} \tag{48}$$

where A, B, and C are the moments of inertia about any three mutually perpendicular axes. This expression also requires modification if the molecule has certain types of symmetry, a matter that is considered in a later section (p. 84).

The total number of degrees of freedom of a molecule is equal to $3N$, where N is the number of atoms in the molecule. Of this number, three relate to the translational motion, and in a nonlinear molecule three are for rotational energy; the remainder, $3N - 6$, therefore apply to vibrational energy. If the molecule is linear, there are only two degrees of rotational freedom and hence $3N - 5$ degrees of vibrational freedom. In a diatomic molecule there is clearly only one degree of vibrational freedom. The partition function for vibrational motion is equal to

$$v = \prod_i (1 - e^{-h\nu_i/kT})^{-1} \tag{49}$$

where ν_i is the vibrational frequency[1] in sec^{-1}, the product being taken over all the modes of vibration; i.e., there is a factor corresponding to each of the $3N - 6$ or $3N - 5$ degrees of freedom. For a diatomic molecule the partition function consists of a single function $(1 - e^{-h\nu/kT})^{-1}$, whereas for a polyatomic molecule each of the factors will have its characteristic ν corresponding to the normal mode of vibration to which it is related. The expressions for partition functions are shown in Table 9, which gives the orders of magnitude.

THE THEORY OF ABSOLUTE REACTION RATES[2]

The treatment of chemical equilibrium in terms of partition functions, making use of relationships like Eq. (40), now has to be extended to the calculation of the rates of chemical reactions. In order for any chemical change to take place, it is necessary for the atoms or molecules involved to come together to form an activated complex. This complex is regarded as being situated at the top of an energy barrier lying between the initial and final states, and the rate of the reaction is controlled by the rate with which the complex travels over the top of the barrier. This type of formulation of the process seems first to have been put forward by Marcelin,[3] who considered the reacting molecules to cross a "critical surface in phase space," and the idea was somewhat further developed by Rodebush[4] and later by O. K. Rice and Gershinowitz.[5] The first calculation of the rates of reactions in terms of specific potential-energy surfaces was done by Pelzer and Wigner,[6] who calculated the rate of the reaction between hydrogen atoms and molecules. A particularly clear formulation of the problem was made by Eyring,[7] who has applied

[1] If wave numbers (ω cm^{-1}) are provided, they must be multiplied by the velocity of light ($\nu = \omega c$).

[2] For a detailed treatment, see S. Glasstone, K. J. Laidler, and H. Eyring, "The Theory of Rate Processes," McGraw-Hill Book Company, New York, 1941.

[3] A. Marcelin, *Ann. Phys.*, **3**, 158 (1915); cf. A. March, *Physik. Z.*, **18**, 53 (1917); R. C. Tolman, *J. Am. Chem. Soc.*, **42**, 2506 (1920); **44**, 75 (1922); E. P. Adams, *ibid.*, **43**, 1251 (1921).

[4] W. H. Rodebush, *ibid.*, **45**, 606 (1923); *J. Chem. Phys.*, **1**, 440 (1933); **3**, 242 (1935); **4**, 744 (1936).

[5] O. K. Rice and H. Gershinowitz, *ibid.*, **2**, 853 (1934); **3**, 479 (1935); G. B. Kistiakowsky and J. R. Lacher, *J. Am. Chem. Soc.*, **58**, 123 (1936).

[6] H. Pelzer and E. Wigner, *Z. Physik. Chem.*, **B15**, 445 (1932).

[7] H. Eyring, *J. Chem. Phys.*, **3**, 107 (1935); W. F. K. Wynne-Jones and Eyring, *ibid.*, 492.

Table 9 PARTITION FUNCTIONS

Motion	Degrees of freedom	Partition function	Order of magnitude
Translational	3	$\dfrac{(2\pi m\mathbf{k}T)^{3/2}}{\mathbf{h}^2}$ (per unit volume)	10^{24}–10^{25}
Rotational (linear molecule)	2	$\dfrac{8\pi^2 I\mathbf{k}T}{\mathbf{h}^2}$	10–10^2
Rotational (nonlinear molecule)	3	$\dfrac{8\pi^2(8\pi^3 ABC)^{1/2}(\mathbf{k}T)^{3/2}}{\mathbf{h}^3}$	10^2–10^3
Vibrational (per normal mode)	1	$\dfrac{1}{1 - e^{-\mathbf{h}\nu/\mathbf{k}T}}$	1–10
Restricted rotation	1	$\dfrac{(8\pi^3 I'\mathbf{k}T)^{1/2}}{\mathbf{h}}$	1–10

I' is the moment of inertia for the restricted rotation.

his method with considerable success to a large number of physical and chemical processes. A somewhat similar formulation of the problem was made by Evans and Polanyi.[1] The method of Eyring will be employed here, but a simplified development of the basic equation will be given first.

The Equilibrium Hypothesis. Consider a reaction

$$\mathrm{A} + \mathrm{B} \rightleftharpoons \mathrm{C} + \mathrm{D}$$

which has proceeded to equilibrium. Under these conditions the activated complexes $X^{\ddagger}$ will also be in equilibrium with the reactants and products, and their concentration may therefore be calculated accurately by the methods of statistical mechanics in terms of the concentrations of A and B. Under these conditions the Eyring method does give a reliable treatment of the rate of the reaction; the theory therefore does apply accurately to the equal and opposite rates for a system at equilibrium.

The theory involves the hypothesis, however, that even when the reactants and products are not at equilibrium with each other, the activated complexes are at equilibrium with the reactants. Some justification for this assumption is provided in the following way. Figure 19 shows a schematic free-energy diagram for a reaction system, and it will first be supposed that the reactants and products are at equilibrium with

[1] M. G. Evans and M. Polanyi, *Trans. Faraday Soc.*, **31**, 875 (1935); **33**, 448 (1937); M. Polanyi, *J. Chem. Soc.*, 629 (1937).

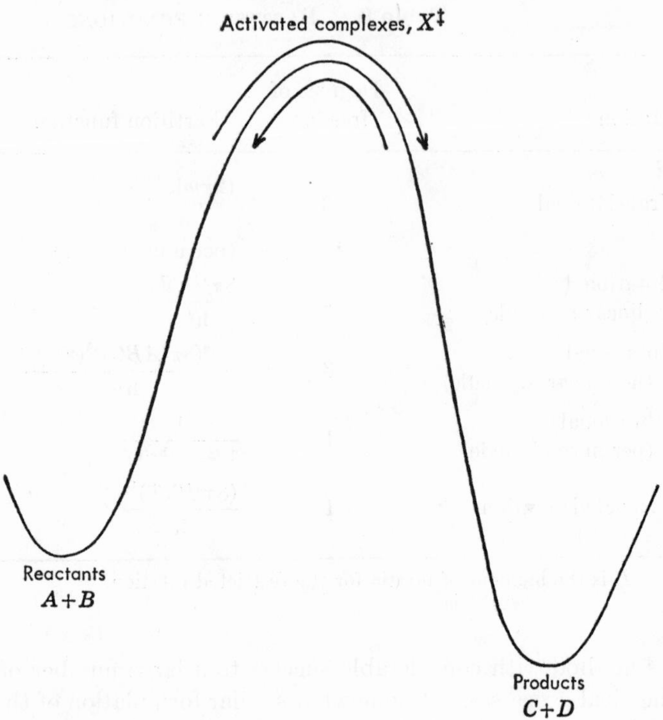

Fig. 19. Free-energy diagram, showing the flow of activated complexes in the two directions.

each other. At any instant of time there will be in the reaction vessel a few activated complexes, some of which are crossing the free-energy barrier in one direction, and some in the other. If the immediate past history of each of these activated complexes is investigated, some will be found to have been reactant molecules, and some product molecules. At equilibrium there will be an equal number of complexes of the two kinds, since the reaction is occurring at equal rates in the two directions.

Suppose that the product molecules are suddenly removed from the reaction system. The flow of those activated complexes that began as products (i.e., the flow from right to left in Fig. 19) will at once cease. There will still be a flow from left to right, however, and the assumption is that the rate of flow in this direction is unaffected by the removal of the products; in other words, the flows in the two directions are assumed to be independent of each other. It should be emphasized that when one states that the activated complexes are in equilibrium with the reactants, one is referring only to those complexes that, in the immediate past, were reactant molecules.

It is to be emphasized that there is no assumption that there is a *classical* type of equilibrium between initial and activated states; addition to the system of activated complexes moving from the initial to the final state would not disturb the equilibrium, as would be required if the equilibrium were classical. The activated complexes are transient species, passing from the initial to the final state and unable to turn back. Their concentration is nevertheless close to what is calculated using equilibrium theory.

It is possible to cast a derivation of the absolute-rate equation in such a form as to avoid the assumption of equilibrium.[1] The basis of the derivation is that one calculates the rate of entrance of systems into the activated state, and equates this to the rate of reaction. Apart from complications arising from statistical factors (cf. p. 84), it is then found that the concentration of complexes is equal to what is calculated assuming equilibrium.

Two other considerations also support the assumption of equilibrium. As noted above, the equilibrium assumption is certainly valid when reactants and products are at equilibrium, since then all species are at equilibrium; the theory therefore correctly predicts rates at equilibrium. If the theory were significantly in error before the establishment of equilibrium, rate constants would be expected to change as equilibrium is approached. Such a phenomenon has not been observed.

In the second place, a few very detailed calculations of rate constants have been made, with the use of methods that do not make the assumption of equilibrium; some of these involve the use of nonequilibrium statistical mechanics, and some are "stochastic" methods. Several such treatments are referred to at the end of this chapter. Here it may simply be noted that these calculations lead to the conclusion that reactions are satisfactorily interpreted on the basis of the equilibrium assumption, provided that E/RT for the reaction has a value of 5 or larger. The significance of this is that if E/RT has a value smaller than 5, the reaction will occur so rapidly that there can no longer be equilibrium even among the reactant molecules; the more energetic species will be removed more rapidly than the supply of them can be replenished, and there will therefore not be a Boltzmann distribution of reactant molecules. Aside from this situation, however, the equilibrium theories lead to no significant error.

Derivations of the Rate Equation. The equilibrium between reactants and activated complexes may be written as

$$\frac{[X^{\ddagger}]}{[A][B]} = K^{\ddagger} \tag{50}$$

[1] D. M. Bishop and K. J. Laidler, *J. Chem. Phys.*, **42,** 1688 (1965); K. J. Laidler and J. C. Polanyi, in G. Porter (ed.), "Progress in Reaction Kinetics," vol. 3, Pergamon Press, Oxford, 1965.

where $K^{\ddagger}$ is the equilibrium constant. This equilibrium constant may be written in terms of the appropriate partition functions,

$$\frac{[X^{\ddagger}]}{[A][B]} = \frac{F^{\ddagger}}{F_A F_B} e^{-E_0/RT} \tag{51}$$

where E_0 is now the difference between the zero-point energy per mole of the activated complexes and that of the reactants. Since this energy is the amount of energy that the reactants must acquire at 0°K before they can react, E_0 is the hypothetical energy of activation at this temperature. The partition functions in this expression must be evaluated with respect to the zero-point levels of the respective molecules.

As was seen earlier, these functions can be factorized into contributions corresponding to translational, rotational, vibrational, and electronic energy. If, for example, the molecule A consists of N_A atoms, there will be $3N_A$ such partition functions, of which three are for translational motion, three for rotational motion (or two if the molecule is linear), and therefore $3N_A - 6$ for vibrational motion ($3N_A - 5$ for a linear molecule). The same is true for the activated complex, which consists of $N_A + N_B$ atoms, giving $3(N_A + N_B) - 6$ vibrational terms if the molecule is nonlinear. One of these vibrational factors is of a different character from the rest, since it corresponds to a very loose vibration which allows the complex to dissociate into the products C and D. For this one degree of freedom one may therefore employ, in place of the ordinary factor $(1 - e^{-\mathbf{h}\nu/\mathbf{k}T})^{-1}$, the value of this function calculated in the limit at which ν tends to zero. This is evaluated by expanding the exponential and taking only the first term,

$$\lim_{\nu \to 0} \frac{1}{1 - e^{-\mathbf{h}\nu/\mathbf{k}T}} = \frac{1}{1 - (1 - \mathbf{h}\nu/\mathbf{k}T)} = \frac{\mathbf{k}T}{\mathbf{h}\nu} \tag{52}$$

The equilibrium constant may therefore be expressed by including this term $\mathbf{k}T/\mathbf{h}\nu$ and replacing $F^{\ddagger}$ by $F_{\ddagger}$, which now refers only to $3(N_A + N_B) - 7$ degrees of vibrational freedom [$3(N_A + N_B) - 6$ for a linear complex]; the resulting expression is

$$\frac{[X^{\ddagger}]}{[A][B]} = \frac{F_{\ddagger}(\mathbf{k}T/\mathbf{h}\nu)}{F_A F_B} e^{-E_0/RT} \tag{53}$$

This expression rearranges to

$$\nu[X^{\ddagger}] = [A][B] \frac{\mathbf{k}T}{\mathbf{h}} \frac{F_{\ddagger}}{F_A F_B} e^{-E_0/RT} \tag{54}$$

The frequency ν is the frequency of vibration of the activated complexes in the degree of freedom corresponding to their decomposition; it is therefore the frequency of decomposition.[1] The expression on the left-hand side of Eq. (54) is therefore the product of the concentration of complexes $X^‡$ and the frequency of their decomposition; it is therefore the rate of reaction, which is thus given by the expression on the right-hand side of the equation, viz.,

$$v = [A][B] \frac{\mathbf{k}T}{\mathbf{h}} \frac{F_‡}{F_A F_B} e^{-E_0/RT} \tag{55}$$

The result that the rate is proportional to the product [A][B] arose from the assumption that the activated complex is composed of one molecule of A and one of B; in the more general case of a complex composed of *a* molecules of A, *b* of B, etc., the rate would be proportional to $[A]^a[B]^b \cdots$. The molecularity of a reaction is in fact equal to the number of reactant molecules that exist in the activated complex.

The rate constant of the reaction, the rate of which is given by Eq. (55), is given by

$$k = \frac{\mathbf{k}T}{\mathbf{h}} \frac{F_‡}{F_A F_B} e^{-E_0/RT} \tag{56}$$

The quantity $\mathbf{k}T/\mathbf{h}$ which appears in these expressions is of great importance in rate theory; it has the dimensions of a frequency, and its value is about 6×10^{12} sec^{-1} at 300°K.

The above derivation of the rate equation is different from the original one of Eyring; it is formally somewhat simpler, but contains some features that cause some uneasiness. In the original derivation, which in some ways is more satisfactory, the vibrational partition function corresponding to the coordinate of decomposition, instead of being retained in the form of $\mathbf{k}T/\mathbf{h}\nu$, is replaced by a translational function. Figure 20 gives a schematic representation of the top of the potential-energy barrier, and it may be considered that all complexes lying within the length δ shown in the diagram are activated complexes; the actual value of δ will be seen to be immaterial. The translational partition function corresponding to the motion of a particle of mass $m_‡$ in a one-dimensional box of length δ is given by

$$f_t = \frac{(2\pi m_‡ \mathbf{k}T)^{1/2}}{\mathbf{h}} \delta \tag{57}$$

and if this expression is substituted for the vibrational partition function corresponding to the coordinate of decomposition, the resulting expression

[1] The frequency ν is the number of times a second a vibrating system passes a given point in *one* direction. The concentration $[X^‡]$ includes complexes moving in *both* directions, and is twice the actual number moving from left to right. The product $\nu[X^‡]$ refers only to the rate from left to right.

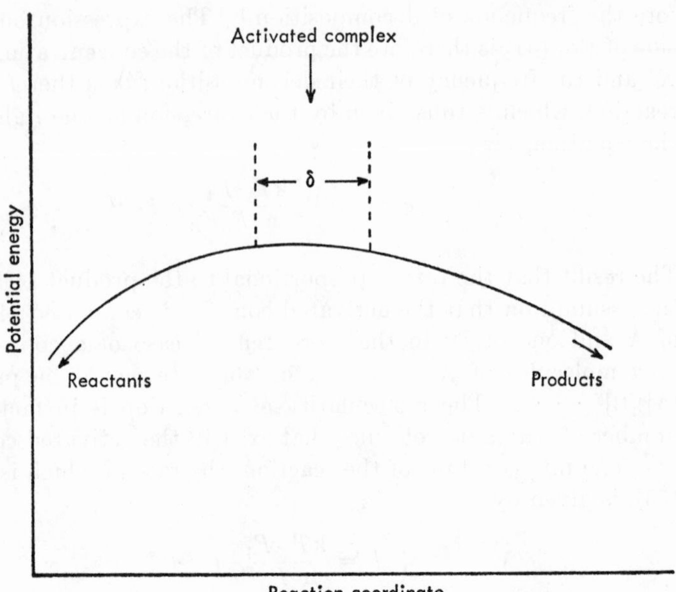

Fig. 20. The top of the potential-energy barrier. A flat portion at the top of the barrier, of length δ, is arbitrarily defined as comprising the activated state.

for the concentration of activated complexes is

$$[X^\ddagger] = [A][B] \frac{(2\pi m_\ddagger \mathbf{k}T)^{1/2}}{\mathbf{h}} \delta \frac{F_\ddagger}{F_A F_B} e^{-E_0/RT} \tag{58}$$

This again includes activated complexes moving in both directions, and is therefore twice the number in which one is interested. The average velocity of the particles *moving from left to right* over the potential-energy barrier is given by kinetic theory as

$$\bar{\dot{x}} = \left(\frac{\mathbf{k}T}{2\pi m_\ddagger}\right)^{1/2} \tag{59}$$

The frequency with which the complexes pass over the barrier from left to right is therefore given by this expression divided by δ, and the rate of reaction is the concentration of complexes multiplied by this frequency. The result is

$$v = [A][B] \frac{(2\pi m_\ddagger \mathbf{k}T)^{1/2}}{\mathbf{h}} \delta \left(\frac{\mathbf{k}T}{2\pi m_\ddagger}\right)^{1/2} \frac{1}{\delta} \frac{F_\ddagger}{F_A F_B} e^{-E_0/RT} \tag{60}$$

$$= [A][B] \frac{\mathbf{k}T}{\mathbf{h}} \frac{F_\ddagger}{F_A F_B} e^{-E_0/RT} \tag{61}$$

Equation (61) is seen to be identical with Eq. (55).

Although the derivations given above appear to be different, they are basically the same. The first regards the passage over the barrier as a very loose vibration, the other as a free translation. If a particle is initially vibrating, and the restoring force on it is gradually reduced to zero, the vibration ultimately becomes a translation. The partition function for a very loose vibration should therefore pass smoothly over into that for a translation. Thus if the frequency corresponding to translational motion,

$$\nu = \left(\frac{\mathbf{k}T}{2\pi m_{\ddagger}}\right)^{1/2} \frac{1}{\delta} \tag{62}$$

is substituted into the expression $\mathbf{k}T/\mathbf{h}\nu$, the result is $(2\pi m_{\ddagger}\mathbf{k}T)^{1/2}\,\delta/\mathbf{h}$, which is the one-dimensional translational partition function for a particle in a length δ [Eq. (57)].

The problem of calculating the rate constant has been reduced by the Eyring treatment to evaluating the partition functions for the normal and activated states; for this to be done, the nature of the activated complex must be known or postulated. In principle, the structure of the activated complex can be determined by the methods of quantum mechanics, as was discussed earlier, but the procedure is laborious and not very accurate; however, in many cases the structure of the activated complex can be estimated with sufficient accuracy on the basis of our general knowledge of molecular structure, and examples in which this is done will be given in later chapters.

Although the theory of absolute reaction rates outlined above is closely linked with the theory of chemical equilibrium, it is important to realize that equilibrium theory alone can give no information about rates. In the present application, equilibrium theory is concerned solely with the calculation of the concentration of activated complexes in terms of those of the reactants; additional theory was required to deal with the question of the frequency with which they decompose.

The Transmission Coefficient. To allow for the possibility that not every activated complex reaching the top of the potential-energy barrier is converted into a reaction product, it is convenient to introduce a "transmission coefficient" κ, the rate constant being written as

$$k = \kappa \frac{\mathbf{k}T}{\mathbf{h}} \frac{F_{\ddagger}}{F_A F_B} e^{-E_0/RT} \tag{63}$$

The function

$$\frac{F_{\ddagger}}{F_A F_B} e^{-E_0/RT}$$

may be regarded as a modified equilibrium constant between the normal and activated states, the modification being the removal of the vibrational factor for the decomposition of the complex. If this modified equilibrium constant is denoted by $K^\ddagger$ the rate expression becomes

$$k = \kappa \frac{\mathbf{k}T}{\mathbf{h}} K^\ddagger \tag{64}$$

This expression has been derived on the assumption that the rate constant is expressed in terms of concentrations; under these conditions $K^\ddagger$ is a concentration equilibrium constant. If pressure units are employed, the same expression holds, but $K^\ddagger$ is now a pressure equilibrium constant. The expressions involving partition functions are, however, valid only for concentration units.

For a great many reactions the transmission coefficient is equal to unity, which means that every activated complex[1] becomes a product. There are, however, two important classes of reactions for which the coefficient may be considerably less than unity. The first comprises bimolecular atom recombinations in the gas phase and the reverse decompositions of diatomic molecules; the mechanisms of such reactions are considered in more detail later. When two atoms collide in the gas phase, there is no energy of activation, and an activated complex may therefore be said to be formed on every collision; however, the resulting molecule still contains, largely as vibrational energy, the energy of the initial atoms, and will therefore decompose in the period of its first vibration; the transmission coefficient of such a reaction is therefore extremely low, and would be zero except for the possibility that the complex loses some of its energy by radiation. If on the other hand the complex is formed in the presence of a "third body," which may be a gas molecule or part of a surface, the energy may be removed by the third body, and the product is therefore stabilized; the transmission coefficient may then approach unity. In the decomposition of a diatomic molecule into atoms, a third body is similarly necessary in order to provide the molecule with the energy required for decomposition.

The second class of reactions in which the transmission coefficient may be appreciably less than unity comprises those in which there is a change from one type of electronic state to another. A certain number of reactions are known in which there is a transition between states of differing multiplicities, so that there is a change in spin angular momentum. Such "electronic switches" occur with only a low probability, and the transmission coefficient assigned to the reaction takes account of this.

Quantum-mechanical Tunneling. Up to now it has been assumed that the reaction system must pass over the top of the energy barrier when the reaction occurs; this is certainly necessary according to classical

[1] By this is meant, of course, every activated complex that originally came from reactants.

mechanics. Quantum-mechanical theory, on the other hand, admits the possibility that a system having less energy than required to surmount the barrier may pass from the initial to the final state; it is said to "tunnel" or "leak" through the energy barrier. This tunneling has been allowed for by the inclusion of the factor[1]

$$1 - \frac{1}{24}\left(\frac{\mathbf{h}\nu_e}{\mathbf{k}T}\right)^2$$

in the rate expression. The quantity ν_e is the frequency of the stretching vibration along the coordinate of decomposition, and is related to the curvature of the surface at the col. The frequency ν_e is an imaginary quantity (there being, as seen above, no restoring force in the activated state), and ν_e^2 is therefore negative; the correction term is therefore greater than unity. It is to be seen that the factor approaches unity at high temperatures and when the curvature of the surface is small (i.e., when the barrier is a flat one).

Quantum-mechanical tunneling is particularly important in electron-transfer reactions, and in reactions involving the transfer of a proton. In most other cases it is unimportant and can be neglected. For gas reactions there is not much experimental evidence of tunneling,[2] and the indications are that the theoretical treatments exaggerate the importance of tunneling;[3] it is not clear whether this is so because of errors in the construction of potential-energy surfaces or because of deficiencies in the theory of tunneling. Good experimental evidence for tunneling has been obtained for certain reactions in solution.[4]

The Reaction Coordinate. In the preceding derivation of the absolute rate equation it was stated (p. 76) that one of the vibrational factors in the partition function for the activated complex is of a different character from the remaining ones. This particular vibration was shown to be equivalent to a translation, and the factor $\mathbf{k}T/\mathbf{h}$ that appears in the

[1] E. P. Wigner, *Z. Physik. Chem.*, **B19**, 903 (1932); C. Eckart, *Phys. Rev.*, **35**, 1303 (1930); R. P. Bell, *Proc. Roy. Soc. (London)*, **A139**, 446 (1933), *Trans. Faraday Soc.*, **55**, 1 (1959).

[2] As of 1965, the only completely reliable evidence of tunneling in a gas-phase reaction has been obtained by W. R. Schulz and D. J. LeRoy [(*J. Chem. Phys.*, **42**, 3869 (1965)] for the $H + H_2$ reaction; the evidence consists of nonlinear Arrhenius plots, the tunneling being relatively more important the lower the temperature.

[3] R. E. Weston, *J. Chem. Phys.*, **31**, 892 (1959); H. S. Johnston, *Advan. Chem. Phys.*, **3**, 131 (1960); H. S. Johnston and D. Rapp, *J. Am. Chem. Soc.*, **83**, 1 (1961); T. E. Sharp and H. S. Johnston, *J. Chem. Phys.*, **37**, 1541 (1962).

[4] R. P. Bell, J. A. Fendley, and J. R. Hulett, *Proc. Roy. Soc. (London)*, **A235**, 453 (1956); *ibid.*, **A251**, 274 (1959); E. F. Caldin and E. Harbron, *J. Chem. Soc.*, 3454 (1962); cf. Caldin, "Fast Reactions in Solution," p. 273, Basil Blackwell & Mott, Ltd., Oxford, 1964; E. F. Caldin and M. Kasparian, *Discussions Faraday Soc.*, **39** (1965).

final rate equation results from this translational motion across the top of the barrier.

This way of looking at the situation actually corresponds to a special case, as may now be seen with particular reference to the linear triatomic activated complex shown in Fig. 21. There are four normal modes of

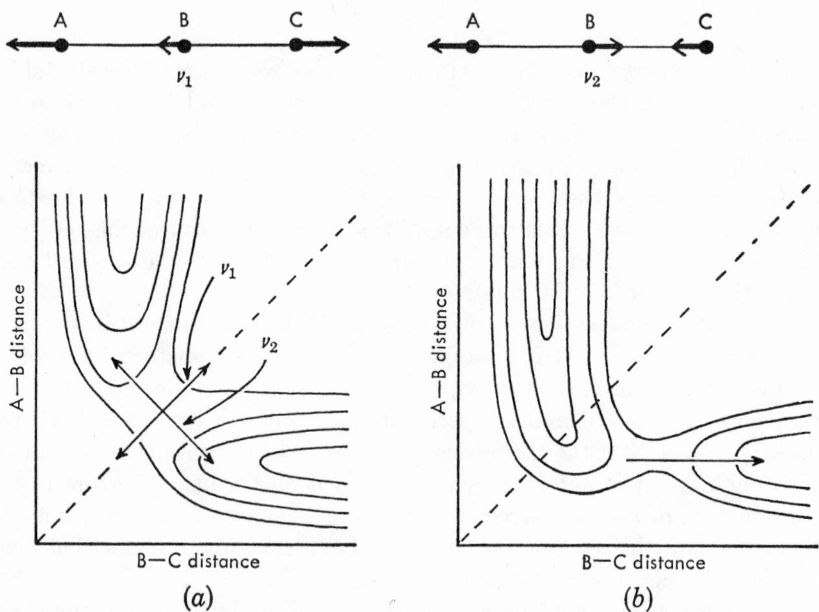

Fig. 21. The two stretching modes of vibration of a linear activated complex A—B—C. In the contour diagram (*a*) the reaction coordinate corresponds to the antisymmetric vibration of frequency ν_2; in (*b*) it corresponds to a simple stretching of the B—C bond.

vibration for this complex; two, shown in the diagram, are for stretching, and two (not shown) are for bending. Two schematic potential-energy surfaces for this system are shown in the figure. One of them (*a*) relates to a situation in which the valleys are arranged symmetrically. The symmetrical vibration of the molecule, of frequency ν_1, is represented by a motion along the line that bisects the axes, the A—B and B—C bonds being extended and contracted in unison. The antisymmetrical vibration of frequency ν_2 corresponds to a motion at right angles to this line that bisects the axis. For this particular case of symmetrical potential-energy surfaces the passage of the system through the activated state corresponds to this antisymmetrical vibration. It would therefore be correct, in treating this problem, to omit the vibration of frequency ν_2

from the partition function for the activated complex, and to consider only the vibration of frequency ν_1 and the two bending vibrations. A similar situation may exist in more complicated cases; the passage across the barrier may again correspond to one particular antisymmetrical vibration. The corresponding partition function would then be omitted, all the others being included.

The nature of the potential-energy surfaces may, however, be such that the passage across the top of the barrier does not correspond simply to one normal mode of vibration. Such a case is illustrated schematically in Fig. 21*b*. The motion of the system across the potential-energy barrier, shown by an arrow in the diagram, now does not correspond to a single normal vibration of the activated complex. The arrow has been drawn so as to be parallel to the axis corresponding to the B—C distance. This means that in the passage of the system over the barrier there is simply an increase in the B—C distance, the A—B distance remaining constant. It is convenient in this case to refer to the B—C distance as the *reaction coordinate*, or as the *critical coordinate*. In the symmetrical case (Fig. 21*a*) the reaction coordinate does not correspond to the extension of a single bond, but rather to the simultaneous extension of the B—C bond and contraction of the A—B bond. The reaction coordinate in this case would be a combination of the A—B and B—C distances. The particular combination that is taken is related to the motions occurring in the antisymmetrical vibration.[1]

In order to make absolute rate calculations for the case (Fig. 21*b*) in which the reaction coordinate corresponds simply to the extension of a single bond, the procedure is to treat this bond length as fixed and to carry out a normal-mode analysis in order to obtain the remaining vibrational frequencies. For the triatomic case represented in Fig. 21*b*, the procedure is very simple; apart from the two bending motions, the only vibration would be that of the atom A relative to B—C, the distance in the latter being fixed. The frequency of this stretching vibration would be

$$\nu^* = \frac{1}{2\pi}\sqrt{\frac{k_{\mathrm{AB}}}{m^*}} \tag{65}$$

where k_{AB} is the force constant for the bond A—B, and m^* is the reduced mass, given by

$$\frac{1}{m^*} = \frac{1}{m_{\mathrm{B}} + m_{\mathrm{C}}} + \frac{1}{m_{\mathrm{A}}} \tag{66}$$

The procedure in more complicated cases is similar; if the reaction

[1] The weighting factors are in fact the amplitude factors for the two distances; these are factors that are proportional to the extensions of the bonds at any time during the antisymmetrical vibration.

coordinate corresponds to a linear combination of two or more interatomic distances, this linear combination must be held fixed, and a normal-mode analysis carried out to determine the relevant vibrational frequencies.

If one is content with approximate estimates of rate constants, the exact choice of reaction coordinate may not be of great importance. For more exact calculations, however, care must be taken to decide which coordinate is the correct one, and this can be done only by obtaining a reliable potential-energy surface. It has been seen earlier in this chapter that the construction of potential-energy surfaces cannot yet be done in a reliable manner, so that it is difficult for exact rate calculations to be made.

This situation leads to particular difficulty in connection with the prediction of kinetic isotope effects, a matter that is discussed later in this chapter. In dealing with these effects, one is concerned with the treatment of very small changes, which are influenced rather strongly by the choice of reaction coordinate. It is indeed this factor that has led to the greatest difficulty in the theory of isotope effects.

Symmetry Numbers and Statistical Factors. Many chemical processes can occur in two or more different ways. In the reaction between a hydrogen atom and a methane molecule, for example,

$$H + CH_4 \rightarrow H_2 + CH_3$$

the hydrogen atom may abstract any one of the four hydrogen atoms, so that there are four equivalent ways in which the reaction can proceed; it is convenient to say that there is a *statistical factor*[1] of 4 for such a reaction. In the analogous reaction

$$H + CH_2D_2 \rightarrow H_2 + CHD_2$$

the statistical factor is obviously 2. It is evident that in applying absolute rate theory it is necessary to take proper account of this question of statistical factors.

For many years it was assumed that the problem was automatically taken care of by introducing the appropriate symmetry numbers into the rotational partition functions for the reactants and activated complexes.

[1] The most reliable way to calculate a statistical factor is to label all identical atoms in the reactants and to count the number of different activated complexes that are formed. In the case of the $H + CH_4$ reaction, for example, the following four activated complexes can be formed from $H^1 + CH^2H^3H^4H^5$:

$$H^1 \cdots H^2 \cdots CH^3H^4H^5 \qquad H^1 \cdots H^3 \cdots CH^2H^4H^5$$
$$H^1 \cdots H^4 \cdots CH^2H^3H^5 \qquad H^1 \cdots H^5 \cdots CH^2H^3H^4$$

If the reactants are identical, the number must be divided by 2, so that the same molecule (or atom) is not counted twice.

This procedure, however, although correct in some cases, has been found to lead to some anomalies. Recent reexaminations of the problem[1] have led to the conclusion that the correct procedure is to *omit the symmetry numbers* for the reactants and activated complexes and to *multiply the rate expression by the statistical factor*. For a discussion of the reason for this the reader is referred to the paper of Bishop and Laidler.

APPLICATIONS OF THE THEORY OF ABSOLUTE REACTION RATES

Reactions between Atoms.[2] The first example to which the general theory of absolute reaction rates will be applied is a reaction between two atoms A and B.[3] The activated complex will in this case be the diatomic molecule AB, which has three degrees of translational freedom and two of rotational; if it were a normal diatomic molecule, it would have one degree of vibrational freedom, but as it is an activated complex, this mode of vibration corresponds to decomposition, and the corresponding partition function is therefore omitted. The partition function $F_{\ddagger}$, with this omission, is therefore

$$F_{\ddagger} = \frac{[2\pi(m_A + m_B)\mathbf{k}T]^{3/2}}{\mathbf{h}^3} \frac{8\pi^2 I\mathbf{k}T}{\mathbf{h}^2} \tag{67}$$

where m_A and m_B are the atomic masses, and I is the moment of inertia of the diatomic complex. The first term in this expression is the contribution from the three degrees of translational freedom, while the second is for rotation. If d_{AB} is the distance between the centers of the atoms in the activated complex, the moment of inertia is given by

$$I = d_{AB}^2 \frac{m_A m_B}{m_A + m_B} \tag{68}$$

The atoms A and B have only translational degrees of freedom, so that the respective partition functions are

$$F_A = \frac{(2\pi m_A \mathbf{k}T)^{3/2}}{\mathbf{h}^3} \tag{69}$$

and

$$F_B = \frac{(2\pi m_B \mathbf{k}T)^{3/2}}{\mathbf{h}^3} \tag{70}$$

[1] D. M. Bishop and K. J. Laidler, *J. Chem. Phys.*, **42**, 1688 (1965); cf. also K. J. Laidler and J. C. Polanyi, in G. Porter (ed.), "Progress in Reaction Kinetics," Pergamon Press, Oxford, 1965; E. W. Schlag, *J. Chem. Phys.*, **38**, 2480 (1963); D. Rapp and R. E. Weston, *J. Chem. Phys.*, **36**, 2807 (1962).

[2] Cf. H. Eyring, *J. Chem. Phys.*, **3**, 107 (1935); C. E. H. Bawn, *Trans. Faraday Soc.*, **31**, 1536 (1935); **32**, 178 (1936); C. N. Hinshelwood, *J. Chem. Soc.*, 635 (1937); R. P. Bell, *Ann. Rept. Progr. Chem. (Chem. Soc., London)*, **36**, 82 (1939).

[3] The question of the necessity for a third body in atomic reactions is ignored in the present section.

If the transmission coefficient κ is taken as unity, the rate constant of the reaction is therefore [cf. Eq. (62)]

$$k = \frac{\mathbf{k}T}{\mathbf{h}} \frac{F_{\ddagger}}{F_{\mathrm{A}}F_{\mathrm{B}}} e^{-E_0/RT} \tag{71}$$

$$= d_{\mathrm{AB}}^2 \left[8\pi\mathbf{k}T \frac{m_{\mathrm{A}} + m_{\mathrm{B}}}{m_{\mathrm{A}}m_{\mathrm{B}}} \right]^{\frac{1}{2}} e^{-E_0/RT} \tag{72}$$

It was seen in Eq. (21) that an identical expression was given by collision theory, on the assumption that the atoms are hard spheres having diameters d_{A} and d_{B} such that $\frac{1}{2}(d_{\mathrm{A}} + d_{\mathrm{B}})$ is equal to d_{AB}.

Agreement between the two treatments is not, however, found when reactions between molecules are considered, as will now be seen.

Reactions between Molecules.[1] The treatment given for atoms can be extended to reactions between molecules of any complexity; however, the equations become rather involved, and a simplified treatment is to be preferred. For this purpose the approximation will be made of regarding the partition function for each type of energy as consisting of equal terms, one for each degree of freedom. This procedure is justified from the point of view of the numerical values of the partition functions, which do not vary to any great extent with the molecular masses or moments of inertia; thus, as seen in Table 9, partition functions for a single degree of translational freedom are generally of the order of 10^8, while those for rotation are often between 10 and 100; those for vibration are close to unity except at elevated temperatures.

If the contributions of single translational, rotational, and vibrational degrees of freedom are written as f_T, f_R, and f_V, the total partition function F for a molecule may be expressed as

$$F = f_T^t f_R^r f_V^v \tag{73}$$

where t, r, and v are the numbers of the degrees of freedom contributing. For the reaction between two atoms, already considered,

$$F_A = f_T^3 \qquad F_B = f_T^3 \qquad F_{\ddagger} = f_T^3 f_R^2 \tag{74}$$

so that the rate constant of the reaction is given by

$$k = \frac{\mathbf{k}T}{\mathbf{h}} \frac{F_{\ddagger}}{F_{\mathrm{A}}F_{\mathrm{B}}} e^{-E_0/RT} \tag{75}$$

$$= \frac{\mathbf{k}T}{\mathbf{h}} \frac{f_R^2}{f_T^3} e^{-E_0/RT} \tag{76}$$

If the general case is now considered, where A and B are complex non-

[1] Cf. Bawn, *loc. cit.*

linear molecules containing N_A and N_B atoms, respectively,

$$F_A = f_T^3 f_R^3 f_V^{3N_A-6}$$
$$F_B = f_T^3 f_R^3 f_V^{3N_B-6} \tag{77}$$

and

$$F_\ddagger = f_T^3 f_R^3 f_V^{3(N_A+N_B)-7} \tag{78}$$

As always, the activated complex has one degree of vibrational freedom less than a normal molecule with $N_A + N_B$ atoms. The rate constant is now

$$k = \frac{\mathbf{k}T}{\mathbf{h}} \frac{f_V^5}{f_T^3 f_R^3} e^{-E_0/RT} \tag{79}$$

The rate constant therefore differs from that obtained in the atomic case by the factor $(f_V/f_R)^5$; the collision theory, by treating the molecules as hard spheres in all cases, is therefore in error by this factor. Since f_V is usually of the order of unity, whereas f_R may be from 10 to 100 for a complex molecule, the ratio f_V/f_R is 10^{-1} to 10^{-2}, so that $(f_V/f_R)^5$ is 10^{-5} to 10^{-10}. Reactions between complex molecules may therefore be expected to proceed very much more slowly than calculated on the basis of collision theory, and this is in fact found to be true, both in the gas phase and in solution. With less complex reacting species the discrepancy is not so great; thus with an atom and a diatomic molecule, forming a nonlinear activated complex, the factor is f_V/f_R, that is, 10^{-1} to 10^{-2}.

When the rate constants of bimolecular reactions are calculated using molecular units, the results are in the units cc molecule^{-1} sec^{-1}; for comparison with experiment these may be converted into liters mole^{-1} sec^{-1}. For reactions between relatively simple molecules the frequency factor A generally has a value of the order of 10^9 to 10^{11} liters mole^{-1} sec^{-1}, but for reactions between complex molecules it may be as low as 10^5. More will be said about the magnitudes of frequency factors in the next chapter.

Temperature Dependence of the Frequency Factor. It follows from the above formulation of the rate constant that the frequency factor A is not necessarily independent of temperature. Thus in rate equations such as (79) the temperature appears in the factor $\mathbf{k}T/\mathbf{h}$ and also in the partition functions for the reactants and the activated complex. Except for the vibrational factors, which are unity in most cases and do not depend strongly on temperature, the partition functions involve the temperature to a simple power, so that the rate constant for a reaction can be expressed in the form

$$k = aT^n e^{-E_0/RT} \tag{80}$$

The value of the exponent n depends upon the form taken by the partition functions; when the collision theory is used [Eq. (72)], n has a value of ½. The fact that plots of the logarithms of k against the reciprocal of the temperature are usually linear for elementary reactions is due to the much stronger temperature dependence of the exponential part than of the preexponential part. When the rate equation is of the above form the apparent energy of activation is temperature-dependent; the way in which it varies with temperature may be deduced as follows.

The experimental energy of activation E_{exp} is defined by

$$\frac{d \ln k}{dT} = \frac{E_{\text{exp}}}{RT^2} \tag{81}$$

since the experimental activation energy is determined by plotting the logarithm of k against the reciprocal of the absolute temperature. Differentiation of the logarithmic form of Eq. (80) gives

$$\frac{d \ln k}{dT} = \frac{n}{T} + \frac{E_0}{RT^2} = \frac{E_0 + nRT}{RT^2} \tag{82}$$

Comparison of these two equations leads to the relationship

$$E_{\text{exp}} = E_0 + nRT \tag{83}$$

At the absolute zero the energy of activation is the difference between the zero-point levels in the initial and the activated states, whereas at any other temperature it is the difference between the average energies of the reactants and of the activated complex. Unless n is very large or E_0 is very small, it may be difficult experimentally to detect this temperature-dependence of the energy of activation. Except for some termolecular reactions, considered in the next chapter, this does not appear to have been done for gas reactions, but there are some reactions in solution where the temperature variations are very large and have been detected.

THE THERMODYNAMICAL FORMULATION OF REACTION RATES

It is frequently convenient to express the rate constants of reactions in terms of thermodynamical functions rather than partition functions; this is often done with reactions in solution, since partition functions of species in the liquid phase are very difficult to evaluate. The thermodynamical formulation of rate constants is based on the fact that the equilibrium between reactants and activated complexes may be expressed in terms of thermodynamical functions as well as by using partition functions.

The equilibrium constant for the process $A + B \rightleftharpoons X^\ddagger$ may be written as

$$K^\ddagger = \left(\frac{[X_\ddagger]}{[A][B]}\right)_{\text{eq}} = \frac{F_\ddagger}{F_A F_B} e^{-E_0/RT} \tag{84}$$

Strictly speaking the partition function of the activated complex that appears in this expression should be $F^{\ddagger}$ instead of $F_{\ddagger}$. The equilibrium constant $K^{\ddagger}$ is therefore a special type of equilibrium constant. Comparison of Eqs. (84) and (56) leads to

$$k = \frac{\mathbf{k}T}{\mathbf{h}} K^{\ddagger} \tag{85}$$

and if $K^{\ddagger}$ is expressed in terms of $\Delta G^{\ddagger}$, the increase in Gibbs free energy in the passage from the initial state to the activated state, the result is

$$k = \frac{\mathbf{k}T}{\mathbf{h}} e^{-\Delta G^{\ddagger}/RT} \tag{86}$$

If this free energy of activation $\Delta G^{\ddagger}$ is expressed in terms of an entropy and a heat of activation, i.e., as $\Delta H^{\ddagger} - T\,\Delta S^{\ddagger}$, the result is

$$k = \frac{\mathbf{k}T}{\mathbf{h}} e^{\Delta S^{\ddagger}/R} e^{-\Delta H^{\ddagger}/RT} \tag{87}$$

This equation was first derived in 1935 by Wynne-Jones and Eyring.[1] If k is expressed in liters mole^{-1} sec^{-1}, the standard state for the free energy and the entropy of activation is 1 mole per liter.

Equation (87) may be expressed in a form that involves the experimental energy of activation, E_{exp}, instead of the heat of activation $\Delta H^{\ddagger}$. Since $K^{\ddagger}$ is a concentration equilibrium constant, its variation with temperature is given by the equation

$$\frac{d \ln K^{\ddagger}}{dT} = \frac{\Delta E^{\ddagger}}{RT^2} \tag{88}$$

where $\Delta E^{\ddagger}$ is the increase in energy in passing from the initial state to the activated state. Differentiation of the logarithmic form of Eq. (85) gives

$$\frac{d \ln k}{dT} = \frac{1}{T} + \frac{d \ln K^{\ddagger}}{dT} \tag{89}$$

and together with Eq. (88) this gives

$$\frac{d \ln k}{dT} = \frac{1}{T} + \frac{\Delta E^{\ddagger}}{RT^2} = \frac{RT + \Delta E^{\ddagger}}{RT^2} \tag{90}$$

Comparison of this equation with Eq. (81) above leads to

$$E_{\text{exp}} = RT + \Delta E^{\ddagger} \tag{91}$$

The relationship between $\Delta E^{\ddagger}$ and $\Delta H^{\ddagger}$ is

$$\Delta H^{\ddagger} = \Delta E^{\ddagger} + P\,\Delta V^{\ddagger} \tag{92}$$

[1] W. F. K. Wynne-Jones and H. Eyring, *J. Chem. Phys.*, **3**, 492 (1935).

where $\Delta V^{\ddagger}$ is the increase in volume in going from the initial state to the activated state. Substitution of this into Eq. (91) gives

$$E_{\text{exp}} = \Delta H^{\ddagger} - P\,\Delta V^{\ddagger} + RT \tag{93}$$

For unimolecular reactions there is no change in the number of molecules as the activated molecule is formed, and $\Delta V^{\ddagger}$ is therefore zero; $\Delta V^{\ddagger}$ is also small for reactions in solution. In these cases

$$E_{\text{exp}} = \Delta H^{\ddagger} + RT \tag{94}$$

and the rate equation may therefore be written as

$$k = \frac{\mathbf{k}T}{\mathbf{h}}\, e^{\Delta S^{\ddagger}/R} e^{-(E_{\text{exp}}-RT)/RT} \tag{95}$$

or as

$$k = e\,\frac{\mathbf{k}T}{\mathbf{h}}\, e^{\Delta S^{\ddagger}/R} e^{-E_{\text{exp}}/RT} \tag{96}$$

For gas reactions the general relationship is

$$P\,\Delta V^{\ddagger} = \Delta n^{\ddagger}\, RT \tag{97}$$

where $\Delta n^{\ddagger}$ is the increase in the number of molecules when the activated complex is formed from the reactants. In a bimolecular reaction, for example, two molecules become one, so that $\Delta n^{\ddagger}$ is equal to -1; in this case the experimental energy of activation is related to the heat of activation by the relationship

$$E_{\text{exp}} = \Delta H^{\ddagger} + 2RT \tag{98}$$

From this it follows that the rate constant may be written as

$$k = e^2\,\frac{\mathbf{k}T}{\mathbf{h}}\, e^{\Delta S^{\ddagger}/R} e^{-E_{\text{exp}}/RT} \tag{99}$$

It is of interest to note that for agreement with the collision theory the entropy of activation, relative to the units of liters mole^{-1} sec^{-1}, must be about -12 eu. If, on the other hand, the standard state is 1 mole per cc, i.e., if the rate-constant units are cc mole^{-1} sec^{-1}, the entropy of activation must be approximately zero for agreement with the collision theory. For this reason the units cc mole^{-1} sec^{-1} are perhaps more convenient.

ISOTOPE EFFECTS ON REACTION RATES[1]

Some information about reactions has been provided by studies of the effects on rates of replacing an atom in a reactant by one of its iso-

[1] For a review see L. Melander, "Isotope Effects on Reaction Rates," The Ronald Press Company, New York, 1960.

topes. Such *kinetic isotope effects* are greatest when an ordinary hydrogen atom is replaced by deuterium or tritium, since these substitutions correspond to large relative changes in the mass of the atom. The isotope effects are particularly great when the reaction involves a complete or almost complete breaking of the bond to the "labeled" atom.

The theory of isotope effects is a very complicated one, and cannot easily be applied in detail to individual reactions. This arises because when an isotopic substitution is made, a number of relatively small effects are involved, and all of them must be treated accurately in order for it to be possible for the overall effect to be predicted. A rigorous theory of isotope effects has been worked out by Bigeleisen, and a brief account of it is given later. First will be given a simple and qualitative treatment of the problem, with emphasis on the directions of the observed effects, and on the conditions under which the effects will be large.

When an atom is replaced by an isotope, there is no change in the potential-energy surface for any reaction that it might undergo. The reason that there is a change in rate is that there is a change in the average vibrational energy of the molecule and of the activated complex. This may be understood with reference to the species H_2, HD, and D_2. The potential-energy curves are identical for all three species, but the zero-point levels are different; their values, relative to the minimum in the curve, are 6.18, 5.36, and 4.39 kcal, respectively. At relatively low temperatures the molecules reside largely at their zero-point levels. It therefore follows that the molecule H_2 requires less energy (103.22 kcal) to reach its dissociated state than does D_2, for which the energy needed is 105.02 kcal. Thus a reaction in which the dissociation of H_2 is involved will, if no other factors are important, occur more rapidly than one involving HD or D_2.

With more complex molecules the situation is qualitatively similar. Consider, for example, a reaction involving a molecule containing a C—H bond. This molecule executes a complicated type of vibration, and there will be $3N - 6$ normal modes, where N is the number of atoms in the molecule. To a very good approximation some of these frequencies can be regarded as associated with individual bonds; most molecules containing a C—H bond, for example, have a vibrational frequency of 2,900 to 3,000 cm^{-1}, and this is attributed to the presence of the C—H bond. Replacement of the H atom by D changes this vibrational frequency to between 2,000 and 2,100 cm^{-1}. The ratio of the two frequencies is approximately equal to the square root of the ratio of the masses of H and D, and this fact supports the conclusion that these frequencies are associated with the individual bonds.

The situation regarding the reaction of a molecule containing a C—H or C—D bond is therefore very similar to that regarding the reactions of H_2, HD, and D_2. An ordinary C—H bond vibration has a zero-point energy that is greater by about 1.2 kcal than that of the C—D bond. The average vibrational energy of the molecule containing the C—H bond will therefore be higher, by approximately this amount, than that of the corresponding molecule in which H has been replaced by D. If, therefore, the two molecules are involved in a reaction for which the C—H or C—D bond is completely or largely broken in the activated complex, the activation energy of the reaction will be higher for the compound in which H has been replaced by D; the rate will therefore be larger for the light molecule.

If on the other hand the bond involving the H or D atom is far from completely broken in the activated state, the situation is different. Figure 22 shows the energy relationships in the normal and activated states. The curve corresponding to the normal state is the potential-energy curve for one particular vibration, such as one involving a C—H or C—D bond. The zero-point levels are shown, with the level for C—H higher

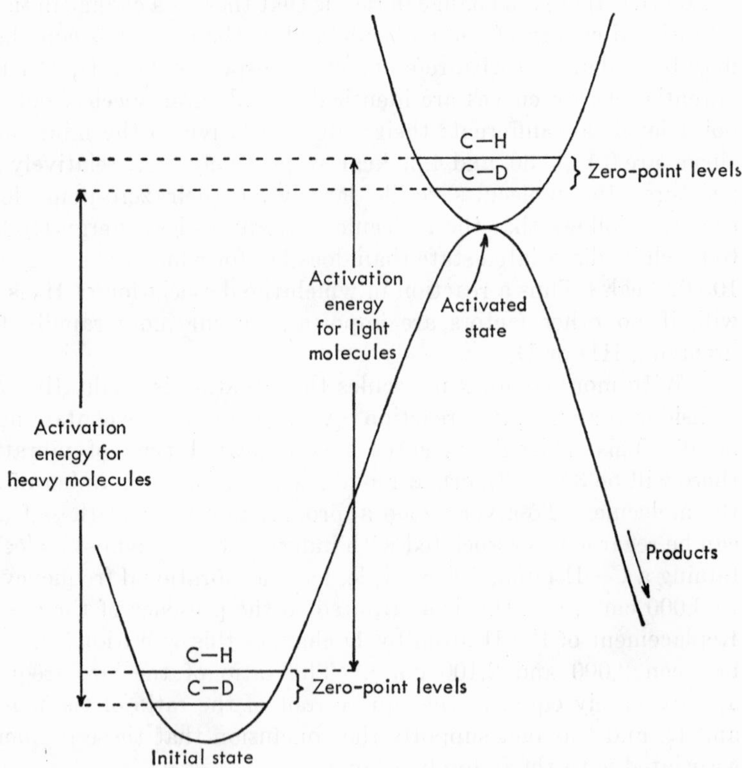

Fig. 22. Potential-energy diagram for a reaction, showing the effect of changing from one isotope to another. For the case illustrated, the C—H or C—D bond remains practically the same in the activated state, so that the isotope effect is very small.

than that for C—D. The upper curve corresponds to one of the vibrations in the activated state. If the C—H or C—D bond is completely broken in the activated state the zero-point levels are obviously the same for the light and heavy complexes and the rate will be greater for the light molecule, as discussed above. If the C—H or C—D bond does not change at all when the activated complex is formed, the difference between the zero-point levels will be the same as in the initial state; the energy of activation will then be the same for both compounds, and the isotope effect will be small. If the C—H or C—D bond is weakened, there will be a smaller isotope effect than when the bond is completely broken.

It is possible for the bond involving a hydrogen atom to become stronger in the activated state; this can occur, for example, if a hydrogen atom is transferred from one atom to another. Replacement of H by D will then lead to a greater decrease in energy in the activated state than in the initial state, and the activation energy will therefore be less for the heavy molecule. Under these circumstances there will be an *inverse* or *reverse* isotope effect, the heavy molecule reacting more rapidly than the light one.

Quantitative Treatments.[1] Since kinetic isotope effects are generally small, they can be treated satisfactorily only by avoiding approximations and making rate calculations in as exact a manner as possible. This at once presents a serious difficulty, since there are still no reliable methods for arriving at potential-energy surfaces. It is true that in the treatment of isotope effects the errors cancel to some extent, since the surfaces are identical for the two reactions that are being compared. In spite of this, the isotope ratios do depend in a rather important way on the exact nature of the activated complexes, and on the reaction coordinate.

The theoretical work that has been done on kinetic isotope effects can be divided into two general classes. In the first place, certain workers have proceeded by arriving at the best potential-energy surfaces for the reaction, and making absolute calculations of the rates of the reactions that are to be compared. Work along these lines has, for example, been done by Polanyi[2] for the various isotopic reactions of the type

$$CH_3 + H_2 \rightarrow CH_4 + H$$

and by Weston[3] and Shavitt[4] on the isotopic reactions of the type

$$H + H_2 \rightarrow H_2 + H$$

[1] This section may well be omitted on first reading.

[2] J. C. Polanyi, *J. Chem. Phys.*, **23**, 1505 (1955).

[3] R. E. Weston, *ibid.*, **31**, 892 (1959); cf. D. Rapp and R. E. Weston, *ibid.*, **36**, 2807 (1962).

[4] I. Shavitt, *ibid.*, **31**, 1359 (1959).

Work of this kind has thrown light on the question of what are the best methods for arriving at potential-energy surfaces.

The second class of theoretical investigations on kinetic isotope effects comprises studies of a more general nature, in which an effort has been made to arrive at conclusions that may be expected to apply to a variety of reactions. Much work along these lines has been carried out by Bigeleisen;[1] his approach to the problem, and related studies, have been reviewed in an article by Bigeleisen and Wolfsberg.[2] Only a very brief account of his treatment can be given in this book.

Consider a general reaction of the type

$$A_1 + B_1 + C_1 + \cdots \rightleftharpoons X_1^{\ddagger} \rightarrow \text{products}$$

where the subscript 1 denotes particular isotopic species; an analogous reaction in which other species are involved may be written as

$$A_2 + B_2 + C_2 + \cdots \rightleftharpoons X_2^{\ddagger} \rightarrow \text{products}$$

The ratio of rate constants, assuming equal transmission coefficients, is then given by

$$\frac{k_1}{k_2} = \frac{F_1^{\ddagger}}{F_2^{\ddagger}} \frac{F_{A_2} F_{B_2} F_{C_2} \cdots}{F_{A_1} F_{B_1} F_{C_1} \cdots} \tag{100}$$

where the F's are the complete partition functions for the species indicated. These partition functions are supposed to be related to the same energy level, and the exponential energy term need therefore not be included.

It is now possible, making use of the Teller-Redlich product rule, to obtain an expression[3] for a ratio of partition functions; in general, this ratio may be written as F_2/F_1, and the following relationship may be derived:

$$\frac{F_2}{F_1} \frac{s_2}{s_1} \prod_{j=1}^{n} \left(\frac{m_{1j}}{m_{2j}} \right)^{3/2} = \prod_{i=1}^{3n-6} \frac{u_{2i}}{u_{1i}} \exp\left(\frac{u_{1i} - u_{2i}}{2} \right) \frac{1 - e^{-u_{1i}}}{1 - e^{-u_{2i}}} \tag{101}$$

In this equation the s's are the symmetry numbers of the respective molecules, the m's are the masses of the constituent atoms of the molecules, and $u_i = \mathbf{h}\nu_i/\mathbf{k}T$, where ν_i is the ith vibrational frequency. It is to be seen that on the left-hand side of this equation there is the product, over all the atoms, of the ratio $(m_1/m_2)^{3/2}$. On the right-hand side there is the product of factors for each degree of vibrational freedom; for linear molecules there will be $3n - 5$ of these instead of $3n - 6$. The subscript

[1] J. W. Bigeleisen, *ibid.*, **17**, 675 (1949) and many later papers.

[2] J. W. Bigeleisen and M. Wolfsberg, in I. Prigogine (ed.), "Advances in Chemical Physics," vol. I, Interscience Publishers, New York, 1958.

[3] J. W. Bigeleisen and M. Goeppert-Mayer, *J. Chem. Phys.*, **15**, 261 (1947).

1 may be taken to refer to the lighter molecule, and Δu_i may be written for $u_{1i} - u_{2i}$; Eq. (101) then becomes

$$\frac{F_2}{F_1}\frac{s_2}{s_1}\prod_{j=1}^{n}\left(\frac{m_{1j}}{m_{2j}}\right)^{3/2} = \prod_{i=1}^{3n-6}\frac{u_i}{u_i + \Delta u_i}\, e^{\Delta u_i/2}\,\frac{1 - \exp\left[-(u_i + \Delta u_i)\right]}{1 - e^{-u_i}} \tag{102}$$

where u_i now refers to the heavier molecule. Since atoms always balance out in any chemical equilibrium, the product $\prod_{j=1}^{n}\left(\frac{m_{1j}}{m_{2j}}\right)^{3/2}$ cancels out in the equilibrium expression, including that for the equilibrium between reactants and activated complexes.

The left-hand side of Eq. (102) is conveniently written as $(s_2/s_1)f$, so that one can write

$$\frac{s_2}{s_1}f = \prod_{i=1}^{3n-6}\frac{u_i}{u_i + \Delta u_i}\, e^{\Delta u_i/2}\,\frac{1 - \exp\left[-(u_i + \Delta u_i)\right]}{1 - e^{-u_i}} \tag{103}$$

For the case of the isotopes of all elements except hydrogen, and except at low temperatures, Δu is much less than unity, and Eq. (103) may then be written as

$$\frac{s_2}{s_1}f = \prod_{i=1}^{3n-6}\left[1 + G(u_i)\,\Delta u_i\right] \tag{104}$$

$$\simeq 1 + \sum_{i=1}^{3n-6} G(u_i)\,\Delta u_i \tag{105}$$

The function $G(u)$ is defined by

$$G(u) = \frac{1}{2} - \frac{1}{u} + \frac{1}{e^u - 1} \tag{106}$$

and has been tabulated. When u and Δu are both small, it can be shown that

$$\frac{s_2}{s_1}f \simeq 1 + \frac{\bar{\gamma}}{24}\sum_{i=1}^{3n-6}\left(u_{1_i}{}^2 - u_{2_i}{}^2\right) \tag{107}$$

where $\bar{\gamma}$ is an average value of γ_i, which is defined as

$$\gamma_i = \frac{12G(u_i)}{u_i} \tag{108}$$

At small values of u the quantity $\bar{\gamma}$ is close to unity. The u's are related to the masses of the atoms in the molecule and to the force constants, and it is found that Eq. (107) may be expressed as

$$\frac{s_2}{s_1} f \simeq 1 + \left(\frac{\mathrm{h}}{2\pi \mathbf{k} T}\right)^2 \frac{\bar{\gamma}}{24} \sum_{j=1}^{3n} \left(\frac{1}{m_{1j}} - \frac{1}{m_{2j}}\right) a_{jj} \tag{109}$$

where a_{jj} is the diagonal force constant. The usefulness of this approximate relationship derives from the fact that $\bar{\gamma}$ does not vary strongly with u, so that its value can be estimated quite accurately even if the u's (i.e., the frequencies) are not known with high accuracy. Estimates of the diagonal force constants a_{jj} can also be made quite satisfactorily.

The situation with regard to $F_1^\ddagger/F_2^\ddagger$ is slightly different, since the partition functions for the activated complexes lack the contributions due to the motion over the top of the energy barrier. By analogy with Eq. (102) one can write

$$\frac{F_2^\ddagger}{F_1^\ddagger} \frac{s_2^\ddagger}{s_1^\ddagger} \prod_{j=1}^{n} \left(\frac{m_{1j}}{m_{2j}}\right)^{3/2} = \prod_{i=1}^{3n-6} \frac{u_{2i}^\ddagger}{u_{1i}^\ddagger} \prod_{i=1}^{3n-7} \exp\left(\frac{\Delta u_i^\ddagger}{2}\right) \frac{1 - \exp(-u_{1i}^\ddagger)}{1 - \exp(-u_{2i}^\ddagger)} \tag{110}$$

In the second product there are only $3n - 7$, instead of $3n - 6$, factors, in view of the lack of the contribution due to motion over the barrier. One of the $3n - 6$ factors appearing in the first product refers to this decomposition mode, and is a nongenuine vibration; the corresponding ν will be written as $\nu_L^\ddagger$. Equation (110) can then be written as

$$\frac{F_2^\ddagger}{F_1^\ddagger} \frac{s_2^\ddagger}{s_1^\ddagger} \prod_{j=1}^{n} \left(\frac{m_{1j}}{m_{2j}}\right)^{3/2} = \frac{\nu_{2L}^\ddagger}{\nu_{1L}^\ddagger} \prod_{i=1}^{3n-7} \frac{u_{2i}^\ddagger}{u_{1i}^\ddagger} \exp\left(\frac{\Delta u_i^\ddagger}{2}\right) \frac{1 - \exp(-u_{1i}^\ddagger)}{1 - \exp(-u_{2i}^\ddagger)} \tag{111}$$

In exactly the same manner as previously [cf. Eq. (105)] this can be reduced to

$$\frac{s_2^\ddagger}{s_1^\ddagger} f^\ddagger \simeq \frac{\nu_{2L}^\ddagger}{\nu_{1L}^\ddagger} \left[1 + \sum_{i=1}^{3n-7} G(u_i^\ddagger)\, \Delta u_i^\ddagger\right] \tag{112}$$

where $(s_2^\ddagger/s_1^\ddagger)f^\ddagger$ is equal to the left-hand side of Eq. (111).

For the case of a reaction involving only one isotopic reactant

$$\frac{k_1}{k_2} = \frac{F_1^\ddagger}{F_2^\ddagger} \frac{F_2}{F_1} \tag{113}$$

where F_1 and F_2 are the partition functions for the isotopic reactants, and $F_1^\ddagger$ and $F_2^\ddagger$ for the corresponding activated complexes. Insertion of Eqs. (105) and (112) into this expression gives, provided that Δu is small,

$$\frac{k_1}{k_2} \frac{s_2 s_1^\ddagger}{s_1 s_2^\ddagger} = \frac{\nu_{1L}^\ddagger}{\nu_{2L}^\ddagger} \left[1 + \sum_{i=1}^{3n-6} G(u_i)\, \Delta u_i - \sum_{i=1}^{3n-7} G(u_i^\ddagger)\, \Delta u_i^\ddagger\right] \tag{114}$$

If one employs the same procedure that led to Eq. (109), the result is

$$\frac{k_1}{k_2}\frac{s_2 s_1^\ddagger}{s_1 s_2^\ddagger} = \frac{\nu_{1L}^\ddagger}{\nu_{2L}^\ddagger}\left[1 + \frac{\bar{\gamma}}{24}\left(\frac{\mathbf{h}}{2\pi \mathbf{k}T}\right)^2 \sum_{i=1}^{3n}\left(\frac{1}{m_{1i}} - \frac{1}{m_{2i}}\right)(a_{ii} - a_{ii}^\ddagger)\right] \quad (115)$$

In some cases a tunneling correction must be applied to this equation.

Equation (115) has proved of value in arriving at predictions of isotope effects in a number of cases. Equation (114) is of particular interest in leading to conclusions about maximum isotope effects. If, by convention, the subscripts 1 and 2 refer to the light and heavy isotopes, respectively, $\nu_{1L}^\ddagger$ is equal to or greater than $\nu_{2L}^\ddagger$. Moreover $G(u)$ and Δu are positive, $G(u)$ increasing with increasing u to the maximum value of ½. Usually the binding is greater in the reacting molecule than in the activated complex, and Eq. (114) then leads to the result that $k_1 > k_2$. In the cases in which the isotopic reactants are atoms, $G(u)\,\Delta u$ is zero, and then k_1/k_2 may be less than unity; there is then an *inverse* or *reverse* isotope effect.

Estimates of maximum regular and inverse isotope effects may be made as follows. For simplicity the symmetry numbers will be omitted. The maximum regular isotope effect will be obtained if there is no isotope effect in the activated complex, which means that there is no binding of the isotopic species in the activated complex. The maximum value of $\nu_{1L}^\ddagger/\nu_{2L}^\ddagger$ is $(m_2/m_1)^{1/2}$, where the m's are the masses of the isotopic atoms. On this basis the maximum values of $k_1 s_2 s_1^\ddagger / k_2 s_1 s_2^\ddagger$ can be estimated using Eq. (115). Some results are given in Table 10.

Table 10 ESTIMATED MAXIMUM REGULAR ISOTOPE EFFECTS AT 25°C

Isotopic forms	$k_1 s_2 s_1^\ddagger / k_2 s_1 s_2^\ddagger$
H, D	18
H, T	60
C^{12}, C^{13}	1.25
C^{12}, C^{14}	1.5
N^{14}, N^{16}	1.25
O^{16}, O^{18}	1.19
Na^{22}, Na^{23}	1.03

Maximum values for inverse isotope effects may be calculated by setting $G(u)\,\Delta u$ equal to zero, and by taking $\nu_{1L}^\ddagger/\nu_{2L}^\ddagger$ as unity, which is the minimum value of this ratio. Maximum values for $G(u_i^\ddagger)\,\Delta u_i^\ddagger$ are estimated by using the values for strongly bonded molecules.

A small isotope effect may be observed when the isotopic atoms are not involved in a bond that is broken or formed during reaction; such isotope effects are referred to as *secondary*. In such cases $\nu_{1L}^\ddagger$ will be very close to $\nu_{2L}^\ddagger$, and the secondary isotope effect can be calculated by considering only $f/f^\ddagger$; the major contribution to this arises from large shifts in high frequencies. Upper limits of secondary isotope effects can be estimated on the basis of the following assumptions and approximations:

1. Only stretching frequencies are considered.
2. The isotope shifts in these frequencies are calculated, assuming the bond to belong to a diatomic molecule.
3. The stretching force constant is assumed to change by a factor of 2 in the activated complex; it will decrease by this factor for a regular secondary isotope effect and increase by this factor for an inverse secondary effect. Some results obtained on this basis are given in Table 11. If a compound is labeled in more than one position (e.g., $—CD_3$ as compared with $—CH_3$), the effects will be proportionately larger.

Table 11 ESTIMATED UPPER LIMITS OF SECONDARY ISOTOPE EFFECTS AT 25°C

Bond	Isotopic forms	Regular secondary isotope effects	Inverse secondary isotope effects
C—H	H, D	1.74	0.46
C—H	H, T	2.20	0.33
O—H	H, D	2.02	0.37
O—H	H, T	2.74	0.24
C—C	C^{12}, C^{13}	1.012	0.983
C—C	C^{12}, C^{14}	1.023	0.968

Even with the use of equations such as (115), the problem of calculating isotopic rate ratios remains a very difficult one. The main uncertainty results from the choice of the reaction coordinate, which can only be decided upon after one has a reliable potential-energy surface. The ratio $\nu_{1L}^{\ddagger}/\nu_{2L}^{\ddagger}$ depends upon this choice of reaction coordinate, as do the values of the force constants $a_{jj}^{\ddagger}$. In making calculations care must be taken that the equation used [e.g., Eq. (114)] does not contain approximations that are serious enough to invalidate the conclusions obtained.

OTHER THEORETICAL TREATMENTS[1]

The previous sections in this chapter have been confined to rather general aspects of potential-energy surfaces and of the theory of absolute

[1] This section might well be omitted by readers who are not concerned with the more advanced aspects of theoretical chemical kinetics. Those who are interested in a more detailed account are referred to a review by K. J. Laidler and J. C. Polanyi, in G. Porter (ed.), "Progress in Reaction Kinetics," vol. 3, Pergamon Press, Oxford, 1965.

reaction rates. During recent years a very considerable amount of theoretical work has been done on the problem of reaction rates, and also on questions such as the way in which energy is transferred in a chemical reaction. This section gives a brief account of some of these investigations, particular attention being devoted to (1) recent quantum-mechanical, semiempirical, and empirical treatments of potential-energy surfaces, (2) classical and quantum-mechanical treatments of the "kinematics" of chemical reactions—that is, of the way in which systems move over potential-energy surfaces, (3) theories of reaction rates in terms of nonequilibrium statistical mechanics, and (4) "stochastic" theories of reaction rates.

Potential-energy Surfaces. Reference has been made to the original calculation, by Eyring and Polanyi, of a potential-energy surface for the system $H + H_2$. This work was based on London's expression for the potential energy of a system of three atoms; this in turn was based on approximations introduced by Heitler and London and also involved other approximations such as the neglect of overlap integrals. Eyring and Polanyi made semiempirical calculations, in terms of a constant fraction of coulombic to exchange energy. They considered the possibility of making a calculation using the actual coulombic and exchange integrals that had previously been computed by Suguira,[1] but did not actually perform the calculations since they felt that the inaccuracies would be too great. Very recently these calculations have been done by Kuntz, Nemeth, and J. C. Polanyi,[2] and their calculated activation energy is about 8.8 kcal, to be compared with the experimental figure of 8 to 9 kcal. This agreement must, however, be regarded as fortuitous since some of the terms that were neglected are larger than the quantity calculated. A full Heitler-London calculation was also carried out some years ago by Magee[3] for the reactions $X + H_2 \rightarrow HX + H$ and $H + HX \rightarrow H_2 + X$, where X is a halogen atom.

The variation method is a much more reliable one for calculating energies, and a number of calculations have been made using it. The nature of a variational calculation is that it cannot yield an energy lower than the true; improvements in the wave functions give lower and lower energies that gradually approach the experimental ones. In a series of papers Hirschfelder, Eyring, and coworkers[4] constructed wave functions on the basis of 1*s* hydrogen-like atomic orbitals, and calculated activation energies ranging from 13.6 to over 30 kcal per mole; these are energies

[1] Y. Suguira, *Z. Physik*, **45**, 484 (1927).

[2] P. J. Kuntz, E. N. Nemeth, and J. C. Polanyi, private communication.

[3] J. L. Magee, *J. Chem. Phys.*, **8**, 677 (1940).

[4] J. O. Hirschfelder, H. Eyring, and N. Rosen, *ibid.*, **4**, 121 (1936); J. O. Hirschfelder, H. Diamond, and H. Eyring, *ibid.*, **5**, 695 (1937); D. P. Stevenson and J. O. Hirschfelder, *ibid.*, 933.

relative to the *calculated* energies of $H + H_2$. Later Hirschfelder[1] used an early computer to evaluate the three-center integrals for nonlinear symmetrical configurations; he showed that the linear H—H—H complex is much more stable than the nonlinear ones.

For some 15 years there was little work on this problem, but with the advent of high-speed computers there has been a considerable revival of interest. Walsh and Matsen[2] calculated the binding energy of H_3, using several molecular-orbital approximations, but appear to have made an error in setting up their wave function.[3] Their most complete treatment was repeated by Ransil[4] who obtained an energy of 13.3 kcal for the H_3 activated complex, relative to their calculated energy for $H + H_2$. Barker and Eyring[5] carried out variational calculations in which the effective charge on the central atom was varied, and obtained an energy of about 20 kcal.

Trulio and Kimball[6] increased the number of atomic orbitals beyond the three used in all previous calculations; they constructed an LCAO-MO wave function from five 1*s* hydrogen-like orbitals with centers equally spaced along the line of nuclei. By varying effective charges and other parameters they calculated an energy for the H_3 activated complex that was lower by 11.7 kcal than that calculated by Ransil. Their calculated energy was still 19.9 kcal above their calculated energy for $H + H_2$, and was 37 kcal higher than the experimental value for $H + H_2$.

The most complete variational treatment to date has been carried out by Boys and Shavitt.[7] Their method was to locate a pair of 1*s* orbitals at each nucleus, with different effective nuclear charges for the members of each pair. As in all previous work they found the linear configuration to be most stable. Their binding energy, however, was only 7.8 kcal better than that calculated by Kimball and Trulio; the energy of the H_3 activated complex was 15.4 kcal higher than their calculated value for $H + H_2$, but 29.2 kcal higher than the true value for $H + H_2$. There thus still remains an unbridged gap of about 21 kcal between the experimental and calculated binding energies. The discrepancy can be reduced by the device of reckoning the energies with respect to the calculated energies for $H + H_2$. However even a value of

[1] J. O. Hirschfelder, *ibid.*, **6**, 795 (1938); J. O. Hirschfelder and C. N. Weygandt, *ibid.*, 806.

[2] J. M. Walsh and F. A. Matsen, *ibid.*, **19**, 526 (1951).

[3] S. F. Boys and I. Shavitt, *Univ. Wisconsin Naval Res. Lab. Tech. Rept.* WIS-AF-13 (1959).

[4] B. J. Ransil, *J. Chem. Phys.*, **26**, 971 (1957); V. Griffing, J. L. Jackson, and B. J. Ransil, *ibid.*, **30**, 1066 (1959).

[5] R. S. Barker and H. Eyring, *ibid.*, **22**, 1182 (1954).

[6] J. G. Trulio and G. E. Kimball, *ibid.*, **28**, 493 (1958).

[7] Boys and Shavitt, *loc. cit.*

15.4 kcal differs considerably from the experimental value of 8 to 9, and would lead to very serious errors in the calculation of rate constants.

In view of this disappointing situation considerable effort has recently been devoted to developing reliable semiempirical procedures for arriving at potential-energy surfaces. The earliest method, that of Eyring and Polanyi, was discussed earlier in this chapter, as was the later procedure suggested by Sato. These treatments are equally empirical, and it is hard to choose between them: the Sato method is to be preferred in view of the fact that it does not give a basin at the activated state, but it seems to be inferior in leading to a barrier that is too thin.

Two recent treatments of potential-energy surfaces, due to Yasumori[1] and to Porter and Karplus,[2] are Heitler-London treatments and are semiempirical in the sense that they make empirical adjustments to some of the integrals. Yasumori used the effective charge as an adjustable parameter, varying it by finding what value best accounted for the difference in energy between bonding and antibonding states. His potential-energy surface was free of basins and had a barrier height of 8.5 kcal. Porter and Karplus evaluated some of the Heitler-London integrals theoretically, and some semiempirically. Each exchange integral, for example, was split into a diatomic exchange integral and a residual term, which was calculated using an adjustable multiplier. Their barrier height was 8.58 kcal, very close to that of Yasumori and in good agreement with experiment. As of 1965, the potential-energy surface of Porter and Karplus appears to be the most satisfactory one that has been obtained.

A very different approach has been taken by Lippincott and Leifer,[3] who applied rigorous quantum mechanics to a very approximate model; they assumed, for example, that a "square-well" attraction law applies to the binding of an electron by its nucleus. Their treatment led to two shallow basins, one at each side of the saddle point, and to a barrier height of 6.8 kcal.

Johnston and coworkers[4] have developed a "bond-energy–bond-order" treatment which involves no adjustable parameters. They made use of Pauling's simple relation between bond length r and bond order n,

$$r = r_S - 0.26 \ln n \tag{116}$$

where r_S is the single-bond length in the particular homologous series.

[1] I. Yasumori, *Bull. Chem. Soc. Japan*, **32**, 1103, 1110 (1959).

[2] R. N. Porter and M. Karplus, *J. Chem. Phys.*, **40**, 1105 (1964).

[3] E. R. Lippincott and A. Leifer, *ibid.*, **28**, 769 (1958); cf. E. R. Lippincott, *ibid.*, **26**, 1678 (1957).

[4] H. S. Johnston, *Advan. Chem. Phys.*, **3**, 131 (1960); H. S. Johnston and P. Goldfinger, *J. Chem. Phys.*, **37**, 700 (1962); H. S. Johnston and C. Parr, *J. Am. Chem. Soc.*, **85**, 2544 (1963).

They relate bond energy D to single-bond energy D_S by the equation

$$D = D_S n^p \tag{117}$$

where p is a constant. Johnston and coworkers base their method on the postulate that for the transfer of a hydrogen atom

$$n_1 + n_2 = 1 \tag{118}$$

where n_1 is the bond order of the bond being broken, and n_2 that of the bond being formed. Through Eq. (116) this determines the changes in bond lengths, and through (117) the changes in energies of the bonds. The procedure involves the assumption that it is legitimate to treat the bonds separately. This simple treatment has been remarkably successful in arriving at reliable estimates of the activation energies of a number of reactions.

Earlier in this chapter reference was made to purely empirical procedures for estimating activation energies. A number of proposals have been made for arriving at the entire potential-energy surface in an empirical manner. Wall and Porter[1] made use of the fact that the section through a potential-energy surface becomes a Morse function when any one of the three atoms is removed to infinity, and generated a surface by rotating a Morse curve through 90°. As it rotated, the Morse curve was distorted in a systematic manner. A very similar procedure, but one that was more suitable for unsymmetrical activated complexes, was employed by Blais and Bunker[2] and by Karplus and Raff.[3] An entirely different approach to an empirical surface has been made by J. C. Polanyi,[4] who added variable parameters to the already largely empirical London-Eyring-Polanyi-Sato expression.

Kinematics: Classical Treatments. So far in this chapter attention has been confined to the theoretical treatment of overall reaction rates—of the rates of production of products and of disappearance of reactants. During recent years there has been increasing interest in what might be called the "fine structure" of reaction rates. Studies with crossed molecular beams (cf. p. 136) and on infrared chemiluminescence (p. 135) have revealed valuable information about the way in which the energy released in a reaction is distributed among the products. In order to gain an understanding of this, it is necessary to treat in more detail the actual passage of a molecular system over a potential-energy surface.

[1] F. T. Wall and R. N. Porter, *J. Chem. Phys.*, **36**, 3256 (1962).

[2] N. C. Blais and D. L. Bunker, *ibid.*, **37**, 2713 (1962).

[3] M. Karplus and L. M. Raff, private communication.

[4] J. C. Polanyi, *J. Quant. Spectr. Radiative Transfer*, **3**, 471 (1963); E. Nemeth, J. C. Polanyi, D. Rosner, and C. Young, to be published.

Theoretical studies of this kind have been referred to as *kinematic* studies, and the subject of *kinematics* may be said to have as its object the elucidation of the connection between the form of the potential-energy surface and the distribution of energy and angular momentum among the products of reaction. The importance of experimental and theoretical studies of this kind stems from the difficulty with which potential-energy surfaces can be arrived at, even when a considerable amount of empiricism is introduced. An experimental study of energy distributions combined with a kinematic treatment for a variety of potential-energy surfaces can yield valuable information about the shapes of potential-energy surfaces: some examples are considered later.

One point that should be made at the outset, since it is frequently misunderstood, is that the result that products are formed with abnormal energy distributions is in no way inconsistent with the assumption that there is equilibrium between initial and activated states in a chemical reaction. It is occasionally stated that the results of molecular-beam and chemiluminescence studies disprove the theory of absolute reaction rates. This conclusion is based on a misconception. The crucial point is that except in special cases (cf. p. 108), equilibrium exists up to the activated state, but that the motion of the system down the valley introduces disequilibrium, depending (as will be seen) on the shape of the surface from the activated state onward. It would, in fact, be possible in kinematic calculations to take the activated state as the starting point and to consider only the motion down the valley. Usually, however, workers have preferred to start with the initial conditions and to consider the entire motion over the surface.

Strictly speaking, the kinematics of a reaction should be treated quantum-mechanically. A few treatments of this kind have been carried out, and will be referred to later, but they have not as yet been highly successful in answering questions in which the experimentalist is interested. Because of the great difficulty of the quantum-mechanical calculations, most of the treatments have been made with reference to greatly oversimplified, and therefore unrealistic, potential-energy surfaces. On the basis of classical mechanics, solutions can be obtained without great difficulty, with the use of computers, for any potential-energy surface that is specified, so that the method is much more versatile. The question that arises, however, is the extent to which it is permissible to treat the atomic motions classically. This is a difficult question to answer precisely, but, broadly speaking, it can be said that provided the barrier is not too thin, and provided also the energies of approach are not too small, classical mechanics will give the same results as quantum mechanics. The uncertainty with regard to this question is related in part to uncertainties with regard to the theory of quantum-mechanical tunneling (cf. p. 80).

The first kinematic calculation was carried out in 1936 by Hirschfelder, Eyring, and Topley[1] on the $H + H_2$ system. Unfortunately, since a hydrogen atom is being transferred, tunneling may well be important and the classical treatment therefore in error. Another drawback in this early treatment is that since computers were not available, it was not possible, without an unreasonable amount of work, to include nonlinear complexes and to cover a sufficient number of approach trajectories to make the results of statistical significance. The first computer calculations of reaction kinematics were made by Wall, Hiller, and Mazur[2] also for the $H + H_2$ system; they used the Eyring-Polanyi potential-energy surface, with a basin. In these calculations the three atoms were restricted to motion in a single plane, and the starting conditions (rotational, vibrational, and translational energies) were chosen by a weighted random ("Monte Carlo") procedure. Later Wall and Porter[3] carried out similar calculations, using a purely empirical surface which had no basin.

Much more extensive calculations on the $H + H_2$ reaction have been carried out by Karplus, Porter, and Sharma,[4] using the very satisfactory potential-energy surface developed by Porter and Karplus (p. 101). The system was treated in three dimensions, and the initial conditions were chosen at random from appropriate distribution functions. The main interest in these calculations is that they led to a rate constant, 1.1×10^{12} cc mole^{-1} sec^{-1} at 1000°K, that agrees very well with the best experimental estimates. Of particular significance is the fact that a plot of log k against $1/T$ yields a straight line; the slope corresponds to an experimental activation energy of 7.4 kcal, which is consistent with the not very reliable experimental evidence. It is to be noted that this value is considerably less than the classical barrier height, 9.13 kcal, for the surface used. This arises from the complex temperature dependencies that result from this model, which includes all angles of approach. The collision time was found in these calculations to be $\sim 3 \times 10^{-14}$ sec, which is roughly the time required for an atom to make a single traversal of the field of force of the molecule.

It was first pointed out by Evans and M. Polanyi[5] that important information about potential-energy surfaces can be revealed by studies of energy distributions in the products of exothermic reactions. In reactions of the type

$$Na_2 + Cl \rightarrow NaCl + Na$$

[1] J. O. Hirschfelder, H. Eyring, and B. Topley, *J. Chem. Phys.*, **4**, 170 (1936).

[2] F. T. Wall, L. A. Hiller, and J. Mazur, *ibid.*, **29**, 255 (1958); **35**, 1284 (1961).

[3] F. T. Wall and R. N. Porter, *ibid.*, **39**, 3112 (1963).

[4] M. Karplus, R. N. Porter, and R. D. Sharma, *ibid.*, **40**, 2033 (1964).

[5] M. G. Evans and M. Polanyi, *Trans. Faraday Soc.*, **31**, 875 (1935); **35**, 178 (1939).

it was found[1] that a high percentage of the heat of reaction was liberated as vibrational energy in the bond formed, and Evans and Polanyi concluded that the surface was of the type they referred to as *purely attractive.* On an attractive surface the heat of reaction is liberated along the coordinate corresponding to the approach of the atom to within normal bonding distance of the molecule; in other words, in the activated state there is very little extension of the bond that is being broken. Figure 21*b* in fact represents a purely attractive surface as far as reaction in the direction A—B + C is concerned; when C approaches A—B (from the right-hand side in the diagram) the activated state is formed without there being any extension of the bond A—B. As the system moves beyond the barrier, to the left, the result will be the formation of BC with a considerable amount of vibration. From the point of view of the reverse reaction, A + BC, on the other hand, the surface is a *purely repulsive* one; now the heat of reaction is liberated along the B-C coordinate, which corresponds to separation of the products AB + C. Very little of the energy liberated now passes into vibrational energy of AB. It is clear that purely attractive and purely repulsive surfaces represent extremes which are rarely realized in practice; surfaces can, however, conveniently be classified according to the extent to which they are attractive or repulsive.

Kinematic calculations on exothermic reactions have more recently been carried out, with particular reference to two sets of experimental data:

1. Molecular-beam studies on reactions of the type

$$\mathrm{M + IR \rightarrow MI + R}$$

where M is an alkali metal, and R an alkyl group. These studies have shown (cf. p. 136) that much of the energy released goes into vibration of the products, a result that is similar to that found in the reactions of the type Na_2 + Cl.

2. Infrared chemiluminescence studies on reactions of the type

$$\mathrm{H\ (or\ D) + X_2 \rightarrow HX\ (or\ DX) + X}$$

where X is Cl or Br. These studies indicate (cf. p. 136) that little of the energy goes into vibration.

The detailed kinematic calculations have largely confirmed the broad generalization of Evans and Polanyi, in terms of attractive and repulsive

[1] H. Beutler and M. Polanyi, *Z. Physik. Chem.*, **B1**, 3 (1928); cf. M. Polanyi, "Atomic Reactions," Ernest Benn, Ltd.—Benn Bros., Ltd., London, 1932.

surfaces, but have indicated that other factors, such as atomic masses, must be taken into account. Blais and Bunker[1] constructed an empirical potential-energy surface which they could vary from moderately attractive to moderately repulsive. They calculated a large number of trajectories for M + CH_3I across this surface, with CH_3 treated as a single particle. Initial conditions were chosen by the Monte Carlo procedure, and the particles were free to move in a plane. When a moderately attractive surface was used, they found, in agreement with experiment, that much of the energy went into vibration of the product. They also investigated the effect of changing the masses of the atoms, by making calculations for light, medium, and heavy atoms. Their conclusion was that almost all combinations of masses led, for an attractive surface, to a large amount of vibration in the product molecule; exceptions tend to occur when the reacting *molecule* is made up of heavy atoms.

Calculations for a repulsive surface have also been made by J. C. Polanyi and coworkers,[2] with special reference to reactions of the type H + X_2. They were able to modify the potential-energy surface in a manner that was reasonable and that led to the experimental result that about 3 per cent of the heat of reaction goes into vibrational energy. They have also studied in detail the way in which changes in the form of the surface, and in the masses of the atoms, affect the results. They concluded, for example, that even a repulsive surface will lead to high vibrational excitation of the products for a reaction in which a heavy atom abstracts a light one.

A very different procedure was applied by Light[3] to certain ion-molecule reactions; the basis of his method is that the probability of each alternative reaction path is taken to be proportional to the amount of phase space available to it. The calculations give satisfactory agreement with experiment for the ion-molecule reactions considered.

Kinematics: Quantum-mechanical Treatments. The quantum-mechanical treatments of the passage over a potential-energy surface involve solving the wave equation for the particular surface. This unfortunately presents a formidable problem, even for the simplest of the realistic potential-energy surfaces. It has therefore nearly always been necessary to use a highly simplified potential function.

The first quantum-mechanical treatment of this problem was that of Hirschfelder and Wigner,[4] who calculated reaction probabilities for the passage of a hydrogen atom over various sloping surfaces. Their general

[1] Blais and Bunker, *loc. cit.*; D. L. Bunker and N. C. Blais, *J. Chem. Phys.*, **41**, 2377 (1964); cf. D. L. Bunker, *ibid.*, **37**, 393 (1962); *Sci. Am.*, **211**, 100 (1964).

[2] J. C. Polanyi and S. D. Rosner, *J. Chem. Phys.*, **38**, 1028 (1963); J. C. Polanyi, *loc. cit.*; Nemeth, Polanyi, Rosner, and Young, *loc. cit.*

[3] J. C. Light, *J. Chem. Phys.*, **40**, 3221 (1964).

[4] J. O. Hirschfelder and E. Wigner, *ibid.*, **7**, 616 (1939).

conclusion was that the results are not far from those predicted on the basis of a classical treatment.

Golden and coworkers[1] carried out a quantum-mechanical treatment on a simplified potential-energy surface for the $Br + H_2$ reaction. One of their simplifications, a rather serious one, is that the exchange and coulombic energies between the outermost atoms are independent of distance. Golden and Peiser made approximate calculations, by perturbation methods, of transition probabilities, and were able to obtain an expression for the rate constant as a function of temperature. Their results agreed very satisfactorily with experiment. One interesting conclusion they reached is that most of the contribution to the rate came from the hydrogen molecules that were in the first excited vibrational state.

Bauer and Wu[2] made a similar treatment of the systems $Cl + H_2$ and $Br + H_2$. They treated only collinear collisions, and simplified the interaction potential by making it effective only at small separations between the reactants. In place of a potential-energy surface they used an intermolecular potential, which depended on the distance between the reacting molecules, and an intramolecular potential that depended only on the H—H distance. They found that the lifetime of the activated complex corresponded to 10 to 100 vibrations, a result that is at variance with the classical calculations and with the results of molecular-beam experiments.

Mazur and Rubin[3] have made computer calculations on exchange reactions. Their potential-energy surface was highly idealized, based on the approximation of three equipotential plateaus, for the initial, intermediate, and final states. Classical calculations were made using the same surface, and significant differences were found between the two methods.

Mortensen and Pitzer[4] have made quantum-mechanical calculations for much more realistic surfaces than those previously considered. Only a preliminary report has so far been published. They found, for the $H + H_2$ system, transmission coefficients of close to unity. One conclusion that they came to is that bending in the activated state has a significant effect on the results.

Nonequilibrium Statistical Mechanics. A number of theoretical treatments of kinetics have been based on the principles of nonequilib-

[1] S. Golden, *ibid.*, **17**, 620 (1949); S. Golden and A. M. Peiser, *ibid.*, 630; *J. Phys. Colloid Chem.*, **55**, 789 (1951).

[2] E. Bauer and T. Y. Wu, *J. Chem. Phys.*, **21**, 726 (1953); cf. E. Bauer, Quantum Theory of Chemical Reaction Rates, *N.Y. Univ. Res. Rept.* CX-33 (1958).

[3] J. Mazur and R. J. Rubin, *J. Chem. Phys.*, **31**, 1395 (1959).

[4] E. M. Mortensen and K. S. Pitzer, *Chem. Soc. (London) Spec. Publ.* **16**, 57 (1962).

rium statistical mechanics, and have been devoted to examining the equilibrium hypothesis that is inherent in the theory of absolute reaction rates.

Curtiss[1] and Prigogine[2] based their treatments on the statistical-mechanical formulations of irreversible processes, and made use of particular values for reaction cross sections. The technique is to derive expressions for the perturbation of the Maxwell-Boltzmann distribution, using various formulations for transition probabilities. Present[3] reexamined the problem using cross sections that are believed to be more reasonable than those previously employed. The reacting molecules were assumed to be spherically symmetrical; steric factors, internal degrees of freedom, and heats evolved in the reaction were neglected. Present's conclusion was that if $\epsilon^*/\mathbf{k}T = 5$ (where ϵ^* is the energy of activation per molecule), the simple collision theory is in error by only 8 percent; for larger values of this ratio, the error is less. In other words, under these conditions depletion of the more energetic molecules has little effect on the rate.

Mahan[4] carried out similar calculations, using the methods of Prigogine, but confined his attention to free-radical combination reactions occurring with zero activation energy. He also found that the equilibrium assumption is justified provided that the radical concentrations are less than 0.1 mole fraction.

The approach taken by Yamamoto[5] was completely different; he also based his treatment on the statistical-mechanical theory of irreversible processes, but used a formulation established by Kubo[6] and by Mori.[7] Near the equilibrium the reaction rate is proportional to the affinity,[8] and Yamamoto expresses the proportionality coefficient as a special type of time-correlation function, in terms of a theory of binary collisions. The rate constant is determined from this proportionality constant, and it is assumed that the same rate constant applied far from equilibrium as close to equilibrium.

Stochastic Methods. The term "stochastic" seems first to have been applied to rate theories by Montroll and Shuler,[9] although an earlier

[1] C. F. Curtiss, *Univ. Wisconsin Rept.* CM-476 (1948).

[2] I. Prigogine and E. Xhrouet, *Physika*, **15**, 913 (1949); I. Prigogine and M. Mahieu, *ibid.*, **16**, 51 (1950).

[3] R. D. Present, *J. Chem. Phys.*, **31**, 747 (1959).

[4] B. H. Mahan, *ibid.*, **32**, 362 (1960).

[5] T. Yamamoto, *J. Chem. Phys.*, **33**, 281 (1960).

[6] R. Kubo, M. Yokota, and S. Nakajima, *J. Phys. Soc. Japan*, **12**, 1203 (1957).

[7] H. Mori, *ibid.*, **11**, 1029 (1956).

[8] T. De Donder, *Bull. Classe Sci. Acad. Roy. Belg.*, **7**, 197, 205 (1922).

[9] E. W. Montroll and K. E. Shuler, *Adv. Chem. Phys.*, **1**, 361 (1958); K. E. Shuler, *J. Chem. Phys.*, **31**, 1375 (1959).

use of the method was that of Kramers.[1] A stochastic theory is one based on the principles of probability, and often makes use of the idea of the "random walk." Stochastic theories are essentially more refined collision theories, in which account is taken of the energy levels in the reacting molecules. In Kramers's treatment the chemical reaction is represented by the diffusion, over a potential-energy barrier, of particles that are subject to Brownian motion as a result of an external field of force. The reactant molecules are trapped in potential holes and become activated through collisions with other molecules of the surrounding medium, which acts as a constant-temperature bath; in course of time a particle escapes after acquiring sufficient energy. For simplicity a one-dimensional model was used. An exact treatment was not possible, but some limiting cases, corresponding to high and low viscosities in the surrounding medium, were worked out. It was concluded that over a wide range of viscosity values the equilibrium theories give results that are correct within 10 percent. Kramers's treatment has been developed by Bak.[2] Montroll and Shuler presented a quantum-mechanical version of the Kramers model. They considered an ensemble of reactant molecules, with quantized energy levels, immersed in a large excess of inert gas which acts as a constant-temperature bath. The reactant molecules are initially in a Maxwell-Boltzmann distribution. By collision with the molecules of the heat bath the reactant molecules are excited in a stepwise process into higher levels; finally they reach the $(n + 1)$st level, when they are removed irreversibly from the reaction system. The collisional transition probabilities between levels n and r are functions of the corresponding quantum numbers. The problem is treated as a random walk; the probability that in unit time a walker will take a step from n to r is a function of the distance between the two positions, and a similar procedure is used for the two energy levels. The time-dependent distribution of the reactant molecules among the energy levels is then given by the fraction that are n levels from the origin at time t. The rate of activation is inversely proportional to the *mean first-passage time*, which is the average time required for a walker to reach the $(n + 1)$st level *for the first time.*

Transition probabilities were obtained by treating the reactant molecules as simple harmonic oscillators and assuming only weak interactions between the oscillators and the heat-bath molecules. The final result of the treatment is that the rate of a chemical reaction with $\epsilon^*/\mathbf{k}T$ equal to 5 will differ by 20 percent from that calculated using equilibrium theory; for $\epsilon^*/\mathbf{k}T > 10$ the deviation is negligible. This conclusion is similar to

[1] H. A. Kramers, *Physika*, **7**, 284 (1940).

[2] T. Bak, "Contributions to the Theory of Chemical Kinetics," W. A. Benjamin, New York, 1963.

that reached by Present and by Zwolinski and Eyring.[1] The treatment of the latter is to some extent an earlier and simpler formulation of the treatment of Montroll and Shuler. Two energy levels only were considered for the reactant molecules, and two for the products, and transition probabilities between the various levels were worked out.

Widom and Bauer[2] developed what is essentially a refined collision theory, and applied it to the problem of energy transfer in mixtures of carbon dioxide and water. Instead of the crude hard-sphere collision model they used a symmetrical Lennard-Jones 6-12 potential for the interactions between the molecules, and on a classical basis calculated transition probabilities between vibrational states on collision; the possibility of conversion into translational energy was taken into account. Widom[3] applied a similar treatment to the case of a dissociation reaction: the dissociating molecules were considered to be dispersed in an inert gas and to gain their energy by collision with the inert-gas molecules. As in the Montroll-Shuler treatment, the theory was developed in terms of mean passage times. Under simplifying conditions, including the condition that $\epsilon^* \gg \mathbf{k}T$, the rate constant reduced to the form $Ze^{-\epsilon^*/\mathbf{k}T}$.

The treatment of Eliason and Hirschfelder[4] is based on a formal kinetic theory of polyatomic molecules developed by Wang-Chang and Uhlenbeck.[5] This theory treats molecules in different internal quantum states as though they were distinct species, and takes into account transitions between these internal states. These changes in internal states in some cases correspond to chemical reaction, and the theory is modified by Eliason and Hirschelder to give a formulation of reaction rates. This theory is essentially a generalized collision theory of bimolecular reactions in which transitions between quantized levels are taken into account. These workers consider in detail the conditions under which their theory reduces to Eyring's absolute rate theory.

THE PRINCIPLE OF MICROSCOPIC REVERSIBILITY

An important principle which relates to the behavior of systems at equilibrium was first formulated by Tolman,[6] who referred to it as the *principle of microscopic reversibility.* This principle has important applications to kinetic problems, but it has not always been applied correctly;

[1] B. Zwolinski and H. Eyring, *J. Am. Chem. Soc.*, **69,** 2702 (1947).

[2] B. Widom and S. H. Bauer, *J. Chem. Phys.*, **21,** 1670 (1953).

[3] B. Widom, *ibid.*, **31,** 1387 (1959).

[4] M. A. Eliason and J. O. Hirschfelder, *ibid.*, **30,** 1426 (1959).

[5] C. S. Wang-Chang and G. E. Uhlenbeck, Transport Phenomena in Polyatomic Molecules, *Univ. Mich. Publ.* CM-681 (1951).

[6] R. C. Tolman, *Phys. Rev.*, **23,** 699 (1924); "The Principles of Statistical Mechanics," Clarendon Press, Oxford. 1938, p. 163.

therefore it is important to state clearly what the principle says and what consequences it has and does not have.

The principle may be stated as follows:

In a system at equilibrium, any molecular process and the reverse of that process occur on the average at the same rate

The proof is as follows. Consider any molecular configuration, having certain bond angles and distances which define it. Such a species may be undergoing a particular motion; this motion can be described by expressing, as vectors, the velocities of the individual atoms. According to the principles of statistical mechanics, the probability of the existence of such a species, having the motion specified, depends only on the energy of the system, which in turn depends upon the squares of the individual velocities. This being so, a species in which all of the motions are exactly reversed, since it has the same energy, will have the same probability of existence. Every molecular species in a system at equilibrium therefore has an exact counterpart which is moving in the opposite direction and which, on the average, is present at the same concentration.

The most important consequence of the principle is that if in a system at equilibrium there is a flow of systems along a given reaction path, there must be an equal flow in the opposite direction. In particular, it can be concluded that the reaction path established as the most probable in one direction (that is, the path along which most systems move) must also be the most probable path in the opposite direction. The activated state for a reaction in one direction must be the same as the activated state in the other direction. Such a conclusion is in any case necessary in terms of absolute rate theory; indeed, if one is working within the framework of that theory, the principle of microscopic reversibility does not introduce anything new.

According to absolute rate theory, the rate of a reaction in one direction depends on the increase in free energy in going from the initial to the activated state. Since the activated states must be the same in both directions, it follows at once that for an elementary reaction the free-energy difference in the two directions must be equal to the overall free-energy difference. It also follows that for an elementary reaction the ratio of rate constants must be equal to the equilibrium constant.

Entirely erroneous conclusions have from time to time been drawn on the basis of the principle. It has been stated, for example, that the rate constants in forward and reverse directions must both be affected in the same way by a change in pH,[1] and by a change in dielectric constant.[2] These conclusions would be true only if the equilibrium constant were independent of pH or of dielectric constant respectively.

[1] "Mechanismen Enzymatischer Reaktionen," p. 47, Springer-Verlag OHG, Berlin, 1964.

[2] *J. Chem. Soc.*, 3682 (1964).

Some comments about the application of the principle to complex systems are made in Chap. 7 (p. 329).

PROBLEMS[1]

1. The rate of reaction at 40°C is three times that at 20°C. Calculate the energy of activation.

2. A reaction has an activation energy of 40 kcal. Calculate the ratio of its rates (**a**) at 0 and 10°C and (**b**) at 100 and 110°C.

3. The following data have been given for the decomposition of dibromosuccinic acid in solution:

T, °C	$k \times 10^4$, hr^{-1}
50.0	1.08
70.1	7.34
89.4	45.4
101.0	138

Plot log **k** against $1/T$ in degrees Kelvin, and determine the activation energy from the slope of the best line. Check the answer using the method of least squares.

4. Two second-order reactions have identical frequency factors, and activation energies differing by 5 kcal. Calculate the ratio of their rate constants (**a**) at 0°C and (**b**) at 500°C.

5. Two reactions of the same order have identical activation energies, and entropies of activation differing by 10 eu. Calculate the ratio of their rate constants at 300°K.

6. One liter of oxygen is maintained at 400 mm pressure and 300°C. Assuming a collision diameter of 2.0 A, calculate (**a**) the total number of collisions per second, (**b**) the number of molecules colliding per second per cubic centimeter, and (**c**) the number of collisions in the 1 liter of gas in which the joint energy is 20 kcal in excess of the average.

[1] The following constants [*Natl. Bur. Std.* (*U.S.*) *Tech. News Bull.*, October, 1963] may be useful in the solution of problems in this and subsequent chapters:

$$\mathbf{k} = 1.381 \times 10^{16} \text{ ergs per deg}$$
$$\mathbf{h} = 6.626 \times 10^{-27} \text{ erg-sec}$$
$$N = 6.023 \times 10^{23} \text{ mole}^{-1}$$
$$R = 1.986 \text{ cal deg}^{-1} \text{ mole}^{-1}$$
$$2.303R = 4.574 \text{ cal deg}^{-1} \text{ mole}^{-1}$$
$$c = 2.998 \times 10^{10} \text{ cm sec}^{-1}$$

Reference should also be made to Appendix B.

7. The frequency factors for two unimolecular reactions occurring at 200°C are 2.75×10^{15} and 3.98×10^{13} sec^{-1}. Calculate the entropy of activation in each case. How do the values obtained depend upon the standard state used?

8. Carry out a corresponding calculation for two bimolecular gas reactions occurring at 300°C, having frequency factors of 7.4×10^{10} and 9.6×10^{9} liters mole^{-1} sec^{-1}. How do the answers now depend upon the standard state used?

★9. On the basis of absolute-rate theory determine the dependence on temperature of the frequency factors for the following types of reactions:

(**a**) A bimolecular reaction between an atom and a diatomic molecule, the complex being linear
(**b**) A bimolecular reaction between two diatomic molecules, the complex being nonlinear
(**c**) A termolecular reaction between three diatomic molecules, forming a nonlinear complex with no free rotation

In each case show how the activation energy at T°K is related to that at 0°K.

Assuming translational partition functions to be 10^8 for each degree of freedom, rotational to be 10, and vibrational to be unity, calculate frequency factors in molecular and in molar units for the above reaction types.

★10. (**a**) In the linear activated complex for the reaction $H + HBr \rightarrow H_2 + Br$, the H—H distance is 1.50 A, and the shorter H—Br distance is 1.42 A. Calculate the moment of inertia of the complex and hence the rotational partition function.
(**b**) The three real vibrational frequencies in the activated complex are 2,340, 460, and 460 cm^{-1}. Calculate the vibrational partition function of the complex.
(**c**) Calculate the total partition function for the activated complex.
(**d**) Calculate the total partition functions for the reactants H and HBr, taking the H—Br distance as 1.414 A and the vibrational frequency as 2,650 cm^{-1}.
(**e**) Obtain a value for the rate constant at 300°K, assuming the activation energy to be 1.2 kcal at that temperature.

★11. The potential energy of the hydrogen molecule can be related to the internuclear distance r by means of the Morse equation

$$E = D[e^{-2a(r-r_0)} - 2e^{-a(r-r_0)}]$$

with $D = 109.4$ kcal per mole, $a = 1.954$ A^{-1}, and $r_0 = 0.74$ A. Calculate the values of the potential energy corresponding to the following

★ Problems marked with a star are more advanced than the others.

internuclear distances:

$$r = 0.5, 0.75, 1.0, 1.5, 2.0, 3.0, 4.0 \text{ A}$$

Draw a graph of the E against r.

On the assumption that the coulombic energy is 14 percent of the total potential energy, calculate the coulombic and exchange energies corresponding to each of the above distances. Plot these two curves on the same graph as used above.

Construct a potential-energy surface for the linear H—H—H system according to the following procedure. First take $r_1 = 0.5$ A and $r_2 = 0.5$ A; calculate the energy using Eq. (13) on page 61. (Take the negative sign.) Repeat this with the series of r_2 values up to $r_2 = 3$, and plot E vs. r_2 corresponding to $r_1 = 0.5$ A. Repeat this procedure with the r_1 values up to $r_1 = 2$, in each case going to $r_1 + r_2 = 4$. Draw the four curves on the one sheet.

On a separate sheet of graph paper prepare rectangular axes corresponding to r_1 and r_2, the values ranging from zero to 3 A. Plot points corresponding to energies of -10, -20, -30, -40, -50, -60, -70, -80, -85, -90, -95, -100 kcal, and draw in the contour lines.

chapter

Elementary Gas-phase Reactions 4

Apart from reactions involving atoms and free radicals, which are of special interest in connection with the part they play in free-radical mechanisms, very few gas reactions are elementary. Examples of bimolecular reactions between stable molecules are the reaction between hydrogen and iodine, the reverse decomposition of hydrogen iodide, the corresponding reactions involving deuterium instead of hydrogen, the dimerization of cyclopentadiene, and the decomposition of nitrogen dioxide. There are a small number of reactions of the third order, all involving nitric oxide, which can be treated as though they involved a simple three-body collision, although in fact two well-defined steps can be distinguished. In addition, a few unimolecular isomerizations and decompositions occur in an elementary manner. A great many other gas-phase reactions have at various times been thought to be elementary, but further study has shown them to be complex. Elementary gas-phase reactions will be treated in some detail in this chapter, since an understanding of them provides a foundation for the study of reactions in other phases and for the study of complex processes.

DECOMPOSITION OF HYDROGEN IODIDE

Gaseous hydrogen iodide decomposes thermally to give an equilibrium mixture of hydrogen, iodine, and hydrogen iodide according to the stoichiometric equation

$$2HI = H_2 + I_2$$

The reaction is of particular interest on account of its kinetic simplicity, and it has been studied in great detail; its investigation by Bodenstein[1] constituted the first comprehensive kinetic study of a reaction occurring in the gas phase. In addition to measuring the rates of the forward and the reverse reactions, Bodenstein determined directly the equilibrium constant; all this work was carried out at various temperatures, ranging from 382 to 508°C.

The experimental technique used by Bodenstein for studying the decomposition of hydrogen iodide consisted in sealing pure hydrogen iodide in bulbs, which were maintained in a vapor bath at the required constant temperature for various intervals of time, and were then removed and cooled rapidly. The contents were analyzed for all three constituents; since there is no volume change, an analytical method was necessary.

Subsequent to Bodenstein's investigations, the reaction has been studied by a number of workers, some of whose methods may be mentioned briefly. H. A. Taylor[2] used a flow system, the hydrogen iodide being caused to stream through a heated Pyrex tube of 600 sq cm surface. The fraction of decomposition was found by analyzing the issuing gas mixture, and from the rate of flow and the volume of the tube the time of contact could be estimated; the rate constant could therefore be calculated. One of the objects of this investigation was to see whether the reaction was occurring to an appreciable extent on the walls; when Pyrex glass powder was introduced into the tube, the rate was very much increased, indicating that under the conditions of the experiments an appreciable amount of the reaction occurred on the surface. However, the rates obtained by Taylor were about 100 times those of Bodenstein; it therefore appears that Taylor's result may be due to his use of another type of glass, and there is good reason to believe that in Bodenstein's work the surface reaction was negligible.

One indication of this is that when log k was plotted against $1/T$ for Taylor's results, a straight line was not obtained, indicating that simultaneous reactions are occurring. With Bodenstein's results, on the other

[1] M. Bodenstein, *Z. Physik. Chem.*, **13**, 56 (1894); **22**, 1 (1897); **29**, 295 (1899).
[2] H. A. Taylor, *J. Phys. Chem.*, **28**, 984 (1924).

hand, a good straight line was obtained, as was shown in Fig. 12. It therefore seems likely that under the conditions used by Bodenstein the reaction takes place largely in the gas phase, and that Taylor's results arose as a result of his use of Pyrex glass.

The suggestion that the decomposition might not be an elementary reaction was made by B. Lewis and Rideal[1] on the basis of their results obtained with hydrogen iodide that had been intensively dried by means of phosphorus pentoxide. Their results appeared to indicate that the decomposition did not stop at the equilibrium position found by Bodenstein, but went to completion, and they concluded that iodine atoms are involved in the reaction. However, Bodenstein and Jost[2] suggested that the process of drying had introduced traces of phosphorus pentoxide into the hydrogen iodide and that this substance was reacting with the iodide to form iodine and water; this explanation is generally accepted.

The reaction was studied by Kistiakowsky[3] over a much wider range of initial concentrations, ranging from 0.02 to 7 moles per liter, the latter value corresponding to a pressure of 150 atm. The reaction was found to take place almost entirely in the gas phase and to be unaffected by intense drying. At the lower pressures the reaction was strictly of the second order, but deviations occurred at higher pressures; however, these could be attributed entirely to departures from ideal-gas behavior. At high concentrations the collision number is somewhat larger than that corresponding to ideal behavior, owing to the volume occupied by the molecules themselves. A correction allowing for this, involving the van der Waals constant b, was found to explain the deviations very accurately. The values of k obtained by Kistiakowsky agree very well with those of Bodenstein.

In view of the simplicity of the overall kinetics, the hydrogen iodide decomposition has for a long time been considered to proceed by a purely molecular mechanism. Recent work on the reverse reaction, the reaction between hydrogen and iodine, has, however, indicated that the reaction proceeds in part by chain processes. This work is considered below; here it is sufficient to note that a reaction must follow the same paths in forward and reverse directions, so that the hydrogen iodide decomposition must also be partly a chain reaction. The molecular process appears, however, to be predominant, so that the various theoretical treatments that have been applied on the assumption that the process is purely molecular are not greatly in error.

Application of the Arrhenius law to the decomposition was made by W. C. McC. Lewis.[4] As seen in the last chapter, the rate constant is

[1] B. Lewis and E. K. Rideal, *J. Am. Chem. Soc.*, **48**, 2553 (1926).
[2] M. Bodenstein and W. Jost, *ibid.*, **49**, 1416 (1927).
[3] G. B. Kistiakowsky, *ibid.*, **50**, 2315 (1928).
[4] W. C. McC. Lewis, *J. Chem. Soc.*, **113**, 471 (1918).

related to the temperature by the equation

$$\ln k = \ln A - \frac{E}{RT} \tag{1}$$

so that a plot of $\log_{10} k$ against $1/T$ should give a straight line; this has been seen to be the case. From the slope of the line the value of E is found to be 44.0 kcal per mole. Actually this treatment is slightly in error, since A varies slightly with the temperature; however for the present purposes this may be ignored.

The collision theory of the absolute magnitude of the rate constant was also due largely to W. C. McC. Lewis, who developed the treatment in a number of papers, in one[1] of which the decomposition of hydrogen iodide was discussed numerically. One feature of the Lewis theory is now known to be incorrect, but fortunately it can be extracted from the treatment without invalidating the rest of the work: this was his concept that molecules acquire the activation energy by absorbing infrared radiation. The molecules of a gas at a constant temperature are in equilibrium with radiant energy, which they constantly absorb and emit, and this was believed at the time to explain the way they gain and lose energy. The frequency of the energy corresponding to a given temperature can readily be calculated, and light of this frequency would, if the hypothesis were true, cause an increase in the rate of reaction. Numerous attempts have been made to bring about such an enhancement of the rates of various reactions by means of infrared radiation, but in no case was success achieved.[2] This indicates that molecules acquire energy by collisions with one another.

The reason that the incorrectness of the radiation theory does not vitiate Lewis's treatment is that the concentration of active molecules is related to that of normal ones by statistical laws and does not depend on the mechanism by which the energy is acquired or lost.

By equating the constant A to the number of molecules entering into collision each second, Lewis arrived at expression (15) on page 64 for the rate of a second-order reaction involving like molecules. For the kinetic-theory diameter d Lewis assumed a value of 2×10^{-8} cm, which is now known to be somewhat too low; this value, together with $\bar{c} = 3.3 \times 10^4$ cm per sec and $E = 44$ kcal per mole, gives for the rate constant at 556°K

$$k = 3.5 \times 10^{-7} \text{ liter mole}^{-1} \text{ sec}^{-1}$$

This is in excellent agreement with Bodenstein's experimental value of 3.52×10^{-7} at this temperature. Lewis extended his calculations over the whole range of temperatures covered by Bodenstein, and the agree-

[1] *Ibid.*

[2] See especially J. E. Mayer, *J. Am. Chem. Soc.*, **49**, 3033 (1927).

ment was satisfactory throughout. The agreement is not quite so good when the more accurate value of 3.5×10^{-8} cm is taken for the molecular diameter; thus at 556°K the calculated rate constant becomes 5.3×10^{-7}, to be compared with the experimental figure of 3.52×10^{-7}. However the agreement is still satisfactory, since a very slight error in the experimental activation energy makes a big percentage change in the calculated rate. It may be noted that the frequency factor for this reaction is about 10^{11} liters mole^{-1} sec^{-1}, or 10^{14} cc mole^{-1} sec^{-1}.

REACTION BETWEEN HYDROGEN AND IODINE

The reverse reaction, between hydrogen and iodine, was studied by Bodenstein with methods similar to those he used for the hydrogen iodide decomposition; hydrogen and iodine were sealed in bulbs, heated at the required temperature, and cooled rapidly, and the contents were analyzed. It was not possible to seal equimolar amounts, so that the rate expression to be used is

$$\frac{dx}{dt} = k_1\left(a - \frac{x}{2}\right)\left(b - \frac{x}{2}\right) - k_{-1}x^2 \tag{2}$$

where k_1 and k_{-1} are the rate constants for the formation and decomposition, respectively, of hydrogen iodide; a and b are the initial concentrations of hydrogen and iodine; and x is the amount of hydrogen iodide formed at time t. Measurements were made at a number of initial pressures, and the rate constant was found to be satisfactorily constant.

This reaction, like the reverse reaction, has been found to exhibit rather simple kinetic behavior, and has long been assumed to be a purely molecular process. Certain results, however, have suggested that chain processes, involving the participation of hydrogen and iodine atoms, also play a small but significant role. Thus Rosenbaum and Hogness[1] allowed the reaction $H_2 + I_2 \rightleftharpoons 2HI$ to proceed to equilibrium, and studied the rate of conversion of parahydrogen into orthohydrogen under these conditions. The object of their work was to see whether rates at equilibrium are the same as rates when the system is far from equilibrium, which was the case under the conditions employed by Bodenstein. Their conclusion was that the rate of conversion of parahydrogen was about twice the rate that was predicted on the assumption that the conversion occurred by the process

$$p\text{-}H_2 + I_2 \rightarrow 2HI \rightarrow o\text{-}H_2 + I_2$$

Their conclusion was that there must be an additional conversion mechanism, and they considered this to be the conversion by the para-

[1] E. J. Rosenbaum and T. R. Hogness, *J. Chem. Phys.*, **2**, 267 (1934).

magnetic iodine atoms. This was the first clear suggestion that these atoms play a role in the reaction.

More recently, Benson and Srinivasan[1] noted that there is a significant temperature dependence of the activation energies for the reaction between hydrogen and iodine, and for the reverse decomposition of hydrogen iodide. They concluded from this that the reactions are not solely molecular, but occur in part by atomic reactions. In the case of the reaction between hydrogen and iodine the main atomic reactions occurring were believed to be

$$I_2 \rightleftharpoons 2I$$
$$I + H_2 \rightarrow HI + H$$
$$H + I_2 \rightarrow HI + I$$

This chain component of the overall mechanism closely parallels the reactions occurring in the analogous hydrogen-bromine and hydrogen-chlorine reactions.

The whole question has been reexamined by Sullivan,[2] who carried out a careful experimental study of the reaction with the object of estimating the importance of the chain processes under various conditions. From the temperature dependence of the activation energy he concluded that when the iodine pressure is ½ atm, the atomic mechanism accounts for about 10 percent of the overall reaction at 633°K, and 27 percent at 738°K. On the basis of his analysis, Sullivan was able to arrive at rate constants and activation energies for some of the elementary steps. Since these are of chief interest in connection with a comparison of the various hydrogen-halogen reactions, they will be considered in a later chapter (Chap. 8).

Application of the collision theory to the results was made by Lewis, using the equations given on page 64. The experimental value of E is 40 kcal per mole, and with d_{AB} equal to 2×10^{-8} cm, the calculated value of k at 700°K is

$$k = 14 \times 10^{-2} \text{ liter mole}^{-1} \text{ sec}^{-1}$$

This is in satisfactory agreement with the observed value of 6.42×10^{-2} at this temperature. The frequency factor is about 2×10^{11} liters mole^{-1} sec^{-1}, or 2×10^{14} cc mole^{-1} sec^{-1}.

The reaction has also been treated in terms of the theory of absolute reaction rates, by Wheeler, Topley, and Eyring.[3] This work included quantum-mechanical calculations of the energy of activation of the reaction, using methods outlined in Chap. 3. The result obtained was 50 kcal, a good deal higher than the experimental value of 40 kcal; how-

[1] S. W. Benson and R. Srinivasan, *ibid.*, **23**, 200 (1955).

[2] J. H. Sullivan, *ibid.*, **30**, 1292, 1577 (1959); **36**, 1925 (1962).

[3] A. Wheeler, B. Topley, and H. Eyring, *ibid.*, **4**, 178 (1936).

ever, as has been seen, the calculations cannot be expected to yield more than a very rough approximation to the true value. The most important outcome of these calculations lies in the fact that they show why the reaction is elementary, whereas the corresponding reactions of chlorine and bromine are complex. These reactions proceed by an initial decomposition of the halogen molecule, followed by the attack on a hydrogen molecule by a halogen atom; the corresponding reactions with iodine would be

$$\tfrac{1}{2}I_2 \rightleftharpoons I$$
$$I + H_2 \rightarrow HI + H$$

The energy required to dissociate an iodine atom is 34 kcal per mole, so that the energy required for the first reaction would be just one-half of this, i.e., 17 kcal. The energy of activation for the second reaction was calculated to be about 40 kcal; consequently the energy of activation required for the formation of 1 mole of hydrogen iodide by the atomic mechanism is $40 + 17 = 57$ kcal. This is considerably higher than the observed activation energy and that calculated assuming the reaction to be elementary; the atomic reaction is therefore less important than the elementary molecular reaction.

According to the theory of absolute reaction rates, the activated complex, which is a molecule of the form

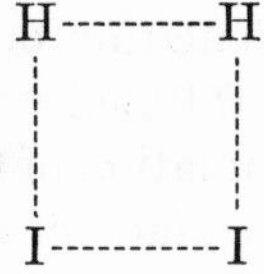

is in equilibrium with the reactants H_2 and I_2, and the rate of the reaction is controlled by the rate of decomposition of the complex. The equilibrium constant for the process

$$H_2 + I_2 \rightleftharpoons H_2I_2$$

is given by the expression

$$K_c = \frac{F^{\ddagger}}{F_{H_2}F_{I_2}} e^{-E_0/RT} \tag{3}$$

where the F's are the partition functions per unit volume, and E_0 is the activation energy per mole at the absolute zero. The rate constant of the reaction is thus given by [cf. Eq. (52), p. 76]

$$k = \frac{\mathbf{k}T}{\mathbf{h}} \frac{F_{\ddagger}}{F_{H_2}F_{I_2}} e^{-E_0/RT} \tag{4}$$

where the partition function $F_{\ddagger}$ differs from $F^{\ddagger}$ by the removal of the vibrational factor corresponding to dissociation into 2HI. The partition functions may now be expressed in terms of the translational, rotational, and vibrational factors. The functions for H_2 and I_2 both contain terms for three degrees of translational freedom, two of rotational (being linear molecules), and one of vibrational, and can be expressed as

$$F_{H_2} = \frac{(2\pi m_{H_2}\mathbf{k}T)^{3/2}}{\mathbf{h}^3} \frac{8\pi I_{H_2}\mathbf{k}T}{\mathbf{h}^2} \frac{1}{1 - \exp(-\mathbf{h}\nu_{H_2}/\mathbf{k}T)} \tag{5}$$

and

$$F_{I_2} = \frac{(2\pi m_{I_2}\mathbf{k}T)^{3/2}}{\mathbf{h}^3} \frac{8\pi I_{I_2}\mathbf{k}T}{\mathbf{h}^2} \frac{1}{1 - \exp(-\mathbf{h}\nu_{I_2}/\mathbf{k}T)} \tag{6}$$

The partition function for the activated complex is given by

$$F_{\ddagger} = \frac{(2\pi m\mathbf{k}T)^{3/2}}{\mathbf{h}^3} \frac{8\pi^2(8\pi^3 ABC)^{1/2}(\mathbf{k}T)^{3/2}}{h^3} \prod^{5} \frac{1}{1 - e^{-\mathbf{h}\nu/\mathbf{k}T}} \tag{7}$$

There are five vibrational degrees of freedom ($3n - 7$ where $n = 4$). In accordance with the discussion on page 84, symmetry numbers have been omitted. The final rate expression must be multiplied by the statistical factor of two, which is the number of ways an H_2 and an I_2 molecule can come together.

The numerical evaluation of the translational factors presents no problem, as the molecular masses are known with precision. Evaluation of the rotational factors involves the moments of inertia; these are known with accuracy for H_2 and I_2 and are known for the complex on the basis of the quantum-mechanical calculation of its properties. A little more uncertainty enters into the vibrational terms, since the calculations do not allow a very accurate determination of the frequencies in the activated complex; however, the vibrational factors are not highly sensitive to these frequencies. Some adjustment to the values was made so as to give agreement at 700°K.

The partition functions being evaluated in this manner, and using the observed activation energy (this is equivalent to 39.7 kcal at the absolute zero), the rate constants were calculated; they are compared with the experimental results at 575 and 781°K in Table 12. The agree-

Table 12 CALCULATED AND OBSERVED RATES FOR THE HYDROGEN-IODINE REACTION

	k, cc mole^{-1} sec^{-1}	
T, °K	Calculated	Observed
575	0.132	0.245
781	1,340	950

ment is seen to be quite satisfactory, although it must be remembered that the treatment is somewhat artificial in view of the adjustment of the vibrational frequencies. In this application the treatment is not superior to collision theory in accuracy and is certainly much more laborious; when the reacting molecules are more complicated, however, the theory of absolute reaction rates gives very much more accurate results.

The rate constant of the reaction can be formulated in an alternative manner, making use of the thermodynamic functions. It was seen in the last chapter that the rate constant is given in general by

$$k = \frac{\mathbf{k}T}{\mathbf{h}} e^{\Delta S^{\ddagger}/R} e^{-\Delta H^{\ddagger}/RT} \tag{8}$$

where $\Delta H^{\ddagger}$ and $\Delta S^{\ddagger}$ are the heat and entropy of activation. The heat of activation is not strictly equal to the energy of activation E, and if the latter is to be used, the rate expression becomes

$$k = e^2 \frac{\mathbf{k}T}{\mathbf{h}} e^{\Delta S^{\ddagger}/R} e^{-E/RT} \tag{9}$$

In the above expression the standard state for the entropy is unit concentration. The separate translational, rotational, and vibrational entropies for H_2, I_2, and the activated complex have been evaluated and are shown in Table 13. The entropies, except for the figure in the last column, all

Table 13 Entropies of activation for the H_2-I_2 reaction

$T = 300°K$

The standard state for $\Delta S_c^{\ddagger}$ is 1 mole per liter.

	Entropy					
Molecule	Translational	Rotational	Vibrational	Total	$\Delta S_p^{\ddagger}$	$\Delta S_c^{\ddagger}$
H_2	28.1	2.1	0	30.3		
I_2	42.8	17.0	0	59.8	−20.3	−13.9
H_2I_2	42.8	23.1	3.9	69.8		

refer to a standard state of 1 atm pressure. If the rate constant is written in the form of the collision theory, i.e., as

$$k = Ze^{-E/RT} \tag{10}$$

it follows that

$$Z = e^2 \frac{\mathbf{k}T}{\mathbf{h}} e^{\Delta S^{\ddagger}/R} \tag{11}$$

and Z calculated in this way is found to have a value of approximately 5×10^{10} liters mole^{-1} sec^{-1} at 300°K; this is slightly less than the value calculated using collision theory, which gives approximately 10^{11}. For an exact correspondence between the two theories $\Delta S_c^\ddagger$ must have a value of about -11.7; however, owing to the different temperature dependence given by the two theories, the particular value of $\Delta S_c^\ddagger$ which gives correspondence between the treatments depends upon the temperature. For a reaction involving two atoms or simple molecules, such as the one under consideration, there is little rearrangement of energy between the various degrees of freedom in the activated state; $\Delta S_c^\ddagger$ will then be close to the above value, and the two theories will give similar results. With more complex molecules the situation is very different, as will be seen from examples given later in this chapter.

OTHER BIMOLECULAR REACTIONS INVOLVING MOLECULES

A number of other elementary gas-phase bimolecular reactions between molecules have been studied. The results are mainly of interest in that they allow a test to be made of the theories of reaction rates. One such reaction is the dimerization of cyclopentadiene,

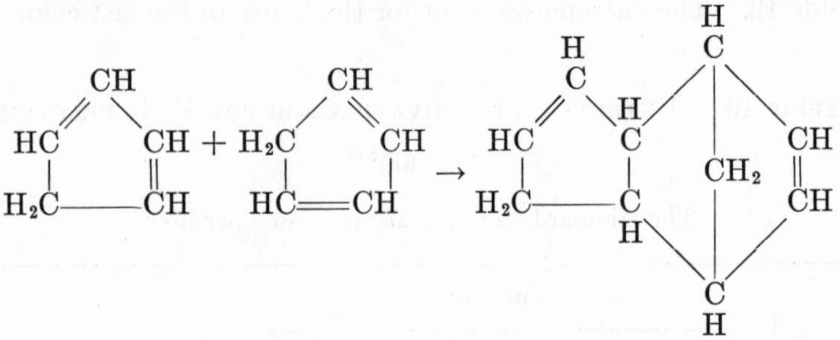

```
                                                        H
                                              H         C
        CH              CH                    C       / | \
      //  \           /   \\                //  \  H /  |  \
    HC     CH + H2C         CH          HC        C     |    CH
    |      ||      |        |      →    |         |    CH2   ||
    H2C----CH      HC=====CH            H2C-------C     |    CH
                                                  H  \  |  /
                                                      \ | /
                                                        C
                                                        H
```

It has been studied by Wassermann and coworkers[1] in the gas phase and in various solvents, and the kinetics were found to be very similar in all cases. The activation energy for the reaction in the gas phase is about 16.7 kcal per mole, and the frequency factor about 10^{10} cc mole^{-1} sec^{-1}. This frequency factor is considerably less than that predicted on the basis of the simple kinetic theory of collisions, which is about 10^{14} cc mole^{-1} sec^{-1}. Absolute-rate-theory calculations, however, lead to a value of about 2×10^{10} cc mole^{-1} sec^{-1}, which is much closer to the observed value. From the standpoint of this theory, the main reason for the low

[1] B. S. Khambata and A. Wassermann, *Nature,* **137**, 496 (1936); **138**, 368 (1936); A. Wassermann, *J. Chem. Soc.,* 1028 (1936); G. A. Benford, B. S. Khambata, and A. Wassermann, *Nature,* **139**, 669 (1937); A. Wassermann, *Trans. Faraday Soc.,* **34**, 128 (1938).

value is that the reactant molecules, because of their complexity, have large values of the rotational partition functions.

Detailed calculations, on the basis of both collision theory and absolute-rate theory, have been made by Herschbach, Johnston, Pitzer, and Powell[1] for a number of other bimolecular reactions. Some of the results of their calculations are shown in Table 14, which gives references

Table 14 KINETIC PARAMETERS FOR SOME BIMOLECULAR REACTIONS

Reaction	Activation energy, kcal per mole	Logarithm of frequency factor, cc mole^{-1} sec^{-1}: Observed	Calculated by absolute-rate theory	Calculated by simple collision theory	Reference
$NO + O_3 \rightarrow NO_2 + O_2$	2.5	11.9	11.6	13.7	*a*
$NO + O_3 \rightarrow NO_3 + O$	7.0	12.8	11.1	13.8	*b*
$NO_2 + F_2 \rightarrow NO_2F + F$	10.4	12.2	11.1	13.8	*c*
$NO_2 + CO \rightarrow NO + CO_2$	31.6	13.1	12.8	13.6	*d*
$2NO_2 \rightarrow 2NO + O_2$	26.6	12.3	12.7	13.6	*e*
$NO + NO_2Cl \rightarrow NOCl + NO_2$	6.9	11.9	11.9	13.9	*f*
$2NOCl \rightarrow 2NO + Cl_2$	24.5	13.0	11.6	13.8	*g*
$NO + Cl_2 \rightarrow NOCl + Cl$	20.3	12.6	12.1	14.0	*h*
$F_2 + ClO_2 \rightarrow FClO_2 + F$	8.5	10.5	10.9	13.7	*i*
$2ClO \rightarrow Cl_2 + O_2$	0	10.8	10.0	13.4	*j*

[a] H. S. Johnston and H. J. Crosby, *J. Chem. Phys.*, **22**, 689 (1954).
[b] H. S. Johnston and D. M. Yost, *ibid.*, **17**, 386 (1949).
[c] R. L. Perrine and H. S. Johnston, *ibid.*, **21**, 2200 (1953).
[d] H. S. Johnston, W. A. Bonner, and D. J. Wilson, *ibid.*, **26**, 1002 (1957).
[e] M. Bodenstein and H. Ramstetter, *Z. Physik. Chem.*, **100**, 106 (1922).
[f] E. C. Freiling, H. S. Johnston, and R. A. Ogg, *J. Chem. Phys.*, **20**, 327 (1952).
[g] G. Waddington and R. C. Tolman, *J. Am. Chem. Soc.*, **57**, 689 (1935).
[h] P. G. Ashmore and J. Chanmugan, *Trans. Faraday Soc.*, **49**, 270 (1953).
[i] P. J. Aynoneno, J. E. Sicre, and H. J. Schumacher, *J. Chem. Phys.*, **22**, 756 (1954).
[j] G. Porter and F. J. Wright, *Discussions Faraday Soc.*, **14**, 23 (1953).

to the original experimental results. It is to be seen that the absolute-rate-theory calculations of the frequency factors are reasonably close to the experimental values. The collision theory, on the other hand, leads

[1] D. R. Herschbach, H. S. Johnston, K. S. Pitzer, and R. E. Powell, *J. Chem. Phys.*, **25**, 736 (1956).

to log A values of close to 14, and which are significantly too high in all cases. The steric factors, which are the ratios of the experimental frequency factors to those calculated using collision theory, vary from about 10^{-1} to 10^{-3}, and there is no simple correlation between the values and the complexity of the reactants. These low steric factors are attributed to the losses of rotational freedom during the formation of the activated complex.

BIMOLECULAR REACTIONS INVOLVING ATOMS AND FREE RADICALS

There are also a number of bimolecular elementary reactions involving atoms and free radicals. One class of these comprises the *abstraction* reactions, in which an atom or radical abstracts an atom from a molecule, giving rise to a new radical and a new molecule; examples are

$$H + CH_4 \rightarrow H_2 + CH_3$$

and

$$CH_3 + C_2H_6 \rightarrow CH_4 + C_2H_5$$

Atoms and free radicals also undergo combination and disproportionation reactions, such as

$$CH_3 + CH_3 \rightarrow C_2H_6$$

and

$$C_2H_5 + C_2H_5 \rightarrow C_2H_4 + C_2H_6$$

Such reactions, however, involve some special features, and consideration of them will be deferred until after the unimolecular reactions are dealt with.

Abstraction Reactions. Reactions in which an atom or radical abstracts an *atom* occur much more readily than those in which it abstracts a *radical;* reactions such as

$$CH_3 + CH_3CHO \rightarrow C_2H_6 + CHO$$

involve much higher energies of activation than those like

$$CH_3 + CH_3CHO \rightarrow CH_4 + CH_3CO$$

The reason for this is that in order for a radical to be abstracted, there must be considerable distortion of the radical; in the example given above the methyl radical must turn inside out (Walden inversion) when it reacts with the attacking free radical, and such a process requires a considerable amount of energy.

The measurement of the rates, activation energies, and frequency factors of such reactions presents a certain amount of difficulty. As an example may be considered the abstraction by a methyl radical of a hydrogen atom from acetone,

$$CH_3 + CH_3COCH_3 \xrightarrow{k_1} CH_4 + CH_2COCH_3$$

The rate of this reaction is

$$v_M = \frac{d[CH_4]}{dt} = k_1[CH_3][CH_3COCH_3] \tag{12}$$

There is no difficulty about measuring v_M, the rate of production of methane, in such a system, but in order to obtain the rate constant k_1, it is necessary for the concentration of the free methyl radicals to be known. This presents a problem, because the concentration of methyl radicals is necessarily very small; it can hardly be greater than 10^{-6}, and such concentrations are very difficult to measure directly.

A method that has frequently been used to overcome this difficulty involves comparing the rate of the hydrogen-atom abstraction reaction with that of the radical recombination reaction

$$CH_3 + CH_3 \xrightarrow{k_2} C_2H_6$$

The kinetics of such reactions are considered later in this chapter, where it will be seen that at sufficiently high total pressures these reactions are second-order processes; the rate of production of ethane is given by

$$v_E = k_2[CH_3]^2 \tag{13}$$

From Eqs. (12) and (13) it follows that

$$\frac{v_M}{v_E^{1/2}} = \frac{k_1}{k_2^{1/2}}[CH_3COCH_3] \tag{14}$$

If, therefore, one can measure the rates of formation of methane and ethane, v_M and v_E, at a given acetone concentration, and knows the magnitude of k_2, one can calculate k_1. If this is known at different temperatures, the activation energies and frequency factors can also be calculated.

The measurement of k_2, the rate constant for the combination of two methyl radicals, is clearly of great importance for the application of this method. The technique used for obtaining this quantity, and the corresponding rate constants for other free-radical combinations, is described later in this chapter (p. 178). The second-order rate constant for the reaction between two methyl radicals has been found to be 5×10^{13} cc mole^{-1} sec^{-1}, and the activation energy to be zero; the frequency factor is therefore also 5×10^{13} cc mole^{-1} sec^{-1}, which is approximately the value calculated by simple collision theory.

Once the rate constant for a radical combination has been measured, the method can be applied to a large variety of molecules, and the appropriate rate constants determined for the abstraction reactions. It is possible, for example, to produce methyl radicals by the action of ultraviolet light on acetone, and to do this in the presence of an additional organic substance which may be represented as RH. The methyl radicals then undergo the following reactions:

$$CH_3 + CH_3COCH_3 \xrightarrow{k_1} CH_4 + CH_2COCH_3$$

$$CH_3 + RH \xrightarrow{k_1'} CH_4 + R$$

$$CH_3 + CH_3 \xrightarrow{k_2} C_2H_6$$

The rates involved are given by Eq. (13) and by

$$v_M = k_1[CH_3][CH_3COCH_3] + k_1'[CH_3][RH] \tag{15}$$

and combination of the two equations gives

$$\frac{v_M}{v_E^{1/2}[CH_3COCH_3]} = \frac{k_1}{k_2^{1/2}} + \frac{k_1'[RH]}{k_2^{1/2}[CH_3COCH_3]} \tag{16}$$

The rates v_M and v_E are measured and k_2 is known, and k_1 is determined by studies in the absence of acetone; the rate constant k_1' can therefore be calculated.

This procedure for obtaining the rate constant of an abstraction reaction is an example of the use of what has been called a *pilot* reaction. Once an accurate rate constant for a given atom or radical reaction has been obtained, this reaction can be used as a standard of comparison for another reaction. Thus if the rate constant for a reaction

$$R + A \rightarrow R' + P_1$$

is known, that for the reaction

$$R + B \rightarrow R'' + P_2$$

can sometimes be obtained by producing the radical R in the presence of both A and B. A comparison of the rates of the two reactions then leads to the rate constant for the second reaction. Radicals and atoms are conveniently generated both by thermal and photochemical methods; some examples are given in Chap. 7.

Table 15 gives a selection of experimental activation energies for a number of abstraction reactions involving atoms and free radicals. Also given in the table are values of $\log_{10} A$, calculated using Eyring's equation, which makes use of the partition functions of the reactant molecules and activated complexes. The results in Table 15 are of special interest in showing the fall in frequency factor as the reacting molecules become more complex; this is explained by activated complex theory in terms of an increase in the importance of the rotational partition functions of the reactants, but finds no interpretation on the basis of the simple kinetic

Table 15 ACTIVATION ENERGIES AND FREQUENCY FACTORS FOR SOME BIMOLECULAR REACTIONS INVOLVING ATOMS AND FREE RADICALS

A in cc mole^{-1} sec^{-1}

Reaction	E, kcal	log A Observed	log A Estimated†
$H + H_2 \rightarrow H_2 + H$	8.8	14.0	13.7[a], 13.8[b], 13.7[c]
$Br + H_2 \rightarrow HBr + H$	17.6	13.5	14.1[c]
$H + CH_4 \rightarrow H_2 + CH_3$	12	13	13.3[b]
$H + C_2H_6 \rightarrow H_2 + C_2H_5$	6.8	12.5	13.1[a]
$CH_3 + H_2 \rightarrow CH_4 + H$	10.0	12.3	12.0[a], 12.4[b], 12.0[c]
$CD_3 + CH_4 \rightarrow CD_3H + CD_3$	14.0	11	11.3[c], 10.9[a] (for CH_3)
$CH_3 + C_2H_6 \rightarrow CH_4 + C_2H_5$	11.2	10.8	11.0[a]
$CD_3 + C_2H_6 \rightarrow CD_3H + C_2H_5$	10.4	11.3	11.3[c]
$CH_3 + \text{iso-}C_4H_{10} \rightarrow CH_4 + C_4H_9$	7.6	10	9.8[a]
$CH_3 + n\text{-}C_5H_{12} \rightarrow CH_4 + C_5H_{11}$	8.1	11.0	
$CH_3 + CH_3COCH_3 \rightarrow CH_4 + CH_2COCH_3$	9.7	11.6	11[d]
$CD_3 + CD_3COCD_3 \rightarrow CD_4 + CD_2COCD_3$	11.3	11.8	
$CD_3 + C_6H_6 \rightarrow CD_3H + C_6H_5$	9.2	10.4	
$CH_3 + C_6H_5CH_3 \rightarrow CH_4 + C_6H_5CH_2$	7	10	
$CF_3 + CH_4 \rightarrow CF_3H + CH_3$	9.5	11.0	
$CF_3 + C_2H_6 \rightarrow CF_3H + C_2H_5$	7.7	11.4	

† The experimental values are discussed, with references, by E. W. R. Steacie, "Atomic and Free Radical Reactions," Reinhold Publishing Corporation, New York, 1954, and by K. O. Kutschke and E. W. R. Steacie, in "Vistas in Free Radical Chemistry," p. 162, Pergamon Press, Oxford, 1959. There is some doubt on the experimental side about the results for the reaction between H and CH_4; the values given represent the author's opinion as to the most reliable figures. Work by J. W. S. Jamieson and G. R. Brown [*Can. J. Chem.*, **42,** 1638 (1964)], however, leads to much lower values of E and log A (7.4 kcal and 12).

[a] S. Bywater and R. Roberts, *Can. J. Chem.*, **30,** 773 (1952).

[b] J. C. Polanyi, *J. Chem. Phys.*, **23,** 1505 (1955); **24,** 493 (1956).

[c] D. J. Wilson and H. S. Johnston, *J. Am. Chem. Soc.*, **79,** 29 (1957).

[d] T. L. Hill, *J. Chem. Phys.*, **17,** 503 (1949).

theory of collisions. The reactions of hydrogen atoms are seen to have "normal" frequency factors, that is, not far from 10^{13} cc mole^{-1} sec^{-1}, the values falling as the complexity of the molecule increases. The methyl radical reactions all have frequency factors that are significantly lower, and which again tend to fall as the molecule becomes more complex. The kinetic theory predicts a value of 10^{13} to 10^{14} cc mole^{-1} sec^{-1} for all these reactions, and is therefore not satisfactory. The absolute-rate calculations are seen to be reasonably satisfactory in all cases, and to predict the general trends.

Attempts have been made to calculate activation energies for abstraction reactions, and to calculate frequency factors on the basis of the potential-energy surfaces. Weston[1] and Shavitt,[2] for example, have carried out such calculations for the following series of reactions:

(1) $H + H_2 \rightarrow H_2 + H$
(2) $D + D_2 \rightarrow D_2 + D$
(3) $D + H_2 \rightarrow HD + H$
(4) $H + D_2 \rightarrow HD + D$
(5) $H + HD \rightarrow H_2 + D$
(6) $D + DH \rightarrow D_2 + H$

Weston calculated a potential-energy surface using the method of Sato (cf. Chap. 3), and varied the Sato parameter S^2 (the square of the overlap integral) until he obtained agreement with the experimental activation energies. Using a treatment of Bell,[3] he calculated, for the $H + H_2$ reaction, the contribution due to tunneling, and found it to be considerable. This result, however, appears to be inconsistent with the experimental results, since it would lead to greater deviations from the Arrhenius law than have been observed. It therefore appears either that Sato's method leads to an unreliable estimate of the potential-energy barrier (making it too thin, so that too much tunneling occurs) or that Bell's treatment overestimates the extent of tunneling.

Shavitt's calculations were based on quantum-mechanical calculations, using the variation method. They led to activation energies that were much too high (15.4 kcal per mole for the $H + H_2$ reaction, as compared with the experimental value[4] of 8 to 9 kcal per mole). Shavitt scaled down his potential-energy surface so that the activation energy would agree with the experimental value for the $H + H_2$ reaction, and then calculated rates of the other reactions.

[1] R. E. Weston, *ibid.*, **31,** 892 (1959); cf. D. Rapp and R. E. Weston, *ibid.*, **36,** 2807 (1962).

[2] I. Shavitt, *ibid.*, **31,** 1359 (1959).

[3] R. P. Bell, *Trans. Faraday Soc.*, **55,** 1 (1959).

[4] Weston, *loc. cit.*

On the whole the calculations of Weston and Shavitt represent the *trends* in rate constants fairly satisfactorily, as is shown[1] by the figures in Table 16. It must be emphasized, however, that both treatments make

Table 16 RATIOS OF RATE CONSTANTS FOR REACTIONS BETWEEN HYDROGEN ATOMS AND HYDROGEN MOLECULES AT 1000°K

Calculations	k_2/k_1	k_3/k_5	k_4/k_6
Experimental	0.35	2.4	1.35
Weston, excluding tunneling	0.52	2.6	1.52
Weston, including tunneling	0.47	2.3	1.53
Shavitt	0.48	2.6	1.52

considerable use of empirical data, without which they would lead to conclusions that are quite inconsistent with the experimental results.

Similar calculations have been made by J. C. Polanyi,[2] who dealt with the $H + H_2$ reactions and also the following series:

$$CH_3 + H_2 \rightarrow CH_4 + H$$
$$CH_3 + D_2 \rightarrow CH_3D + D$$
$$CD_3 + H_2 \rightarrow CD_3H + H$$
$$CD_3 + D_2 \rightarrow CD_4 + D$$
$$CH_3 + DH \rightarrow CH_3D + H$$
$$CH_3 + HD \rightarrow CH_4 + D$$
$$CD_3 + HD \rightarrow CD_3H + D$$
$$CD_3 + DH \rightarrow CD_4 + H$$

He employed the semiempirical method of Eyring and M. Polanyi (cf. Chap. 3), and his calculated activation energies were again much greater than the experimental ones. Despite adjustment of the classical barrier height, it proved impossible to account for the variations in rate constants between the isotopic reactions. When the energy surface was readjusted to give a symmetrical activated state, fair agreement was obtained among experiment and theory. In Table 15 are included some of the results of these calculations.

[1] For a more detailed discussion of the experimental and calculated values see K. J. Laidler and J. C. Polanyi, in G. Porter (ed.), "Progress in Reaction Kinetics," vol. 3, Pergamon Press, Oxford, 1965.

[2] Polanyi, *loc. cit.*

Efforts have also been made to devise empirical relationships between energies of activation and other properties, such as bond energies and heats of reaction. Such relationships as do exist are not at all exact, but they are useful in allowing rough estimates of activation energies to be made.

It was suggested by Hirschfelder[1] that if a reaction of the type

$$\mathrm{A + BC \rightarrow AB + C}$$

is exothermic, the activation energy E is related to the dissociation energy D_{BC} of the bond BC by the equation

$$E = 0.055D_{\mathrm{BC}} \tag{17}$$

This relationship predicts that the energy of activation is independent of the nature of the atom or radical A, which is certainly not the case; however, the equation allows activation energies to be estimated to within a few kilocalories. If the reaction is endothermic, the procedure is to estimate the activation energy for the reverse reaction, using Eq. (17), and to use the heat of reaction to calculate that of the forward reaction.

Slightly different types of relationship have also been developed[2] and have been generalized by Semenoff.[3] For a wide variety of abstraction reactions Semenoff plots the energy of activation E against the heat evolved Q, and finds that for exothermic reactions (Q positive) almost all the points lie fairly close to the line represented by the equation

$$E = 11.5 - 0.25Q \tag{18}$$

As shown in Fig. 23, the activation energies rarely deviate from this relationship by more than 1 kcal. For endothermic reactions the best procedure is to estimate the energy of activation of the reverse reaction, using Eq. (18), and then to calculate that for the forward reaction; this is equivalent to saying that for a negative value of Q the relationship is

$$E = 11.5 + 0.75Q \tag{19}$$

A new empirical formulation that includes terms for bond forming and bond breaking has been proposed recently by Szabó[4] and applied to several homologous series.

[1] J. O. Hirschfelder, *J. Chem. Phys.*, **9,** 645 (1941).

[2] M. G. Evans and M. Polanyi, *Trans. Faraday Soc.*, **34,** 11 (1938); K. S. Bagdasaryan, *Zh. Fiz. Khim.*, **23,** 1375 (1949); N. N. Tikhomirova and V. V. Voevodsky, *Dokl. Akad. Nauk. SSR*, **79,** 993 (1951).

[3] N. N. Semenoff, "Some Problems in Chemical Kinetics and Reactivity," chap. 1, Pergamon Press, London, and Princeton University Press, Princeton, N.J., 1958.

[4] Z. G. Szabó, *Chem. Soc. (London) Spec. Publ.* **16,** 113 (1962).

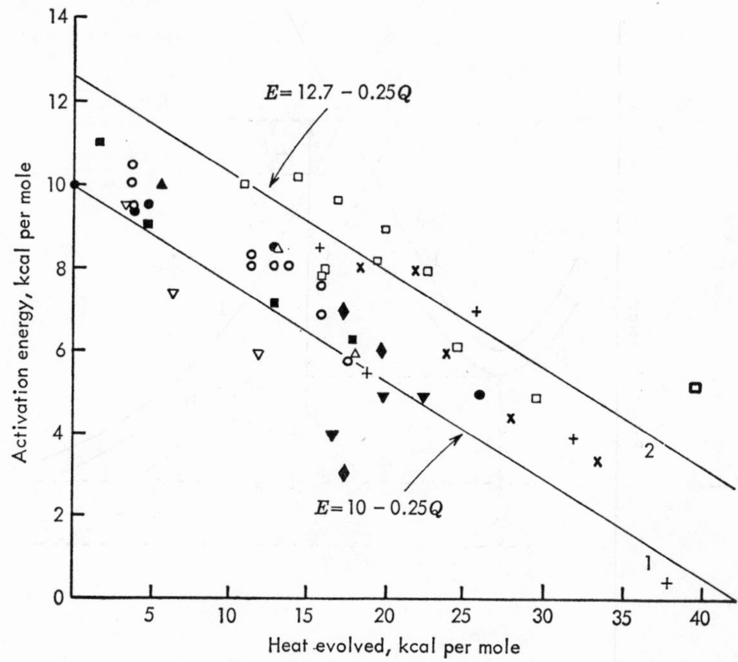

Fig. 23. Plot of activation energy against heat evolved, for a number of exothermic reactions, as follows:

●	$H + RH \rightarrow H_2 + R$
○	$CH_3 + RH \rightarrow CH_4 + R$
■	$D + RH \rightarrow HD + R$
+	$OH + RH \rightarrow H_2O + R$
△	$H + RCHO \rightarrow H_2 + RCO$
×	$H + RCl \rightarrow HCl + R$
▼	$CH_3 + RCl \rightarrow CH_3Cl + R$
◆	$H + RBr \rightarrow HBr + R$
▲	$CH_3 + RBr \rightarrow CH_3Br + R$
□	$Na + RCl \rightarrow NaCl + R$

Various theoretical discussions have been given of relationships of this kind; most are based on an early treatment of Evans and Polanyi.[1] Figure 24 shows potential-energy profiles (sections through the potential-energy surface) for a reaction of the type

$$A + BC \rightarrow AB + C$$

[1] Evans and Polanyi, *loc. cit.;* cf. also C. N. Hinshelwood, K. J. Laidler, and E. W. Timm, *J. Chem. Soc.*, 848 (1938); S. Glasstone, K. J. Laidler, and H. Eyring, "The Theory of Rate Processes," pp. 139–146, McGraw-Hill Book Company, New York, 1941.

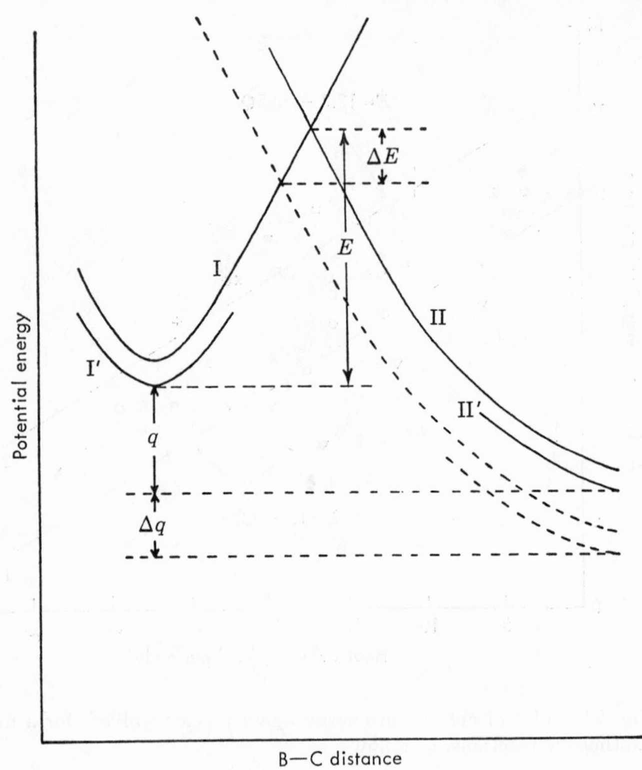

Fig. 24. Potential-energy profiles for a reaction A + BC → AB + C, showing the relationship between the increase in heat evolved Δq and the decrease in energy of activation ΔE.

Curve I relates to the system A + BC and shows the variation of potential energy with B—C distance at the particular A—B distance in the activated state, while curve II shows the corresponding variation for the system AB + C. Curve I′ is part of the potential-energy curve for BC when A is an infinite distance away, and curve II′ is the curve for AB + C with the A—B distance that corresponds to the normal molecule. The overall heat of reaction q and the activation energy E are shown on the diagram; actually there is a resonance splitting at the crossing point of curves I and II.

The dashed curve shows the change that occurs if A is replaced by another radical. If the A—B bond is now stronger, the curve is lowered and the heat evolved increases by an amount Δq. The change in the curve I is generally small when A is changed (this is equivalent to saying that there is usually little repulsive energy between A and BC). If this is the case, the change in E will closely parallel that in q. If the curves I and II are symmetrical where they intersect, the decrease in E would be one-half the increase in q. Semenoff's equation shows that the effect is actually a good deal less than this.

Similar arguments can be used to interpret the changes in activation energy that occur when B or C is changed.

ENERGY TRANSFER IN BIMOLECULAR REACTIONS[1]

When a bimolecular reaction involves the evolution of heat (i.e., is exothermic), there is an important question as to the distribution of this energy between the products of reaction and between the different types of motion. All the energy might, for example, pass into translational energy of the product molecules; alternatively, much of it might pass into vibrational modes. The answer to the question of the distribution of energy can in principle be provided from theory on the basis of a detailed consideration of the potential-energy surfaces; as has been seen, however, the construction of these surfaces cannot be done in an accurate manner, so that reliable conclusions cannot be drawn. As was discussed in the last chapter, significant advances have been made by carrying out experimental studies on energy transfer and interpreting them in the light of theoretical kinematic studies; in this way it has been possible to arrive at conclusions about the shapes of potential-energy surfaces.

Two important experimental techniques that have been used in this connection are measurements of chemiluminescence and molecular-beam studies, and some of the main results will now be reviewed briefly.

Chemiluminescence. Important results in this field have been obtained on reactions of the type

$$X + Na_2 \rightarrow Na + NaX$$

where X is a halogen atom. Work of this kind was initiated by work done by M. Polanyi,[2] who studied the emission of light when sodium reacts with halogens. Polanyi's work showed that the sodium halide molecule (NaX) emerging from the reaction was vibrationally excited, and on collision could transfer its vibrational energy to a sodium atom, which then became electronically excited. A similar situation occurs with the exothermic reaction

$$H + Cl_2 \rightarrow H + HCl$$

[1] For a number of papers on this subject see *Discussions Faraday Soc.*, **33** (1962).

[2] M. Polanyi, "Atomic Reactions," Ernest Benn, Ltd.–Benn Bros., Ltd., London, 1932.

Studies of the chemiluminescence emitted in many reactions of this type have been carried out by J. C. Polanyi and his coworkers.[1] The procedure for the $H + Cl_2$ reaction, for example, is to mix atomic hydrogen (formed in a discharge or at a hot wire) with chlorine at very low pressures, and to observe in the infrared region the radiation emitted by the HCl molecules formed. In all the exothermic reactions studied there was found to be preferential formation of product molecules in certain vibrationally excited states. In reactions of the type

$$H + Cl_2 \rightarrow HCl + Cl$$

however, most of the energy liberated goes into translation, and only a small amount into vibration. In the sodium-halogen reactions, on the other hand, most goes into vibrational modes. The significance of these results, in terms of the shapes of potential-energy surfaces, was considered in the last chapter.

A number of other conclusions have already emerged from investigations of this kind.[2] In systems in which more than three atoms are involved, such as[3]

$$O + O_3 \rightarrow O_2 + O_2^*$$
$$NO + O_3 \rightarrow NO_2 + O_2^*$$

the energy may reside largely as vibrational energy in one of the product molecules, as indicated in the equations above. Smith[4] has discussed the theory of processes of this kind and has suggested that there is a theoretical limit to the proportion of energy that can pass into vibrational modes. Experimental evidence has also been obtained[5] for the formation of product molecules containing large amounts of rotational energy.

Reactions in Crossed Molecular Beams. The first investigation of the kinetics of a chemical reaction by the molecular-beam technique was that of Taylor and Datz,[6] who studied the reaction

$$K + HBr \rightarrow KBr + H$$

[1] J. D. McKinlay and J. C. Polanyi, *Can. J. Chem.*, **36**, 107 (1958); J. K. Cashion and J. C. Polanyi, *J. Chem. Phys.*, **31**, 316, 317 (1959); P. E. Charters and J. C. Polanyi, *Can. J. Chem.*, **38**, 1742 (1960); J. K. Cashion and J. C. Polanyi, *Proc. Roy. Soc.* (*London*), **A258**, 529, 564, 570 (1960); J. C. Polanyi and C. M. Sadowski, *J. Chem. Phys.*, **36**, 2239 (1962); P. E. Charters and J. C. Polanyi, *Discussions Faraday Soc.*, **33**, 107 (1962); J. C. Polanyi, *J. Quant. Spectrosc. Radiat. Transfer*, **3**, 471 (1963).

[2] Cf. R. G. W. Norrish, *Proc. Chem. Soc.*, 247 (1958); J. C. Polanyi, *J. Chem. Phys.*, **31**, 1338 (1959); D. Garvin, H. P. Broida, and H. J. Kostowski, *ibid.*, **32**, 880 (1960).

[3] W. D. McGrath and R. G. W. Norrish, *Proc. Roy. Soc.* (*London*), **A254**, 317 (1960); F. J. Lipscomb, R. G. W. Norrish, and B. A. Thrush, *ibid.*, **A233**, 455 (1956).

[4] F. T. Smith, *J. Chem. Phys.*, **31**, 1352 (1959).

[5] G. B. Kistiakowsky and F. D. Tabbutt, *ibid.*, **30**, 577 (1959).

[6] E. H. Taylor and S. Datz, *ibid.*, **23**, 1711 (1955).

Beams of potassium atoms and hydrogen bromide were crossed, and the products detected using heated tungsten and platinum filaments. It was possible to distinguish the small amounts of KBr formed from the large background of elastically scattered K atoms, and a value of about 10^{-3} was found for the collision yield; this is the ratio of KBr molecules detected to K atoms scattered. From the variation of the yield with beam "temperatures"—calculated from the energy and other characteristics of the beams—Taylor and Datz estimated an activation energy of 3 kcal per mole for the reaction. In a later study of the same reaction, Greene, Roberts, and Ross[1] used more refined apparatus, and obtained more detailed information about the collision yields.

Herschbach and his coworkers[2] have studied reactions of the type

$$K + CH_3I \rightarrow KI + CH_3$$
$$K + C_2H_5I \rightarrow KI + C_2H_5$$

They have measured not only reaction cross sections but also the angular distribution of the reaction products. By the use of the theory of molecular beams, the angular distribution of the product KI yields information about the partitioning of the energy of reaction between translation, vibration, and rotation in the product molecules.

The main results of these investigations have been summarized in the previous chapter in connection with kinematic calculations. They have shown that in reactions of alkali metals the major part of the heat of reaction goes into internal energy, with only a small part going into translation. These results suggest that the surfaces are of the attractive type.

TERMOLECULAR REACTIONS

A few reactions take place with velocities that are proportional to the product of three concentrations. The activated complex is made up of three molecules, and its concentration can be calculated by the usual methods of statistical mechanics. Since, moreover, the reactions appear to be comparatively free from side reactions, they may conveniently be treated as elementary.

All the known gaseous reactions of the third order involve nitric oxide as one of the reacting molecules. The first reaction of this type was studied in 1914 by Trautz,[3] who investigated the reaction between nitric oxide and chlorine over the range of temperatures from 8 to 283°C. The

[1] E. F. Greene, R. W. Roberts, and J. Ross, *ibid.*, **32**, 940 (1960).

[2] D. R. Herschbach, *ibid.*, **33**, 1870 (1960); *Vortex*, **22**, 1 (1961); *Discussions Faraday Soc.*, **33**, 149 (1962); D. R. Herschbach, G. H. Kwei, and J. A. Norris, *J. Chem. Phys.*, **34**, 1842 (1961).

[3] M. Trautz, *Z. Anorg. Chem.*, **88**, 285 (1914).

product of the reaction is nitrosyl chloride, the overall process being

$$2NO + Cl_2 = 2NOCl$$

There is therefore a decrease in volume, so that the progress of the reaction can be followed by confining the gases in a bulb maintained at the required temperature and observing the change in pressure as a function of the time. Trautz later did further work on the reaction and on the equilibrium,[1] as did von Kiss.[2] Later Krauss and Saracini[3] confirmed that the reaction is homogeneous and of the third order over a wide range of pressures.

Other reactions of the third order were studied during the same period. In 1918 Bodenstein investigated the reaction between nitric oxide and oxygen to give nitrogen dioxide[4]

$$2NO + O_2 = 2NO_2$$

The reacting gases were allowed to stream into a bulb at constant temperature, and the change in pressure was measured using a manometer containing bromonaphthalene. The rate of reaction is high at ordinary pressures, but can be measured sufficiently accurately at low ones. The third-order law was obeyed, and the rate decreased with rise of temperature.

Similar results were obtained with the reaction between nitric oxide and bromine,[5]

$$2NO + Br_2 = 2NOBr$$

The reaction between nitric oxide and hydrogen,[6]

$$2NO + 2H_2 = 2H_2O + N_2$$

differs from the other reactions in having a high temperature coefficient, and more recent work[7] has indicated that the reaction becomes more complicated at lower pressures. The reaction with deuterium has also been studied.[8]

There has been a good deal of discussion, on the basis of the collision theory, about the mechanism by which these reactions take place. A

[1] M. Trautz and L. Wachenheim, *ibid.*, **97**, 241 (1916); M. Trautz and F. A. Hengheim, *ibid.*, **110**, 237 (1920); M. Trautz and H. Schlueter, *ibid.*, **136**, 1 (1924).

[2] A. von Kiss, *Rec. Trav. Chim.*, **42**, 112, 665 (1923); **43**, 68 (1924).

[3] W. Krauss and M. Saracini, *Z. Physik. Chem.*, **A178**, 245 (1937).

[4] M. Bodenstein, *Z. Elektrochem.*, **24**, 183 (1918); *Z. Physik. Chem.*, **100**, 68 (1922). Cf. E. Briner, W. Pfeiffer, and G. Malet, *J. Chim. Phys.*, **21**, 25 (1924); G. Kornfeld and E. Klinger, *Z. Physik. Chem.*, **4**, 37 (1929).

[5] M. Trautz and V. P. Dalal, *Z. Anorg. Chem.*, **102**, 149 (1918).

[6] C. N. Hinshelwood and T. E. Green, *J. Chem. Soc.*, 730 (1926).

[7] C. N. Hinshelwood and J. W. Mitchell, *ibid.*, 378 (1936); H. A. Taylor and C. Tanford, *J. Chem. Phys.*, **12**, 47 (1944).

[8] Hinshelwood and Mitchell, *loc. cit.*

collision between three molecules will obviously take place much less frequently than one between two; consequently, if a reaction of the third order had the same activation energy as one of the second order, its rate would be much lower. The only third-order reactions that are likely to proceed at conveniently measurable rates may therefore be expected to involve rather low activation energies. This is true for all the reactions studied except that involving hydrogen, and this takes place only at very high temperatures and is complex.

In 1916 Trautz[1] suggested that true ternary collisions between molecules are probably so rare that it is better to regard the termolecular reactions as taking place in two stages; in 1918 he proposed[2] the mechanism

$$NO + Br_2 \rightleftharpoons NOBr_2$$
$$NOBr_2 + NO \rightarrow 2NOBr$$

for the bromine reaction, and later gave corresponding mechanisms for the other reactions.[3] According to this scheme, a small concentration of $NOBr_2$ is maintained in equilibrium with NO and Br_2, its concentration being proportional to $[NO][Br_2]$. The overall rate of the reaction is determined by the collision between $NOBr_2$ and NO, so that the rate is proportional to $[NOBr_2][NO]$, i.e., to $[NO]^2[Br_2]$. Increase in temperature tends to dissociate the $NOBr_2$, with the result that the rate of the reaction may be reduced.

Such mechanisms are formally equivalent to the assumption of collisions of long duration ("sticky collisions") between two of the reacting molecules: NO and Br_2 in the above example. Bodenstein[4] explained the experimental results in a rather more general way than Trautz, without specifying the molecules between which a long collision time had to be postulated. He made a rough estimate of the number of triple collisions by assuming that the ratio between the chance of a molecule hitting another molecule which is actually in collision with a third molecule, to the chance that it hits a single molecule, is equal to the ratio of the molecular diameter to the mean free path. On this basis the ratio of ternary to binary collisions came out to be about 1:1,000. However this gives about 10^5 more collisions than correspond to reaction for the cases in which the energy of activation is zero. The reason for this discrepancy is that the collision theory, by assuming the molecules to behave as hard spheres, neglects the considerable loss of entropy when three molecules unite in the activated state.

[1] M. Trautz, *Z. Elektrochem.*, **22**, 104 (1916).

[2] Trautz and Dalal, *loc. cit.*

[3] Trautz and Schlueter, *loc. cit.*

[4] M. Bodenstein, *Z. Physik. Chem.*, **100**, 118 (1922); cf. K. F. Herzfeld, *Z. Physik.*, **8**, 132 (1921).

The theory of absolute reaction rates has the virtue of allowing for this effect and of circumventing the question of the mechanism by which the ternary complex is formed. As long as it can be assumed that the complex is in equilibrium with the reacting molecules, the manner of its formation is irrelevant to the calculation of its concentration.

The detailed application of the theory has been worked out by Gershinowitz and Eyring.[1] For a reaction of the type

$$2NO + X_2 \rightarrow 2NOX$$

where X may be oxygen, chlorine, or bromine, the rate constant is given by

$$k = l^\ddagger \frac{\mathbf{k}T}{\mathbf{h}} \frac{F_\ddagger}{F_{NO}^2 F_{X_2}} e^{-E_0/RT} \tag{20}$$

where $l^\ddagger$ is the statistical factor, in this case equal to unity. Evaluation of the partition functions in terms of their translational, rotational, and vibrational factors gives the expression

$$k = \frac{\mathbf{k}T}{\mathbf{h}} \frac{g_\ddagger}{g_i} \frac{\frac{(2\pi m_\ddagger \mathbf{k}T)^{3/2}}{\mathbf{h}^3} \frac{8\pi^2(8\pi^3 ABC)^{1/2}(\mathbf{k}T)^{3/2}}{\mathbf{h}^3} \prod^{11} (1 - e^{-\mathbf{h}\nu_*/\mathbf{k}T})^{-1}}{\prod^{3} \frac{(2\pi m_i \mathbf{k}T)^{3/2}}{\mathbf{h}^3} \prod^{3} \left(\frac{8\pi^2 I_i \mathbf{k}T}{\mathbf{h}^2}\right) \prod^{3} (1 - e^{-\mathbf{h}\nu_i/\mathbf{k}T})^{-1}} e^{-E_0/RT} \tag{21}$$

In these two equations the transmission coefficient has been taken as unity; the subscript i refers to the initial state. Since the activated complex contains six atoms, there are 11 vibrational factors. With the removal of temperature-independent factors, including the vibrational factors, which vary only slightly with the temperature, this expression may be written as

$$k = \mathbf{k}' T^{-7/2} e^{-E_0/RT} \tag{22}$$

It is evident that if E_0 is zero or very small, the rate constant will decrease with temperature, as is actually found in the reaction involving oxygen.

In order to carry out an absolute calculation of the rate constant, it is necessary to have some knowledge of the configuration and vibration frequencies of the activated complex. For the reaction between nitric oxide and oxygen, the configuration depicted in Fig. 25 has been assumed. This necessitates a slight modification to the treatment given previously [Eq. (21)], owing to the possibility of free rotation about the O—O bond. This is done by replacing one of the vibrational factors for the activated complex by the expression

$$\frac{(8\pi^3 I_D \mathbf{k}T)^{1/2}}{\mathbf{h}}$$

[1] H. Gershinowitz and H. Eyring, *J. Am. Chem. Soc.*, **57**, 985 (1935).

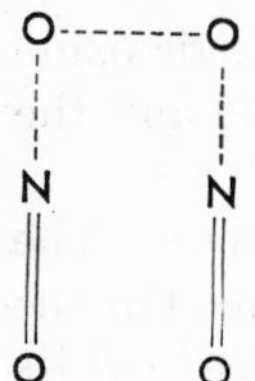

Fig. 25. The general shape of the activated complex in the reaction between nitric oxide and oxygen.

where I_D is the moment of inertia for rotation about the bond. The effect of this is to replace the term $T^{-7/2}$ by T^{-3}. Upon substituting the numerical values for the universal constants and expressing molecular weights M in grams and moments of inertia in g-A² per mole, the rate constant for the reaction is given by

$$k = 1.6 \times 10^{19} \frac{g_\ddagger}{g_i} \left(\frac{M}{\prod\limits^{3} M_i} \right)^{3/2} \frac{(ABC)^{1/2} I_D^{1/2}}{T^3 \prod\limits^{3} I_i} \frac{\prod\limits^{10} (1 - e^{-h\nu_\ddagger/kT})^{-1}}{\prod\limits^{3} (1 - e^{-h\nu_i/kT})^{-1}} e^{-E_0/RT} \tag{23}$$

the units being cc² mole⁻² sec⁻¹. To a good approximation the vibrational frequencies $\nu_\ddagger$ for the activated state may be taken to be the same as in N_2O_4, the values of which are known.[1] The frequencies for oxygen and nitric oxide are so high that the corresponding partition functions are practically unity. Making this approximation, and taking logarithms of both sides of Eq. (23), one finds that a plot of

$$\ln k + 3 \ln T - \ln \prod^{7} (1 - e^{-h\nu_\ddagger/kT})^{-1}$$

against $1/T$ should be a straight line of slope equal to $-E_0/R$. This has been plotted in Fig. 26, in which it is seen that E_0 is extremely close to

[1] G. B. B. M. Sutherland, *Proc. Roy. Soc.* (*London*), **A141**, 342 (1933).

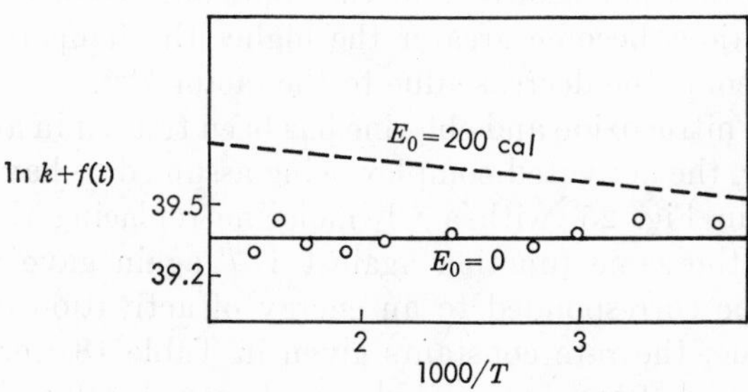

Fig. 26. A plot of $\ln k + f(T)$ against $1/T$ for the nitric oxide-oxygen reaction.

zero. This result may be associated with the fact that both nitric oxide and oxygen are paramagnetic, the former molecule having one and the latter two unpaired electrons.

The rate constant is therefore calculated with E_0 taken as zero. The moments of inertia are derived from spectroscopic measurements, but the evaluation of those of the activated complex requires a knowledge of its configurations and dimensions. The relevant values are not very critical, and estimates were made on the basis of the normal interatomic distances in other molecules.

The observed results, and those calculated by the methods outlined above, are shown in Table 17. The agreement is very satisfactory,

Table 17 Calculated and observed rate constants for the nitric oxide–oxygen reaction

	$k \times 10^{-3}$, liter^2 mole^{-2} sec^{-1}	
T, °K	Calculated	Observed
80	86.0	41.8
143	16.2	20.2
228	5.3	10.1
300	3.3	7.1
413	2.2	4.0
564	2.0	2.8
613	2.1	2.8
662	2.0	2.9

especially in that both theory and experiment show a minimum rate at about the same temperature; the reason is that the contributions of the vibrational partition functions become greater the higher the temperature, and eventually overcome the decrease due to the factor T^{-3}.

The reaction between nitric oxide and chlorine has been treated in an essentially similar manner, the activated complex being assumed to have the configuration shown in Fig. 25, with a Cl_2 molecule replacing the O_2 molecule. A plot of the same function against $1/T$ again gave a straight line, but the slope corresponded to an energy of activation of 4.8 kcal. Using this value, the rate constants given in Table 18 were calculated. The agreement between calculated and observed values is again quite satisfactory, especially in view of the assumptions made in the theory and the fact that the data are not very accurate.

The experimental results for the reaction between nitric oxide and bromine are not accurate enough to allow an estimate of the value of E_0 to be made; however, certain qualitative remarks can be made about the reaction. Because bromine is heavier than chlorine, the vibration frequencies are probably lower, and the activation energy will be lower since the Br—Br bond is weaker than the Cl—Cl bond. It therefore follows from Eq. (21) that the rate of this reaction should be greater than that of the reaction with chlorine at the same temperature. This conclusion is in agreement with experiment.

The satisfactory agreement with experiment that is achieved by the theory of absolute reaction rates indicates that the theory is adequate for interpreting elementary reactions of the third order from the standpoint of an equilibrium between the complex and the reacting molecules. The question of the way in which the complex is formed is therefore irrelevant to the study of the rate of reaction.

Table 18 CALCULATED AND OBSERVED RATES FOR THE NITRIC OXIDE–CHLORINE REACTION

	$k \times 10^{-12}$, liter^2 mole^{-2} sec^{-1}	
T, °K	Calculated	Observed
273	1.4	5.5
333	2.2	9.5
355	8.6	27.2
401	18.3	72.2
451	25.4	182
506	64.5	453
566	120.2	1,130

UNIMOLECULAR REACTIONS

In a unimolecular reaction the activated complex is a single reactant molecule which has gained the necessary energy of activation by collisions with other molecules. Unimolecular reactions are of two types. They may be isomerizations, such as the isomerization of cyclopropane into propylene:

$$\begin{array}{c} CH_2 \\ / \quad \backslash \\ CH_2{-}CH_2 \end{array} \rightarrow CH_3CH{=}CH_2$$

They may also be decompositions, such as the dissociation of ethane into two methyl radicals,

$$C_2H_6 \rightarrow 2CH_3$$

As will be seen later, most decompositions occur not in a single stage but by free-radical mechanisms; the first step is, however, generally a unimolecular decomposition, and the dissociation of ethane into two methyl radicals is in fact the first stage in the thermal decomposition of ethane.

Some difficulty arose at first concerning the manner in which molecules became activated in unimolecular reactions. It appeared that activation by collision would give rise to second-order kinetics, since the number of collisions is proportional to the square of the concentration. In 1922, however, Lindemann[1] showed how activation by collision can give rise to first-order kinetics under certain circumstances. Lindemann's theory is the basis of all modern theories of unimolecular reactions, although a number of important modifications had to be made to it. An account will be given first of the elementary theory of Lindemann, and then the various modifications referred to above will be treated in some detail.

Lindemann's Theory. According to Lindemann's theory, reactant molecules receive energy by collisions with one another, and at any given time a small fraction of the molecules have sufficient energy to pass into the final state without having to receive any additional energy; such molecules will be referred to as *energized* molecules. If the energized molecules are converted into products at a rate that is small compared to the rate with which they are deenergized by collision, a stationary concentration of them may be built up. Since these energized molecules are in equilibrium with the normal molecules, their concentration is proportional to that of the normal molecules. The rate of reaction is proportional to the concentration of energized molecules, and is therefore proportional to the concentration of normal molecules; the reaction is therefore of the first order. At low pressures, however, the collisions cannot maintain a supply of energized molecules; the rate of the reaction then depends upon the rate of energization, and is therefore proportional to the square of the concentration of reacting molecules.

The processes of energization and deenergization by collision may be represented by the equation

$$\text{(1)} \qquad A + A \underset{k_{-1}}{\overset{k_1}{\rightleftharpoons}} A^* + A$$

where A represents a normal reactant molecule, and A* an energized molecule. The subsequent reaction (decomposition or isomerization)

[1] F. A. Lindemann, *Trans. Faraday Soc.*, **17**, 598 (1922).

of the energized molecule is represented by tne equation

(2) $$A^* \xrightarrow{k_2} \text{products}$$

A steady concentration of energized molecules will be established, and the net rate of formation of A* may be set equal to zero:[1]

$$\frac{d[A^*]}{dt} = k_1[A]^2 - k_{-1}[A^*][A] - k_2[A^*] = 0 \tag{24}$$

From this equation it follows that the concentration of energized molecules is

$$[A^*] = \frac{k_1[A]^2}{k_{-1}[A] + k_2} \tag{25}$$

The rate of formation of products is therefore

$$v = k_2[A^*] = \frac{k_1 k_2 [A]^2}{k_{-1}[A] + k_2} \tag{26}$$

At sufficiently high pressures $k_{-1}[A] \gg k_2$, and under these conditions the rate is given by

$$v = \frac{k_1 k_2}{k_{-1}} [A] = k_\infty [A] \tag{27}$$

The reaction is then of the first order. In this equation k_∞ is the first-order constant at high pressures and is equal to $k_1 k_2 / k_{-1}$. At low pressures, on the other hand, $k_{-1}[A] \ll k_2$; the rate equation then reduces to

$$v = k_1[A]^2 \tag{28}$$

so that the reaction is now of the second order.

Changes from first-order to second-order kinetics as the pressure is lowered have been observed experimentally in a number of unimolecular reactions. Lindemann's theory therefore does give a satisfactory qualitative interpretation of unimolecular reactions, but quantitatively it is not completely satisfactory. This may be seen as follows.

A first-order rate coefficient k^1 may be defined by the equation

$$v = k^1[A] \tag{29}$$

Equations (26) and (29) give rise to

$$k^1 = \frac{k_1 k_2 [A]}{k_{-1}[A] + k_2} = \frac{k_\infty}{1 + k_2/k_{-1}[A]} \tag{30}$$

A plot of k^1 against [A] gives a curve of the form shown in Fig. 27. The coefficient k^1 is constant in the higher pressure range, but falls to zero at

[1] This is an example of the application of the *steady-state treatment*, the basis of which is discussed later.

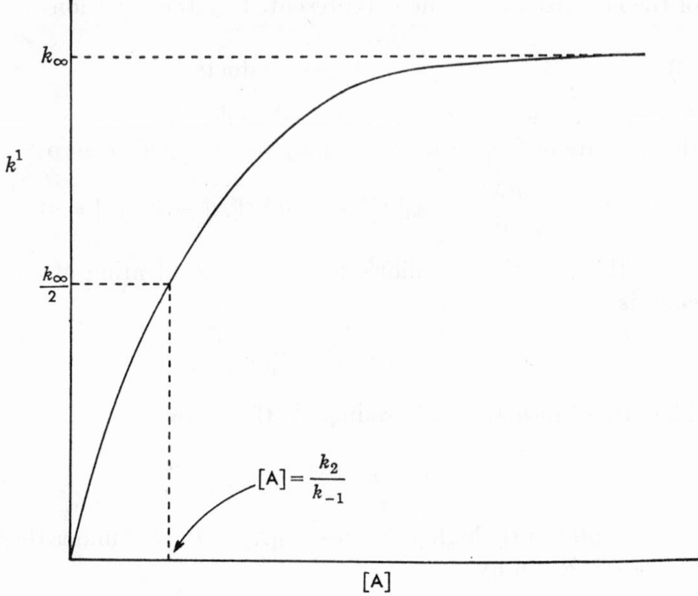

Fig. 27. The variation of the first-order rate coefficient with the concentration, for a unimolecular reaction.

lower pressures. It follows from Eq. (30) that k^1 becomes equal to one-half of k_∞ when

$$k_{-1}[\text{A}]_{1/2} = k_2 \tag{31}$$

Therefore, when $k^1 = k_\infty/2$,

$$k_1[\text{A}]_{1/2} = \frac{k_1 k_2}{k_{-1}} = k_\infty \tag{32}$$

or

$$[\text{A}]_{1/2} = \frac{k_\infty}{k_1} \tag{33}$$

The value of k_∞, the first-order rate constant at high pressures, is found from experiment, and, according to the simple collision theory, k_1 should be equal to $Z_1 e^{-E^*/RT}$, where E^* is the energy of activation. In all cases, however, this procedure leads to the prediction that the first-order rate constant should fall off at a much higher pressure than is actually observed. There can be no doubt about k_∞, which is an experimental quantity; the error must therefore be in the estimation of k_1. It is thus necessary for the collision theory to be modified in such a manner as to give larger values for k_1. Such a modification was made by Hinshelwood, whose treatment is discussed in the next section.

Another difficulty with the simple Lindemann theory of unimolecular reactions becomes apparent when the equation is considered from another point of view. Equation (30) may be written as

$$\frac{1}{k^1} = \frac{k_{-1}}{k_1 k_2} + \frac{1}{k_1[\mathrm{A}]} \tag{34}$$

and a plot of $1/k^1$ against the reciprocal of the concentration should give a straight line. Deviations from linearity are found, however, of the kind shown schematically in Fig. 28. These deviations are explained,

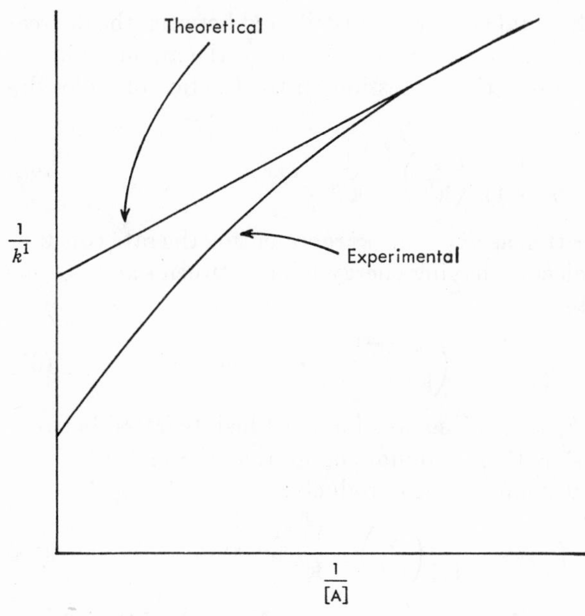

Fig. 28. Predicted [by Eq. (30)] and observed behavior when $1/k^1$ is plotted against $1/[A]$.

as will be seen, by the theories of Kassel, of Rice and Ramsperger, and of Slater.

Hinshelwood's Treatment. An explanation for the fact that the first-order rates are maintained down to lower concentrations than permitted by the simple Lindemann theory was first given by Hinshelwood.[1] The basis of his modification to the Lindemann theory is that the rate constant for the energization process k_1 may be much greater for a complex molecule than for a simple molecule. This is so because the energy

[1] C. N. Hinshelwood, *Proc. Roy. Soc. (London)*, **A113**, 230 (1927); cf. also G. N. Lewis and D. F. Smith, *J. Am. Chem. Soc.*, **47**, 1508 (1925); R. H. Fowler and E. K. Rideal, *Proc. Roy. Soc. (London)*, **A113**, 570 (1927).

possessed by a complex molecule may be distributed among a considerable number of degrees of vibrational freedom. According to statistical mechanics, if a molecule has s degrees of vibrational freedom, the fraction of molecules having a total energy between ϵ and $\epsilon + d\epsilon$, distributed in such a manner that the energy in the first degree of freedom is between ϵ_1 and $\epsilon_1 + d\epsilon_1$, that in the second degree of freedom is between ϵ_2 and $\epsilon_2 + d\epsilon_2$, and so on, is given by

$$f = \frac{e^{-\epsilon/\mathbf{k}T}\, d\epsilon_1\, d\epsilon_2 \cdots d\epsilon_s}{(\mathbf{k}T)^s} \tag{35}$$

If, on the other hand, the total energy ϵ is distributed between the degrees of freedom in any way, without any restriction as to the amounts in the individual degrees of freedom, the expression for the fraction of molecules becomes

$$f = \frac{1}{(s-1)!}\left(\frac{\epsilon}{\mathbf{k}T}\right)^{s-1} \frac{1}{\mathbf{k}T}\, e^{-\epsilon/\mathbf{k}T}\, d\epsilon \tag{36}$$

This fraction may be written as dk_1/k_{-1}, dk_1 representing the rate constant for the formation of molecules having energy lying between ϵ and $\epsilon + d\epsilon$; one may therefore write

$$\frac{dk_1}{k_{-1}} = \frac{1}{(s-1)!}\left(\frac{\epsilon}{\mathbf{k}T}\right)^{s-1} \frac{1}{\mathbf{k}T}\, e^{-\epsilon/\mathbf{k}T}\, d\epsilon \tag{37}$$

To obtain the value of k_1/k_{-1}, this expression must be integrated between ϵ^* and infinity, where ϵ^* is the minimum energy that the molecule must have in order for it to decompose into products:

$$\frac{k_1}{k_{-1}} = \int_{\epsilon^*}^{\infty} \frac{1}{(s-1)!}\left(\frac{\epsilon}{\mathbf{k}T}\right)^{s-1} \frac{1}{\mathbf{k}T}\, e^{-\epsilon/\mathbf{k}T}\, d\epsilon \tag{38}$$

Provided that $\epsilon^*/s\mathbf{k}T$ is much greater than unity, the result of the integration is approximately

$$\frac{k_1}{k_{-1}} = \frac{1}{(s-1)!}\left(\frac{\epsilon^*}{\mathbf{k}T}\right)^{s-1} e^{-\epsilon^*/\mathbf{k}T} \tag{39}$$

If the collision frequency corresponding to k_{-1} is written as Z_{-1}, the expression for k_1 becomes

$$k_1 = Z_{-1}\frac{1}{(s-1)!}\left(\frac{\epsilon^*}{\mathbf{k}T}\right)^{s-1} e^{-\epsilon^*/\mathbf{k}T} \tag{40}$$

This expression is to be compared with the expression

$$k_1 = Z_1 e^{-\epsilon^*/\mathbf{k}T} \tag{41}$$

which is the expression originally employed on the basis of the simple collision theory.

In employing Eq. (40) it must be noted that, whereas in Eq. (41) the quantity ϵ^* is the experimental energy of activation per molecule, that in Eq. (40) differs from the experimental value ϵ_{exp} according to the relationship

$$\epsilon^* = \epsilon_{\text{exp}} + (s - 1)\mathbf{k}T \tag{42}$$

This arises because of the temperature dependence of the frequency factor (p. 87). It may easily be shown by inserting numerical values that the new theory gives rise to a much higher rate of energization, and therefore to a much higher value of k_1/k_{-1}, than does the old. If, for example, the experimental energy of activation is taken as 40 kcal per mole, and s as 12, Eq. (40) gives rise to a value of 9.9×10^{-12} for k_1/k_{-1}. The simple theory [Eq. (41)] gives 3.1×10^{-18}. The difference in this example is of the order of 10^6, and the new theory will therefore predict that the first-order rate constant will begin to fall off at pressures lower by this order of magnitude than predicted by the old theory. In practice s is usually found by a method of trial and error, and it has always been found possible to explain the results using a value of s that is equal to, or less than, the total number of normal modes in the molecule. The best agreement is usually obtained by taking s as equal to about half the total number. The explanation is presumably that the energy that is ultimately involved in the formation of the activated complex comes not from all the normal modes but only from some of them; the significance of this is considered again later.

Hinshelwood's treatment, and the other modifications to Lindemann's theory that are now to be discussed, are to be considered in terms of the following scheme of reactions:

$$\mathrm{A} + \mathrm{A} \underset{k_{-1}}{\overset{k_1}{\rightleftharpoons}} \mathrm{A}^* + \mathrm{A}$$

$$\mathrm{A}^* \xrightarrow{k_2} \mathrm{A}^\ddagger$$

$$\mathrm{A}^\ddagger \xrightarrow{k^\ddagger} \text{products}$$

A distinction has here been made between an *activated* complex, represented by the symbol $\mathrm{A}^\ddagger$, and an *energized* molecule, represented by A^*. By an activated complex $\mathrm{A}^\ddagger$ is meant one that is passing smoothly into the final state. An energized molecule is one that has sufficient energy and can become an activated molecule without the acquisition of further energy; it must, however, undergo vibrational changes before it can become an activated complex, in which the energy has become localized in the particular bond or bonds that are to be broken during the reaction. According to the point of view of the Hinshelwood treatment, the molecules may become energized much more readily than had been considered possible on the basis of simple collision theory; a long period of time may elapse, however, before an energized molecule can become an activated molecule. Hinshelwood's treatment predicts an abnormally large value for k_1, and k_2 is correspondingly low. The theories that are now to be discussed also postulate a large value for k_1, but they consider that k_2 is larger, the greater the amount of energy residing in the energized molecule. The theories of Kassel and of Rice and Ramsperger, on the one hand, and of Slater, on the other, represent two alternative ways of treating this problem.

The Treatment of Kassel, and of Rice and Ramsperger. In order to explain the type of behavior shown in Fig. 27, Kassel[1] and Rice and Ramsperger[2] developed a theory which is based on the assumption that k_2 will be a function of the energy possessed by the energized molecule A*. The theories of Kassel and of Rice and Ramsperger, are very similar; the version that will be given here is essentially that of Kassel.

The postulate that is made in these theories is that the rate constant k_2 for the decomposition of the active molecule increases with the energy possessed by the molecule in its various degrees of freedom; at high pressures, where there is a greater number of highly activated molecules, the rate will therefore be higher than predicted by the simple theory. It is supposed that on every vibration there is a reshuffling of energy between the normal modes, and after a number of vibrations the critical energy ϵ^* may be found in one particular normal mode, and reaction then occurs; this mode may be referred to as the *critical* mode. The larger the energy ϵ possessed by the excited molecule, the greater is the chance that the necessary amount ϵ^* can pass into the critical mode, and the greater is therefore the rate of the reaction.

In terms of a quantum model, the Kassel-Rice-Ramsperger relationship may be obtained as follows. The statistical weight of a system of s degrees of vibrational freedom containing j quanta of vibrational energy is equal to the number of ways in which j objects can be divided among s boxes, each of which can contain any number; the number of such ways is

$$\frac{(j + s - 1)!}{j!(s - 1)!}$$

The statistical weight for states in which the s oscillators have j quanta among them, and a particular one has m quanta, is similarly

$$\frac{(j - m + s - 1)!}{(j - m)!(s - 1)!}$$

[1] L. S. Kassel, *J. Phys. Chem.*, **32**, 225 (1928); "Kinetics of Homogeneous Gas Reactions," chap. 5, Reinhold Publishing Corporation, New York, 1932.

[2] O. K. Rice and H. C. Ramsperger, *J. Am. Chem. Soc.*, **49**, 1617 (1927); **50**, 617 (1928).

The probability that a particular oscillator has m quanta, and all s oscillators have j quanta, is the ratio of these

$$\frac{(j-m+s-1)!j!}{(j-m)!(j+s-1)!}$$

This is approximately equal to

$$\left(\frac{j-m}{j}\right)^{s-1}$$

provided that j is very large. The total number of quanta j may be taken as proportional to ϵ, the total energy of the molecule, while m is proportional to ϵ^*, the minimum energy that a molecule must have for reaction to take place. The expression given above is therefore equal to

$$\left(\frac{\epsilon-\epsilon^*}{\epsilon}\right)^{s-1}$$

The rate with which the required energy passes into the particular degree of freedom is proportional to this quantity, so that one may write

$$k_2 = k^\ddagger \left(\frac{\epsilon-\epsilon^*}{\epsilon}\right)^{s-1} \tag{43}$$

In this expression $k^\ddagger$ is the rate constant corresponding to the free passage of the system over the potential-energy barrier; when ϵ is sufficiently large, the energized molecule is essentially an activated molecule and therefore can pass immediately into the final state. The variation of k_2 with ϵ is shown schematically in Fig. 29.

In order to obtain an expression for k_∞, Kassel employed the same expression as Hinshelwood for dk_1/k_{-1}, namely, Eq. (37), and used Eq. (43) for k_2. The expression for k_∞ is therefore as follows:

$$k_\infty = \frac{k_1k_2}{k_{-1}} = k^\ddagger \int_{\epsilon^*}^{\infty} \left(\frac{\epsilon-\epsilon^*}{\epsilon}\right)^{s-1} \frac{1}{(s-1)!}\left(\frac{\epsilon}{\mathbf{k}T}\right)^{s-1} \frac{1}{\mathbf{k}T} e^{-\epsilon/\mathbf{k}T} \tag{44}$$

The integration must be carried out between the limits of ϵ^* and infinity, and when this is done the result is simply the Arrhenius equation

$$k_\infty = k^\ddagger e^{-\epsilon^*/\mathbf{k}T} \tag{45}$$

It is of interest to note that Slater[1] has shown that when Eq. (37) is employed for dk_1/k_1, the only expression that will give rise to Eq. (45) is Eq. (43).

[1] N. B. Slater, *Proc. Leeds Phil. Soc.*, **4**, 259 (1955).

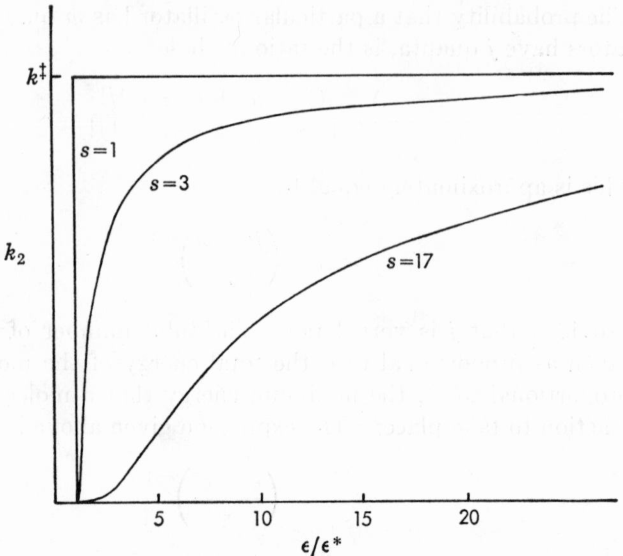

Fig. 29. The variation of k_2 with ϵ/ϵ^*, according to Eq. (43), for different values of s, the number of degrees of freedom.

Equation (45) could have been arrived at immediately using the method of absolute reaction rates; according to this theory, $k^\ddagger$ would be equal to $\mathbf{k}T/\mathbf{h}$, and Eq. (45) would result, provided that the partition functions are the same in the initial and activated states. From the standpoint of absolute theory, Kassel's equation (45) would therefore predict that frequency factors of first-order reactions should be of the order of $\mathbf{k}T/\mathbf{h}$, that is, of the order of 10^{13} at ordinary temperatures. This conclusion, however, requires some modification (cf. p. 165). In Kassel's original formulation no particular significance was attached to the magnitude of $k^\ddagger$.

An important aspect of the Kassel theory is the manner in which it predicts the variation of k^1 with the pressure of the reacting gas. Equation (30) can be written in the form

$$k^1 = \frac{k_1 k_2/k_{-1}}{1 + k_2/k_{-1}[\mathrm{A}]} \tag{46}$$

and, considering the rate constant associated with molecules having energy lying between ϵ and $\epsilon + d\epsilon$, one may write

$$dk^1 = \frac{(dk_1)k_2/k_{-1}}{1 + k_2/k_{-1}[\mathrm{A}]} \tag{47}$$

Insertion of expressions (37) and (43), and integration between the limits

ϵ^* and ∞, gives rise to

$$k^1 = \int_{\epsilon^*}^{\infty} \frac{\frac{1}{(s-1)!}\left(\frac{\epsilon}{\mathbf{k}T}\right)^{s-1} e^{-\epsilon^*/\mathbf{k}T} k^\ddagger \left(\frac{\epsilon - \epsilon^*}{\epsilon}\right)^{s-1} \frac{d\epsilon}{\mathbf{k}T}}{1 + \frac{k^\ddagger}{k_{-1}[\mathrm{A}]}\left(\frac{\epsilon - \epsilon^*}{\epsilon}\right)^{s-1}} \tag{48}$$

This equation may be conveniently reduced by making the following substitutions:

$$x = \frac{\epsilon - \epsilon^*}{\mathbf{k}T} \qquad b = \frac{\epsilon^*}{\mathbf{k}T}$$

The result is

$$k^1 = \frac{k^\ddagger e^{-\epsilon^*/\mathbf{k}T}}{(s-1)!} \int_0^{\infty} \frac{x^{s-1}e^{-x}\,dx}{1 + \frac{k^\ddagger}{k_{-1}[\mathrm{A}]}\left(\frac{x}{b+x}\right)^{s-1}} \tag{49}$$

With the use of Eq. (45) this relationship may be written as

$$\frac{k^1}{k_\infty} = \frac{1}{(s-1)!} \int_0^{\infty} \frac{x^{s-1}e^{-x}\,dx}{1 + \frac{k^\ddagger}{k_{-1}[\mathrm{A}]}\left(\frac{x}{b+x}\right)^{s-1}} \tag{50}$$

The integral in the above expressions, for a fixed value of s, corresponds to a particular variation with the concentration [A]. In order to test the theory, the procedure is therefore to see, usually by trial and error, what value of s will predict the observed variation of k^1 with the pressure.[1] The application of this theory to a number of reactions has been extremely satisfactory. The value of s that is required generally corresponds to about half the total number of normal modes in the molecule.

It may be emphasized that in the treatments of Kassel and of Rice and Ramsperger the only condition for energization is that the molecule must acquire the critical amount of energy ϵ^*; any molecule that has acquired this energy will, unless it is deenergized by collision, pass through the activated state into the final state. This involves the assumption that the energy "flows" freely between the normal modes of vibration; the frequency $k^\ddagger$ that appears in the above expressions is really the frequency of such energy redistributions. For agreement with experi-

[1] An IBM program for the Kassel integral, with tabulated results, has been described by E. M. Willbanks, Los Alamos Scientific Laboratory Report LA-2178 (1958); available from the Office of Technical Services, U.S. Dept. of Commerce, Washington 25, D.C.

ment, $k^\ddagger$ must usually be at least of the order of magnitude of a vibrational frequency; the treatment therefore implies that there is a complete redistribution of energy within the period of a vibration.

Marcus[1] has developed what is essentially a quantum-mechanical formulation of the Kassel-Rice-Ramsperger theories; zero-point energies, for example, are taken into account. Because of lack of data for individual molecules it is difficult to apply the theory to many reactions, but where it has been applied it has proved very satisfactory.[2]

Slater's Treatment.[3] The main difference between Slater's treatment and those of Hinshelwood, Kassel, Rice, and Ramsperger relates to this question of the flow of energy between the modes. The point of view of the latter theories (which will from now on be referred to collectively as the HKRR theories) is that there is rapid flow; Slater's theory, on the other hand, does not permit energy to flow at all. The HKRR theories consider that reaction occurs when the necessary amount of energy passes into a particular mode; according to Slater, reaction occurs when a "critical coordinate"—a bond length or a combination of bond lengths—becomes extended by a specified amount. Such an extension will occur when different normal modes of vibration come into phase.

The main features of Slater's treatment may most easily be understood with reference to the dissociation of a diatomic molecule A—B, and of a linear triatomic molecule A—B—C. A potential-energy curve for a diatomic molecule is shown schematically in Fig. 30. In dealing with the dissociation of this molecule from Slater's point of view, the vibration is assumed to be a pure harmonic vibration, as indicated by the dashed line. Decomposition is considered to occur when the distance between the atoms has increased by the critical distance x_0 shown in the diagram. The variation of the extension x with the time is, for harmonic motion, given by

$$x = \sqrt{\frac{2\epsilon}{b}} \cos 2\pi\nu t \tag{51}$$

where ϵ is the total energy relative to the nonvibrating system, b is the force constant, and ν is the frequency.

[1] R. A. Marcus, *J. Chem. Phys.*, **20**, 359 (1952); R. A. Marcus and O. K. Rice, *J. Phys. Colloid Chem.*, **55**, 894 (1951); G. M. Wieder and R. A. Marcus, *J. Chem. Phys.*, **37**, 1835 (1962).

[2] For a review see B. S. Rabinovitch and D. W. Setzer, *Advances in Photochemistry*, **3** (1964).

[3] N. B. Slater, *Proc. Cambridge Phil. Soc.*, **35**, 56 (1939); *Proc. Roy. Soc.* (*London*), **A194**, 112 (1948); *Phil. Trans.*, **A249**, 57 (1953); *Proc. Roy. Soc.* (*London*), **A218**, 224 (1953); *Proc. Leeds Phil. Soc.*, **4**, 259, 268 (1955); *Proc. Roy. Soc. Edinburgh*, **A44**, 161 (1955); *Chem. Soc.* (*London*) *Spec. Publ.* **16**, 29 (1962); for a general account see N. B. Slater, "Theory of Unimolecular Reactions," Cornell University Press, Ithaca, N.Y., 1959.

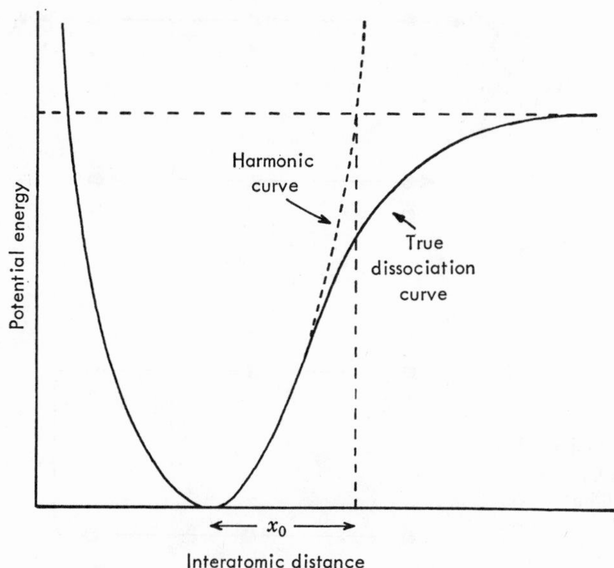

Fig. 30. Potential-energy curve for a diatomic molecule.

The condition that the molecule contains enough energy that x may attain the value x_0 is given by

$$\sqrt{\frac{2\epsilon}{b}} \geqslant x_0 \tag{52}$$

whence

$$\epsilon \geqslant \frac{bx_0^2}{2} \tag{53}$$

Any molecule that contains enough energy to satisfy the inequality (53) will dissociate in the period of the first vibration; a molecule that has less than this amount of energy cannot dissociate. The fraction of molecules having energy in excess of ϵ^*, the amount that just satisfies the inequality (i.e., $\epsilon^* = bx_0^2/2$), is $e^{-\epsilon^*/\mathbf{k}T}$, and the frequency of the dissociation of these molecules is ν. The first-order rate constant for the dissociation is therefore given by

$$k = \nu e^{-\epsilon^*/\mathbf{k}T} \tag{54}$$

This case of the diatomic molecule is a somewhat trivial one, and more insight into Slater's theory is provided by a consideration of its application to the decomposition of a linear triatomic molecule. There are four normal modes of vibration for such a molecule, and these are shown in Fig. 31. Only the two stretching modes, of frequency ν_1 and ν_2, give rise to extensions in the bond distances, and only these modes

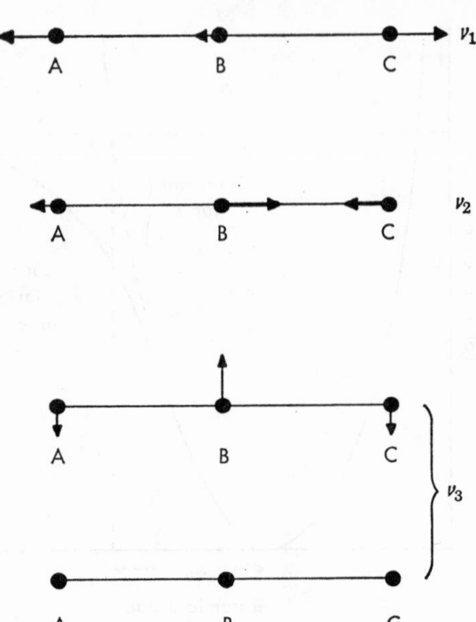

Fig. 31. The four normal modes of vibration of A—B—C, a linear triatomic molecule. The lower two are equivalent bending vibrations in two planes at right angles to each other.

need be considered if the critical coordinate is the stretching of a bond, or the combination of the stretchings of two bonds. For a reaction of the type

$$\text{A—B—C} \rightarrow \text{A—B} + \text{C}$$

it might be reasonable to regard the critical coordinate as simply the stretching of the bond B—C. When the molecule is energized by a collision with another molecule, a certain amount of energy passes into the mode of frequency ν_1, and a certain amount into the mode of frequency ν_2. The amounts are not necessarily the same, and if the motion is strictly harmonic, as assumed by Slater, there is no flow between the modes. As a result of the vibration of frequency ν_1, the B—C distance varies harmonically with time, and it also varies because of the vibration of frequency ν_2; the net variation results from a superposition of the modes. Figure 32 shows how the B—C distance will vary as a result of the two modes of vibration, and it is seen that from time to time the vibrations come essentially into phase in such a way that there is a very large extension of the bond; dissociation may then occur.

The theory of the way in which harmonic vibrations come into phase has been developed by Slater, and his theory leads to a complete formulation of the rates of unimolecular reactions, over the entire pressure range. The application of his theory to particular reactions is a matter of some difficulty, and has been carried out in detail for only a few molecules for

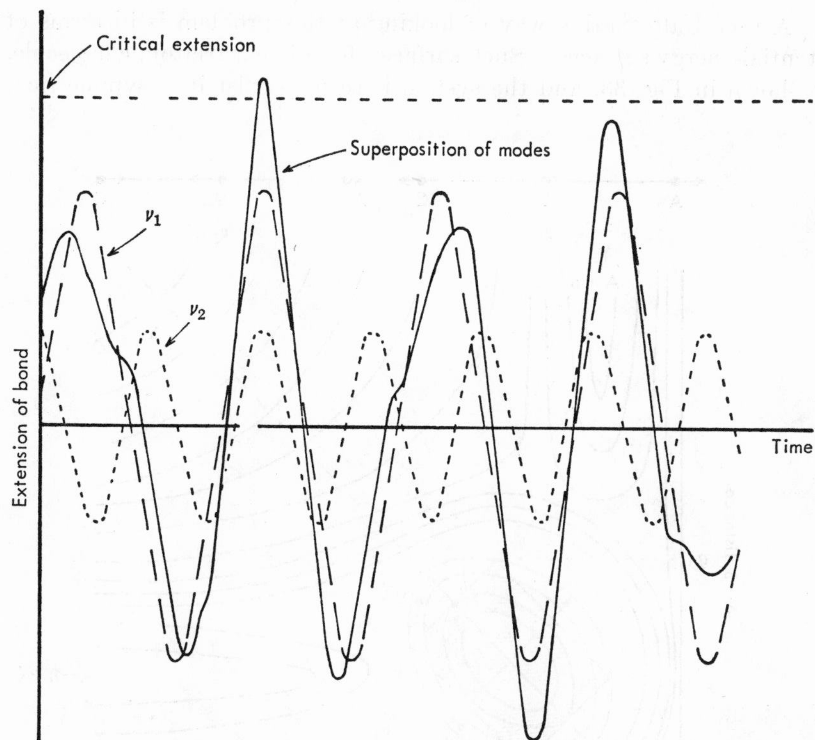

Fig. 32. The extension of a bond due to motion in two normal modes, and the resultant extension.

which it has been possible to work out a complete vibrational analysis. One very important aspect of Slater's theory is that it imposes a very much more stringent condition for energization than do the HKRR theories. This may be seen to be the case with reference to the dissociation of the linear molecule A—B—C (Fig. 31). The HKRR theories would say that the molecule was energized, and therefore capable of reacting, provided that the critical energy ϵ^* was distributed in *any* way among the four modes of vibration. According to Slater's treatment, on the other hand, if the critical coordinate is the B—C distance, the bending modes can make no contribution; the energy ϵ^* would therefore have to be in the two stretching modes, and would even have to be suitably distributed between them. Energy in the bending modes would make no contribution to reaction. As a result of this, the rate of energization predicted by Slater's treatment is usually very much less than that given by Hinshelwood's formula [Eq. (40)], which is the formula used in the various versions of the HKRR theories.

A useful alternative way of looking at this problem is in terms of potential-energy surfaces. Such surfaces, for a linear triatomic molecule, are shown in Fig. 33, and the system is seen to exist in a symmetrical

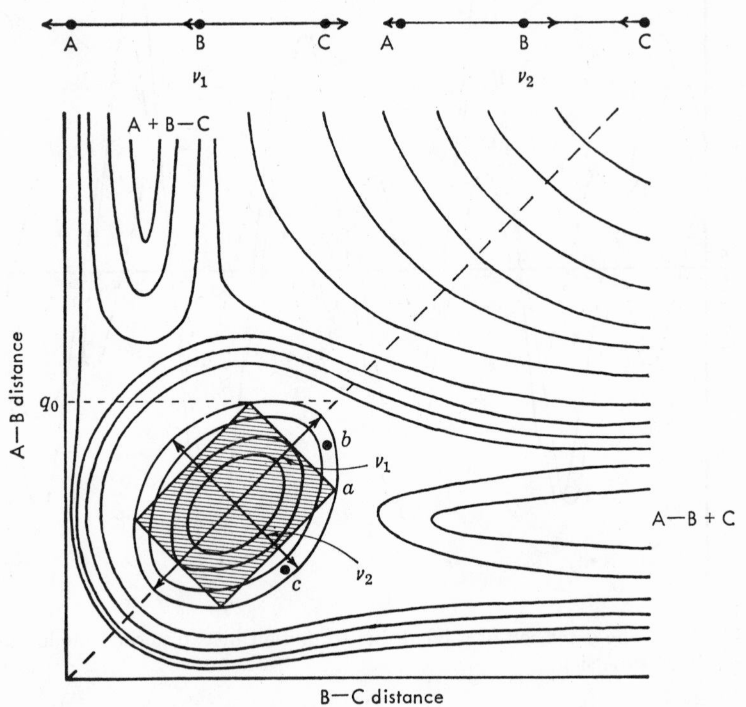

Fig. 33. Schematic potential-energy surface for the linear symmetric molecule A—B—C, showing the axial normal modes of vibration.

potential-energy basin. The symmetric vibration, of frequency ν_1, corresponds to motion along the line bisecting the axes, since along this line the A—B and B—C distances increase simultaneously. The asymmetric vibration corresponds to motion at right angles to this line, as shown in the diagram.

Suppose now that the molecule is distorted to a configuration corresponding to point *a* in the diagram. It will execute a vibration which is a superposition of the two normal modes, and if the motions are strictly harmonic, the configuration will at all times remain within the shaded rectangle in the diagram. Configurations such as those represented by points *b* and *c*, which lie outside the rectangle, are inaccessible to the molecule, even though these points correspond to a lower total energy than that possessed by the molecule. This is the point of view of the Slater theory.

In the HKRR theories, on the other hand, the vibrations are somewhat anharmonic, and strictly speaking there are no normal modes; to a useful approximation it may be considered that there are normal modes which are loosely coupled with one another. Energy can now flow between the modes, and the result is that if the molecule starts to vibrate at point *a* in Fig. 33 all points inside the ellipse through *a* are accessible; the molecule can therefore, after a number of vibrations, attain the configurations represented by *b* and *c*.

For more complex molecules the situation is naturally more complicated, but the general principles remain the same. An important virtue of the Slater theory is that it leads to a very clear formulation of the mechanism by which an energized molecule undergoes reaction. According to the theory, the activated complex is defined in a very precise manner, in terms of the critical coordinate for the system. The idea that reaction occurs when a critical coordinate reaches a given extension is a more realistic one than the idea, contained in the Kassel-Rice-Ramsperger theories, that the energy must find its way into a particular bond.

In its original form the theory is, however, deficient in not permitting flow between modes; there seems to be no doubt that such flow does occur, and in several cases where a comparison has been made with experimental results the Slater rate of energization has been found to be considerably too low.[1] Similar conclusions have been reached by Bunker[2] on the basis of Monte Carlo calculations of the dissociation rates of triatomic molecules. A modified theory, in which flow is allowed for, has been considered by Slater,[3] but its detailed application to the experimental results will probably prove to be rather difficult.

Isomerization of Cyclopropane. Space does not permit consideration of the many unimolecular reactions that have now been studied in detail. Many of the experimental investigations that have been made have demonstrated the falling off of the first-order rate coefficient at low pressures, in qualitative agreement with Lindemann's theory. Application of the HKRR theories has usually led to good agreement between theory and experiment, provided that the number of normal modes is taken not as the total number in the molecule, but as about half that number. The reason for this is not clear; it has been suggested[4] that for reasons of the symmetry of the activated complex only certain modes

[1] E. K. Gill and K. J. Laidler, *Proc. Roy. Soc. (London)*, **A250**, 121 (1959); K. J. Laidler and B. W. Wojciechowski, *Chem. Soc. (London) Spec. Publ.* **16**, 37 (1962).

[2] D. L. Bunker, *J. Chem. Phys.*, **37**, 393 (1962); **40**, 1946 (1964).

[3] N. B. Slater, *Chem. Soc. (London) Spec. Publ.* **16**, 29 (1962).

[4] Laidler and Wojciechowski, *loc. cit.*

contribute toward a lengthening of the critical coordinate, and that energy flows between these modes.

The thermal isomerization of cyclopropane into propylene,

$$\underset{H_2C—CH_2}{\overset{CH_2}{/\backslash}} \rightarrow CH_3—CH=CH_2$$

is one of the few overall reactions that are of a simple unimolecular nature and involve no complications. A number of experimental studies of the reaction have been made; Chambers and Kistiakowsky,[1] for example, followed the reaction over the temperature range of 469 to 519°, the products being analyzed by oxidation of the propylene by potassium permanganate. They found that the high-pressure rate constant was given by

$$k_\infty = 1.5 \times 10^{15} e^{-65,000/RT} \quad \text{sec}^{-1}$$

A significant decrease in the value of the first-order rate coefficient was observed as the pressure was lowered to 10 mm. A more detailed study of the reaction was made by Pritchard, Sowden, and Trotman-Dickenson,[2] who worked at 492°C and at pressures down to below 0.1 mm; they used improved analytical techniques which enabled more accurate rates to be obtained. A plot of their results is shown in Fig. 34, and there is seen to be a very definite falling off of the rate coefficient at the low pressures. Addition of chemically inert gases markedly increased the rate of reaction at the lower pressures; such gases increase the rate of energization, in a manner to be considered later.

Slater[3] has applied both his theory and the Kassel theory to the results, and has shown that both theories can be made to fit the results by the choice of a suitable value for the number of degrees of freedom. This is shown in Fig. 34, where it is seen that the Kassel and Slater curves are very close together except at the lowest pressures. Agreement with the Kassel theory was obtained by taking the number of effective degrees of freedom to be 12. The total number of vibrational modes in the molecule is 21, so that apparently only about half of these are active.

Slater's theory leads to good agreement when all 21 modes are taken into consideration, and when the reaction coordinate is taken to be the distance between a carbon atom and a hydrogen atom that is attached to one of the other carbon atoms. At first sight this agreement might be

[1] T. S. Chambers and G. B. Kistiakowsky, *J. Am. Chem. Soc.*, **56**, 399 (1934).

[2] H. O. Pritchard, R. G. Sowden, and A. F. Trotman-Dickenson, *Proc. Roy. Soc.* (*London*), **A217**, 563 (1953).

[3] N. B. Slater, *ibid.*, **A218**, 224 (1953).

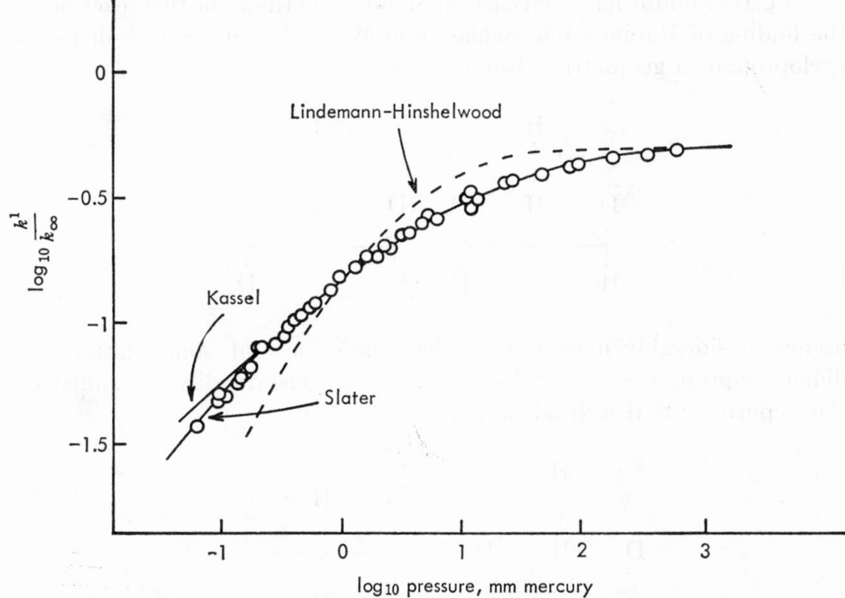

Fig. 34. Plots of $\log_{10} (k^1/k_\infty)$ against $\log_{10}$ pressure for the thermal isomerization of cyclopropane at 492°C. The points are the experimental ones, the curves those calculated from the theories. The experimental values have been displaced 0.3 units to the right.

taken to indicate that this theory was more satisfactory than the Kassel theory. Difficulty arises, however, when one compares the behavior of *cis*-dideuteriocyclopropane, for which it has been found[1] that the falling off of the rate coefficient occurs in the same pressure region as for cyclopropane. With cyclopropane 14 of the vibrational modes are doubly degenerate, and according to Slater's theory each pair can only be counted[2] as one; consequently, only 14 modes (7 nondegenerate modes and 7 of the 14 doubly degenerate ones) contribute to the lengthening of the critical coordinate. In dideuteriocyclopropane, on the other hand, there are no degenerate vibrations, and all 21 should therefore make a contribution. If they did so, the rate coefficient would fall off for the deuterated compound at a very much lower pressure than for cyclopropane itself. Since this is certainly not the case, the Slater theory is apparently inapplicable, and it seems better to apply the HKRR theories and to conclude that not all the modes contribute.

[1] E. W. Schlag and B. S. Rabinovitch, *J. Am. Chem. Soc.*, **82**, 5996 (1960).

[2] The physical reason for this is that if two vibrations are of the same frequency they cannot come into phase if they once start out of phase; they therefore act as one as far as coming into phase with other vibrations is concerned.

Further doubt has been cast on Slater's treatment of this reaction by the finding of Rabinovitch, Schlag, and Wiberg[1] that with *cis*-deuteriocyclopropane a geometrical isomerization

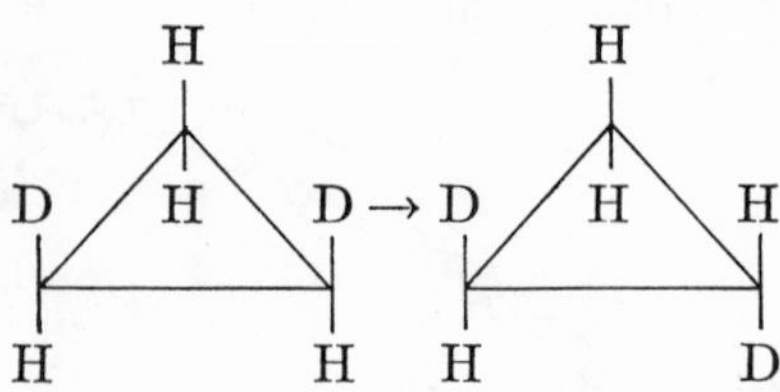

occurs considerably more rapidly than the structural isomerization into dideuteriopropylene. This isomerization is most readily explained on the hypothesis that a diradical is formed initially,

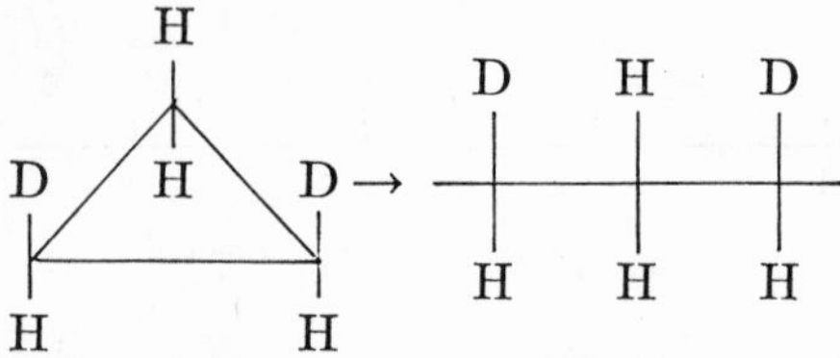

and that this can either form the cyclic molecule again, with the possibility of geometrical isomerization, or form the dideuteriopropylene. Alternatively, as proposed by Smith,[2] the activated complex may involve the extension of a C—C bond and a twisting of the opposite CH_2 group until the two hydrogen atoms are in the plane of the ring. Objections to this suggestion have, however, been raised[3] on energetic grounds. The matter is by no means settled, but it does seem clear that Slater's mechanism and reaction coordinate cannot apply to this reaction.

The isomerizations of several substituted cyclopropanes have also been studied, with somewhat similar results to those with cyclopropane. A very careful study of methylcyclopropane has been made[4] in the temperature range of 440 to 490°C, and at pressures from 200 down to 6×10^{-2} mm. The high-pressure rate constant is given by

$$k_\infty = 2.8 \times 10^{15} e^{-65,000/RT} \qquad \text{sec}^{-1}$$

and the rate coefficient begins to fall at about one-thirtieth of the pressure at which it falls in the cyclopropane isomerization; this is consistent with

[1] B. S. Rabinovitch, E. W. Schlag, and K. B. Wiberg, *J. Chem. Phys.*, **28**, 504 (1958).

[2] F. T. Smith, *ibid.*, **29**, 235 (1958); cf. Laidler and Wojciechowski, *loc. cit.*

[3] S. W. Benson, *J. Chem. Phys.*, **34**, 521 (1961).

[4] J. P. Chesick, *J. Am. Chem. Soc.*, **82**, 3277 (1960).

the fact that more degrees of freedom are effective, and a value of 19 gives satisfactory agreement. Similar studies have been made with 1,1-dimethylcyclopropane,[1] the first-order rate constant for which is

$$k_\infty = 1.12 \times 10^{15} e^{-62,600/RT} \qquad \text{sec}^{-1}$$

The transition pressure range is somewhat lower again than that for methylcyclopropane. The molecule 1,2-dimethylcyclopropane[2] undergoes both a thermal unimolecular cis-trans isomerization and a unimolecular structural isomerization to give *cis*- and *trans*-pent-2-ene, 2-methylbut-2-ene, and 2-methylbut-1-ene. A falling off of rate coefficient was observed at a pressure of about 0.1 mm.

Decomposition of Ozone. The thermal decomposition of ozone occurs by a complex mechanism the details of which are considered in Chap. 8. The initial step is undoubtedly

$$O_3 \rightarrow O_2 + O$$

and from an analysis of the overall kinetics Benson and Axworthy[3] have concluded that this reaction is in its low-pressure second-order region. The second-order rate constant can be expressed as

$$k_1 = 4.6 \times 10^{15} e^{-2,400/RT} \qquad \text{cc mole}^{-1}\ \text{sec}^{-1}$$

The fact that under ordinary conditions the reaction is second-order is to be expected in view of the small number of vibrational modes in the molecule. As yet work has not been done at sufficiently high pressures to cause the process to become of the first order.

Both the Slater and HKRR theories have been shown[4] to lead to a satisfactory interpretation of the second-order rate constant for this reaction.

Decomposition of Hydrogen Peroxide. The decomposition of hydrogen peroxide is also a complex reaction, but the initial reaction is the unimolecular dissociation into hydroxyl radicals,

$$H_2O_2 \rightarrow 2OH$$

The second-order rate constant for this reaction has been found[5] to be

[1] M. C. Flowers and H. M. Frey, *J. Chem. Soc.*, 3953 (1959).

[2] M. C. Flowers and H. M. Frey, *Proc. Roy. Soc.* (*London*), **A257,** 121 (1960).

[3] S. W. Benson and H. E. Axworthy, *J. Chem. Phys.*, **26,** 1718 (1957).

[4] E. K. Gill and K. J. Laidler, *Trans. Faraday Soc.*, **55,** 753 (1959).

[5] W. Forst, *Can. J. Chem.*, **36,** 1308 (1958); cf. P. A. Giguère and I. D. Liu, *ibid.*, **35,** 283 (1957); D. E. Hoare, J. B. Protheroe, and A. D. Walsh, *Trans. Faraday Soc.*, **55,** 548 (1959).

given by

$$k_1 = 10^{18} e^{-45,000/RT} \qquad \text{cc mole}^{-1}\ \text{sec}^{-1}$$

The hydrogen peroxide molecule has six degrees of vibrational freedom. Agreement with the Hinshelwood equation for the rate of energization is obtained if four degrees of freedom are used.[1] A detailed application of Slater's theory was made by Gill and Laidler,[1] who concluded that no choice of critical coordinate could lead to a rate that was as high as the experimental rate; the most likely critical coordinate, the O—O distance, led to a rate that was too low by a factor of 1,000. The conclusion is therefore that Slater's assumption of no flow is incorrect; energy appears to flow freely among four of the six normal modes.

Decomposition of Ethane. The decomposition of ethane is also a complex reaction, the mechanism of which is considered in Chap. 8. There is no doubt that the initial reaction is the dissociation into two methyl radicals,

$$C_2H_6 \rightarrow 2CH_3$$

The rate of this process cannot be obtained from the overall kinetics, but can be calculated in a fairly reliable manner from the rate of the reverse reaction, use being made of the equilibrium constant. By methods to be considered later in this chapter, Dodd and Steacie[2] have studied the kinetics of the methyl radical combination over a range of pressures. From their results, and using the value of 85 kcal per mole for the dissociation energy of the C—C bond in ethane, it can be calculated that the first-order rate constant for the dissociation of ethane at 200°C is approximately

$$3 \times 10^{-16} = 10^{17} e^{-85,000/RT} \qquad \text{sec}^{-1}$$

The rate coefficient begins to fall off at a pressure of 10 mm, and the reaction is probably essentially in its second-order region below 1 mm at this temperature.

A complete vibrational analysis of the ethane molecule has not as yet been carried out, so that a detailed application of Slater's treatment cannot be made. It has been concluded,[3] however, that no plausible choice of reaction coordinate can lead to agreement with experiment. The HKRR theories, however, are satisfactory if eight or nine degrees of freedom are considered to be effective.

Isomerization of *cis*-but-2-ene. It was originally reported that a number of cis-trans isomerizations occur with extremely low frequency factors, but more recent work has cast doubt on this conclusion. The

[1] E. K. Gill and K. J. Laidler, *Proc. Roy. Soc.* (*London*), **A251**, 66 (1959).
[2] R. E. Dodd and E. W. R. Steacie, *ibid.*, **A223**, 283 (1954).
[3] E. K. Gill and K. J. Laidler, *ibid.*, **A250**, 121 (1959).

conversion of *cis*-but-2-ene into *trans*-but-2-ene, for example,

$$\begin{matrix} CH_3 & & CH_3 \\ & C{=}C & \\ H & & H \end{matrix} \rightarrow \begin{matrix} CH_3 & & H \\ & C{=}C & \\ H & & CH_3 \end{matrix}$$

has been found[1] to be a unimolecular reaction with a first-order rate constant given by

$$k_\infty = 6.1 \times 10^{13} e^{-62,800/RT} \qquad \text{sec}^{-1}$$

The first-order coefficient begins to fall off at pressures below 2 mm, and the behavior can be interpreted on the basis of the HKRR theory using 16 effective degrees of freedom; the total number in the molecule is 30.

Unimolecular Dissociations in Shock Tubes. The kinetics of the thermal dissociation of several simple molecules have been studied by using a bursting-diaphragm shock tube (p. 45) to produce sudden heating of the gas. Several diatomic molecules have been analyzed by this technique, and there has been particular interest in the way in which the internal energies of rotation and vibration of the colliding molecules may contribute to the energy required to produce dissociation. Palmer and Hornig,[2] for example, studied the rate of dissociation of bromine in pure bromine and in bromine-argon mixtures and concluded that several modes of the internal energy may contribute to the dissociation of Br_2 by Br_2.

Similar studies have been made with polyatomic molecules including dinitrogen tetroxide,[3] nitrogen dioxide,[4] cyanogen,[5] nitrous oxide,[6] nitrosyl chloride,[7] and various simple hydrocarbons.

Abnormal Frequency Factors.[8] According to Slater's theory in its simplest form, the frequency factor for a unimolecular reaction in its first-order region should be a weighted mean of all the vibrational frequencies of the molecule; it should therefore be of the order of 10^{13} sec^{-1}. According to absolute-rate theory, the rate constant is given by

$$k_\infty = \frac{\mathbf{k}T}{\mathbf{h}} \frac{F_\ddagger}{F_A} e^{-E_0/\mathbf{k}T} \tag{55}$$

[1] B. S. Rabinovitch and K. W. Michel, *J. Am. Chem. Soc.*, **81,** 5065 (1959).
[2] H. B. Palmer and D. F. Hornig, *J. Chem. Phys.*, **26,** 98 (1957).
[3] T. A. Carrington and N. Davidson, *J. Phys. Chem.*, **57,** 418 (1953).
[4] R. E. Huffman and N. Davidson, *J. Am. Chem. Soc.*, **81,** 2311 (1959).
[5] H. T. Knight and J. P. Rink, *J. Chem. Phys.*, **35,** 199 (1961).
[6] J. N. Bradley and G. B. Kistiakowsky, *ibid.*, 256.
[7] B. Deklau and H. B. Palmer, "Eighth Symposium on Combustion," p. 139, The Williams & Wilkins Company, Baltimore, 1962.
[8] Cf. C. Steel and K. J. Laidler, *J. Chem. Phys.*, **34,** 1827 (1961).

where $F_{\ddagger}$ and F_A are the partition functions for the activated and initial states. If the ratio $F_{\ddagger}/F_A$ is close to unity, a value of about 10^{13} sec^{-1} is again expected for the frequency factor. Frequency factors of this magnitude are conveniently referred to as "normal," although it now appears that for the majority of reactions the value differs from the normal value by at least a power of 10.

Frequency factors are commonly higher than 10^{13}, but for one reaction, the decomposition of nitrous oxide,[1]

$$N_2O \rightarrow N_2 + O$$

the value is about 8×10^{11} sec^{-1}. This abnormally low value has been explained[2] in terms of the fact that the process involves a change in multiplicity. The ground state of N_2O is a $^1\Sigma$ state, and this correlates with $N_2(^1\Sigma) + O^*(^1D)$, whereas the products appear as $N_2(^1\Sigma) + O(^3P)$. The potential-energy curves for the system are shown in Fig. 35, and at the "crossing" point of the repulsive and attractive curves there is a resonance splitting, which gives rise to a low transmission coefficient.

[1] H. S. Johnston, *ibid.*, **19,** 663 (1951).

[2] A. E. Stearn and H. Eyring, *ibid.*, **3,** 778 (1935); cf. also E. K. Gill and K. J. Laidler, *Can. J. Chem.*, **36,** 1570 (1958).

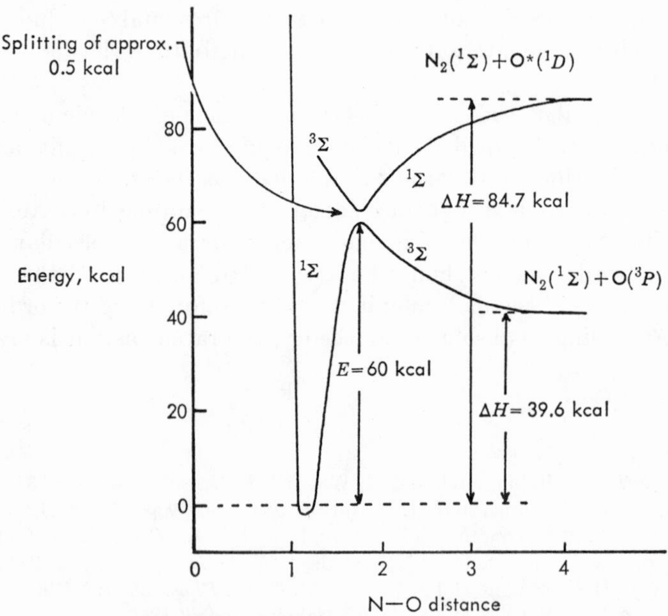

Fig. 35. Potential-energy curves for the N_2O molecule, showing the dissociations into $N_2 + O$ and $N_2 + O^*$.

The splitting probably amounts to about 500 cal per mole, and arises from spin-orbit interaction energies. Such a splitting gives a transmission coefficient of 10^{-1} to 10^{-2}, in agreement with experiment.

A somewhat similar situation exists with regard to the decomposition of sulfur dioxide, the kinetics of which have been studied in a shock tube.[1] The slow step in the decomposition appears to be

$$SO_2 + M \rightarrow SO_3^* + M$$

which is endothermic by 73.6 kcal. The reaction is in its low-pressure region, with three or four effective degrees of freedom, so that the frequency factor would be expected on this basis to be high; there is also, however, a change in multiplicity from singlet to triplet, and this introduces a low transmission coefficient.

The reactions listed in Table 19 have abnormally high frequency factors, which are shown in the form of $\log_{10} A$. The theory of these high frequency factors has been considered in some detail by Steel and Laidler, who relate them to high entropies of the activated complexes. These high entropies arise in general from the looseness of certain vibrations in the activated state. This is shown schematically in Fig. 36 for certain of the vibrations of the activated complex formed from the ethane molecule as it dissociates into two methyl radicals. Since the carbon-carbon bond is greatly extended, there is little restoring force on the displacements of the methyl radicals, and motions such as the rocking motion shown in the

[1] A. G. Gaydon, G. H. Kimbell, and H. B. Palmer, *Proc. Roy. Soc.* (*London*), **A276**, 461 (1963).

Table 19 UNIMOLECULAR GAS REACTIONS HAVING HIGH FREQUENCY FACTORS†

Decomposition of	Activation energy, kcal per mole	log A (A in sec^{-1})
$CH_3CO—O—O—C(CH_3)_3$	38	16.7
$(CH_3)_3C—CO—O—O—C(CH_3)_3$	31	16.1
$CH_3N{=}NCH_3$	51.2	15.7
$C_2H_5N{=}NC_2H_5$	48.5	15.7
$Hg(CH_3)_2$	51	13.3
$Hg(C_2H_5)_2$	43	14.1
$Hg(n\text{-}C_3H_7)_2$	46	15.2
C_6H_5HgBr	63	14.3

† These values are taken from a compilation made by C. Steel and K. J. Laidler, *J. Chem. Phys.*, **34**, 1827 (1961).

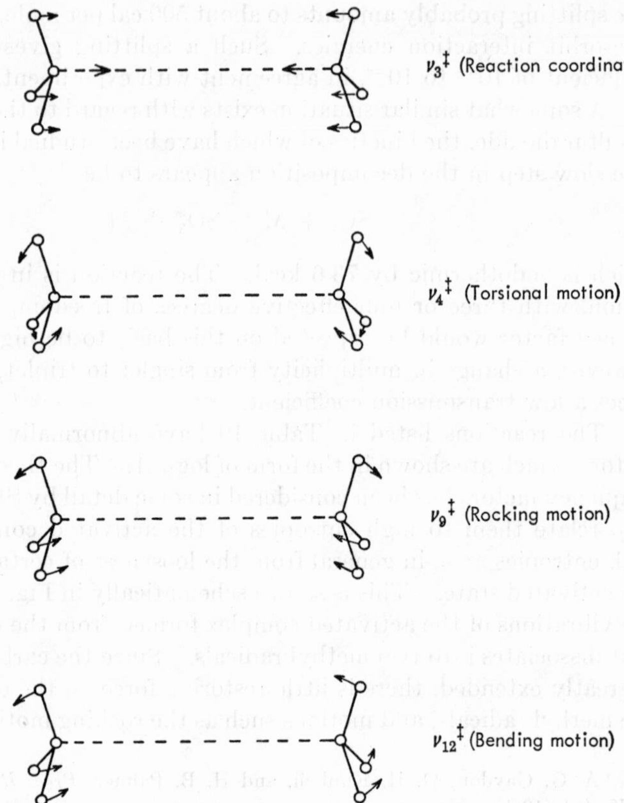

Fig. 36. Some of the normal modes of vibration for the activated complex for a process such as $C_2H_6 \rightarrow 2CH_3$.

figure occur with very low frequency. The effect has sometimes been described in terms of the idea that the radicals rotate freely in the activated state, but this alone is not sufficient to explain the very large frequency factor: it is necessary to invoke a loosening of a considerable number of the vibrations.

One special situation that leads to abnormally high frequency factors occurs when a molecule decomposes with the simultaneous breaking of two bonds, as represented by the equation

$$A—B—C \rightarrow A + B + C$$

Examples are to be found in the decompositions of azo compounds and of mercury alkyls,

$$CH_3N{=}NCH_3 \rightarrow CH_3 + N_2 + CH_3$$
$$C_2H_5HgC_2H_5 \rightarrow C_2H_5 + Hg + C_2H_5$$

In such cases the energy required to form A + B + C is less than that to form AB + C or A + BC; the dissociation energies of AB and BC are negative, so that both bonds rupture at once. A schematic potential-energy surface for such a system is shown in Fig. 37, and is seen to be

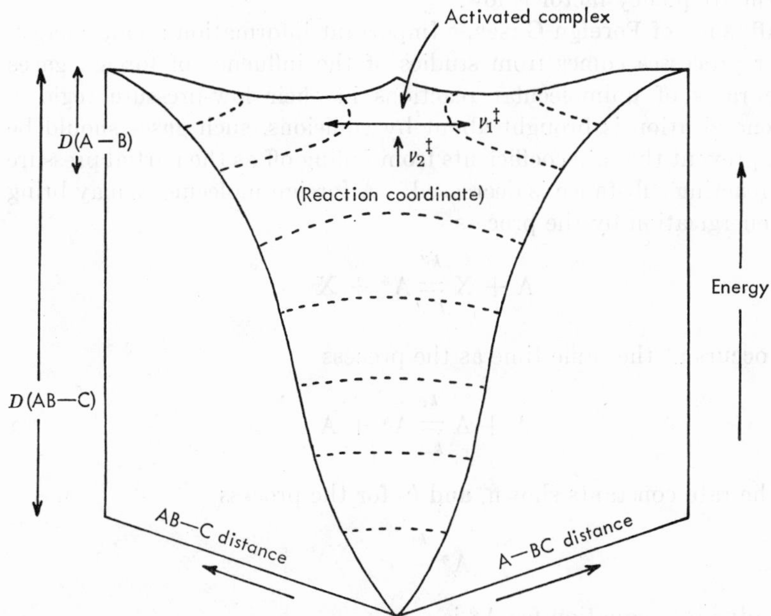

Fig. 37. Schematic potential-energy surface for the dissociation of ABC into A + B + C. The state A + B + C is of lower energy than either AB + C or A + BC.

very shallow at the activated state. The symmetric vibration corresponds to the reaction coordinate, and all the other vibrations are very loose in the activated state because of the form of the surface. This leads to a large partition function for the activated complex, and therefore to a large frequency factor.

One question of importance that arises in this connection is whether abnormally large rates of energization are observed when the high-pressure frequency factor is abnormally large. Both theory and experiment lead to the conclusion that rates of energization can still be predicted satisfactorily by the Hinshelwood formula even when the frequency factor is greatly different from 10^{13} sec^{-1}. The significance of this is that it is the activated complex, and not the energized molecule, that is in a state of high entropy. A similar conclusion is reached for the nitrous oxide decomposition where the frequency factor is very small; the low transmission coefficient arises when the system passes through the activated state, and not during the process of energization.

It follows from this that abnormally high frequency factors will result in an abnormally high transition pressure between the first- and second-order regions, and that a low transition pressure will be found when the frequency factor is low.

Influence of Foreign Gases. Important information about energy-transfer processes comes from studies of the influence of foreign gases on the rates of unimolecular reactions in their low-pressure regions. Since energization is brought about by collisions, such gases should be able to prevent the rate coefficients from falling off as the partial pressure of the reacting substance is decreased. A foreign molecule X may bring about energization by the process

$$A + X \underset{k_{-1}'}{\overset{k_1'}{\rightleftharpoons}} A^* + X$$

which occurs at the same time as the process

$$A + A \underset{k_{-1}}{\overset{k_1}{\rightleftharpoons}} A^* + A$$

With the rate constants shown, and k_2 for the process

$$A^* \xrightarrow{k_2} P$$

the steady-state equation for A* is

$$k_1[A]^2 - k_{-1}[A^*][A] + k_1'[A][X] - k_{-1}'[A^*][X] - k_2[A^*] = 0 \quad (56)$$

Therefore

$$[A^*] = \frac{k_1[A]^2 + k_1'[A][X]}{k_{-1}[A] + k_{-1}'[X] + k_2} \quad (57)$$

and the rate is given by

$$v = \frac{k_2(k_1[A]^2 + k_1'[A][X])}{k_{-1}[A] + k_{-1}'[X] + k_2} \quad (58)$$

By studying rates at various concentrations of A and X it is possible to calculate a value for k_1'/k_1, which is the relative effectiveness with which A and X transfer energy to A.

Work of this kind has been done for a number of unimolecular reactions, with a variety of foreign gases, and some results are shown in Table 20. The decompositions of fluorine monoxide,[1] nitrous oxide,[2] and azomethane[3] are complex reactions, but the inert-gas effect probably

[1] W. Koblitz and H. J. Schumacher, *Z. Physik. Chem.*, **B20**, 406 (1933).

[2] M. Volmer et al., *ibid.*, **B19**, 85 (1932); **B21**, 257 (1933); **B25**, 81 (1934).

[3] D. V. Sickman and O. K. Rice, *J. Chem. Phys.*, **4**, 608 (1936).

relates to the initiating step, which is the dissociation of the molecule into two fragments. The reactions of cyclopropane[1] and cyclobutane[2] are, however, almost certainly elementary, so that the results for these reactions are more reliable.

Table 20 THE EFFICIENCIES OF MOLECULES IN TRANSFERRING ENERGY IN UNIMOLECULAR REACTIONS

Molecule	Decomposition of F_2O (250°C)	Decomposition of N_2O (653°C)	Decomposition of azomethane (310°C)	Isomerization of cyclopropane (492°C)	Dissociation of cyclobutane (448°C)
Reactant	1.0	1.0	1.0	1.0	1.0
He	0.40	0.66	0.07	0.05	0.07
Ne	—	0.47	—	—	0.12
Ar	0.82	0.20	—	0.07	0.21
H_2	—	—	—	0.12	0.10
D_2	—	—	0.46	—	—
N_2	1.01	0.24	0.21	0.07	0.21
O_2	1.13	0.23	—	—	—
F_2	1.13	—	—	—	—
CO	—	—	0.03	0.08	—
CO_2	—	1.32	0.25	—	—
H_2O	—	1.50	0.46	0.7	0.44
CH_4	—	—	0.20	0.24	0.38
SiF_4	0.88	—	—	—	—
$C_6H_5CH_3$	—	—	—	1.10	1.12

On the whole the results shown in Table 20 follow a self-consistent pattern; there are particularly close parallelisms among the results with azomethane, cyclopropane, and cyclobutane. The inert gases are relatively ineffective, and the efficiency of energy transfer increases with increasing complexity of the molecule. A limiting efficiency seems to be reached as the complexity of the molecule increases, and it may well be that this limiting efficiency corresponds to unit probability of energy transfer on collision. It has been seen that this assumption was indeed

[1] H. O. Pritchard, R. G. Sowden, and A. F. Trotman-Dickenson, *Proc. Roy. Soc. (London)*, **A217**, 563 (1953).

[2] H. O. Pritchard, R. G. Sowden, and A. F. Trotman-Dickenson, *ibid.*, **A218**, 416 (1953).

made in treating experimental data from the standpoint of the theories of unimolecular reactions.

The values in Table 20 suggest the possibility that molecules that are capable of reacting together chemically will transfer energy more readily than ones that will not. This result can be interpreted in terms of the fact that there will be some distortion of potential-energy surfaces arising from chemical interaction, and that such distortion will lead to an interconversion of energy. This effect is illustrated schematically in Fig. 38, which shows how relative translational energy may be converted

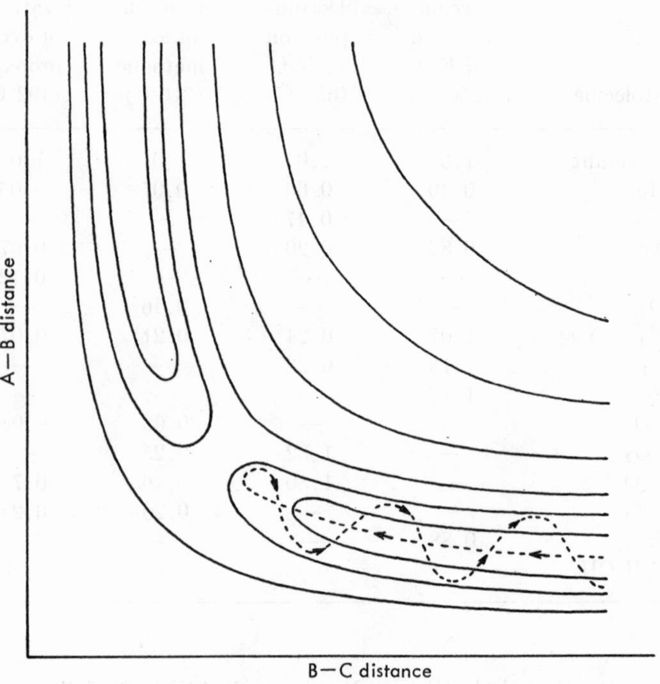

Fig. 38. The conversion of translational energy into vibrational energy when a molecule A—B collides with C. Because there is the possibility of chemical reaction, there is a distortion of the energy valleys, and on collision the A—B distance is altered, so that the molecule gains vibrational energy.

into the vibrational energy of a molecule when it collides with another for which it has some chemical affinity.

Additional information about energy transfer is provided by the effects of inert gases on the efficiencies of atom and free-radical combination reactions; this matter will be discussed later.

The Decomposition of Ions. In the mass spectrometer it is possible to study the unimolecular decompositions of ions; examples of such processes are

$$C_2H_6^+ \rightarrow CH_3^+ + CH_3$$
$$CH_3CH_2NH_2^+ \rightarrow CH_3 + CH_2NH_2^+$$

A general theory of such reactions has been developed by Eyring and his coworkers,[1] and is commonly referred to as the "statistical theory of mass spectra" (STMS). The theory resembles the HKRR theories of unimolecular reactions, but has to be applied to the experimental data in a somewhat empirical manner; values of frequency factors, for example, are usually assigned rather arbitrarily. Experimental work, with the object of testing the theory, has been done on a variety of systems, including hydrocarbons,[2] alcohols,[3] ketones,[3] and amines;[3,4] the variation of the rate constant with the internal energy of the ions has been studied. The agreement with the theory is not very good for the smallest molecules, but becomes better as the number of normal modes increases. In some cases the relative frequency factors that have to be assumed to give satisfactory agreement are not very plausible. Attempts have also been made to interpret the results by a modification of Slater's theory, but so far this has not been very successful.

Unimolecular Reactions of "Hot" Molecules and Radicals.[5] Work has also been done on the unimolecular reactions of "hot" molecules, which are molecules that are produced with excessive amounts of energy. One technique for producing such molecules involves the initial formation of methylene radicals, which are then allowed to add on to certain types of molecules. Methylene radicals are conveniently produced by the action of light on ketene,

$$CH_2{=}C{=}O + \mathbf{h}\nu \rightarrow CH_2 + CO$$

and also by the action of light on diazomethane,

$$CH_2N_2 + \mathbf{h}\nu \rightarrow CH_2 + N_2$$

By using light of various wavelengths it is possible to vary the amount of kinetic energy in the methylene radical produced.

[1] See especially H. M. Rosenstock, M. B. Wallenstein, A. L. Wahrhaftig, and H. Eyring, *Proc. Natl. Acad. Sci. U.S.*, **38,** 667 (1952); E. M. Eyring and A. L. Wahrhaftig, *J. Chem. Phys.*, **34,** 23 (1961).

[2] L. Friedman, F. A. Long, and M. Wolfsberg, *ibid.*, **30,** 1605 (1959).

[3] W. A. Chupka, *ibid.*, 191.

[4] W. A. Chupka and J. Berkowitz, *ibid.*, **32,** 1546 (1960).

[5] For a review see H. M. Frey, Reactions of Methylene and Some Simple Carbenes, in G. Porter (ed.), "Progress in Reaction Kinetics," vol. 2, Pergamon Press, Oxford, 1964.

The methylene radicals may be caused to react with various molecules, and since the reactions that occur are usually highly exothermic, molecules of very high energy are produced. Methylene radicals add on, for example, to the double bond in ethylene to give excited cyclopropane:[1]

$$CH_2 + CH_2{=}CH_2 \rightarrow \underset{\diagdown\;/\;CH_2}{H_2C{-}CH_2^*}$$

If the methylene radicals start with no excess energy, this reaction liberates 80 kcal per mole, which must reside in the cyclopropane unless removed by collisions. The activation energy for the isomerization of cyclopropane to propylene is 62 kcal, so that unless at least 18 kcal of energy is removed by collisions, the excited cyclopropane will undergo isomerization. Work of this kind allows much valuable information to be obtained about the reactions of excited molecules, and about the manner in which they lose energy on collision.

A second type of reaction of methylene radicals is addition to a C—H bond with the formation of a methyl group; an example is the addition of methylene to cyclopropane with the formation of methylcyclopropane,

$$CH_2 + \underset{\diagdown\;/\;CH_2}{H_2C{-}CH_2} \rightarrow CH_3{-}\underset{\diagdown\;/\;CH_2}{CH{-}CH_2^*}$$

Butler and Kistiakowsky[2] employed this reaction and also the reaction

$$CH_2 + CH_3{-}CH{=}CH_2 \rightarrow CH_3{-}\underset{\diagdown\;/\;CH_2}{CH{-}CH_2^*}$$

to produce hot methylcyclopropane having a wide range of excess energies, and a corresponding range of lifetimes. They found that the same products were obtained in the subsequent reaction of the methylcyclopropane, whatever the amount of excess energy. The various methyl cyclopropanes had different initial distributions of energy within the normal modes, so that the conclusion is that the energy can readily distribute itself between these modes.

Similar investigations have been made on the unimolecular reactions of hot radicals produced by the addition of atoms to olefins. Thus

[1] H. M. Frey and G. B. Kistiakowsky, *J. Am. Chem. Soc.*, **79**, 6373 (1957); J. H. Knox and A. F. Trotman-Dickenson, *Chem. Ind. (London)*, 1039 (1957).

[2] J. N. Butler and G. B. Kistiakowsky, *J. Am. Chem. Soc.*, **82**, 759 (1960).

Rabinovitch and Diesen[1] caused hydrogen atoms to add on to *cis*-but-2-ene,

$$H + CH_3CH{=}CHCH_3 \rightarrow CH_3CH_2CHCH_3^*$$

and then studied the subsequent decomposition and deenergization of the excited *sec*-butyl radicals,

$$CH_3CH_2CHCH_3^* \rightarrow CH_3 + CH_3CH{=}CH_2$$
$$CH_3CH_2CHCH_3^* + M \rightarrow CH_3CH_2CHCH_3 + M$$

Similar work has been done by the addition of deuterium atoms to *cis*-but-2-ene;[2] this produces radicals having slightly more energy than those from hydrogen atoms, owing to differences in zero-point energies, and the heavy radicals were found to decompose somewhat more rapidly. Hydrogen and deuterium atoms have also been caused to add on to but-1-ene, with the formation of light and heavy *sec*-butyl radicals.[3] The radicals formed from but-1-ene and but-2-ene must originally have significantly different distributions of vibrational energy, but the decomposition could be interpreted in terms of a treatment which considers only the total excess energy, and not its distribution. The conclusion is therefore that there can be flow of energy among the various vibrational modes before reaction occurs, in agreement with the assumption of the HKRR theories.

COMBINATION AND DISPROPORTIONATION REACTIONS

Reactions in which atoms and free radicals combine together to give an addition product play a very important role in chemical kinetics; such reactions, for example, have a significant bearing on the course of many complex reactions. Examples of such reactions are

$$H + H \rightarrow H_2$$

and

$$I + I \rightarrow I_2$$

A similar process is the reaction between methyl radicals,

$$CH_3 + CH_3 \rightarrow C_2H_6$$

and that between ethyl radicals,

$$C_2H_5 + C_2H_5 \rightarrow C_4H_{10}$$

[1] B. S. Rabinovitch and R. W. Diesen, *J. Chem. Phys.*, **30**, 735 (1959).

[2] R. E. Harrington, B. S. Rabinovitch, and R. W. Diesen, *ibid.*, **32**, 1245 (1960).

[3] R. E. Harrington, B. S. Rabinovitch, and H. M. Frey, *ibid.*, **33**, 1271 (1960); cf. also H. M. Frey, *Trans. Faraday Soc.*, **56**, 51 (1960); B. S. Rabinovitch, D. H. Dills, W. H. Mahain, and J. H. Current, *J. Chem. Phys.*, **32**, 493 (1960).

Reactions between different atoms or radicals are also, of course, possible; examples are

$$H + CH_3 \rightarrow CH_4$$
$$H + C_2H_5 \rightarrow C_2H_6$$

Another type of process is *disproportionation;* two ethyl radicals, for example, may produce a molecule of ethylene and one of ethane:

$$C_2H_5 + C_2H_5 \rightarrow C_2H_4 + C_2H_6$$

A related type of reaction comprises those in which an atom or radical adds on to a molecule containing a double bond, with the formation of a molecule or radical; examples are

$$H + C_2H_4 \rightarrow C_2H_5$$

$$O + C_2H_4 \rightarrow \begin{array}{c} CH_2 \\ | \diagdown \\ |\quad O \\ | \diagup \\ CH_2 \end{array}$$

and $$CH_3 + C_2H_4 \rightarrow CH_3CH_2CH_2$$

At first sight processes of these types might seem to be straightforward examples of bimolecular reactions, showing second-order kinetics. The combination reactions are, however, the reverse of unimolecular dissociations, and must therefore show similar features. That this is so may be seen from the fact that the equilibrium expression must be the same under all conditions of pressure. Since the equilibrium constant is the ratio of the rate constants in the forward and reverse directions, it follows that if one of these "constants" shows some variation with total pressure, the other must show a parallel variation. Consider, for example, the combination of methyl radicals

$$CH_3 + CH_3 \xrightarrow{k_1} C_2H_6$$

and the reverse association of ethane

$$C_2H_6 \xrightarrow{k_{-1}} CH_3 + CH_3$$

Under all conditions of pressure the equilibrium constant for this reaction is given by

$$K = \frac{[C_2H_6]}{[CH_3]^2} \tag{59}$$

At sufficiently high pressures the first-order rate coefficient k_{-1} for the dissociation is constant, and the rate of dissociation is then

$$v_{-1} = k_{-1}[C_2H_6] \tag{60}$$

This expression can be reconciled with Eq. (59) only if the rate of the combination reaction is given by

$$v_1 = k_1[CH_3]^2 \tag{61}$$

with k_1 constant. At equilibrium, v_1 is equal to v_{-1}, so that

$$k_1[CH_3]^2 = k_{-1}[C_2H_6] \tag{62}$$

whence

$$\frac{k_1}{k_{-1}} = \frac{[C_2H_6]}{[CH_3]^2} \tag{63}$$

For agreement with Eq. (59) it follows that if k_{-1} is constant, k_1 is also constant. Whenever the dissociation reaction is first order, the combination reaction is second order.

In an exactly similar way it can be shown that if the dissociation reaction is in the second-order (low pressure) region, the combination reaction must be third order. Thus, if the rate of the dissociation reaction is given by

$$v_1 = k_1'[C_2H_6]^2 \tag{64}$$

that of the combination reaction must, for agreement with the equilibrium expression, be given by

$$v_{-1} = k_{-1}'[CH_3]^2[C_2H_6] \tag{65}$$

The orders of the forward and reverse reactions are thus related to each other, that for the combination reaction always being one greater than that for the dissociation.

It follows that if one has information as to the pressure region in which there is a change in order for one of these reactions, one can conclude that at the same pressure there will also be a change for the reverse reaction. The mechanisms of dissociation reactions have been considered earlier in this chapter, and the mechanism of the reverse combination reaction may be readily deduced. In the combination of methyl radicals, for example, the initial step is the collision between two radicals to give rise to a complex that still contains all the energy released by the formation of the bond,

(1) $$CH_3 + CH_3 \rightleftharpoons C_2H_6^*$$

Either the excited C_2H_6 formed may dissociate again or it may have its energy removed by collision with another molecule,

(2) $$C_2H_6^* + C_2H_6 \rightarrow 2C_2H_6$$

At sufficiently high pressures the average time that elapses between such deenergizing collisions will be much shorter than the average time that it takes for $C_2H_6^*$ to dissociate into $2CH_3$; practically every $C_2H_6^*$ that is formed will therefore be stabilized. Under these circumstances the overall rate of reaction will be controlled by the rate of the collisions between methyl radicals. Experimentally it is found that under these circumstances the activation energy is zero, and the frequency factor is that which would be predicted by simple collision theory; the second-order rate constant is in fact

$$k_1 = 5 \times 10^{13} \text{ cc mole}^{-1} \text{ sec}^{-1}$$

At low pressures, on the other hand, a considerable time elapses between collisions, and it is then likely that $C_2H_6^*$ will dissociate again into radicals. The equilibrium concentration of $C_2H_6^*$ is therefore established, and the rate-controlling step is then reaction (2), the deactivation of the $C_2H_6^*$. The rate of reaction is therefore, under these conditions,

$$v = k_2[C_2H_6][C_2H_6^*] = k_2K[C_2H_6][CH_3]^2 \tag{66}$$

where K is the equilibrium constant for reaction (1).

The more complicated the complex, the longer is its life, since the species may undergo many vibrations before the modes come into phase in such a way that it redissociates. The recombinations of complex radicals therefore remain second order down to much lower pressures than do the recombinations of simple radicals or atoms. The extreme case is to be found in the recombination reactions of atoms, such as hydrogen and iodine atoms. One possible mechanism for the recombination of such atoms is by the initial formation of a complex which, as shown in Fig. 39, must redissociate within the period of the first vibration. The lifetime of these energized species is of the order of a vibrational frequency, 10^{13} sec^{-1}. Stabilization of the complex will occur only if a collision takes place within this period of time. At ordinary pressures and temperatures the average frequency with which a molecule undergoes a collision is of the order of 10^8 to 10^9 sec^{-1}; it is therefore only at very high pressures, of the order of 10^4 to 10^5 times greater than atmospheric pressure, that there is a high probability that the collision between two atoms will lead to a stable molecule. At such pressures the reactions will be second order in the atom concentrations; at ordinary pressures the reactions will be third order (second order in the atom and first order in the molecule bringing about deenergization), and the rates will be exceedingly low. It will be seen later that for atom recombinations an alternative mechanism, which sometimes leads to more efficient combination, is possible.

The Measurement of Combination Rates. A very useful method for determining the rate constants for radical combination and disproportionation reactions involves the use of a rotating sector. This method involves producing the radicals by photochemical means, and interrupting the light at a known rate by the use of the sector. The method was

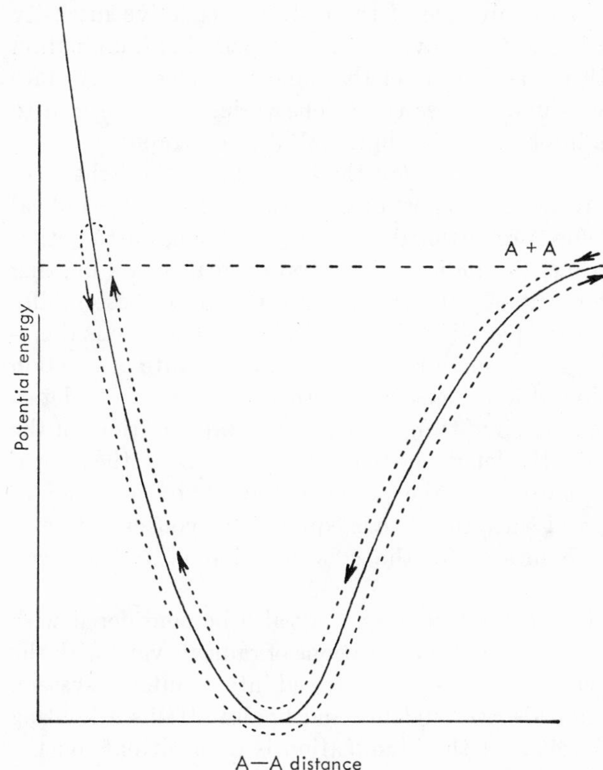

Fig. 39. Potential-energy curve for a diatomic molecule A_2, showing that when the two A atoms come together, they separate in the first vibration.

first used in kinetic studies by Briers, Chapman, and Walter,[1] and has been more recently developed by Melville and his coworkers[2] with particular reference to polymerization reactions. A general theory applicable to experiments in which the sector methods are used has been given by Shepp.[3] The principle of the method is as follows. By means of rotating slotted disks placed between the source of radiation and the reaction vessel, the system experiences periods of illumination and darkness. Suppose, for example, that the disk is of such a form that the periods of illumination and darkness are equal to each other. If I is the

[1] E. Briers, D. L. Chapman, and E. Walter, *J. Chem. Soc.*, 502 (1926).

[2] See, for example, H. W. Melville, *ibid.*, 274 (1947); G. M. Burnett and H. W. Melville, *Nature,* **156,** 661 (1945); H. W. Melville, *Proc. Roy. Soc.* (*London*), **A237,** 149 (1956).

[3] A. Shepp, *J. Chem. Phys.*, **24,** 939 (1956).

intensity of the light in the absence of the disk, the effective intensity when the disk is operating is $I/2$, provided that the period of illumination is short compared with the active life of the radicals. The steady-state concentration of radicals under these conditions varies in proportion to the square root of the intensity of the light. With very rapid rotation, therefore, the system behaves as though the intensity of the light were $I/2$, and the rate of reaction, proportional to the steady-state radical concentration, is therefore proportional to $(I/2)^{1/2}$. When, on the other hand, the rotation is slow, the radical concentration reaches its limiting value before the light is cut off, and in this case the system essentially adsorbs I during half of the period of the experiment. The rate is therefore proportional to $I^{1/2}/2$. At high rates of rotation the rate of reaction is therefore $2^{1/2}$ times that at lower speeds; it is therefore possible to determine the lifetime of a radical by fitting the experimental variations of the rate of the reaction with the length of the light flash, to the theoretical variation. Since in a photochemical experiment the rate of formation of the radicals is known, and since this rate is equal to the concentration of radicals divided by the mean life, the concentration of radicals can readily be calculated.

The principle of the sector technique may also be considered with reference to the way in which the concentrations of radicals vary with the time. When light of constant intensity is passed into a suitable system, the concentration of radicals rises steadily and finally attains a limiting value, as shown in Fig. 40. If the illumination is intermittent, on the

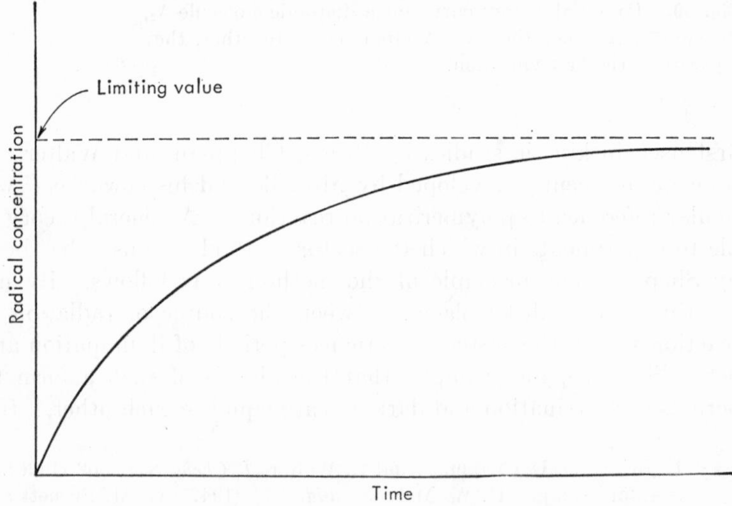

Fig. 40. The increase of radical concentration with time, for the case of constant illumination.

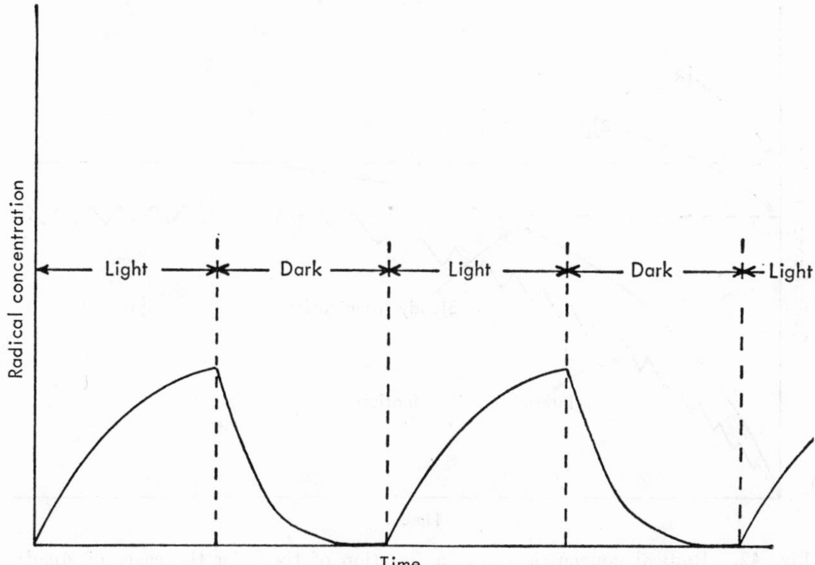

Fig. 41. Radical concentration as a function of time, for intermittent illumination in which the periods of light and dark are long compared with the half life of the radicals.

other hand, the periods of light and darkness being long, the variation with time will be as shown in Fig. 41, and it is evident that the average concentration will be less than in the case of constant illumination. If the sector is rotated rapidly so that the radicals do not have time to decay completely during the dark period, the variation of radical concentration with time will be as shown in Fig. 42; after a certain period of time the average radical concentration will attain a limiting value that will be less than the value for steady illumination with light of the same intensity. The method depends on the fact that the limiting average concentration for slow rotation (Fig. 41) differs from that for rapid (Fig. 42), and that the transition between the two cases is obtained when the time of illumination is of the same order of magnitude as the half life of the radicals.

Figure 43 shows the theoretical variation of the mean radical concentration with the logarithm of the sector speed, for the case in which the sector design is such that the period of darkness is three times the period of illumination. For rapid rotation the mean radical concentration is $(\frac{1}{4})^{\frac{1}{2}}$, or one-half the concentration for continuous illumination. For slow rotation the light acts as if it were of one-quarter of its intensity, so that the radical concentration is one-quarter of that for continuous illumination. If the ratio of dark to light is r, the mean radical concen-

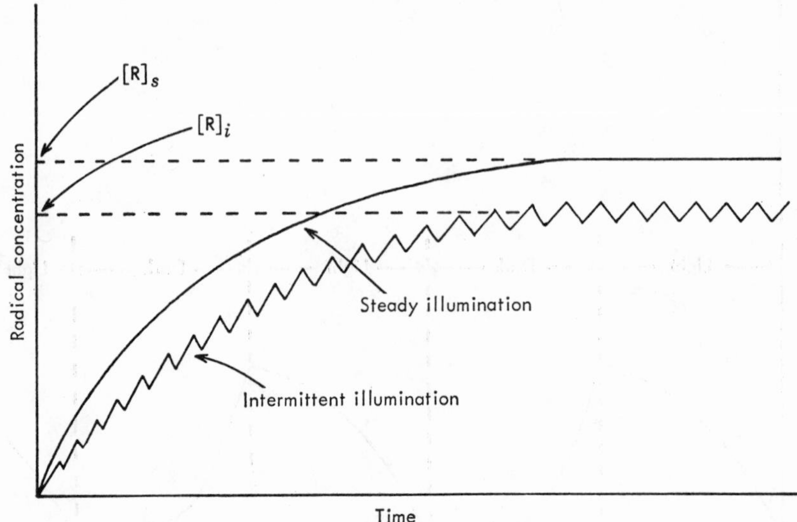

Fig. 42. Radical concentration as a function of time, for the cases of steady illumination and intermittent illumination. The steady-state concentrations in the two cases are $[R]_s$ and $[R]_i$, respectively.

tration for rapid rotation is

$$\frac{1}{(1+r)^{1/2}}$$

of the value for steady illumination; for slow rotation it is

$$\frac{1}{1+r}$$

of that value.

For different half lives the curve in Fig. 43 is simply displaced to one side or the other. By fitting experimental curves to theoretical ones the half life is readily determined, and the rate constant for the reaction can be calculated.

Table 21 lists some rate constants for radical combinations in their second-order regions. The values for the first three reactions were obtained using the sector technique. That for the last reaction was calculated from the rate constant for the reverse reaction, which was determined by the shock-tube technique, as described in Chap. 2.

Another technique that has been used for measuring the rates of combination reactions may be considered with special reference to the recombination of iodine atoms,

$$I + I + M \rightarrow I_2 + M$$

The apparatus employed is shown schematically in Fig. 44. Iodine vapor at a pressure of less than 1 mm is present in the cell, together with the

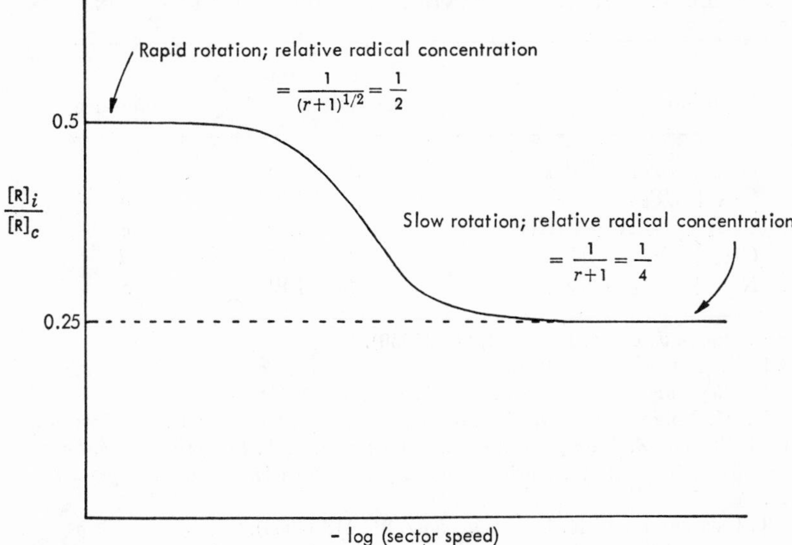

Fig. 43. The variation of $[R]_i/[R]_c$, the ratio of the steady-state concentrations for intermittent and constant illuminations, with sector speed. The ratio r of light to dark is 3.

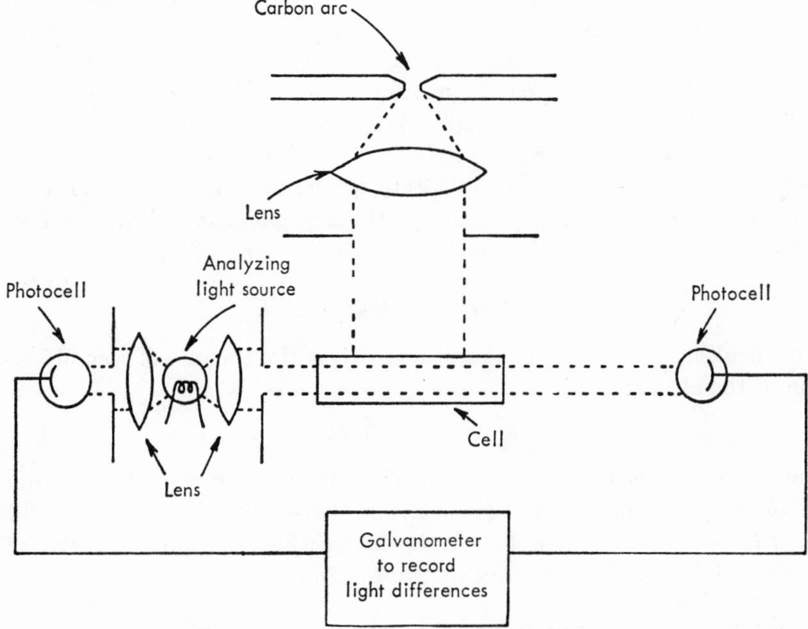

Fig. 44. Schematic diagram of apparatus employed for the study of atom combination reactions (steady-state method).

Table 21 RATE CONSTANTS FOR COMBINATION REACTIONS

Reaction	Rate constant, cc mole^{-1} sec^{-1}	Reference
$CH_3 + CH_3 \rightarrow C_2H_6$	2.2×10^{13}	*a*
$CF_3 + CF_3 \rightarrow C_2F_6$	2.3×10^{13}	*b*
$C_2H_5 + C_2H_5 \rightarrow C_4H_{10}$	2×10^{13}	*c*
$CH_3 + NO \rightarrow CH_3NO$	2×10^{11}	*d*
$NO_2 + NO_2 \rightarrow N_2O_4$	5×10^{11}	*e*

[a] A. Shepp, *J. Chem. Phys.*, **24**, 939 (1956).
[b] P. B. Ayscough, *ibid.*, 944.
[c] A. Shepp and K. O. Kutschke, *ibid.*, **26**, 1020 (1957).
[d] D. M. Miller and E. W. R. Steacie, *ibid.*, **19**, 73 (1951); R. A. Marcus and E. W. R. Steacie, *Z. Naturforsch.*, **4a**, 332 (1949); J. S. A. Forsyth, *Trans. Faraday Soc.*, **37**, 312 (1941); R. W. Durham and E. W. R. Steacie, *J. Chem. Phys.*, **20**, 582 (1952).
[e] T. Carrington and N. Davidson, *ibid.*, **21**, 418 (1953).

foreign gas M. A beam of light of suitable wavelength passes through the cell and falls on a photocell which records the light absorption, which is a measure of the concentration of iodine molecules. This photocell is coupled to a second photocell which is activated by a beam of light, which comes from the same light source but which does not pass through the cell; in this way small changes in light absorption, due to changes in molecular concentrations, can be measured accurately. The dissociation of the iodine molecules is brought about by a powerful beam of light, coming from a carbon arc; this light is caused to fall on the cell by the opening of a shutter, and a steady state is then established within a very short period of time. The intensity of the arc light that is absorbed, I_{abs}, is a measure of the rate of dissociation of iodine molecules,

$$I_{abs} = k_{-1}[I_2][M]$$

and when the steady state is established, this is also the rate of recombination of the atoms:

$$I_{abs} = k_1[I]^2[M]$$

The intensity absorbed I_{abs} is determined in separate experiments, and the iodine-atom concentration is determined from the absorption of light as measured by the photocells. A method of this type was employed by Rabinowitch and Wood for both bromine[1] and iodine atoms.[2]

[1] E. Rabinowitch and W. C. Wood, *J. Chem. Phys.*, **4**, 497 (1936).
[2] E. Rabinowitch and W. C. Wood, *Trans. Faraday Soc.*, **32**, 907 (1936).

When high-intensity flash tubes were developed, a modification of these methods could be employed, involving a dynamic measurement of recombination rates. The apparatus is shown schematically in Fig. 45.

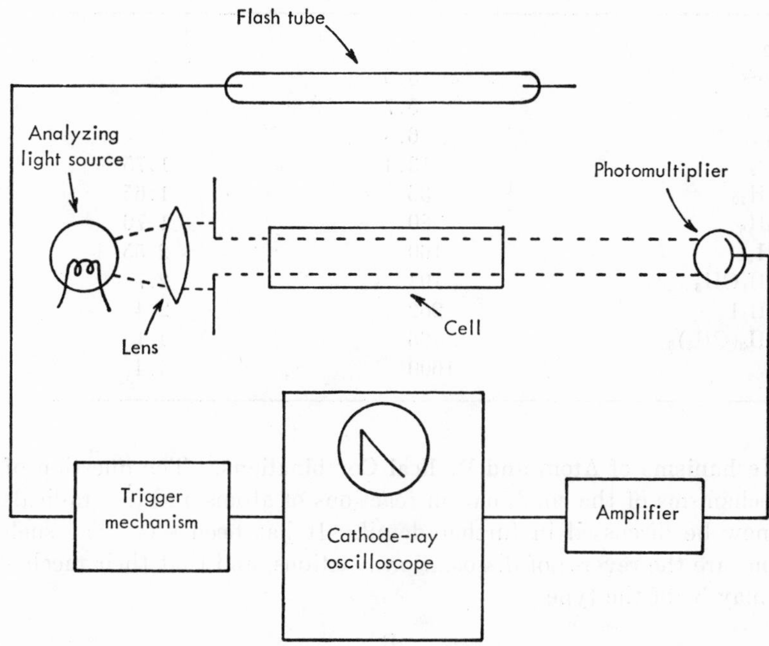

Fig. 45. Schematic diagram of apparatus employed for the study of atom combination reactions (dynamic method).

A mixture of iodine and the foreign gas is irradiated by a light pulse lasting about 1 μsec, and this may lead to dissociation of about 20 percent of the iodine molecules. The light passing along the tube falls on a photomultiplier, the output from which passes through an amplifier to an oscilloscope. The time sweep of this is triggered when the light flash takes place; in this way a trace on the oscilloscope screen is obtained, from which may be deduced the changes of concentration as a function of time. Several groups of workers have employed this method for the study of the combination of iodine atoms.[1] Some values, collected by Porter,[2] are given in Table 22. The significance of the energy E^* is discussed later.

[1] R. Marshall and N. Davidson, *J. Chem. Phys.*, **21,** 659 (1953); M. I. Christie, R. G. W. Norrish, and G. Porter, *Proc. Roy. Soc.* (*London*), **A216,** 152 (1953); K. E. Russell and J. Simons, *ibid.*, **A217,** 271 (1953); G. Porter and J. A. Smith, *ibid.*, **A261,** 28 (1961).

[2] G. Porter, *Discussions Faraday Soc.*, **33,** 198 (1962).

Table 22 THIRD-ORDER CONSTANTS FOR THE COMBINATION OF IODINE ATOMS

Foreign molecule	$k_r \times 10^{-12}$, cc² mole⁻² sec⁻¹	E^*, kcal per mole
He	1.5	
Ar	3.0	
H_2	5.7	
O_2	6.8	
CO_2	13.4	1.75
C_4H_{10}	36	1.65
C_6H_6	80	1.70
CH_3I	160	2.55
$C_6H_5CH_3$	194	2.7
C_2H_5I	262	2.4
$C_6H_3(CH_3)_3$	405	4.1
I_2	1600	4.4

Mechanisms of Atom and Radical Combinations. The question of the mechanisms of the combination reactions of atoms and free radicals must now be discussed in further detail. It has been seen that such reactions are the reverse of dissociation reactions, and that their mechanisms may be of the type

$$2R \underset{k_{-1}}{\overset{k_1}{\rightleftharpoons}} R_2^*$$

$$R_2^* + X \xrightarrow{k_2} R_2 + X$$

where X is a third body. The essential feature of this mechanism is that there is a transfer of energy in the second step, and the term *energy-transfer mechanism* will therefore be employed. It is undoubtedly the case that such mechanisms are very common, especially when radicals of any complexity are involved.

Another mechanism is possible, and is particularly likely for atom combinations when the third body X is a molecule that can readily form a complex with one of the atoms. Such a complex formation may be represented as

$$R + X \underset{k_{-3}}{\overset{k_3}{\rightleftharpoons}} RX^*$$

The resulting complex retains the energy released in its formation, and may be deenergized by collision with another molecule X:

$$RX^* + X \underset{k_{-4}}{\overset{k_4}{\rightleftharpoons}} RX + X + E^*$$

Here E^* is the energy released, equal to the binding energy of the complex RX. Finally RX may react with R, giving rise to

$$RX + R \xrightarrow{k_5} R_2 + X$$

This mechanism is referred to as the *radical-molecule*, or *atom-molecule, complex mechanism.*

The kinetic consequences of these two mechanisms have recently been considered by Porter,[1] with particular reference to the experimental results for the recombination of iodine atoms in the presence of various chaperons[2] X. The following elementary treatment of the problem is adequate to bring out the main principles. The treatment is equivalent to the Lindemann-Hinshelwood formulation of unimolecular reactions; it can readily be modified following the methods of Kassel, Rice and Ramsperger, and Slater.

Application of the steady-state treatment to the scheme of reactions shown for the *energy-transfer* mechanism leads to

$$k_1[R]^2 - k_{-1}[R_2^*] - k_2[R_2^*][X] = 0 \tag{67}$$

Therefore

$$[R_2^*] = \frac{k_1[R]^2}{k_{-1} + k_2[X]} \tag{68}$$

and the rate of disappearance of R is

$$v = \frac{2k_1k_2[R]^2[X]}{k_{-1} + k_2[X]} \tag{69}$$

When [X] is sufficiently large ($k_2[X] \gg k_{-1}$),

$$v = 2k_1[R]^2 \tag{70}$$

so that the rate is controlled by the rate of combination of the radicals to form R_2^*. At sufficiently low pressures, on the other hand,

$$v = \frac{2k_1k_2}{k_{-1}}[R]^2[X] \tag{71}$$

$$= 2K_1k_2[R]^2[X] \tag{72}$$

where K_1 is the equilibrium constant for the formation of R_2^* from 2R.

[1] *Ibid.;* cf. K. J. Laidler, *ibid.*, p. 294; M. Eusuf and K. J. Laidler, *Trans. Faraday Soc.*, **59**, 2750 (1963).

[2] Some doubt has been cast on the propriety of using the word *chaperon* for a substance that facilitates union. N. K. Adam's definition ("Physical Chemistry," p. 460, Clarendon Press, Oxford, 1956) provides the answer: "A chaperon is a third person who accompanies young girls on social occasions, to prevent too ardent affinity for a person of opposite sex resulting in a hasty and unstable association: in places where both sexes have acquired sufficient degrees of freedom chaperons have become obsolete."

This equilibrium constant may be written as

$$K_1 = \frac{f_{R_2}}{f_R^2}\left(\frac{\epsilon_0}{\mathbf{k}T}\right)^{s-1}\frac{1}{(s-1)!} \tag{73}$$

where the f's are the conventional partition functions, s is the number of effective[1] degrees of vibrational freedom in R_2, and ϵ_0 is the energy of R_2^* with reference to the ground vibrational state of the molecule R_2. No exponential term enters into Eq. (73), since no energy is released when the combination of radicals occurs.

The constant k_2 will have the order of magnitude of a collision frequency Z. Insertion of numerical values leads to the result that the third-order recombination coefficient k_r, equal to $2K_1k_2$, has the value

$$k_r \approx 10^{13}\left(\frac{\epsilon_0}{\mathbf{k}T}\right)^{s-1}\frac{1}{(s-1)!} \quad \text{cc}^2\ \text{mole}^{-2}\ \text{sec}^{-1} \tag{74}$$

This value will be much greater than 10^{13} if ϵ_0 and s are large. A large number of effective degrees of freedom, and a large recombination energy, will therefore favor this mechanism. For atom recombinations, $s = 1$ and the mechanism is not favored; it will only be found if the alternative mechanism is unimportant.

Application of the steady-state treatment to the *radical-molecule complex* mechanism gives rise to

$$k_3[R][X] - k_{-3}[RX^*] - k_4[RX^*][X] + k_{-4}[RX][X] = 0 \tag{75}$$

(for RX^*) and to

$$k_4[RX^*][X] - k_{-4}[RX][X] - k_5[RX][R] = 0 \tag{76}$$

(for RX). Addition gives

$$k_3[R][X] - k_{-3}[RX^*] - k_5[RX][R] = 0 \tag{77}$$

From Eq. (76),

$$[RX^*] = \frac{k_{-4}[X] + k_5[R]}{k_4[X]}[RX] \tag{78}$$

and insertion of this in (77) gives

$$k_3[R][X] - \frac{k_{-3}[RX](k_{-4}[X] + k_5[R])}{k_4[X]} - k_5[RX][R] = 0 \tag{79}$$

whence

$$[RX] = \frac{k_3k_4[R][X]^2}{k_{-3}k_{-4}[X] + k_{-3}k_5[R] + k_4k_5[R][X]} \tag{80}$$

The rate of disappearance of R is therefore

$$v = \frac{2k_3k_4k_5[R]^2[X]^2}{k_{-3}k_{-4}[X] + k_{-3}k_5[R] + k_4k_5[R][X]} \tag{81}$$

[1] Between which flow can occur.

Under most conditions [R] will be sufficiently small that only the first term in the denominator need be considered; the rate equation is then

$$v = 2k_5K_3K_4[\mathrm{R}]^2[\mathrm{X}] \tag{82}$$

where K_3 and K_4 are the equilibrium constants. It is to be noted that according to this mechanism the reaction does not become second order at high pressures of X.

The equilibrium constants K_3 and K_4 may now be expressed in terms of partition functions and of the numbers of effective degrees of freedom s' in the complex RX. The constant K_3 may be written as

$$K_3 = \frac{f_{\mathrm{RX}}}{f_{\mathrm{R}}f_{\mathrm{X}}}\left(\frac{\epsilon^*}{\mathbf{k}T}\right)^{s'-1}\frac{1}{(s'-1)!} \tag{83}$$

where the f's are the conventional partition functions, and ϵ^* is the energy of RX* with reference to the energy level of ordinary RX. The term $(\epsilon^*/\mathbf{k}T)^{s'-1}/(s'-1)!$ is introduced because the energy ϵ^* flows within the s' degrees of freedom. The constant K_4 may be written as

$$K_4 = \frac{e^{\epsilon^*/\mathbf{k}T}(s'-1)!}{(\epsilon^*/\mathbf{k}T)^{s'-1}} \tag{84}$$

The exponential term takes account of the fact that there is a loss of energy ϵ^* during the process, the conventional partition functions remaining approximately the same. The term $(s'-1)!/(\epsilon^*/\mathbf{k}T)^{s'-1}$ must be added because, whereas in RX* the energy ϵ^* flows within s' normal modes, it no longer does so in RX.

The value of k_5 will be approximately the collision number Z, and introduction of the expressions for k_5, K_3, and K_4 into Eq. (82) gives rise to

$$k_r = 2Z\frac{f_{\mathrm{RX}}}{f_{\mathrm{R}}f_{\mathrm{X}}}e^{\epsilon^*/\mathbf{k}T} \tag{85}$$

for the third-order recombination coefficient. Introduction of typical numerical values leads to

$$k_r \approx 10^{13}e^{\epsilon^*/\mathbf{k}T} \qquad \mathrm{cc^2\ mole^{-2}\ sec^{-1}} \tag{86}$$

This mechanism is therefore favored when ϵ^* is large, i.e., if a considerable amount of energy is released when the normal molecule RX is formed from R and X. It is to be noted that s', the number of effective degrees of freedom in the complex RX, does not enter into the final rate expression; the complexity of the chaperon has therefore no bearing on its effectiveness.

Table 22 on page 186 gave some third-order rate constants for the iodine-atom combination in the presence of a number of foreign molecules. These results are consistent with the point of view that with the inert gases, and probably hydrogen and oxygen, the reaction proceeds by the energy-transfer mechanism. There is little affinity between R and X in such cases, so that E^*, equal to $N\epsilon^*$, will be very small. The energy-transfer mechanism, with s equal to unity in Eq. (74), predicts a value of about 10^{13} cc^2 mole^{-2} sec^{-1} for k_r, in agreement with experiment. In atom recombinations, for which $s = 1$, higher values of k_r are not explicable in terms of this mechanism, so that the other results in Table 22 must be explained on the basis of the atom-molecule complex mechanism. Values of E^* that are required to give agreement on the basis of this theory, using Eq. (86), are included in Table 22, and are seen to be reasonable. The applicability of Eq. (86) implies negative temperature coefficients for the reactions, and these have in fact been observed.

In radical recombinations, on the other hand, for which some data were given in Table 21, the energy-transfer mechanism probably applies. The equation for the rate constant is (74), and this can lead to large values if s is greater than unity. The effect of this is probably to make this mechanism predominant for all except the recombinations of atoms and very simple radicals such as diatomic ones; even in the methyl radical recombination the process is believed to occur mainly by the energy-transfer mechanism.

Combination-Disproportionation Ratios. Two radicals such as ethyl radicals may undergo the disproportionation reaction

$$C_2H_5 + C_2H_5 \xrightarrow{k_{\text{disp}}} C_2H_4 + C_2H_6$$

as well as the combination reaction

$$C_2H_5 + C_2H_5 \xrightarrow{k_{\text{comb}}} C_4H_{10}$$

It is easier to measure the ratio $k_{\text{disp}}/k_{\text{comb}}$ than it is to measure the individual rate constants, since it is not necessary to measure absolute radical concentrations, or half lives. The ratio can be studied by producing the radical in a reaction system and following the rate of production of the products C_2H_4, C_2H_6, and C_4H_{10}. With the development of vapor-phase chromatography the analysis of such a mixture is usually quite simple.

In principle, the disproportionation of radicals such as ethyl radicals could occur in various ways. The radicals might meet head to head and form an excited butane molecule, which could decompose into ethane and ethylene. Alternatively the radicals could meet head to tail (again forming a species of excited butane), and one radical could abstract a hydrogen atom from the other. Studies have been made[1] on the disproportionation of CH_3CD_2, and the products were found to be exclu-

[1] M. H. J. Wijnan and E. W. R. Steacie, *Can. J. Chem.*, **29**, 1092 (1951); J. R. McNesby, C. M. Drew, and A. S. Gordon, *J. Phys. Chem.*, **59**, 988 (1955).

sively CH_3CD_2H and CH_2CD_2:

$$CH_3CD_2 + CH_3CD_2 \rightarrow CH_3CD_2H + CH_2CD_2$$

This result excludes the head-to-head mechanism, and is consistent with the head-to-tail mechanism. It is also, however, consistent with a mechanism occurring through an intermediate of structure

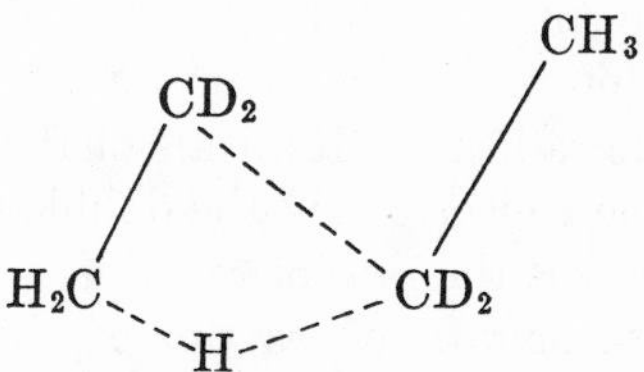

Such an intermediate, which might lead to either combination or disproportionation, has been suggested by various authors;[1] so far there is no conclusive evidence with regard to it.

ADDITION OF RADICALS TO DOUBLE BONDS[2]

Another group of reactions that are the reverse of unimolecular reactions is those processes in which atoms and radicals undergo additions to molecules containing single and double bonds; examples are

$$M + H + C_2H_4 \rightarrow C_2H_5 + M$$

and

$$M + CH_2 + C_2H_4 \rightarrow \begin{array}{l} CH_2 \\ | \quad \diagdown \\ | \quad\quad CH_2 + M \\ | \quad \diagup \\ CH_2 \end{array}$$

In the first of these reactions the product is a radical, in the second a molecule (since CH_2 is a diradical). A foreign molecule M is involved in all reactions of these types, since the excess energy must be removed in order for the resulting radical or molecule to be stabilized.

The study of such addition reactions is of special interest from several points of view. It provides a means, for example, of producing radicals and molecules with excess energies, so that the mechanisms of their decomposition can be studied; reference has already been made to work with methylene radicals in which the decompositions of energized

[1] J. N. Bradley, *J. Chem. Phys.*, **35**, 748 (1961); J. A. Kerr and A. F. Trotman-Dickenson, The Reactions of Alkyl Radicals, in G. Porter (ed.), "Progress in Reaction Kinetics," vol. 1, p. 105, Pergamon Press, Oxford, 1961; P. S. Dixon, A. P. Stefani, and M. Szwarc, *J. Am. Chem. Soc.*, **85**, 2551 (1963).

[2] Cf. H. M. Frey, Reactions of Methylene and Some Simple Carbenes, in G. Porter (ed.), "Progress in Reaction Kinetics," vol. 2, Pergamon Press, Oxford, 1964.

products have led to the conclusion that there is flow of energy between the normal modes. Secondly, on the basis of work with a variety of radicals and saturated molecules it has been possible to obtain information about the factors influencing addition reactions of this type.

Work of this kind has led to the conclusion[1] that there are two different types of atoms and radicals, as follows:

1. *Electrophilic* reagents, which become attached more readily to a double bond at a position of high electron density. Oxygen atoms are examples of electrophilic radicals. Radicals of this type are believed to interact initially with the π electrons of the double bond, so that increase of electron density increases the rate of reaction.

2. *Radical* reagents, the rates of reaction of which are not affected by the electron density. Hydrogen atoms and methyl radicals are of this type. Their reactions with double bonds can be regarded as being influenced by the interaction between the radical and the bond that is broken, rather than that between the radical and the π electrons.

SOME REACTIONS OF DIRADICALS

During recent years there has been considerable interest in the kinetics of reactions involving diradicals; examples are oxygen atoms and methylene radicals. Both these species can exist in both triplet and singlet states, the lowest state being a triplet state in which the two odd electrons have the same spin. When methylene radicals are formed initially by photochemical means, they are in singlet states, but after experiencing a number of collisions with foreign molecules, they are converted into the triplet species.[2]

Methylene radicals are generally produced experimentally by the photolysis of ketene,

$$CH_2CO + \mathbf{h}\nu \rightarrow CH_2 + CO$$

or by the photolysis of diazomethane,

$$CH_2N_2 + \mathbf{h}\nu \rightarrow CH_2 + N_2$$

Radicals having various amounts of energies can be made by using light of different wavelengths, and with different pressures of foreign gas. Methylene radicals may also be produced by the thermal decomposition

[1] R. J. Cvetanovic, *Can. J. Chem.*, **36**, 623 (1958); *J. Chem. Phys.*, **30**, 19 (1959); *Can. J. Chem.*, **38**, 1687 (1960); *Advan. Photochemistry*, **1**, 115 (1963); S. Sato and R. J. Cvetanovic, *Can. J. Chem.*, **37**, 953 (1959).

[2] G. Herzberg and J. Shoosmith, *Nature*, **183**, 1801 (1959); F. A. L. Anet, R. F. W. Bader, and A. van der Auwera, *J. Am. Chem. Soc.*, **82**, 3217 (1960); H. M. Frey, *ibid.*, 5947; R. F. W. Bader and J. I. Generosa, *Can. J. Chem.*, **43**, 1631 (1965).

of diazomethane and of its isomer diazerine,

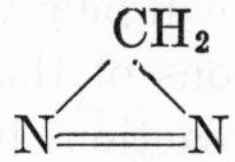

$$\begin{array}{c} CH_2 \\ / \quad \backslash \\ N{=\!=}N \end{array}$$

Three main types of reactions are undergone by methylene radicals, as follows.

1. *Addition to Double Bonds.* An example is

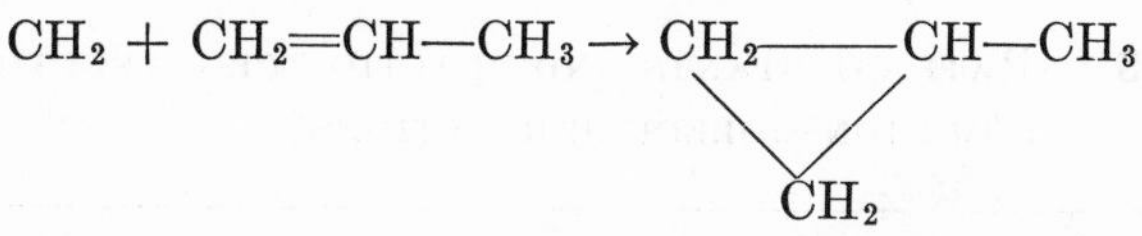

$$CH_2 + CH_2{=}CH{-}CH_3 \rightarrow \underset{\diagdown \; CH_2 \; \diagup}{CH_2{-\!-\!-}CH{-}CH_3}$$

the methylcyclopropane formed being in an excited state.

2. *Insertion in Single Bonds, such as Carbon-Hydrogen Bonds.* Examples are

$$CH_2 + CH_3CH_2CH_3 \rightarrow CH_3CH_2CH_2CH_3 \text{ and } CH_3\underset{\displaystyle CH_3}{\underset{|}{C}}HCH_3$$

and

$$CH_2 + \underset{\diagdown \; CH_2 \; \diagup}{CH_2{-\!-\!-}CH_2} \rightarrow \underset{\diagdown \; CH_2 \; \diagup}{CH_2{-\!-\!-}CH{-}CH_3}$$

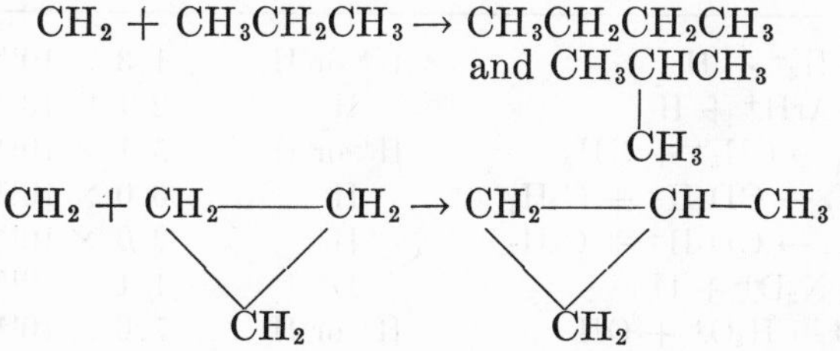

The product of the last reaction is the same as that when CH_2 is inserted into the double bond in propylene; it was seen earlier (p. 174) that Frey made use of these reactions to produce methylcyclopropanes having various amounts of energy and various initial energy distributions.

3. *Abstraction Reactions.* The evidence for these is not so extensive as for the other types of reactions, but it is believed that reactions such as

$$CH_2 + CH_3CH_2CH_3 \rightarrow CH_3 + CH_2CH_2CH_3$$

can occur.

Sometimes methylene radicals interact in different ways with the same molecule; some examples have been studied by Back,[1] who has followed the fate of the molecules produced by the addition of CH_2 radicals to acetaldehyde and propionaldehyde.

GAS-PHASE REACTIONS INVOLVING IONS

A considerable amount of work has been done on gas-phase reactions involving ionic species. Such processes play important roles in reactions induced by ionizing radiations, in electrical discharges, and in flames, and

[1] M. H. Back, *Can. J. Chem.*, **43**, 106 (1965).

they also occur in the chambers of mass spectrometers. Only a very brief account of these reactions can be given here.[1]

The most important reactions of this type are either unimolecular decompositions or bimolecular reactions between ions and neutral molecules. The former have been referred to earlier (p. 173). Some examples of bimolecular reactions between an ion and a neutral molecule are given in Table 23. This table indicates the species that is transferred in each

Table 23 RATE CONSTANTS AND REACTION CROSS SECTIONS FOR SOME ION-MOLECULE REACTIONS†

Reaction	Entity transferred	Rate constant, cc mole^{-1} sec^{-1}	Reaction cross section, A^2
$H_2^+ + H_2 \rightarrow H_3^+ + H$	H^+ or H	1.3×10^{15}	27.4
$Ar^+ + H_2 \rightarrow ArH^+ + H$	H	2.1×10^{14}	14.1
$CH_4^+ + CH_4 \rightarrow CH_5^+ + CH_3$	H^+ or H	5.1×10^{14}	61.0
$CD_4^+ + C_2H_6 \rightarrow CD_4H^+ + C_2H_5$	H	6.0×10^{13}	8.1
$CD_4^+ + C_3H_8 \rightarrow CD_4H^+ + C_3H_7$	H	3.0×10^{13}	4.0
$N_2^+ + D_2 \rightarrow N_2D^+ + D$	D	1.1×10^{15}	86.3
$H_2O^+ + H_2O \rightarrow H_3O^+ + OH$	H^+ or H	7.6×10^{14}	95.0
$D_2O^+ + H_2 \rightarrow HD_2O^+ + H$	H	3.9×10^{14}	63.0
$C_2H_6^+ + D_2O \rightarrow HD_2O^+ + C_2H_5$	H^+	4.5×10^{15}	440.0
$H_2^+ + O_2 \rightarrow HO_2^+ + H$	H^+	5.8×10^{15}	126.0
$C_3H_5^+ + \text{neo-}C_5H_{12} \rightarrow C_5H_{11}^+ + C_3H_6$	H^-	—	14.0
$CD_3^+ + CD_4 \rightarrow C_2D_5^+ + D_2$	§	2.2×10^{15}	161.0
$C_2H_3^+ + C_2H_6 \rightarrow C_3H_5^+ + CH_4$	§	8.7×10^{14}	78.0
$C_2H_4^+ + C_2H_4 \rightarrow C_4H_7^+ + H$	§	3.0×10^{13}	4.0

† The values are taken from F. W. Lampe, J. L. Franklin, and F. H. Field, Kinetics of the Reactions of Ions with Molecules, in G. Porter (ed.), "Progress in Reaction Kinetics," vol. 1, p. 87, Pergamon Press, Oxford, 1961.

§ "Condensation" reaction.

case, and gives the rate constant of the reaction and the collision cross section. The last is the square of the collision diameter d_{AB} that has to be used in collision theory [Eq. (22) of Chap. 3] in order to interpret the rate constant on the assumption of a zero energy of activation. Most reactions of this type do appear to have no activation energy, reaction occurring on almost every collision.

[1] For a review see F. W. Lampe, J. L. Franklin, and F. H. Field, Kinetics of the Reactions of Ions with Molecules, in G. Porter (ed.), "Progress in Reaction Kinetics," vol. 1, Pergamon Press, Oxford, 1961.

It appears that reactions involving the transfer of a proton occur about ten times as rapidly as those involving the transfer of a hydrogen atom; no explanation for this has been given. Some of the reactions in Table 23 involve the transfer of a hydride ion (H^-). Some of the reactions in the table, such as

$$CD_3^+ + CD_4 \rightarrow C_2D_5^+ + D_2$$

do not occur by a simple atom transfer but involve considerably more molecular rearrangement. Reactions of this type are usually known as *condensation* reactions.

The nature of the activated complex in bimolecular reactions between ions and molecules is a matter of some interest. One possibility is that the ions largely retain their identity in the activated state, the ion and molecule being held together by polarization forces; the second is that considerable rearrangement of chemical bonds has taken place by the time the activated complex is formed. The evidence indicates that both types of activated complex can exist. In reactions such as

$$CH_4^+ + CD_4 \rightarrow CH_4D^+ + CD_3$$

there is no mixing of hydrogen and deuterium, and this implies that the ions remain largely intact in the activated complex. On the other hand, in reactions like

$$CD_4^+ + C_2H_4 \rightarrow C_3H_4D^+ + D_2 + D$$

there is essentially complete isotopic mixing, the ionic products being $C_3H_4D^+$, $C_3H_3D_2^+$, $C_3H_2D_3^+$, and $C_3HD_4^+$. The activated complex must therefore be one in which there has been considerable molecular rearrangement. This appears to be so when the complex corresponds to a fairly stable species in which the ordinary valency rules are satisfied.

PROBLEMS

1. Using collision theory, calculate the rate constant at 300°K for the decomposition of hydrogen iodide, assuming a collision diameter of 3.5 A and an activation energy of 44 kcal. To what entropy of activation does the result correspond?

2. Using the values given on page 123, calculate the rate at 400°C of the reaction between hydrogen and iodine, both present at ½ atm pressure.

3. Using the entropy values given in Table 13, calculate the rate at 500°C of the hydrogen-iodine reaction when both reactants are present at ½ atm pressure.

4. The frequency factor for the gas-phase dissociation of the dimer of cyclopentadiene is 1.3×10^{13} sec^{-1}, and the activation energy is 35.0 kcal.

Calculate (a) the entropy of activation, (b) the rate constant at 100°C, and (c) the rate at 100°C and 1 atm pressure.

5. Calculate the frequency factor for the hypothetical gas-phase combination of two hydrogen atoms, assuming the interatomic separation in the activated state to be 0.74 A. Assume the transmission coefficient to be unity.

6. Using the following rate constants for the nitric oxide–oxygen reaction:

T, °K	$k \times 10^{-9}$, cc^2 mole^{-2} sec^{-1}
80	86.0
143	16.2
228	5.3
300	3.3

and assuming the activation energy to be zero, determine to the nearest half power the temperature dependence of the frequency factor.

7. The following are the rate constants of the termolecular reaction between nitric oxide and chlorine:

T, °K	$k \times 10^{-6}$, cc^2 mole^{-2} sec^{-1}
273	5.5
355	27.2
451	182
566	1130

Assuming that the frequency factor is inversely proportional to T^3, determine the energy of activation.

8. The following first-order rate coefficients were obtained[1] for the conversion of cyclopropane into propylene at 469.6°C:

Pressure, mm	$k \times 10^4$, sec^{-1}
760	1.11
388	1.08
210	1.04
110	0.96
51	0.84
26	0.79

By plotting $1/k$ against 1/pressure, obtain a value for k_∞.

[1] H. O. Pritchard, R. G. Sowden, and A. F. Trotman-Dickenson, *Proc. Roy. Soc.* (*London*), **A217**, 563 (1953).

★9. According to the work of J. P. Chesick[1] on the thermal unimolecular decomposition of methylcyclopropane, the high-pressure first-order constant is given by

$$k_\infty = 2.8 \times 10^{15} e^{-65{,}000/RT} \qquad \text{sec}^{-1}$$

At 446.9°C the first-order rate coefficients at various pressures are as follows:

P, cm	$k \times 10^4$, *sec*$^{-1}$	*P, cm*	$k \times 10^4$, *sec*$^{-1}$
13.58	0.535	0.037	0.376
4.93	0.531	0.531	0.337
1.79	0.518	0.021	0.321
0.60	0.500	0.013	0.275
0.217	0.456	0.0108	0.279
0.157	0.443	0.0076	0.245
0.079	0.415	0.0052	0.227
0.057	0.403	0.0038	0.208

Apply Kassel's theory to these data, and deduce a value for the effective number of degrees of freedom.

★10. The low-pressure third-order rate constant for the methyl radical combination,

$$CH_3 + CH_3 + M \rightarrow C_2H_6 + M$$

has been estimated to be 3×10^{20} cc^2 mole^{-2} sec^{-1} at 200°C. If 9 normal modes of vibration are effective, and the high-pressure activation energy is zero, estimate the third-order rate constant at 400°C.

[1] J. P. Chesick, *J. Am. Chem. Soc.*, **82**, 3277 (1960).

chapter

Elementary Reactions in Solution 5

When a chemical reaction takes place in solution, the solvent is usually in such great excess that its concentration cannot change appreciably as the reaction proceeds, and the rate expression accordingly need not involve it. In some cases, moreover, the stoichiometric equation for the reaction does not involve the solvent, which may then merely provide a physical environment for the reaction. In other instances there is reason to believe that the solvent enters into the chemical change and may or may not be regenerated at the end of the process; in these cases the solvent would be said to exert a chemical effect on the reaction, this being superimposed on its physical effect. Since the physical forces are much less well understood than the purely chemical ones, no completely satisfactory treatment of solvent effects has been given. In the first part of the present chapter will be presented some of the more significant experimental results which may throw some light on the problem, and the various theories that have been put forward will be outlined.[1]

[1] For reviews of solvent effects on reaction rates, see E. A. Moelwyn-Hughes, "Kinetics of Reactions in Solution," Clarendon Press, Oxford, 1947; K. J. Laidler

Valuable evidence concerning the influence of the solvent on the rates of reactions in solution has come from two types of investigation. In the first, studies have been made both in solution and in the gas phase; only a few reactions have been studied in this way, largely because a great many reactions which occur in solvents will not take place homogeneously in the gas phase. Accordingly, much of the information on the influence of the solvent has had to come from the second type of investigation, which is less definite and more difficult to interpret: this comprises the work that has been done on reactions in different solvents.

COMPARISON BETWEEN GAS-PHASE AND SOLUTION REACTIONS

In reactions that do occur in the gas phase as well as in solution the solvent generally appears to play a subsidiary role; it seems to act as a mere space filler and has only a minor influence on the rate of reaction. Such reactions are little affected by a change in solvent, and occur in the gas phase at much the same rate as in solution. An example of such a reaction is the thermal decomposition of nitrogen pentoxide, some data[1] for which are given in Table 24. The rate constants, frequency factors, and activation energies are seen to be very much the same in most of the solvents and in the gas phase. In nitric acid solution, on the other hand, the rate constant is significantly lower and the activation energy higher, indicating that this solvent plays a more active role in the reaction.

The dimerization of cyclopentadiene and the reverse dissociation of the dimer have been studied in the gas phase, in the pure liquid state, and in the solvents carbon tetrachloride, carbon disulfide, benzene, and paraffin.[2] The values of $\log_{10} A$ and E for both reactions are given in Table 25. It is seen that with the exception of the dimerization in paraffin solution the values are identical within the experimental error; in paraffin the activation energy and the frequency factor seem to be appreciably higher.

Solvents that have no effect on rates, frequency factors, and activation energies probably do not interact very much with the reactant mole-

---

and H. Eyring, *Ann. N.Y. Acad. Sci.*, **39**, 303 (1940); R. P. Bell, "Handbuch der Katalyse," vol. II, p. 319, J. Springer, Berlin, 1940 (reprinted by J. W. Edwards, Publisher, Incorporated, Ann Arbor, Mich., 1944); S. Glasstone, K. J. Laidler, and H. Eyring, "The Theory of Rate Processes," chap. 8, McGraw-Hill Book Company, New York, 1941.

[1] F. Daniels and E. H. Johnston, *J. Am. Chem. Soc.*, **43**, 53 (1921); H. Eyring and F. Daniels, *ibid.*, **52**, 1473 (1930).

[2] B. S. Khambata and A. Wassermann, *Nature*, **137**, 496 (1936); **138**, 368 (1936); A. Wassermann, *J. Chem. Soc.*, 1028 (1936); G. A. Benford, B. S. Khambata, and A. Wassermann, *Nature*, **139**, 669 (1937); A. Wassermann, *Trans. Faraday Soc.*, **34**, 128 (1938).

Table 24 VALUES OF k, LOG$_{10}$ A, AND E FOR THE DECOMPOSITION OF NITROGEN PENTOXIDE IN VARIOUS SOLVENTS

Solvent	$k \times 10^5$ (at 25°C)	$\log_{10}$ A	E, kcal
(Gas phase)†	3.38	13.6	24.7
Carbon tetrachloride§	4.09	13.8	25.5
Carbon tetrachloride¶	4.69	13.6	24.2
Chloroform§	3.72	13.6	24.5
Chloroform¶	5.54	13.7	24.6
Ethylene dichloride¶	4.79	13.6	24.4
Ethylidine dichloride¶	6.56	14.2	24.9
Pentachloroethane¶	4.30	14.0	25.0
Nitromethane¶	3.13	13.5	24.5
Bromine¶	4.27	13.3	24.0
Nitrogen tetroxide¶	7.05	14.2	25.0
Nitric acid¶	0.147	14.8	28.3
Propylene dichloride¶	0.510	14.6	27.0

† F. Daniels and E. H. Johnston, *J. Am. Chem. Soc.*, **43**, 53 (1921).
§ R. H. Lueck, *ibid.*, **44**, 757 (1922).
¶ H. Eyring and F. Daniels, *ibid.*, **52**, 1473 (1930).

Table 25 VALUES OF LOG$_{10}$ A AND E FOR THE DIMERIZATION OF CYCLOPENTADIENE AND THE REVERSE DISSOCIATION

	Dimerization		Dissociation	
Medium	$\log_{10} A$	E, kcal	$\log_{10} A$	E, kcal
Gas phase	6.1	16.7	13.1	35.0
Pure liquid	5.7	16.0	13.0	34.5
Carbon tetrachloride	5.9	16.2		
Carbon disulfide	5.7	17.7		
Benzene	7.1	16.4		
Paraffin	8.1	17.4	13.0	34.2

cules or the activated complexes. An important question that arises in such cases is the frequency of collisions between solute molecules as compared with the frequency in the gas phase. This matter has been treated theoretically from the point of view both of the kinetic theory of collisions and of the absolute-rate theory. The point of view of the collision theory was employed by Rabinowitch,[1] who based his treatment on a theoretical study made in 1930 by Debye and Menke of the structure of liquid mercury. Using a distribution function for mercury given by Debye and Menke, Rabinowitch calculated the frequency of collisions between a given pair of mercury atoms, and compared this frequency with the frequency in the gas phase. His conclusion was that in the liquid the frequency of collisions is approximately two to three times greater than that in the gas phase.

Absolute-rate theory was applied to this problem by M. G. Evans and M. Polanyi,[2] and by R. P. Bell.[3] It is difficult to write satisfactory partition functions for molecules in the liquid phase (because of the complicated nature of their translational, rotational, and vibrational motions); it is therefore more convenient to apply the theory of absolute reaction rates in terms of entropies of activation rather than of partition functions. In Bell's treatment empirical values for entropies of nonpolar molecules in solution were employed, and from them were estimated the entropies of activation for reactions involving such molecules. In agreement with collision theory, his conclusion was that the frequency factor for a reaction in solution should be approximately three times as great as in the gas phase. On the assumption that the energies of activation are the same in the gas phase, both the collision theory and the theory of absolute reaction rates would therefore indicate that the rates in solution should be approximately three times as great as in the gas phase.

Another important problem is the distribution of collisions in time when reactions are occurring in solution. This problem was studied experimentally by Rabinowitch and Wood,[4] who employed a tray on which spheres were allowed to roll. Agitation of the tray caused the spheres to move around, and by an electrical method the number of collisions between a given pair of spheres was determined. The behavior in the gas phase is represented by the behavior when very few spheres are present, whereas that in the liquid phase is represented by the situation in which the spheres are comparatively closely packed. The frequency of collisions between a given pair of spheres was found to be almost independent of the total number of spheres present, but the distribution was quite different when many spheres were present. Collisions, in fact, occurred in sets when the spheres were fairly closely packed, but not when only a few spheres were present. The explanation is that in the case of the closely packed spheres the surrounding spheres form a "cage," which

[1] E. Rabinowitch, *ibid.*, **33**, 1225 (1937); E. Rabinowitch and W. C. Wood, *ibid.*, **32**, 1381 (1936).

[2] M. G. Evans and M. Polanyi, *ibid.*, 1333.

[3] R. P. Bell, *ibid.*, **33**, 496 (1937); cf. also J. A. V. Butler, *ibid.*, 171, 229; I. M. Barklay and J. A. V. Butler, *ibid.*, **34**, 1445 (1938).

[4] Rabinowitch and Wood, *loc. cit.*

holds the colliding spheres together and causes them to collide a number of times before they finally separate. This tendency for collisions to occur in sets has no effect on ordinary reactions, which involve an activation energy, since reaction may occur at any collision within the set. With reactions that do not involve an activation energy, such as free-radical combinations, this tendency of collisions to occur in sets makes a difference to the frequency factors since reaction occurs at the first collision in any set, with the result that the remaining collisions do not contribute to the rate. The frequency factor is therefore related to the reciprocal of the average time elapsing between successive sets of collisions, i.e., between successive *encounters*.

This *cage effect*, also known as the *Franck-Rabinowitch effect*,[1] has other important consequences. In photochemical reactions in solution, for example, a pair of free radicals produced initially may, owing to their being caged in by the surrounding solvent molecules, be caused to recombine before they can separate from each other. This phenomenon is known as *primary recombination*, as opposed to *secondary recombination* which occurs after the free radicals have separated from each other.

COMPARISON BETWEEN DIFFERENT SOLVENTS

The reactions considered above are those in which there are no great differences between the kinetics in solution and in the gas phase. It would, however, be unwise to conclude from this that the influence of the solvent is in general not important, as the similarity between the rates to some extent depends upon the ability of the reaction to occur in the gas phase as well as in solution. When reactions that do not occur in the gas phase are considered, it is found that the influence of the solvent, as judged by comparing the kinetics in different solvents, is very much more marked.

In considering such reactions it is of interest to compare the values of A obtained in solution with those expected on the basis of simple collision theory or the theory of absolute reaction rates. It has been seen that collision theory gives a value of 10^{10} to 10^{11} liters mole^{-1} sec^{-1} for the frequency factor[2] and that this value is also obtained for second-order reactions involving relatively simple molecules by the theory of absolute rates. When complex molecules react in a bimolecular manner, the latter theory predicts that the frequency factor should be much less than that given above. As will be seen in this section, a number of reactions in solution have been found to have very low frequency factors and are sometimes spoken of as "slow" reactions; well-known examples are the

[1] J. Franck and E. Rabinowitch, *Trans. Faraday Soc.*, **30**, 120 (1934).

[2] Rates and frequency factors for second-order reactions in solution are generally expressed in liters mole^{-1} sec^{-1}; those for reactions in the gas phase are now more commonly given as cc mole^{-1} sec^{-1}.

formation of quaternary ammonium salts and the benzoylation of amines. To exactly what extent these low frequency factors are due to specific solvent influences is difficult to ascertain in view of the failure of the reactions to proceed in the gas phase. However, it is important to note that the dimerization of cyclopentadiene has a very low frequency factor in the gas phase as well as in solution (cf. Table 25), so that in this instance, at least, the low frequency factor cannot be attributed to a solvent influence; the decrease in entropy as the two molecules become one is clearly an important factor.

In general, it is found that reactions between an ion and a neutral molecule have a "normal" frequency factor, i.e., 10^{10} to 10^{11}, even when the neutral molecule is of some complexity; the rates of such reactions would therefore agree with their hypothetical rates in the gas phase as predicted by either of the theories. Reactions between ions of opposite sign have high frequency factors and those between ions of the same sign low ones. This is due to the electrostatic forces and will be considered quantitatively in a later section of this chapter.

The results obtained with one or two reactions in various solvents will now be discussed briefly.

The reaction between triethylamine and ethyl iodide was studied in 22 different solvents by Menschutkin,[1] who found variations in the velocity of about a thousandfold. He measured no activation energies, but this was done by Grimm, Ruf, and Wolff,[2] some of whose results are included in Table 26. The reaction between pyridine and methyl iodide

[1] N. Menschutkin, *Z. Physik. Chem.*, **6**, 41 (1890).

[2] H. G. Grimm, H. Ruf, and H. Wolff, *ibid.*, **B13**, 301 (1931).

Table 26 FORMATION OF QUATERNARY AMMONIUM SALTS IN VARIOUS SOLVENTS

	Ethyl iodide and triethylamine			Pyridine and methyl iodide	
Solvent	$k \times 10^5$ (at 100°C)	E, kcal	$\log_{10} A$	E, kcal	$\log_{10} A$
Hexane	0.5	16.0	4.0		
Toluene	25.3	13.0	4.0	14.5	5.5
Benzene	39.8	11.4	3.3	14.2	5.4
Bromobenzene	166.0	12.5	4.6	13.7	5.7
Acetone	265.0	11.9	4.4	14.0	6.5
Benzonitrile	1,125.0	11.9	5.0	13.7	6.5
Nitrobenzene	1,383.0	11.6	4.9	13.7	6.6

has also been investigated,[1] and some of the results are given in the table. It is seen that in both reactions the variation in the rate is largely determined by the activation energy, the value of $\log_{10} A$ being comparatively constant. The reaction is seen to be a "slow" one; this is probably largely due to entropy effects.

A similar variation in rate and activation energy with change of solvent was found with the benzoylation of *m*-nitroaniline,[2] some of the results for which are given in Table 27. Again the variation in A is somewhat less important than that in E.

Table 27 BENZOYLATION OF *m*-NITROANILINE IN VARIOUS SOLVENTS

Solvent	E, kcal	$\log_{10} A$
Carbon tetrachloride	13.6	5.5
Isopropyl ether	10.9	4.4
Benzene	10.3	4.2
Chlorobenzene	11.4	4.8
Nitrobenzene	9.4	5.0
Benzonitrile	10.1	6.4

The addition of cyclopentadiene to benzoquinone is a simple reaction which has been studied in a variety of solvents;[3] some of the results are included in Table 28. The main variations are again in the energy of

[1] N. J. T. Pickles and C. N. Hinshelwood, *J. Chem. Soc.*, 1353 (1936); R. A. Fairclough and C. N. Hinshelwood, *ibid.*, 538, 1573 (1937).

[2] Pickles and Hinshelwood, *loc. cit.*

[3] A. Wassermann, *Ber.*, **66**, 1932 (1933); *Nature*, **137**, 497 (1936); *Trans. Faraday Soc.*, **34**, 128 (1938); R. A. Fairclough and C. N. Hinshelwood, *J. Chem. Soc.*, 236 (1938).

Table 28 REACTION BETWEEN CYCLOPENTADIENE AND BENZOQUINONE

Solvent	E, kcal	$\log_{10} A$
Ethyl alcohol	12.7	7.0
Carbon tetrachloride	9.2	4.5
Benzene	11.5	6.3
Nitrobenzene	8.8	5.0

activation, but the changes in $\log_{10} A$ are here greater than those cited previously.

The thermal decomposition of trinitrobenzoic acid is an example of a first-order decomposition that has been studied in a variety of solvents;[1] some results are given in Table 29. It is seen that a thousandfold variation in the rate is observed with the solvents used but that the values of E and $\log_{10} A$ are rather scattered. The examples of reactions studied in different solvents could be continued, but the reactions quoted are sufficient to illustrate the general type of behavior that is observed.

Table 29 DECOMPOSITION OF TRINITROBENZOIC ACID

Solvent	$9 + \log_{10} k$ (at 70°C)	E, kcal	$\log_{10} A$
Toluene	0.21	31.6	12.0
Nitrobenzene	0.6	35.0	14.6
Anisole	2.29	30.7	13.5
Acetophenone	2.76	25.5	10.5
Water	3.52	30.0	14.3

FACTORS DETERMINING REACTION RATES IN SOLUTION

Rate-determining Step in Solution. The reaction between two molecules in solution can be thought of as occurring in three well-defined stages: (1) diffusion of the molecules to each other, (2) the actual chemical transformation, and (3) diffusion of the products away from each other. Diffusion in a liquid, like many other physical processes, has an activation energy, but the magnitude of this is generally not greater than 5 kcal. Many chemical reactions have activation energies of more than this and thus cannot involve diffusion as the slow step, which must therefore be step 2, the purely chemical process. This conclusion is supported by the fact that the rates of these reactions do not depend upon the viscosity of the solvent, as they would if diffusion were important, diffusion and viscosity being very closely related. Most of the discussion in this book will be devoted to such reactions in which step 2 is slow and rate determining.

[1] E. A. Moelwyn-Hughes and C. N. Hinshelwood, *Proc. Roy. Soc. (London)*, **A131,** 177 (1931).

On the other hand, there are some processes occurring in solution in which the diffusion is rate controlling; these are certain reactions which occur very rapidly. Ionic recombinations are of this type; the rates of such reactions are too rapid to be measured conveniently, but it would no doubt be found that diffusion was rate controlling. The quenching of fluorescence in solution also involves diffusion as the slow step.[1] Certain heterogeneous reactions between solids and liquids are also of this type.

Since the chemical interaction between the molecules is of primary importance in determining the rate in most cases, a study of rates in different solvents will be concerned largely with the influence of the solvent on this step. This problem will be considered in terms of the theory of absolute reaction rates, which offers the most constructive approach to the problem.

Theory of Absolute Reaction Rates.[2] The application of the theory of absolute reaction rates to reactions in solution is simple in principle but is difficult to carry out quantitatively, owing to our imperfect knowledge of the liquid state. As with gas reactions, the rate can be expressed in terms of partition functions for the reacting species and the activated state, but they should contain terms for the influence of the solvent environment. However, since there is so much uncertainty about partition functions in solution, it is better to treat rates in solution in a less fundamental manner, by using activity coefficients.

It has been seen in Chap. 3 that the rate of a reaction is proportional to the concentration $[X^\ddagger]$ of the activated complexes, i.e.,

$$v \propto [X^\ddagger] \tag{1}$$

For the reaction

$$A + B \rightleftharpoons X^\ddagger \rightarrow \text{products}$$

the concentration $[X^\ddagger]$ may be expressed as

$$[X^\ddagger] = K^*[A][B]\frac{\alpha_A \alpha_B}{\alpha_\ddagger} \tag{2}$$

Here K^* is the true equilibrium constant, and the α's are the activity coefficients, previously neglected since in the gas phase they are close to

[1] Cf. R. W. Roughton and G. K. Rollefson, *J. Am. Chem. Soc.*, **61**, 2634 (1939); **62**, 2264 (1940); V. K. LaMer and M. E. Kamner, *ibid.*, **57**, 2662 (1935); P. Debye, *Trans. Electrochem. Soc.*, **82**, 265 (1942); J. Q. Umberger and V. K. LaMer, *J. Am. Chem. Soc.*, **67**, 1099 (1945).

[2] Cf. W. F. K. Wynne-Jones and H. Eyring, *J. Chem. Phys.*, **3**, 493 (1935); A. E. Stearn and H. Eyring, *ibid.*, **5**, 113 (1937); K. J. Laidler and H. Eyring, *Ann. N.Y. Acad. Sci.*, **39**, 303 (1940).

unity. Substitution of this expression in Eq. (1) leads to

$$v \propto [\mathrm{A}][\mathrm{B}]K^* \frac{\alpha_\mathrm{A}\alpha_\mathrm{B}}{\alpha_\ddagger} \tag{3}$$

The rate constant is thus given by

$$k \propto K^* \frac{\alpha_\mathrm{A}\alpha_\mathrm{B}}{\alpha_\ddagger} \tag{4}$$

For an ideal gaseous system the activity coefficients are unity, so that the rate constant reduces to

$$k_g \propto K^* \tag{5}$$

The rate constant in solution can therefore be related to that in the gas phase by the equation

$$k = k_g \frac{\alpha_\mathrm{A}\alpha_\mathrm{B}}{\alpha_\ddagger} \tag{6}$$

This equation can be used for relating the rate constant in solution not only to that in the gas phase but also to that in very dilute solution, where the substances behave ideally; this will be considered later.

If the rates in solution and in the gas phase are to be equal, the activity-coefficient factor $\alpha_\mathrm{A}\alpha_\mathrm{B}/\alpha_\ddagger$ must be equal to unity. This may easily arise for a unimolecular reaction, for which the appropriate factor is $\alpha_\mathrm{A}/\alpha_\ddagger$; if the reactant and the activated complex have similar structures, as is often the case, α_A and $\alpha_\ddagger$ will not differ greatly, and the rate of reaction in solution will be similar to that in the gas phase. It has been seen that this similarity in rates is approximately true for the decomposition of nitrogen pentoxide in a number of solvents (see Table 24). The abnormally slow rate of decomposition in nitric acid and propylene dichloride, and the correspondingly high energies of activation, may be due to the formation of a complex between the reactant and the solvent; such compound formation decreases α_A and consequently the rate of reaction.

Influence of Internal Pressure. The application of the theory of solutions to reaction rates has revealed some interesting regularities concerning the relationship between rate and internal pressure. The activity coefficient α, which appears in Eq. (6), is proportional to the more usual activity coefficient γ, which relates the behavior of a solute to its behavior in an ideal solution, so that the rate of reaction can be written as

$$\frac{k_s}{k_0} = \frac{\gamma_\mathrm{A}\gamma_\mathrm{B}}{\gamma_\ddagger} \tag{7}$$

where k_0 is now the rate in the ideal solution. For a regular solution, i.e., one in which the molecular distribution is entirely random in spite of the nonideality, the activity coefficient γ_1 of a solute can be expressed in the form[1]

$$RT \ln \gamma_1 = v_1 \left(\frac{N_2 v_2}{N_1 v_1 + N_2 v_2} \right)^2 \left[\left(\frac{E_1}{v_1} \right)^{1/2} - \left(\frac{E_2}{v_2} \right)^{1/2} \right]^2 \tag{8}$$

where N_1 and N_2 are the mole fractions of solute and solvent, v_1 and v_2 their molar volumes, and E_1 and E_2 the energies of vaporization of solute and solvent when in the form of pure liquids. If the solution is dilute, $N_1 v_1$ may be neglected in comparison with $N_2 v_2$, and the expression reduces to

$$RT \ln \gamma_1 = v_1 \left[\left(\frac{E_1}{v_1} \right)^{1/2} - \left(\frac{E_2}{v_2} \right)^{1/2} \right]^2 \tag{9}$$

The quantities E/v are approximately equal to a/v^2, where a is the van der Waals attraction constant, and are hence roughly equal to the internal pressure P of the liquid; thus

$$RT \ln \gamma_1 = v_1 (P_1^{1/2} - P_2^{1/2})^2 = v_1 \Delta \tag{10}$$

Here Δ is an abbreviation for $(P_1^{1/2} - P_2^{1/2})^2$ and is always a positive quantity. Taking logarithms of Eq. (7) and inserting the values of $\ln \gamma$ given by Eq. (10) gives

$$RT \ln k_s = RT \ln k_0 + v_A \Delta_A + v_B \Delta_B - v_\ddagger \Delta_\ddagger \tag{11}$$

For regular solutions the influence of the solvent is therefore determined by the molar volumes and the internal-pressure terms.

The molar volumes do not vary greatly; hence the internal-pressure factor is the more important. If the internal pressures of solvent, of A and B, and of the activated complex are all similar, the solvent will have little effect on the rate of reaction as compared with a solvent in which the reaction behaves ideally. If the internal pressure of the solvent is close to the values for the reactants, i.e., if Δ_A and Δ_B are small, but appreciably different from that of the complex, i.e., $\Delta_\ddagger$ is large, the factor $v_A \Delta_A + v_B \Delta_B - v_\ddagger \Delta_\ddagger$ will have a relatively large negative value, and in accordance with Eq. (11) the rate in this solvent will be low. If, on the other hand, the solvent has an internal pressure similar to that of the activated complex, but different from those of one or both of the reactants, the factor $v_A \Delta_A + v_B \Delta_B - v_\ddagger \Delta_\ddagger$ will be large and positive, and the reaction rate will be high. Since the activated complex has properties which approach those of the products of reaction, and which may resemble them very closely in some cases, it follows as a general rule that if the reaction is one in which the products are of higher internal pressure than the reactants,

[1] G. Scatchard, *Chem. Rev.*, **8**, 321 (1931); J. H. Hildebrand and S. E. Wood, *J. Chem. Phys.*, **1**, 817 (1933); cf. J. H. Hildebrand and R. L. Scott, "Regular Solutions," Prentice-Hall, Inc., Englewood Cliffs, N.J., 1962.

it is accelerated by solvents of high internal pressure. This rule was first stated empirically by Richardson and Soper[1] and was arrived at theoretically by Glasstone.[2]

This rule may now be applied to some of the examples quoted earlier in this chapter. In general, for bimolecular associations of the type $A + B \rightarrow C$, the activated complex may be expected to resemble C; thus for the formation of quaternary ammonium salts the complex will resemble the ionic product and consequently have a high internal pressure. It should therefore be accelerated by solvents of high internal pressure; this is confirmed by the first column of figures given in Table 30, the solvent internal pressures increasing roughly in the order given. On the other hand, solvents which favor the formation of quaternary ammonium salts tend to slow down reactions like the dissociation of sulfonium salts and esterifications (cf. Table 30) in which the products are of lower internal pressure than the reactants. However, deviations from these rules are often found and can frequently be explained as solvation effects, the solutions no longer being regular.

Table 30 Influence of solvents on specific rates

Solvent	Triethylamine and ethyl iodide (at 100°C)	Acetic anhydride and ethyl alcohol (at 50°C)
Hexane	0.00018	0.0119
Chlorobenzene	0.023	0.0053
Benzene	0.0058	0.0046
Anisole	0.040	0.0029
Nitrobenzene	70.1	0.0024

Influence of Solvation. The degree of solvation of the reactants and the activated complex has a very pronounced influence on the rate of reaction. If the reactants are not appreciably solvated but the activated complex is, the activity coefficient of the complex is smaller than it is in a solvent that does not solvate it; consequently, by Eq. (2), the rate of the reaction will be greater than in a nonsolvating solvent. This explains at least in part the very high rate of formation of quaternary ammonium salts in nitrobenzene as compared with benzene (see Table 30); the activated complex probably resembles the product in being a

[1] M. Richardson and F. G. Soper, *J. Chem. Soc.*, 1873 (1929).
[2] S. Glasstone, *ibid.*, 723 (1936).

polar substance and hence is solvated to a considerable degree by nitrobenzene but not by benzene. On the other hand, a reaction occurring in a solvent which solvates the reactants to a greater degree than the activated complex will take place less rapidly than it would in a solvent in which the reactants are not solvated.

The preceding comments are strictly valid only for reactions in an inert solvent which has little effect on the kinetic behavior. There are many reactions that do not occur at all in the gas phase; an example is the formation of the quaternary ammonium salt $(C_2H_5)_4N^+I^-$ from ethyl iodide and triethylamine, some results for which are included in Table 30. The activated complex for this reaction will have some of the properties of the product, and in particular will be fairly polar. Ionizing solvents, which will stabilize the activated complex, are therefore expected to favor the reaction. This explanation is supported by the results in Table 30, which shows that the rate is very much greater in an ionizing and polar solvent such as nitrobenzene than it is in a nonpolar solvent such as hexane or benzene. The frequency factors in all the solvents listed are 10^4 to 10^5 liters mole^{-1} sec^{-1}, much lower than expected on the basis of simple collision theory. The small values cannot be explained in terms of structural effects; there is, for example, no large loss of rotational entropy in the liquid phase. The explanation must be in terms of specific solvent effects, to be discussed later.

In this reaction, and in many other reactions in which the solvent has an important influence, the situation is dominated by the electrostatic forces between solvent and solute molecules. In some reactions, such as those between ions, these forces exert a predominant effect on the kinetic behavior, which can be treated fairly satisfactorily by considering only these electrostatic forces. In other cases, such as reactions between highly polar molecules or reactions in which a highly polar activated complex is formed, the electrostatic forces are also quite important and must be considered, although other factors are also significant. Reactions in which electrostatic effects are important will now be considered in further detail.

REACTIONS BETWEEN IONS

The electrostatic forces between ions are much stronger than the nonelectrostatic ones, and they are understood quite satisfactorily. The theoretical treatment that will be outlined will apply particularly to reactions in which covalent chemical bonds are broken and formed; simple ion-recombination reactions are diffusion controlled and are considered later.

The frequency factors of ionic reactions depend in a very simple and important way on the ionic charges, as is to be seen from Table 31 on page 215. For reactions between ions of opposite signs the frequency factors are much higher than "normal" ($\sim 10^{10}$ liters mole^{-1} sec^{-1}), whereas if the ions are of the same sign, the frequency factors are abnormally low. The effects of electrostatic attraction or repulsion are obviously important. The situation can be considered in terms of collision theory; if the ions are of opposite signs, the frequency of collisions will be increased by the attractive forces, but if they are of the same sign, the frequency of collisions will be reduced. Scatchard[1] and Moelwyn-Hughes[2] have in fact proceeded in this way and have modified the collision theory to allow for such electrostatic interactions. Alternatively one may use absolute-rate theory, which is the procedure that will be used here. The problem of the influence of the solvent on the rates and frequency factors of reactions in solution will be considered first; afterward, with the aid of the Debye-Hückel theory, the influence of the ionic strength will be treated.

Influence of Solvent. Estimates may be made of the free-energy change in going from the initial state of a reaction to the activated state. According to the theory of absolute reaction rates the rate constant is related to the free energy of activation by the equation [cf. Eq. (86) of Chap. 3]

$$k = \frac{\mathbf{k}T}{\mathbf{h}} e^{-\Delta G^{\ddagger}/RT} \tag{12}$$

In reactions between ions the electrostatic interactions make the most important contribution to the free energy of activation. According to the simplest treatment of electrostatic interactions, the charged ions are considered to be conducting spheres, and the solvent is regarded as a continuous dielectric, having a fixed dielectric constant ϵ. Such a treatment represents a gross oversimplification, but it has proved surprisingly useful; it certainly leads to conclusions that are semiquantitatively correct, as will be seen later. Some improvement to the theories can be effected in various ways, such as by taking account of the variation in dielectric constant with field strength; unfortunately the treatment is then very complicated and does not lead to clear-cut conclusions.

This treatment, in which emphasis is placed on the increase in free energy when the system passes from the initial state to the activated state, is to be contrasted with the collision-theory approach; according to the latter, the collision frequency is regarded as modified by the electrostatic interaction. The absolute-rate method is more flexible than that of the collision theory, since the structure of the activated complex can be formulated in various ways, regard being paid to the detailed processes

[1] G. Scatchard, *Chem. Rev.*, **10**, 229 (1932).

[2] E. A. Moelwyn-Hughes, *Proc. Roy. Soc.* (*London*), **A155**, 308 (1936); "Kinetics of Reactions in Solution," chap. 4, Clarendon Press, Oxford, 1947.

that occur. In ideal cases, when the reactant molecules simply approach one another and remain intact in the activated state, the two theories become equivalent.

A very simple model for a reaction between two ions in solution is represented in Fig. 46. The reacting molecules are regarded as conduct-

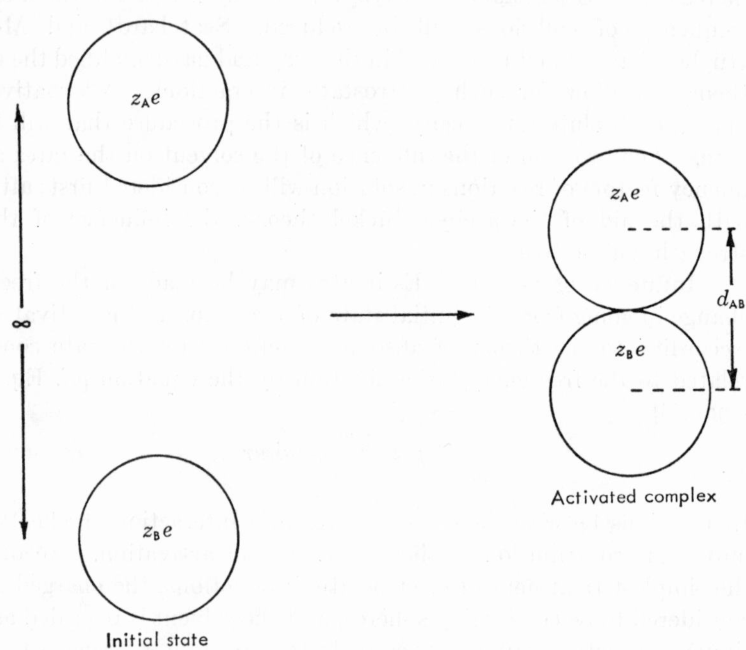

Fig. 46. A simple model for a reaction between two ions, of charges $z_A e$ and $z_B e$, in a medium of dielectric constant ϵ. This is known as the "double-sphere" model.

ing spheres; the radii are r_A and r_B and the charges $z_A e$ and $z_B e$, e being the electronic charge, and z_A and z_B being whole numbers (positive or negative) which indicate the numbers of charges on the ion. Initially the ions are at an infinite distance from each other, and in the activated state they are considered to be intact (i.e., there is no "smearing" of charge), and they are at a distance d_{AB} apart. This model is frequently referred to as the *double-sphere* model. When the ions are at a distance x apart, the force acting between them is equal to

$$f = \frac{z_A z_B e^2}{\epsilon x^2} \tag{13}$$

The work that must be done in moving them together a distance dx is

$$dw = -\frac{z_A z_B e^2}{\epsilon x^2}\,dx \tag{14}$$

(The negative sign is used because x *decreases* by dx when the ions move together by a distance dx.) The work that is done in moving the ions from an initial distance of infinity to a final distance of d_{AB} is therefore

$$w = -\int_{\infty}^{d_{AB}} \frac{z_A z_B e^2}{\epsilon x^2}\,dx \tag{15}$$

$$= \frac{z_A z_B e^2}{\epsilon d_{AB}} \tag{16}$$

If the signs on the ions are the same, this work is positive; if they are different, it is negative. This work is equal to the electrostatic contribution to the free-energy increase as the ions are moved up to each other.

There is also a molar nonelectrostatic term, $\Delta G^{\ddagger}_{\text{n.e.s.}}$. The free energy of activation per molecule may therefore be written as

$$\frac{\Delta G^{\ddagger}}{N} = \frac{\Delta G^{\ddagger}_{\text{n.e.s.}}}{N} + \frac{z_A z_B e^2}{\epsilon d_{AB}} \tag{17}$$

and introduction of this into Eq. (12) gives

$$k = \frac{\mathbf{k}T}{\mathbf{h}} \exp\left(-\frac{\Delta G^{\ddagger}_{\text{n.e.s.}}}{RT}\right) \exp\left(-\frac{z_A z_B e^2}{\epsilon d_{AB}\mathbf{k}T}\right) \tag{18}$$

This equation may be written in the logarithmic form

$$\ln k = \ln \frac{\mathbf{k}T}{\mathbf{h}} - \frac{\Delta G^{\ddagger}_{\text{n.e.s.}}}{RT} - \frac{z_A z_B e^2}{\epsilon d_{AB}\mathbf{k}T} \tag{19}$$

and this may be simplified to[1]

$$\ln k = \ln k_0 - \frac{z_A z_B e^2}{\epsilon d_{AB}\mathbf{k}T} \tag{20}$$

The rate constant k_0 is seen to be the value of k in a medium of infinite dielectric constant, when the final term in (20) becomes zero (i.e., when there are no electrostatic forces).

Equation (20) leads to the prediction that the logarithm of the rate constant of a reaction between ions should vary linearly with the reciprocal of the dielectric constant. Many tests of this relationship have been made, particularly by causing a reaction to occur in a series of mixed solvents of varying dielectric constant. On the whole, the relationship is obeyed to a good approximation, although there are usually serious deviations at very low dielectric constants. An example of a test of Eq.

[1] An expression of this form was first obtained by G. Scatchard, *Chem. Rev.*, **10**, 229 (1932), but his method of derivation was quite different.

(20) is shown in Fig. 47. Deviations from linearity can be explained as due to failure of the simple approximations involved in deriving Eq. (20), and in some cases to change in reaction mechanism as the solvent is varied.

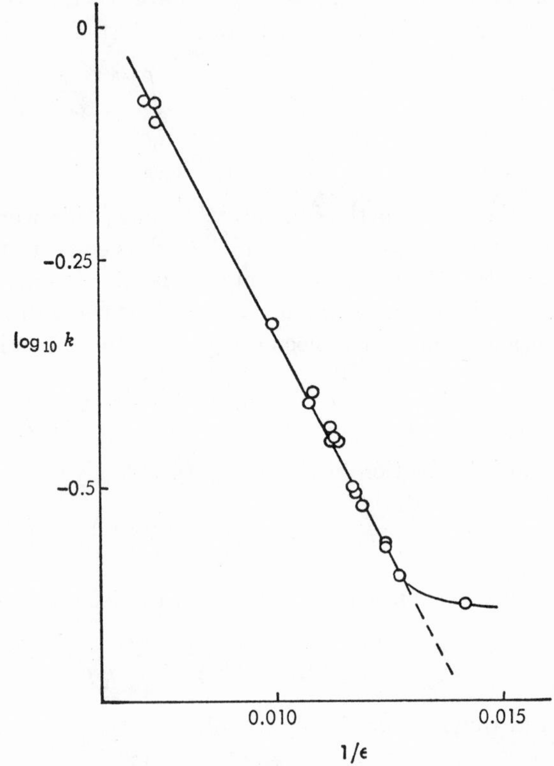

Fig. 47. A plot of $\log_{10} k$ against the reciprocal of the dielectric constant, for the reaction between bromoacetate and thiosulfate ions in aqueous solution. [*K. J. Laidler and H. Eyring, Ann. N.Y. Acad. Sci.* **39**, 303 (1940).]

The slope of the line obtained by plotting ln k against $1/\epsilon$ is given by Eq. (20) as $z_A z_B e^2/d_{AB}\mathbf{k}T$. Since everything in this expression is known except d_{AB}, it is possible to calculate d_{AB} from the experimental slope. This has been done in a number of cases, and the values obtained, of the order of a few angstroms, have always been entirely reasonable; for the data shown in Fig. 47 the value of d_{AB} is 5.1 A.

Frequency Factors. This treatment can be extended to give an interpretation of the magnitudes of the frequency factors of reactions of this type. The electrostatic contribution to the free energy of activation (per mole) has been seen to be given by

$$\Delta G^{\ddagger}_{\text{e.s.}} = \frac{N z_A z_B e^2}{\epsilon d_{AB}} \tag{21}$$

The thermodynamical relationship between entropy and free energy is

$$S = -\left(\frac{\partial G}{\partial T}\right)_P \tag{22}$$

so that the electrostatic contribution to the entropy of activation is

$$\Delta S^{\ddagger}_{\text{e.s.}} = -\left(\frac{\partial\, \Delta G^{\ddagger}_{\text{e.s.}}}{\partial T}\right)_P \tag{23}$$

The only quantity in (21) that is temperature-dependent is ϵ, and it therefore follows that

$$\Delta S^{\ddagger}_{\text{e.s.}} = \frac{N z_A z_B}{\epsilon^2 d_{AB}}\left(\frac{\partial \epsilon}{\partial T}\right)_P \tag{24}$$

$$= \frac{N z_A z_B}{\epsilon d_{AB}}\left(\frac{\partial \ln \epsilon}{\partial T}\right)_P \tag{25}$$

In aqueous solution ϵ is about 80 and $(\partial \ln \epsilon/\partial T)_P$ remains constant at -0.0046 over a considerable temperature range. If d_{AB} is taken as equal

Table 31 SOME OBSERVED AND PREDICTED FREQUENCY FACTORS AND ENTROPIES OF ACTIVATION

Frequency factors are in liters mole^{-1} sec^{-1}

	Experimental values†		Estimated values§	
Reactants	A	$\Delta S\ddagger$	A	$\Delta S\ddagger$
$[Cr(H_2O)_6]^{3+} + CNS^-$	10^{19}	30	10^{19}	30
$Co(NH_3)_5Br^{2+} + OH^-$	5×10^{17}	22	10^{17}	20
$CH_2BrCOOCH_3 + S_2O_3^{2-}$	1×10^{14}	6	10^{13}	0
$CH_2ClCOO^- + OH^-$	6×10^{10}	-12	10^{11}	-10
$ClO^- + ClO_2^-$	9×10^{8}	-20	10^{11}	-10
$CH_2BrCOO^- + S_2O_3^{2-}$	1×10^{9}	-17	10^{9}	-20
$Co(NH_3)_5Br^{2+} + Hg^{2+}$	1×10^{8}	-24	10^{5}	-40
$S_2O_4^{2-} + S_2O_4^{2-}$	2×10^{4}	-40	10^{5}	-40
$S_2O_3^{2-} + SO_3^{2-}$	2×10^{6}	-30	10^{5}	-40

† For references to experimental values see A. A. Frost and R. G. Pearson, "Kinetics and Mechanism," 2d ed., p. 144, John Wiley & Sons, Inc., New York, 1961; D. T. Y. Chen and K. J. Laidler, *Can. J. Chem.*, **37**, 599 (1959).

§ For the purpose of these rough estimates the frequency factor in the absence of electrostatic effects has been taken as 10^{13}, and the entropy of activation as zero.

to 2×10^{-8} cm, it follows from Eq. (25) that

$$\Delta S^{\ddagger}_{\text{e.s.}} \simeq -10 z_A z_B \tag{26}$$

The entropy of activation in aqueous solution should thus decrease by about 10 units for each unit of $z_A z_B$. Moreover, since the frequency factor is proportional to $e^{\Delta S\ddagger/R}$, which equals $10^{\Delta S\ddagger/2.303R}$ or $10^{\Delta S\ddagger/4.57}$, it follows that the frequency factor should decrease by a factor of $10^{10/4.57}$, i.e., by about one-hundredfold, for each unit of $z_A z_B$. Table 31 shows that these relationships are obeyed in a very approximate manner. The

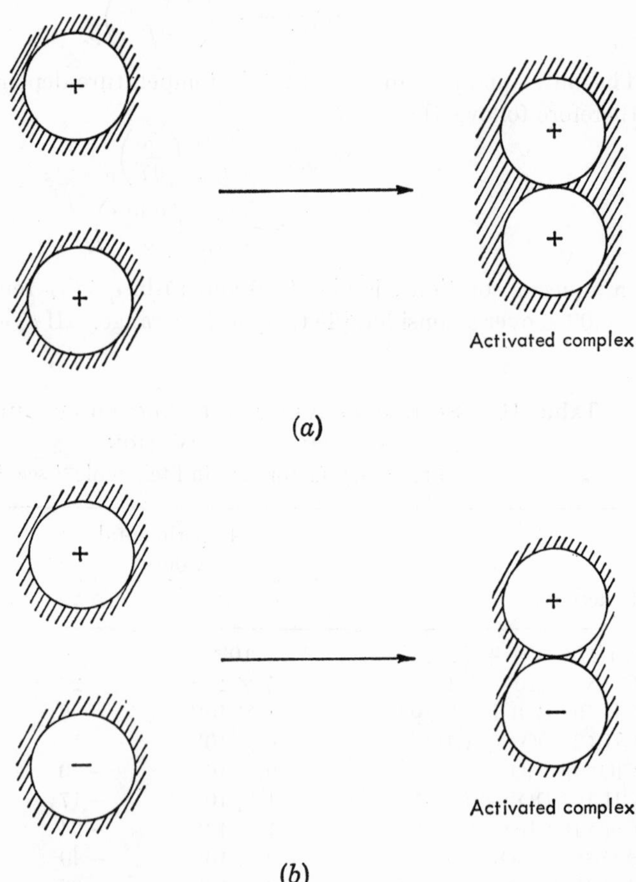

Fig. 48. An interpretation of entropies of activation in terms of the electrostriction of solvent molecules. In (*a*) the ions are of the same sign, and there is more electrostriction in the activated complex; there is therefore a decrease in entropy (and volume). In (*b*) there is less electrostriction in the activated complex.

treatment is too crude to allow reliable predictions to be made, but is evidently along the right lines.

The physical model that lies behind the above relationships is represented schematically in Fig. 48. In (*a*) the ions are shown as having single positive charges, and the activated complex therefore bears a double positive charge. The solvent molecules in the neighborhood of an ion are acted upon by strong electrostatic forces which restrict their freedom of motion; this effect is known as *electrostriction.* There is a consequent loss of entropy, and this loss is greater the larger the charge. In the case under consideration there is some loss of entropy in the initial state, resulting from the fact that the reactant species are ions. In the activated state, however, there is a much greater loss of entropy since the charge is greater. There is therefore a loss of entropy when the activated complex is formed.

In case (*b*) the reacting ions are of opposite signs, and there is therefore *less* charge on the activated complex than on the reactant molecules. There is a consequent decrease in electrostriction when the activated complex is formed, and an increase in entropy.

AN ALTERNATIVE MODEL: THE SINGLE-SPHERE ACTIVATED COMPLEX

Slightly different relationships have been obtained using a different model for the activated complex.[1] In the treatment just described the activated complex was regarded as having the form of a double sphere, the original charges residing at the center of the two spheres and being separated by a distance d_{AB}. The two spheres may alternatively be regarded as becoming merged into one single sphere which has a charge equal to the algebraic sum of the charges on the ions. It will be seen that the results to which these alternative treatments lead are quite similar to each other, and it is likely that the truth usually lies somewhere between the two.

The *single-sphere* activated complex is represented schematically in Fig. 49, which is to be contrasted with Fig. 46. The derivation of the rate equation for this case is based on an expression obtained by Born[2] for the free energy of charging an ion in solution. Born's expression is derived as follows. Consider the process of charging a conducting sphere of radius r from an initial charge of zero to a final charge equal to ze. This process will be carried out by transporting, from an infinite distance, small increments of charge equal to $e\,d\lambda$, where λ is a parameter that varies from zero to z. At any time the charge on the sphere may be

[1] K. J. Laidler and H. Eyring, *Ann. N.Y. Acad. Sci.*, **39**, 303 (1940).

[2] M. Born, *Z. Physik.*, **1**, 45 (1920).

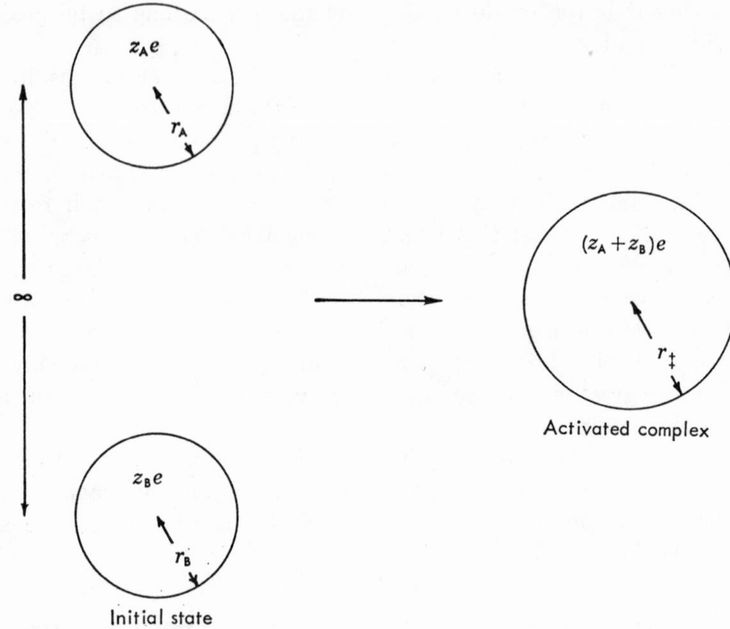

Fig. 49. The single-sphere activated complex.

written as λe, and if at a given instant the increment of charge is at a distance x from the ion, the force acting on it is

$$df = \frac{\lambda e^2 \, d\lambda}{\epsilon x^2} \tag{27}$$

The work of moving the increment from x to $x - dx$ is

$$dw = \frac{\lambda e^2 \, d\lambda \, dx}{\epsilon x^2} \tag{28}$$

The total work of charging is obtained by carrying out the double integration, x being allowed to vary from infinity to r, and λ from zero to z. The total work is thus

$$w = \frac{e^2}{\epsilon} \int_0^z \int_\infty^r \frac{\lambda \, d\lambda \, dx}{x^2} \tag{29}$$

$$= \frac{z^2 e^2}{2\epsilon r} \tag{30}$$

This work is the electrostatic contribution to the free energy of the ion,

$$G_{\text{e.s.}} = \frac{z^2 e^2}{2\epsilon r} \tag{31}$$

For the process represented in Fig. 49 the electrostatic free energies of the reactant ions and the activated complex are given by

$$G_{\text{e.s.}}(\text{A}) = \frac{z_{\text{A}}^2 e^2}{2\epsilon r_{\text{A}}} \tag{32}$$

$$G_{\text{e.s.}}(\text{B}) = \frac{z_{\text{B}}^2 e^2}{2\epsilon r_{\text{B}}} \tag{33}$$

$$G_{\text{e.s.}}(\ddagger) = \frac{(z_{\text{A}} + z_{\text{B}})^2 e^2}{2\epsilon r_\ddagger} \tag{34}$$

The increase in electrostatic free energy when the activated complex is formed is thus

$$\Delta G^\ddagger_{\text{e.s.}} = \frac{e^2}{2\epsilon}\left[\frac{(z_{\text{A}} + z_{\text{B}})^2}{r_\ddagger} - \frac{z_{\text{A}}^2}{r_{\text{A}}} - \frac{z_{\text{B}}^2}{r_{\text{B}}}\right] \tag{35}$$

Use of the same procedure that led to Eq. (20) gives rise to

$$\ln k = \ln k_0 - \frac{e^2}{2\epsilon \mathbf{k} T}\left[\frac{(z_{\text{A}} + z_{\text{B}})^2}{r_\ddagger} - \frac{z_{\text{A}}^2}{r_{\text{A}}} - \frac{z_{\text{B}}^2}{r_{\text{B}}}\right] \tag{36}$$

This equation is to be compared and contrasted with Eq. (20), which is based on the double-sphere model. Equation (36) reduces to Eq. (20) if one puts $r_{\text{A}} = r_{\text{B}} = r_\ddagger$. The experimental results may be fitted by Eq. (36) as readily as by Eq. (20), and there is little to choose between the two models of the activated complex. There will be some merging of the electrical charges during the formation of the activated complex, at least in some cases, although perhaps not the complete merging that is assumed with the single-sphere complex.

Influence of Ionic Strength. Theoretical treatments of the influence of ionic strength on the rates of reactions between ions were given by Brønsted,[1] Bjerrum,[2] Christiansen,[3] and Scatchard.[4] Their discussion may be considered with reference to a reaction of the general type

$$\text{A} + \text{B} \rightarrow \text{X} \rightarrow \text{products}$$

In the treatments of Brønsted and Bjerrum the intermediate X is some complex formed by the addition of the reactant molecules A and B, and is not necessarily an activated complex; however, in the present formulation it is convenient to regard X as an activated complex. The basis of the treatment is that the rate of a reaction will be proportional to the *concentration* of the activated complexes $\text{X}^\ddagger$, and not to their activity. The rate is therefore given by

$$v = k'[\text{X}^\ddagger] \tag{37}$$

[1] J. N. Brønsted, *Z. Physik. Chem.*, **102**, 169 (1922).
[2] N. Bjerrum, *ibid.*, **108**, 82 (1924).
[3] J. A. Christiansen, *ibid.*, **113**, 35 (1924).
[4] G. Scatchard, *Chem. Rev.*, **10**, 229 (1932).

The equilibrium between the activated complexes and the reactants A and B may be expressed as

$$K = \frac{a_\ddagger}{a_A a_B} = \frac{[X^\ddagger]}{[A][B]} \frac{f_\ddagger}{f_A f_B} \tag{38}$$

where the a's are the activities, and the f's the activity coefficients. Introduction of Eq. (38) into Eq. (37) gives rise to

$$v = k[A][B] = k_0[A][B] \frac{f_A f_B}{f_\ddagger} \tag{39}$$

Taking logarithms,

$$\log_{10} k = \log_{10} k_0 + \log_{10} \frac{f_A f_B}{f_\ddagger} \tag{40}$$

According to the Debye-Hückel theory, the activity coefficient of an ion is related to its valency z and the ionic strength u by the equation

$$\log_{10} f = -Qz^2 \sqrt{u} \tag{41}$$

The coefficient Q in this expression is given by

$$Q = \frac{N^2 e^3 (2\pi)^{1/2}}{2.303(\epsilon \mathbf{k} T)^{3/2}(1{,}000)^{1/2}} \tag{42}$$

and the ionic strength is defined, following G. N. Lewis, by the equation

$$u = \frac{1}{2} \sum_i z_i^2 c_i \tag{43}$$

Here z_i is the valency of the ion and c_i its concentration, the summation being taken of all of the ions in the solution.[1] The introduction of Eq. (41) into the rate equation (40) gives rise to

$$\begin{aligned} \log_{10} k &= \log_{10} k_0 + \log_{10} f_A + \log_{10} f_B - \log_{10} f_\ddagger & (44)\\ &= \log_{10} k_0 - Q\sqrt{u}\,[z_A{}^2 + z_B{}^2 - (z_A + z_B)^2] & (45)\\ &= \log_{10} k_0 + 2Qz_A z_B \sqrt{u} & (46) \end{aligned}$$

The value of Q is approximately 0.51 for aqueous solutions at 25°C; Eq. (46) may therefore be written as

$$\log_{10} k = \log_{10} k_0 + 1.02 z_A z_B \sqrt{u} \tag{47}$$

This equation has been tested a considerable number of times, particularly by Brønsted and LaMer, and more recently by Davies.[2] The

[1] For a solution of a uni-univalent electrolyte the ionic strength is identical with the molar concentration, but it is greater than the concentration when the salt contains ions of higher valencies.

[2] C. W. Davies, in G. Porter (ed.), "Progress in Reaction Kinetics," vol. 1, p. 161, Pergamon Press, Oxford, 1961.

procedure has usually been to measure the rates of ionic reactions in media of varying ionic strength; according to Eq. (47), a plot of $\log_{10} k$ against $\sqrt{u}$ will give a straight line of slope $1.02z_Az_B$. Figure 50 shows a plot of results for reactions of various types; the lines drawn are those with theoretical slopes, and the points are seen to lie very close to them. If one of the reactants is a neutral molecule, z_Az_B is zero, and the rate constant is expected to be independent of the ionic strength; this is true,

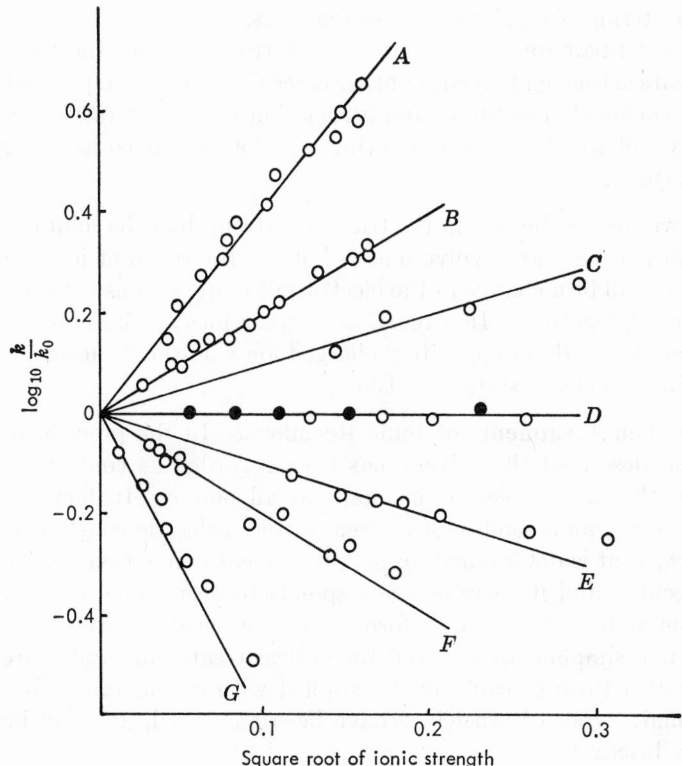

Fig. 50. Plots of $\log_{10}(k/k_0)$ against the square root of the ionic strength, for ionic reactions of various types. The lines are drawn with slopes equal to z_Az_B. The reactions are:

A	$Co(NH_3)_5Br^{2+} + Hg^{2+}$	$(z_Az_B = 4)$
B	$S_2O_8^{2-} + I^-$	$(z_Az_B = 2)$
C	$CO(OC_2H_5)N{:}NO_2^- + OH^-$	$(z_Az_B = 1)$
D	$(Cr(urea)_6)^{3+} + H_2O$ (open circles)	$(z_Az_B = 0)$
	$CH_3COOC_2H_5 + OH^-$ (closed circles)	$(z_Az_B = 0)$
E	$H^{+}+Br^- + H_2O_2$	$(z_Az_B = -1)$
F	$Co(NH_3)_5Br^{2+} + OH^-$	$(z_Az_B = -2)$
G	$Fe^{2+} + Co(C_2O_4)_3^{3-}$	$(z_Az_B = -6)$

for example, for the base-catalyzed hydrolysis of ethyl acetate, shown in the figure. It will be seen later that a somewhat more elaborate treatment of the effects of the ionic strength on reactions between ions and neutral molecules indicates that there is a small ionic-strength effect.

Davies's study of the applicability of Eq. (47) to reactions between ions leads to the conclusion that the equation holds with high accuracy for a number of such reactions. Some deviations have been observed, particularly in more concentrated solutions where the Debye-Hückel equation breaks down, and these deviations can usually be explained satisfactorily in terms of the formation of ion pairs.

Sometimes ion-pair formation is purely electrostatic, and the term *Bjerrum ion pairs* is then employed; in other cases the association product has a definite chemical structure. Ion association can affect rates in a number of ways, of which the two following may be mentioned as being the most important:

1. There will be a reduction in the true ionic strength of the solution.
2. The ion pairing may involve one or both of the reactant ions, in which case there will be a change in the electrostatic interactions between the ions that react together. In a reaction between ions of like sign, for example, association with an oppositely charged ion will lead to acceleration by reducing the electrostatic repulsion.

More Detailed Treatments of Ionic Reactions. In the procedures that have been described the solvent has been regarded as continuous and as having the same dielectric constant at all points. In fact the solvent is, of course, an assembly of molecules; the dielectric constant is a gross property that is determined by making a measurement on a large group of molecules, and it therefore corresponds to an average kind of behavior. The assumption of a uniform dielectric constant leads to a very considerable simplification in the theoretical treatment, and more exact and detailed theories can only be applied with considerable difficulty. Two main types of procedure have been employed, and will be described very briefly.

The first type of improved treatment still regards the solvent as continuous, but takes account of the change in dielectric constant in the neighborhood of ions. The dielectric behavior of a liquid is actually due to the orientation of molecules in an electric field, and at very high fields there is a tendency toward saturation, so that the dielectric constant approaches a low limiting value. As the solvent molecules become completely aligned in the field, there can be no further orientation polarization, and the dielectric constant then has the very low value characteristic of hydrocarbons and other nonpolar substances. This effect is known as *dielectric saturation*.

Close to an ion the electric field is very high, and the dielectric constant is very much lower than in the rest of the solution. The problem has been treated quantitatively in terms of the known variation of dielectric constant with field strength. Figure 51 shows the results of such

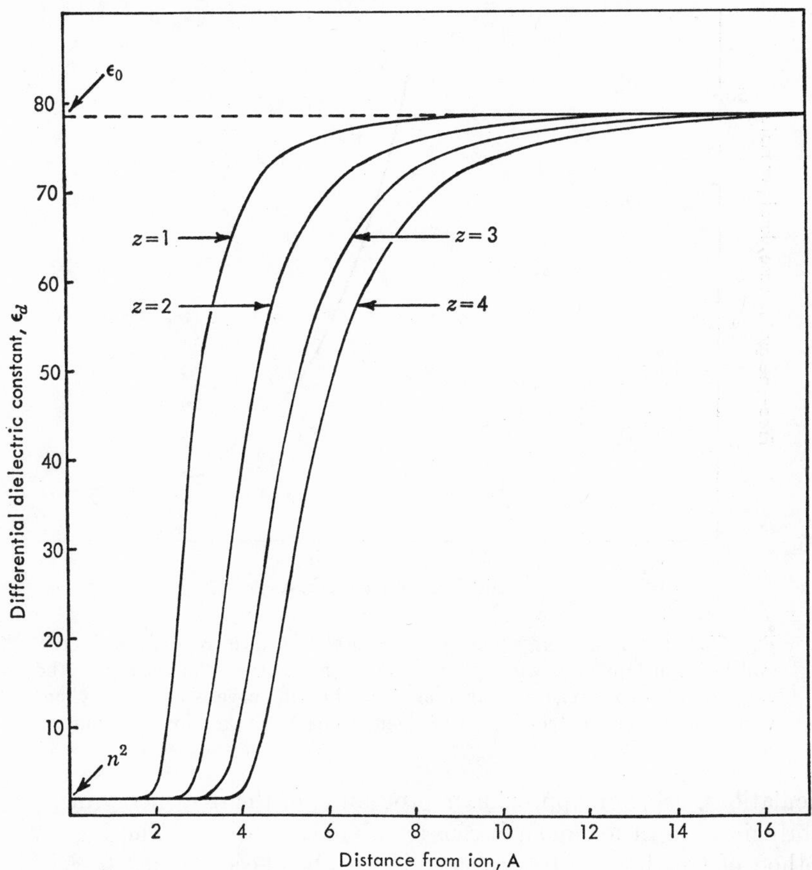

Fig. 51. The differential dielectric constant as a function of the distance from an ion.

calculations,[1] for the case of simple ions of various valencies in aqueous solution. Close to the ions the dielectric constant is seen to have a value of 1.78, and it rises quite steeply to a value of 78.5. As a result of this modification in dielectric constant, the electrostatic interactions between ions in aqueous solutions are, particularly at short distances, significantly different from what they would be if the dielectric constant had a uniform

[1] K. J. Laidler, *Can. J. Chem.*, **37**, 138 (1959); cf. K. J. Laidler and C. Pegis, *Proc. Roy. Soc.* (*London*), **A241**, 80 (1957).

value of 78.5. The free-energy increase in bringing ions together is enhanced by this effect, particularly when the ions are brought to within a few angstroms of each other. Figure 52 shows the results of actual

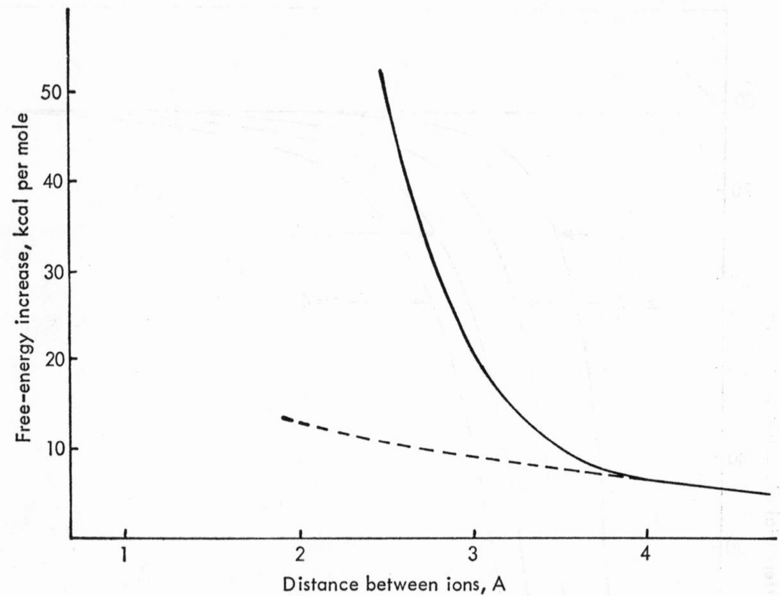

Fig. 52. The free-energy increase due to electrostatic repulsions when Fe^{2+} and Fe^{3+} ions approach each other. The dashed curve is for the simple theory with the dielectric constant taken as 78.5; the full curve is obtained when the variation of dielectric constant with field strength is taken into account.

calculations, using an approximate procedure, of the free-energy increase in bringing a ferric ion and a ferrous ion up to each other. This improved method of treating the free-energy changes has been applied to certain electron-transfer reactions,[1] but similar methods do not seem to have been applied to reactions in which bonds are formed and broken.

The alternative procedure treats the solvent as having a molecular structure, and considers in detail the interactions between the ions and the individual solvent molecules. Frank and his coworkers[2] have in particular considered from this point of view the thermodynamic and other properties of ions in solution. They have shown that next to an ion in aqueous solution there is generally a layer of water molecules that are held fairly rigidly and that can be regarded as forming a "hydration shell"; these molecules have low entropies and volumes. Outside this

[1] E. Sacher and K. J. Laidler, *Trans. Faraday Soc.*, **59**, 396 (1963).

[2] H. S. Frank and M. W. Evans, *J. Chem. Phys.*, **13**, 507 (1945); H. S. Frank and W. Y. Wen, *Discussions Faraday Soc.*, **24**, 133 (1957).

layer there is a "disorder zone," where the water molecules are arranged in a less orderly manner than in the remainder of the solution; this zone arises because of the competition between the forces due to the ion and the hydrogen-bonding forces due to the surrounding water molecules. The molecules in this disorder zone have a higher entropy than those in the rest of the solution. Levine and Bell[1] have calculated interaction energies between two ions in aqueous solution, their procedure being to take explicit account of the hydration shell and to treat the rest of the water as continuous. An application of these ideas to the kinetics of ionic reactions does not appear to have been made.

The two types of approach lead to quite similar conclusions since the layer of frozen water molecules corresponds roughly to the region of very low dielectric constant. From some points of view the first type of improvement, in which the change in dielectric constant is considered, is easier to apply in complicated cases and may perhaps be more fruitful in dealing with the kinetics of reactions between ions.

It is an interesting fact that crude theories of solutions may lead to fairly reliable conclusions as far as free energies (and free energies of activation) are concerned, but may be much less satisfactory for dealing with enthalpies and entropies (including energies of activation and frequency factors). The reason for this is that, as will be discussed, there is a tendency for entropy and enthalpy changes to compensate each other, so that a small change in some parameter, such as a substituent, may bring about only a very small change in free energy but a much larger change in enthalpy. It is for this reason that the very simple theories in which the solvent is regarded as having a constant dielectric constant are quite satisfactory for dealing with solvent and ionic-strength effects on *rates*. They are less satisfactory in treating activation energies and frequency factors, for which improved methods are needed.

In this section it has been assumed throughout that the ions are simple, having no dipolar character. Most of the ions of interest in chemical kinetics have dipoles, and the ion-dipole and dipole-dipole interactions must also be taken into account. Such interactions are considered in the next section.

REACTIONS INVOLVING DIPOLES[2]

Influence of Solvent. The treatment that will be given for reactions between dipolar molecules or ions is based on an expression derived

[1] S. Levine and G. M. Bell, in B. Pesce (ed.), "Electrolytes," p. 77, Pergamon Press, Oxford, 1962; cf. S. Levine and H. E. Wrigley, *Discussions Faraday Soc.*, **24**, 43 (1957).

[2] K. J. Laidler and H. Eyring, *Ann. N.Y. Acad. Sci.*, **39**, 303 (1940); K. J. Laidler and P. A. Landskroener, *Trans. Faraday Soc.*, **52**, 200 (1956); K. J. Laidler, *Suomen Kemistilehti*, **A33**, 44 (1960); K. Hiromi, *Bull. Chem. Soc. Japan*, **33**, 1251, 1264 (1960).

by Kirkwood[1] for the free energy of charging a sphere that has charges imbedded in it in a number of specified positions. This treatment will reduce to the equations derived above for the special case in which the sphere contains a single ion at its center. Kirkwood's expression is for the free-energy increase when a sphere containing a distribution of charges is transferred from a vacuum of unit dielectric constant to a medium where the dielectric constant is ϵ; it involves functions Q_n, which relate to the charges on the sphere and their positions, and are defined by

$$Q_n = \sum_{k=1}^{n} \sum_{l=1}^{n} e_k e_l r_k{}^n r_l{}^n P_n(\cos \theta_{kl}) \tag{48}$$

In this expression the e's are the charges on the sphere, the r's their distance from the center, and $P_n(\cos \theta_{kl})$ is the Legendre polynomial. The summation in Eq. (48) converges rapidly, and it is usually not necessary to go beyond $n = 1$. The two polynomial values that will be required for the present treatment are

$$P_0(x) = 1 \tag{49}$$

and

$$P_1(x) = x \tag{50}$$

Kirkwood's general expression for the free-energy increase when the sphere of radius r is transferred from a medium of unit dielectric constant to one of dielectric constant ϵ is

$$\Delta G = \frac{1}{2} \sum_{n=0}^{\infty} \frac{(n+1)Q_n}{\epsilon_i r^{2n+1}} \left[\frac{\epsilon_i - \epsilon}{(n+1)\epsilon + n\epsilon_i} - \frac{\epsilon_i - 1}{n + 1 + n\epsilon_i} \right] \tag{51}$$

where Q_n is defined by Eq. (48), and ϵ_i is generally taken as 2. If only the first two terms are accepted, Eq. (51) becomes, with $\epsilon_i = 2$,

$$\Delta G = \frac{1}{2} \left[\frac{Q_0}{2r} \left(\frac{2 - \epsilon}{\epsilon} - 1 \right) + \frac{Q_1}{r^3} \left(\frac{2 - \epsilon}{2\epsilon + 2} - \frac{1}{4} \right) \right] \tag{52}$$

It may easily be shown that Q_0 is simply the square of the total net charge ze on the sphere, and that Q_1 is the square of the dipole moment μ of the molecule. Equation (52) therefore reduces to

$$\Delta G = \frac{z^2 e^2}{2r} \left(\frac{1}{\epsilon} - 1 \right) + \frac{3\mu^2}{8r^3} \left(\frac{1 - \epsilon}{\epsilon + 1} \right) \tag{53}$$

The first term of this is simply Born's expression for the free energy of transfer from a vacuum to a dielectric; the second represents the additional effect of the charge distribution on the sphere.

The application of these equations to the rate constant for reaction between a species (molecule or ion) A and a species B is as follows. For the molecules A and B and for the activated complex X‡ one may write

[1] J. G. Kirkwood, *J. Chem. Phys.*, **2**, 351 (1934).

the equations

$$\Delta G_{\mathrm{A}} = \frac{z_{\mathrm{A}}{}^2 e^2}{2r_{\mathrm{A}}}\left(\frac{1}{\epsilon} - 1\right) + \frac{3\mu_{\mathrm{A}}{}^2}{8r_{\mathrm{A}}{}^3}\left(\frac{1-\epsilon}{\epsilon+1}\right) \tag{54}$$

$$\Delta G_{\mathrm{B}} = \frac{z_{\mathrm{B}}{}^2 e^2}{2r_{\mathrm{B}}}\left(\frac{1}{\epsilon} - 1\right) + \frac{3\mu_{\mathrm{B}}{}^2}{8r_{\mathrm{B}}{}^3}\left(\frac{1-\epsilon}{\epsilon+1}\right) \tag{55}$$

$$\Delta G_{\ddagger} = \frac{(z_{\mathrm{A}} + z_{\mathrm{B}})^2 e^2}{2r_{\ddagger}}\left(\frac{1}{\epsilon} - 1\right) + \frac{3\mu_{\ddagger}{}^2}{8r^3}\left(\frac{1-\epsilon}{\epsilon+1}\right) \tag{56}$$

It follows from these expressions that the difference between the free energy of activation for the reaction in solution and that in the gas phase ($\epsilon = 1$) is given by

$$\Delta G^{\ddagger}_{\mathrm{soln}} - \Delta G^{\ddagger}_{\mathrm{gas}} = \frac{e^2}{2}\left(\frac{1}{\epsilon} - 1\right)\left[\frac{(z_{\mathrm{A}} + z_{\mathrm{B}})^2}{r_{\ddagger}} - \frac{z_{\mathrm{A}}{}^2}{r_{\mathrm{A}}} - \frac{z_{\mathrm{B}}{}^2}{r_{\mathrm{B}}}\right] + \frac{3}{8}\left(\frac{1-\epsilon}{\epsilon+1}\right)\left[\frac{\mu_{\ddagger}{}^2}{r_{\ddagger}{}^3} - \frac{\mu_{\mathrm{A}}{}^2}{r_{\mathrm{A}}{}^3} - \frac{\mu_{\mathrm{B}}{}^2}{r_{\mathrm{B}}{}^3}\right] \tag{57}$$

Since the rate constant depends exponentially on the negative of the free energy of activation divided by $\mathbf{k}T$, the relationship between the rate constant in solution and that in the gas phase is given by the expression

$$\ln k = \ln k_g + \frac{e^2}{2\mathbf{k}T}\left(\frac{1}{\epsilon} - 1\right)\left[\frac{z_{\mathrm{A}}{}^2}{r_{\mathrm{A}}} + \frac{z_{\mathrm{B}}{}^2}{r_{\mathrm{A}}} - \frac{(z_{\mathrm{A}} + z_{\mathrm{B}})^2}{r_{\ddagger}}\right] + \frac{3}{8\mathbf{k}T}\left(\frac{1-\epsilon}{\epsilon+1}\right)\left[\frac{\mu_{\mathrm{A}}{}^2}{r_{\mathrm{A}}{}^3} + \frac{\mu_{\mathrm{B}}{}^2}{r_{\mathrm{B}}{}^3} - \frac{\mu_{\ddagger}{}^2}{r_{\ddagger}{}^3}\right] \tag{58}$$

The second term of this equation is equivalent to the term obtained above [Eq. (36)] for a reaction between two simple ions. For such reactions the final term is less important than the second and can generally be neglected. For a reaction between two dipoles having no net charge, the second term disappears, and the solvent effect is given entirely by the last term. For a reaction between an ion and a dipole, or between two dipoles, both terms must be included; however, the second term is then frequently small, and the main effect of the dielectric is predicted by the last term.

Equation (58) may readily be put into a form which is more convenient for the analysis of experimental data. The term $(1 - \epsilon)/(1 + \epsilon)$ appearing in this equation may be shown to be approximately equal to $2/\epsilon - 1$ provided that ϵ is sufficiently large. Equation (58) therefore becomes

$$\ln k = \ln k_g + \frac{e^2}{2\mathbf{k}T}\left(\frac{1}{\epsilon} - 1\right)\left[\frac{z_{\mathrm{A}}{}^2}{r_{\mathrm{A}}} + \frac{z_{\mathrm{B}}{}^2}{r_{\mathrm{B}}} - \frac{(z_{\mathrm{A}} + z_{\mathrm{B}})^2}{r_{\ddagger}}\right] + \frac{3}{8\mathbf{k}T}\left(\frac{2}{\epsilon} - 1\right)\left[\frac{\mu_{\mathrm{A}}{}^2}{r_{\mathrm{A}}{}^3} + \frac{\mu_{\mathrm{B}}{}^2}{r_{\mathrm{B}}{}^3} - \frac{\mu_{\ddagger}{}^2}{r_{\ddagger}{}^3}\right] \tag{59}$$

This equation predicts that the logarithm of k will vary linearly with the reciprocal of the dielectric constant, and gives an explicit expression for the slope in terms of the charges, radii, and dipole moments.

Various procedures may be employed for the application of this equation to the experimental data. In employing these, it is important to realize that the equation cannot be expected to do more than give the right order of magnitude for the variation of the logarithm of the rate constant with the reciprocal of the dielectric constant. If data are available for a series of mixed solvents, one procedure is to plot the logarithm of the rate constant against the reciprocal of the dielectric constant, and to determine the slope. Once this slope has been obtained, one may then see whether its sign and magnitude may be predicted in terms of Eq. (59), using reasonable values for the radii and the μ terms. This procedure depends, of course, upon devising a suitable model for the activated complex; in particular, one must postulate how the charges are distributed, and what the radius of the sphere is.

On the whole, it is probably most satisfactory to regard Eq. (59) as giving a semiquantitative formulation which allows only very rough predictions to be made as to the effect of changing the dielectric constant. For example, the equation predicts that if a reaction between neutral molecules occurs with the formation of an activated complex that is very polar (i.e., $\mu_{\ddagger}$ is much greater than either μ_A or μ_B), there will be an increase in rate constant with increasing dielectric constant. The physical significance of this result is that a high dielectric constant favors the production of any species of high dipole moment, and thus favors the production of the activated complex.

Frequency Factors. The modifications to the entropy of activation resulting from electrostatic interactions between neutral molecules are generally fairly small, but important effects can arise if a reactant or the activated complex has a high dipole moment. A good example of this is to be found in the reaction between a tertiary amine and an alkyl iodide, with the formation of a quaternary ammonium salt. Since the product is a salt, the activated complex is expected to be highly polar; as a result, the complex tends to bind solvent molecules much more strongly than do the reactant molecules. This effect results in a considerable negative entropy of activation, and a correspondingly low frequency factor, as seen in Table 33. A similar type of behavior is to be found in the acid and base hydrolyses of esters, where the activated complexes are probably quite polar, owing to the ionization of the carbonyl group; the actual mechanisms are discussed in Chap. 9. Owing to the electrostriction of solvent by the activated complexes in such reactions, the entropies of activation are low. The reactions are accelerated by an increase in the dielectric constant of the solvent.

The conclusions can be summarized by saying that if the formation of the activated complex involves a separation of opposite charges, or an approach of like charges, there will be an abnormally low frequency factor; in this case the reaction will be accelerated by an increase in the dielectric constant. Conversely a reaction in which the formation of the activated complex involves an approach of opposite charges, or a separation of like charges, will have an abnormally high frequency factor. The rate will in such cases be reduced by increasing the dielectric constant. These conclusions are summarized in Table 34 on page 237, where the pressure effects are included.

Influence of Ionic Strength. Equation (47) predicts that a reaction between an ion and a neutral molecule should not be affected by the ionic strength of the solution. This equation was, however, obtained using approximations that hold only in very dilute solutions, and an extension of the treatment is necessary. The activity coefficient of an ion is given to a good approximation if, in addition to the Debye-Hückel term, the term bu introduced by Hückel[1] is added; the equation for the ion A should therefore be written as

$$\log_{10} f_A = -Qz_A^2 \sqrt{u} + b_A u \tag{60}$$

If B has no net charge, its activity coefficient may be expressed by an approximate equation due to Debye and McAulay:[2]

$$\log_{10} f_B = b_B u \tag{61}$$

The activated complex must have the same net charge as A, and its activity coefficient is therefore given by an equation of the same form as Eq. (60). The introduction of these equations into Eq. (40) gives rise to

$$\log_{10} k = \log_{10} k_0 + (b_A + b_B - b_\ddagger)u \tag{62}$$

The Debye-Hückel term involving the square root of the ionic strength has disappeared, since it occurs in the expressions for both A and the activated complex; as a result of this, it is important to include the terms that are linear in the ionic strength, as was done above. Equation (62) predicts that the logarithm of the rate constant of a reaction between an ion and a neutral molecule should vary with the first power of the ionic strength instead of with the square root; the effect, however, is much smaller than for reactions between ions. This conclusion has received experimental support from the work of Brønsted and Wynne-Jones[3] on the hydrolysis of acetals by hydroxide ions.

Equation (62) may be written as

$$k = k_0 e^{b'u} \tag{63}$$

[1] E. Hückel, *Physik. Z.*, **26**, 93 (1925).

[2] P. Debye and J. McAulay, *ibid.*, 22.

[3] J. N. Brønsted and W. F. K. Wynne-Jones, *Trans. Faraday Soc.*, **25**, 59, (1929).

If $b'u$ is much smaller than unity, the exponential may be expanded and only the first term accepted, the result being

$$k = k_0(1 + b'u) \tag{64}$$

The rate constant should therefore vary linearly with u under these conditions, and this has been found to be the case for several reactions.[1]

There is still no completely satisfactory treatment that permits the calculation of the magnitude of the coefficients b, in terms of the structures of the molecules concerned. The term $b_A u$ that occurs in the expression for the activity coefficient of an ion was introduced by Hückel on the basis of an argument that takes into consideration the effects of dielectric saturation, and a quantitative treatment has been given by Stokes and Robinson.[2] The b coefficient that appears in the expression for a neutral molecule, as in Eq. (61), has been discussed by many authors,[3] but reliable estimates of its magnitude can still not be made. There is much scope for additional work in this important field.

Summary of Results. In Table 32 the qualitative results arrived at in the preceding sections, and some examples, are summarized.

[1] J. N. Brønsted and C. Grove, *J. Am. Chem. Soc.*, **52,** 1394 (1930).

[2] R. H. Stokes and R. A. Robinson, *ibid.*, **70,** 1870 (1948); R. A. Robinson and R. H. Stokes, "Electrolyte Solutions," p. 246, Butterworth Scientific Publications, London, 1959.

[3] For a review see F. A. Long and W. F. McDewit, *Chem. Rev.*, **51,** 119 (1952).

Table 32 INFLUENCE OF DIELECTRIC CONSTANT AND IONIC STRENGTH ON RATES OF VARIOUS TYPES OF REACTIONS

	Effect of increasing		
Reaction type	Dielectric constant	Ionic strength	Examples
Two molecules forming a polar product	Increase	Small effect	$R_3N + RX$ $H_2O + RX$
Two ions:			
Same sign	Increase	Increase	$BrAc^- + S_2O_3^{2-}$ OH^- + bromophenol blue$^-$
Opposite sign	Decrease	Decrease	$OH^- + Me_3S^+$
Ion and neutral molecule	Small effect	Small effect	$OH^- + RX$ $OR^- + RX$ $X^- + RX$ $Me_2BuS^+ + H_2O$

INFLUENCE OF PRESSURE ON RATES IN SOLUTION[1]

An increasing amount of work is being carried out on reactions in solution at high hydrostatic pressures. Only a few reactions have yet been investigated in this way, but the results have yielded valuable information about reaction mechanisms. Pressure studies provide at least as much insight into mechanisms as do temperature studies, and there is need for much more work in this field.

The theory of hydrostatic-pressure effects on reaction rates was first formulated in 1901 by van't Hoff; his treatment will be given here in terms of more modern concepts. The theory is based on the equation for the effect of pressure on the equilibrium constant. The equilibrium constant for a reaction such as

$$A + B \underset{k_{-1}}{\overset{k_1}{\rightleftharpoons}} AB$$

is related to the standard Gibbs free-energy change ΔG by the equation

$$\Delta G = -RT \ln K \tag{65}$$

The thermodynamical relationship between the volume, the Gibbs free energy, and the hydrostatic pressure is

$$V = \left(\frac{\partial G}{\partial P}\right)_T \tag{66}$$

so that

$$\Delta V = \left(\frac{\partial \Delta G}{\partial P}\right)_T \tag{67}$$

From (65) and (67),

$$\left(\frac{\partial \ln K}{\partial P}\right)_T = -\frac{\Delta V}{RT} \tag{68}$$

If a reaction occurs with an increase in volume (ΔV positive), the equilibrium constant therefore decreases with increasing pressure; conversely, if ΔV is negative, the equilibrium constant increases with increasing pressure. The proportion of products at equilibrium is therefore decreased or increased by pressure according as the volume change is positive or negative.

In order to obtain a corresponding equation for the variation with pressure of the rate constant, van't Hoff employed an argument which is analogous to the one that he used in connection with temperature effects (p. 51). The volume change ΔV is equal to the difference between the

[1] For a review see S. D. Hamann, "Physico-chemical Effects of Pressure," chap. 9, Butterworth Scientific Publications, London, 1957.

volume of the products V_p and that of the reactants V_r,

$$\Delta V = V_p - V_r \tag{69}$$

If $V^\ddagger$ is the volume of the activated complex, this can be written as

$$\Delta V = (V^\ddagger - V_r) - (V^\ddagger - V_p) \tag{70}$$

$$= \Delta V_1^\ddagger - \Delta V_{-1}^\ddagger \tag{71}$$

In this equation $\Delta V_1^\ddagger$ is the increase in volume in passing from the initial state to the activated state, and is known as the *volume of activation* for the forward reaction; $\Delta V_{-1}^\ddagger$ is the volume of activation for the reverse reaction. Since K is equal to k_1/k_{-1}, Eq. (68) may be written as

$$\left(\frac{\partial \ln k_1}{\partial P}\right)_T - \left(\frac{\partial \ln k_{-1}}{\partial P}\right)_T = -\frac{\Delta V}{RT} \tag{72}$$

and together with Eq. (71) this gives

$$\left(\frac{\partial \ln k_1}{\partial P}\right)_T - \left(\frac{\partial \ln k_{-1}}{\partial P}\right)_T = -\frac{\Delta V_1^\ddagger}{RT} + \frac{\Delta V_{-1}^\ddagger}{RT} \tag{73}$$

The assumption was then made that the behavior of the forward reaction depends only on the volume change in going from the initial state to the activated state, which means that Eq. (73) can be split into the two equations

$$\left(\frac{\partial \ln k_1}{\partial P}\right)_T = -\frac{\Delta V_1^\ddagger}{RT} \tag{74}$$

and

$$\left(\frac{\partial \ln k_{-1}}{\partial P}\right)_T = -\frac{\Delta V_{-1}^\ddagger}{RT} \tag{75}$$

These equations can also be derived by making use of the fact that, according to absolute-rate theory, the rate constant k is proportional to the equilibrium constant $K^\ddagger$ between initial and activated states. According to Eq. (85) of Chap. 3 (p. 89),

$$k = \frac{\mathbf{k}T}{\mathbf{h}} K^\ddagger \tag{76}$$

The variation of the equilibrium constant $K^\ddagger$ with pressure is given by [cf. Eq. (68)]

$$\left(\frac{\partial \ln K^\ddagger}{\partial P}\right)_T = -\frac{\Delta V^\ddagger}{RT} \tag{77}$$

where $\Delta V^\ddagger$ is the volume of activation. Equations (76) and (77) then lead to

$$\left(\frac{\partial \ln k}{\partial P}\right)_T = -\frac{\Delta V^\ddagger}{RT} \tag{78}$$

According to this equation, the rate constant of a reaction increases with increasing pressure if $\Delta V^\ddagger$ is negative, i.e., if the activated state has a smaller volume than the initial state. Conversely, pressure has an adverse effect on rates if there is a volume increase when the activated complex is formed. By using Eq. (78), values of $\Delta V^{\ddagger}$ can be determined from experimental measurements of rates at different pressures. In practice, it is necessary to use fairly high pressures for this purpose (of the order of thousands of pounds per square inch), since otherwise the changes in rate are too small for accurate $\Delta V^{\ddagger}$ values to be obtained. The procedure involves plotting the logarithm of the rate constant against the pressure; according to Eq. (78), the slope at any pressure is equal to $-\Delta V^{\ddagger}/RT$ (or $-\Delta V^{\ddagger}/2.303RT$ if common logarithms are used). In some cases such plots are straight lines, which means that the volume of activation is independent of the pressure. If this is so, Eq. (78) can be integrated to give

$$\ln k = \ln k_0 - \frac{\Delta V^{\ddagger}}{RT} P \tag{79}$$

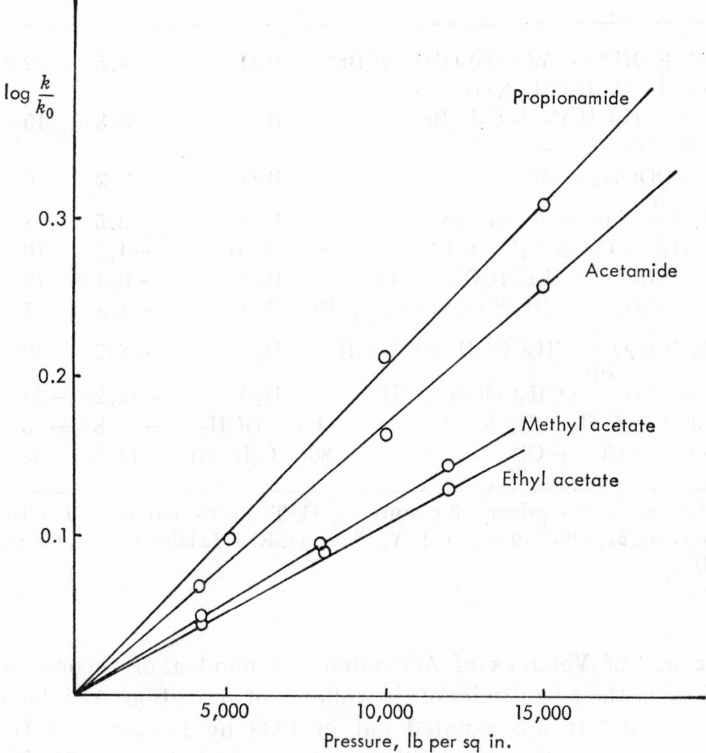

Fig. 53. Plot of log (k/k_0) against the hydrostatic pressure, for the alkaline hydrolyses of esters and amides. [*Data of K. J. Laidler and D. Chen, Trans. Faraday Soc.*, **54,** 1020 (1958).]

where k_0 is the rate constant at zero pressure (this is always very close to the value at atmospheric pressure). If Eq. (79) is obeyed, a plot of $\ln (k/k_0)$ against P will be a straight line through the origin. Examples of such linear plots are shown in Fig. 53. A number of reactions of widely different types obey Eq. (79), so that for them it can be concluded that $\Delta V^{\ddagger}$ is independent of pressure over the range investigated, which usually covers from atmospheric pressure up to about 20,000 lb per sq in. Table 33 shows some value of $\Delta V^{\ddagger}$ for a number of reactions in various solvents, and also gives the entropies of activation $\Delta S^{\ddagger}$.

Table 33 VOLUMES AND ENTROPIES OF ACTIVATION†

Reaction	Solvent	$\Delta V^{\ddagger}$, cc mole^{-1}	$\Delta S^{\ddagger}$, cal deg^{-1} mole^{-1}
$Co(NH_3)_5Br^{2+} + OH^- \rightarrow Co(NH_3)_5OH^{2+} + Br^-$	H_2O	8.5	22
$(CH_3)(C_2H_5)(C_6H_5)(C_6H_5CH_2)N^+Br^- \rightarrow (CH_3)(C_6H_5)(C_6H_5CH_2)N + C_2H_5Br$	H_2O	3.3	15
$CH_2BrCOOCH_3 + S_2O_3^{2-} \rightarrow CH_2(S_2O_3^-)COOCH_3 + Br^-$	H_2O	3.2	6
Sucrose + $H_2O \xrightarrow{H^+}$ glucose + fructose	H_2O	2.5	8
$C_2H_5O^- + C_2H_5I \rightarrow C_2H_5OC_2H_5 + I^-$	C_2H_5OH	−4.1	−10
$CH_2ClCOO^- + OH^- \rightarrow CH_2OHCOO^- + Cl^-$	H_2O	−6.1	−12
$CH_2BrCOO^- + S_2O_3^{2-} \rightarrow CH_2(S_2O_3^-)COO^- + Br^-$	H_2O	−4.8	−17
$CH_3COOCH_3 + H_2O \xrightarrow{H^+} CH_3COOH + CH_3OH$	H_2O	−8.7	−10
$CH_3CONH_2 + H_2O \xrightarrow{OH^-} CH_3COOH + NH_3$	H_2O	−14.2	−34
$C_5H_5N + C_2H_5I \rightarrow C_5H_5(C_2H_5)N^+I^-$	CH_3COCH_3	−16.8	−35
$C_6H_5CCl_3 \rightarrow C_6H_5CCl_2^+ + Cl^-$	80% C_2H_5OH	−14.5	−35

† For references to the original literature see C. T. Burris and K. J. Laidler, *Trans. Faraday Soc.*, **51**, 1497 (1955); D. T. Y. Chen and K. J. Laidler, *Can. J. Chem.*, **37**, 599 (1959).

Significance of Volumes of Activation. A number of theoretical interpretations of the magnitudes of the volumes of activation, $\Delta V^{\ddagger}$, have been put forward. It was pointed out in 1938 by Perrin[1] that the reactions studied up to that time fell into three broad classes, and that these classes differ from one another in other kinetic characteristics.

[1] M. W. Perrin, *Trans. Faraday Soc.*, **34**, 144 (1938).

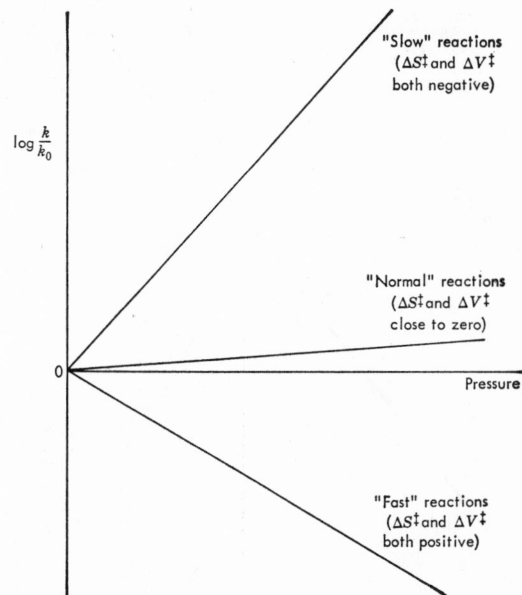

Fig. 54. Three classes of reactions, as indicated by the pressure effects.

These classes are illustrated schematically in Fig. 54, and in terms of more modern concepts may be described as follows:

1. *"Slow" reactions*, which are bimolecular reactions having abnormally low frequency factors and therefore negative entropies of activation. These reactions are markedly accelerated by pressure, which means, according to Eq. (78), that their volumes of activation are negative.

2. *"Normal" reactions*, which are bimolecular reactions whose frequency factors are "normal" ($\sim 10^{11}$ liters mole^{-1} sec^{-1}) so that their entropies of activation are close to zero. Such reactions are usually very slightly accelerated by pressure, which means that they have slightly negative volumes of activation.

3. *"Fast" reactions*, for which the entropies of activation are positive. These reactions are retarded by pressure, so that the $\Delta V^\ddagger$ values are positive.

Perrin's conclusions can all be summarized by the statement that entropies of activation and volumes of activation tend to fall in line with each other. A plot of the volumes of activation against the entropies of activation for a number of reactions in aqueous solution is shown in Fig. 55, and there is seen to be a fairly good linear correlation.

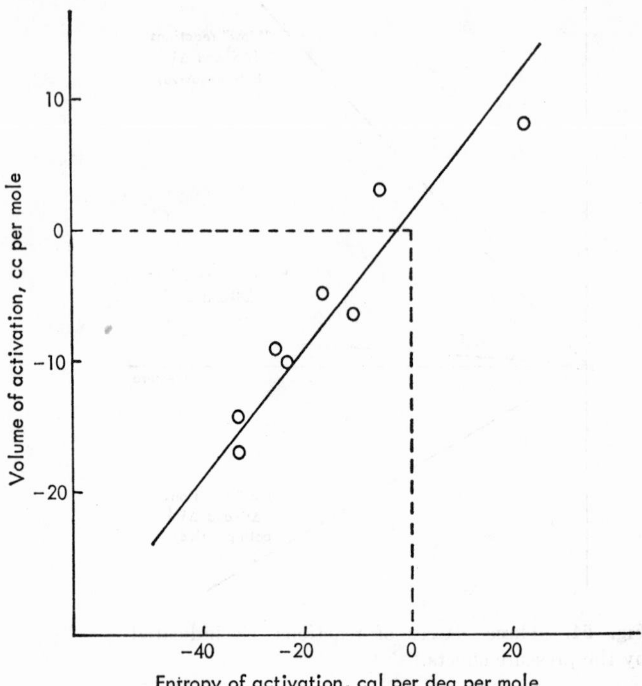

Fig. 55. The correlation between volumes and entropies of activation for reactions in aqueous solution. [*For data see K. J. Laidler and D. T. Y. Chen, Can. J. Chem.*, **37**, 599 (1959).]

Evans and Polanyi[1] pointed out that two distinct effects must be considered in connection with the interpretation of volumes of activation. Firstly, there may be a change, due to structural factors, in the volume of the reactant molecules themselves as they pass into the activated state; for a bimolecular process this always leads to a volume decrease, while for a unimolecular process there is a volume increase. Secondly, there may be a volume change resulting from reorganization of the solvent molecules. Studies of a variety of reactions[2] have led to the conclusion that for reactions in which ions or fairly strong dipoles are concerned the solvent effects are generally more important than the structural ones.

These effects of solvent on volumes are explained in a manner similar to the effects of solvent on entropies of activation, a fact that explains the correlation between volumes and entropies of activation (Fig. 55).

[1] M. G. Evans and M. Polanyi, *ibid.*, **31**, 875 (1935); **32**, 1333 (1936); M. G. Evans, *ibid.*, **34**, 49 (1938).

[2] J. Buchanan and S. D. Hamann, *ibid.*, **49**, 1425 (1953); C. T. Burris and K. J. Laidler, *ibid.*, **51**, 1497 (1955).

Thus if a reaction occurs with the approach of ions of the same sign, or a separation of ions of the opposite sign, there is an intensification of the electric field, and therefore an increase in electrostriction and a resulting decrease in volume; there is also a decrease in entropy owing to the loss of freedom of the solvent molecules. Conversely, if the electric field is weakened when the activated complex is formed (as when two ions of opposite signs come together), there will be some release of bound solvent molecules, and the volumes and entropies of activation will be positive. Reference to the reactions listed in Table 33 shows that all the results can be qualitatively explained on this basis. The above conclusions are summarized in Table 34, which shows the three main types of reactions.

Table 34 SUMMARY OF PRESSURE EFFECTS ON REACTIONS

Classification	Ionic character	Examples	Volume of activation	Entropy of activation
"Slow"	Formation of opposite charges, or approach of like charges	Reactions between ions of same sign, ester hydrolyses, esterifications, Menschutkin reactions, unimolecular solvolyses	Large negative	Large negative
"Normal"	Electrostatic effects unimportant	Negative-ion replacements	Small negative	Small negative
"Fast"	Approach of opposite charges, or spreading of charges	Reverse Menschutkin reactions, reactions between ions of opposite sign	Positive	Positive

Whalley[1] has made use of the results of pressure studies in order to arrive at conclusions about reaction mechanisms. He has shown that volumes of activation are more reliable than entropies of activation in suggesting the type of reaction that is taking place. This is the case because entropies of activation are quite sensitive to factors such as the loosening or strengthening of chemical bonds, whereas volumes depend to a much greater extent on electrostriction effects than on any other effects. Volume changes are therefore much more constant for reactions

[1] E. Whalley, *ibid.*, **55**, 798 (1959).

of a given type than are entropies, and therefore lead to more clear-cut conclusions about the processes taking place. Some examples of the use of this procedure are given in Chap. 10.

INFLUENCE OF SUBSTITUENTS ON REACTION RATES

An important aspect of chemical reactions in solution arises from the fact that a great many series of homologous reactions are known and provide important information about the effects of substituents on reaction rates. As an example may be mentioned the benzoylation of amines; the reaction between benzoyl chloride and aniline can be studied, as well as the reactions between these molecules carrying various substituents. A great deal of work has accumulated on the influence of substituents on reactions of this kind; only the purely kinetic aspects of the problem can be discussed here.

It has been seen that the rate constant of any reaction may be expressed by means of the equation

$$k = \frac{\mathbf{k}T}{\mathbf{h}} e^{\Delta S^{\ddagger}/R} e^{-\Delta H^{\ddagger}/RT} \tag{80}$$

where $\Delta S^{\ddagger}$ is the entropy of activation, and $\Delta H^{\ddagger}$ the heat of activation, a quantity that is closely related to the experimental energy of activation. Sometimes substituents exert their effect primarily on the energy of activation, changes in the entropy of activation or in the frequency factor being rather incidental.[1] Among reaction types in which the entropy of activation remains constant within the experimental error, while the activation energy varies significantly, may be mentioned the benzoylation of amines,[2] the alkaline hydrolysis of benzoic esters,[3] the alcoholysis of triarylmethyl chlorides,[4] and the reaction between substituted dimethyl anilines and methyl iodide.[5]

Electronic Theories of Organic Reactivity. The influence of substituents on the rates of organic reactions has been interpreted in terms of electrical effects, the developments along these lines being due to a considerable number of workers of whom J. Stieglitz, G. N. Lewis, H. J. Lucas, A. Lapworth, R. Robinson, and C. K. Ingold may be men-

[1] A. E. Bradfield and B. Jones, *J. Chem. Soc.*, 1006 (1928); 2903 (1931); B. Spencer and J. Spencer, *ibid.*, 2907 (1931); C. N. Hinshelwood, K. J. Laidler, and E. W. Timm, *ibid.*, 848 (1938).

[2] E. G. Williams and C. N. Hinshelwood, *ibid.*, 1079 (1934).

[3] W. B. S. Newling and C. N. Hinshelwood, *ibid.*, 1357 (1936); D. P. Evans, J. J. Gordon, and H. B. Watson, *ibid.*, 1430 (1937).

[4] A. C. Nixon and G. E. K. Branch, *J. Am. Chem. Soc.*, **58**, 492 (1936).

[5] K. J. Laidler, *J. Chem. Soc.*, 1786 (1938).

tioned in particular. This type of treatment provided the basis for the kinetic work on this problem, and a brief account of the modern views will be given.[1]

A substituent changes the reactivity of a parent compound by altering the availability of electrons at the seat of reaction. Certain types of reactions are favored by an increase of electron density in a certain region, and substituents which effect such an increase cause the rate to increase; as seen previously, they usually do this by decreasing the energy of activation. An example of this is found in the reaction between pyridine and methyl iodide, which is favored by an increase in the electron density in the neighborhood of the nitrogen atom, the formation of the carbon-nitrogen bond being facilitated by this. Substituents such as methyl groups are known, from general evidence to be referred to later, to repel electrons, and their introduction into the pyridine ring thus increases the rate of reaction. This reaction is also aided by substituents which decrease the electron density in the neighborhood of the central carbon atom on the iodide.

Studies of the effects of meta and para substituents on reaction rates, combined with other evidence such as dipole moment measurements,[2] have led to the conclusion that two different effects are involved, as follows.

1. *The Inductive or Polar Effect.* This mode of electron displacement is transmitted along a chain of atoms without any reorganization of the formal chemical bonds in the molecule. The substitution of a methyl group in the pyridine ring, for example, involves a displacement of electrons to the nitrogen atom from the methyl group. The inductive effect of a group falls off rapidly with distance.

2. *The Electromeric or Resonance Effect.* When certain types of electronic structures occur, molecules exist in a resonance state between two extreme structures; this occurs particularly when there are conjugate double bonds. Chlorobenzene, for example, exists in a resonance state consisting mainly of the structures

[1] For further details reference should be made to C. K. Ingold, *Chem. Rev.*, **15**, 225 (1934); R. Robinson, "Outline of an Electrochemical Theory of the Course of Organic Reactions," The Institute of Chemistry, London, 1932; W. A. Waters, "Physical Aspects of Organic Chemistry," D. Van Nostrand Company, Inc., Princeton, N.J., 1935; L. P. Hammett, "Physical Organic Chemistry," McGraw-Hill Book Company, New York, 1940; A. E. Remick, "Electronic Interpretations of Organic Chemistry," John Wiley & Sons, Inc., New York, 1943; G. E. K. Branch and M. Calvin, "The Theory of Organic Chemistry," Prentice-Hall, Inc., Englewood Cliffs, N.J., 1941; M. J. S. Dewar, "The Electronic Theory of Organic Chemistry," Oxford University Press, Fair Lawn, N.J., 1941; J. Hine, "Physical Organic Chemistry," 2d ed., McGraw-Hill Book Company, New York, 1962.

[2] L. E. Sutton, *Proc. Roy. Soc. (London)*, **A133**, 668 (1931).

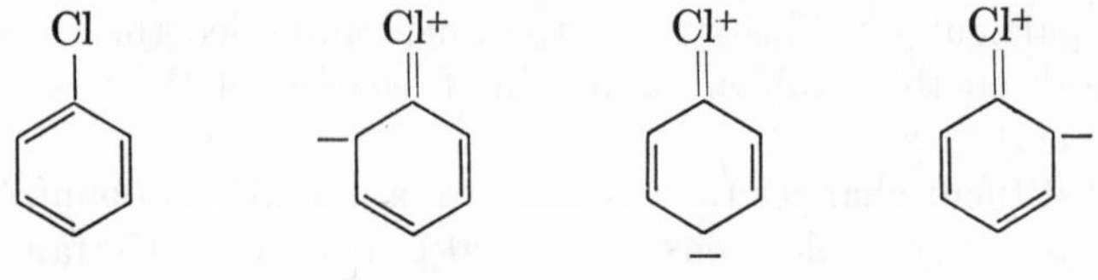

As a result, chlorobenzene has an excess electron density in the ortho and para positions.

Table 35 gives an indication of the directions of the effects brought about by various common groups.

Table 35 INDUCTIVE AND ELECTROMERIC EFFECTS OF SUBSTITUENTS

Substituent	Inductive (polar) effect	Electromeric (resonance) effect
CH_3, C_2H_5, etc.	+	+
COO^-	+	0
O^-	+	+
O^+R_2	−	0
NR_3	−	0
NO_2	−	−
NR_2	−	+
F	−	+
Cl	−	+
Br	−	+
I	−	+
OH	−	+
OR	−	+
COOH	−	−
COOR	−	−

A positive sign implies an electron-repelling effect, a negative sign an electron-attracting effect, and a zero no effect.

In some treatments of substituent effects, particularly those of Ingold and Robinson and their coworkers, a distinction is made between permanent effects and those that come into play during reaction. In their work the term "inductive" is reserved for the permanent effect, the effect that is brought about during the chemical reaction being referred to as an "inductomeric" effect; similarly the term "electromeric" is reserved for a temporary effect, the word "mesomeric" applying to the corresponding permanent one. From the point of view of activated-complex theory, the kinetic effects depend upon the difference between the substituent effects in the activated state and those in the initial state. It is therefore not essential to distinguish between the permanent and temporary effects, and it is slightly simpler to use the terms inductive and electromeric to refer to these differences. This will be the procedure employed here.

Influence of Substituents on the Energy of Activation. The ideas outlined above have been extended somewhat in a theoretical treatment of the influence of substituents on the energy of activation.[1] If the reaction

$$\mathrm{X + Y{-}Z \rightarrow X{-}Y + Z}$$

is considered, the introduction of a substituent into the molecule YZ will bring about changes in the bond energies and interaction energies and will in this way influence the energy of activation and hence the rate of reaction. Suppose, for example, that X is a negative ion, or the negative end of a dipolar molecule, and that the substituent has the effect of increasing the positive charge on Y and the negative charge on Z, in the following manner:

$$\mathrm{X + Y^{\delta+}{-}Z^{\delta-} \rightarrow X{-}Y + Z}$$

Here $\delta+$ and $\delta-$ represent the changes in the effective charges. The effect of these changes brought about by the introduction of the substituent is an increase in the attraction between Y and Z and a decrease in the repulsion between X and Y. The first of these, the increase in the attraction between Y and Z, will clearly tend to increase the activation energy; on the other hand, the increased attraction between X and Y will tend to lower the activation energy. The two effects therefore act in opposite directions. In the majority of reactions studied, the influence of a substituent is in the direction that would be predicted if only the second effect were taken into consideration; in other words, the attraction between molecules seems to be of chief importance. An example of this type of behavior is found in the formation of quaternary ammonium salts, some results for which[2] are shown in Table 36. The figures are for the reactions of the two bases triethylamine and pyridine with methyl, ethyl, and isopropyl iodides. Methyl groups exert a positive inductive, i.e., electron-repelling, effect, so that the introduction of a methyl group in passing, for example, from methyl to ethyl iodide makes the central atom more negative; its attraction for the negative reagent therefore becomes less, and the observed increase in energy of activation is to be

[1] C. N. Hinshelwood, K. J. Laidler, and E. W. Timm, *J. Chem. Soc.*, 848 (1938).

[2] C. A. Winkler and C. N. Hinshelwood, *ibid.*, 1147 (1935); K. J. Laidler and C. N. Hinshelwood, *ibid.*, 858 (1938).

Table 36 ACTIVATION ENERGIES FOR THE FORMATION OF QUATERNARY AMMONIUM SALTS

Amine	Iodide	*E*, cal
Triethylamine	Methyl	9.7
Triethylamine	Ethyl	11.4
Triethylamine	Isopropyl	17.1
Pyridine	Methyl	14.3
Pyridine	Ethyl	15.8
Pyridine	Isopropyl	18.0

expected. A further increase is found on passing from ethyl to isopropyl iodide.

Additional proof that the repulsion energy between the base and the iodide is of chief importance in this type of reaction comes from experiments in which the strength of the base is varied by the introduction of substituents into dimethylaniline.[1] The figures in Table 37 in which the bases are arranged in order of decreasing strength, i.e., decreasing effective negative charge on the nitrogen atom, show that the increased repulsion between the base and the positive carbon atom gives rise to an increase in the energy of activation.

Table 37 ACTIVATION ENERGIES FOR THE REACTION BETWEEN METHYL IODIDE AND SUBSTITUTED DIMETHYLANILINES

Substituent	*E, kcal*
p-OCH_3	11.7
p-CH_3	12.3
(H)	12.8
p-Br	13.7
p-Cl	13.9

Many other reactions are known in which the influence of the repulsion energy between the two reacting molecules is of chief importance in determining the influence of substituents. One example is benzene substitution, which is considered in more detail in Chap. 10. Here the influence of a substituent on the rate of reaction can be predicted from a consideration of the electrostatic interactions between the reagent and the aromatic molecule; the ease with which the carbon-hydrogen bond is

[1] Laidler, *loc. cit.*; D. P. Evans, H. B. Watson, and L. Williams, *ibid.*, 1345 (1939).

broken is of minor importance. A further example is in the acid-catalyzed prototropic changes of substituted acetophenones,[1] the reaction mechanism being

$$\underset{\underset{\displaystyle O}{\|}}{CH_3CC_6H_4X} + H^+ \rightarrow H\text{—}\underset{\underset{\displaystyle O^+\text{—}H}{\|}}{CH_2CC_6H_4X} \rightarrow H^+ + \underset{\underset{\displaystyle OH}{|}}{CH_2{=}CC_6H_4X}$$

The activation energies vary in the manner determined by the attraction between the acetophenone and the hydrogen ion, the ease with which the C—H bond is ionized being unimportant.

Particularly interesting reactions are the acid- and base-catalyzed hydrolyses of ordinary esters such as methyl acetate, for which the evidence (cf. Chap. 10) indicates the slow and rate-determining processes to be as follows:

Alkaline Hydrolysis

$$OH^- + R\text{—}\overset{\overset{\displaystyle O}{\|}}{C}\text{—}OR' \rightarrow R\text{—}\underset{\underset{\displaystyle OH}{\vdots}}{\overset{\overset{\displaystyle O^-}{|}}{C}}\cdots OR' \rightarrow R\text{—}\overset{\overset{\displaystyle O}{\|}}{C}\text{—}OH + OR'^-$$

(activated complex)

Acid Hydrolysis

$$H_2O + R\text{—}\overset{\overset{\displaystyle O}{\|}}{C}\text{—}O^+\begin{matrix}\diagup R' \\ \diagdown H\end{matrix} \rightarrow R\text{—}\underset{\underset{\displaystyle H\text{—}\underset{\underset{\displaystyle H}{|}}{O^+}}{\vdots}}{\overset{\overset{\displaystyle O^-}{|}}{C}}\cdots O^+\begin{matrix}\diagup R' \\ \diagdown H\end{matrix} \rightarrow R\text{—}\overset{\overset{\displaystyle O}{\|}}{C}\text{—}OH + R'OH + H^+$$

(activated complex)

In agreement with these schemes it is found[2] that the introduction of a substituent into the R group of the ester brings about the same type of change in the activation energy for both acid and base catalysis; the effect is attributed to the change in the effective charge on the carbonyl carbon atom, which therefore operates in the same way in both types of hydrolysis. The activation energy for the base-catalyzed reaction of a given ester is lower by 5 to 7 kcal than that for the acid-catalyzed hydrolysis; this is due to the fact that in acid hydrolysis the uncharged water molecule attacks the carbonyl carbon atom, so that the repulsion energy is greater than when the hydroxyl ion attacks it. In agreement with this

[1] D. P. Evans, V. G. Morgan, and H. B. Watson, *ibid.*, 1167 (1935).

[2] C. K. Ingold and W. S. Nathan, *ibid.*, 222 (1936); E. W. Timm and C. N. Hinshelwood, *ibid.*, 862 (1938).

explanation, the effect of a substituent is greater in alkaline than in acid hydrolysis.

In contrast to the reactions discussed above, a number of reactions are also known in which the influence of a substituent on the energy of activation seems to be determined by its influence on the bond strength of the bond that is broken—more exactly, since most of the reactions under consideration are ionic, by the influence of the substituent on the ionizability of the bond. It is to be expected that this situation will be found when the repulsion between the reacting molecules is large, so that a greater degree of ionization will occur in reaching the activated state. A trend in this direction is to be seen in the values quoted in Table 36. It has been noted that the substitution of methyl groups, by increasing the repulsion between the reactants, increased the energy of activation; this effect is much less with the weak base pyridine than with the stronger triethylamine. This may be explained as due to the fact that with pyridine, where the repulsion between the reacting molecules is greater, the ionization of the C-I bond plays a more important role than with the stronger base.

In these reactions the repulsion energy still controls the energy of activation, but cases are known in which the ionization of the bond determines the influence of a substituent upon the energy. An example of this is the hydrolysis of triarylmethyl chlorides,[1] activation energies for which are given in Table 38. A methoxy group, which aids the ionization

Table 38 ACTIVATION ENERGIES FOR ALCOHOLYTIC REACTIONS

Triarymethyl chlorides	E, kcal	Acyl chlorides	E, kcal
$(p\text{-}NO_2C_6H_4)_3CCl$	16.7	$p\text{-}NO_2C_6H_4COCl$	11.1
$(p\text{-}ClC_6H_4)_3CCl$	13.5	$p\text{-}ClC_6H_4COCl$	13.9
$(C_6H_5)_3CCl$	13.4	C_6H_5COCl	14.4
$(p\text{-}CH_3OC_6H_4)(C_6H_5)_2CCl$	12.5	$p\text{-}CH_3OC_6H_4COCl$	18.7

but increases the repulsion of the reacting hydroxyl ion, decreases the energy of activation; the ionization is therefore controlling. These results are to be contrasted with those obtained for the hydrolysis of acyl chlorides[2] (cf. Table 38), in which reactions the substituents have the opposite effect; here the repulsion energy is apparently more important. The difference in behavior is associated with the easier ionizability of the

[1] A. C. Nixon and G. E. K. Branch, *J. Am. Chem. Soc.*, **58**, 492 (1936).

[2] G. E. K. Branch and A. C. Nixon, *ibid.*, 2499.

triarylmethyl chlorides, and with the larger positive charge residing on the carbon atom of the carbonyl group in the acyl chlorides; in the former case there will therefore be more ionization and a less close approach of the hydroxide ions in the activated state.

The hydrolyses and alcoholyses of alkyl halides offer examples of an intermediate type of behavior, the two effects being of about equal magnitude and canceling each other out. Some figures[1] are given in Table 39, and it will be seen that there is very little change in activation energy on changing the halide. If the repulsion-energy factor were the more important, the change from methyl through ethyl to isopropyl would increase the energy of activation; if the ionic character were dominant, the effect would be the opposite. Apparently the two effects approximately balance each other.

Table 39 ACTIVATION ENERGIES FOR ALKYL HALIDE REACTIONS

	Activation energy with		
Reaction	$R = CH_3$	$R = C_2H_5$	$R = CH(CH_3)_2$
$RCl + OH^-$	—	23.0	23.0
$RBr + OH^-$	—	23.0	21.7
$RI + C_6H_5O^-$	22.1	22.0	22.1
$RI + C_6H_5CH_2O^-$	20.6	21.9	21.4

If the reactant molecule is a water molecule instead of a negative ion, the repulsion energy is larger, since the electrostatic attraction between the water molecule and the carbon atom of the halide is less than in the case of the ion. Since the effects of the repulsion energy and the bond strength approximately balance in the case of the ions, it would be anticipated that when the water molecule effects the hydrolysis, the ionizability of the bond will be more important than the repulsion energy. Changing from methyl through ethyl to isopropyl should therefore decrease the activation energy by increasing the ionizability of the bond. Experimental values are not available, but it is known that isopropyl and tertiary butyl halides are more rapidly hydrolyzed by water than are the corresponding methyl and ethyl halides;[2] since rates are generally deter-

[1] G. H. Grant and C. N. Hinshelwood, *J. Chem. Soc.*, 258 (1933); E. D. Hughes, C. K. Ingold, and U. G. Shapiro, *ibid.*, 225 (1936); K. A. Cooper and E. D. Hughes, *ibid.*, 1138 (1937).

[2] E. D. Hughes, *ibid.*, 255 (1935).

mined by activation energies, this can be taken as evidence that the energies actually fall in the predicted order. Another example of the same thing has been seen in the alcoholysis of the triarylmethyl chlorides.

Substituent Effects and Dipole Moments. In connection with the influence of substituents on rates and activation energies, a number of attempts have been made to correlate the observed effects with other properties of the reactants. In particular, relationships with the dipole moment have been sought, and the activation energies of reactions involving substituents in the meta position to the reaction center have been found empirically[1] to be related to the dipole moment μ by

$$E = E_0 - c(\mu + b\mu^2) \tag{81}$$

where E_0 is the activation energy in the absence of a substituent, and b and c are constants. Alternatively it has been proposed by Jenkins[2] that the direction of operation of the dipole moment should be taken into account, and it was found that the activation energy varied linearly with the electrostatic potential produced by the substituent at the reaction center. This relationship of Jenkins is obeyed more accurately than Eq. (81), but ortho and para compounds are always found to be anomalous.[3]

Linear Free-energy Relationships. A number of quantitative relationships have been suggested in connection with the effects of substituents on the rate constants of reactions. One of the best known and most useful of these is an equation proposed by Hammett,[4] which relates equilibrium and rate constants for the reactions of meta- and para-substituted benzene derivatives. The equation applies to series of aromatic compounds having the same reaction center present as a side chain and having a substituent in the meta or para position to this reaction center; an example is a group of substituted benzoic esters. According to the Hammett relationship, a rate or equilibrium constant for reaction of any one of these compounds is related to the value for the unsubstituted ("parent") compound in terms of two parameters ρ and σ. In the case of rate constants the relationship is

$$\log k = \log k_0 + \sigma\rho \tag{82}$$

[1] W. S. Nathan and H. B. Watson, *ibid.*, 893 (1933); J. F. J. Dippy and H. B. Watson, *J. Soc. Chem. Ind.* (*London*), **54,** 735 (1935); *J. Chem. Soc.*, 436 (1936); W. A. Waters, *Phil. Mag.*, **8,** 436 (1938).

[2] H. O. Jenkins, *J. Chem. Soc.*, 640, 1137, 1780 (1939).

[3] Cf. H. B. Watson, "Modern Theories of Organic Chemistry," p. 205, Oxford University Press, Fair Lawn, N.J., 1937; *Ann. Rept. Progr. Chem.* (*Chem. Soc. London*), **35,** 243 (1938).

[4] L. P. Hammett, "Physical Organic Chemistry," pp. 184–199, McGraw-Hill Book Company, New York, 1940; H. H. Jaffe, *Chem. Rev.*, **53,** 191 (1953).

where k_0 is the rate constant for the parent compound. For equilibrium constants

$$\log K = \log K_0 + \sigma\rho \tag{83}$$

Of these two constants, σ depends only on the substituent, while ρ is a reaction constant, varying with the reaction and the external conditions such as the solvent. A value of unity is arbitrarily chosen for ρ for the ionization equilibrium constant for benzoic acid in aqueous solution, and for the substituted benzoic acids; it follows that σ is the logarithm of the ratio of the ionization constant of a substituted benzoic acid to that of benzoic acid itself. By using values of σ determined in this way, the values of ρ for other reactions can be determined. Hammett's equation applies quite accurately to a large number of rate and equilibrium constants, and is therefore of value for predicting such constants from a small number of values of σ and ρ. Table 40 gives a selection of values of substituent constants, and Table 41 gives a few reaction constants for both rates and equilibria. Substituents with positive σ values are

Table 40 SUBSTITUENT CONSTANTS

	Substituent constant	
Group	Meta	Para
CH_3	−0.07	−0.17
C_2H_5	−0.04	−0.15
OH	0.00	−0.46
OCH_3	0.12	−0.27
Cl	0.37	0.23
NO_2	0.71	0.78
$N(CH_3)_3^+$	0.91	0.86

Table 41 REACTION CONSTANTS

Reaction	Reaction constant
Ionization of benzoic acids in H_2O (eq.)	1.000
Ionization of phenols in H_2O (eq.)	2.113
Alkaline hydrolysis of methyl benzoates in 60% acetone (rate)	2.460
Acid hydrolysis of ethyl benzoates in 60% ethanol (rate)	0.144
Benzoylation of aromatic amines in benzene (rate)	−2.781

stronger electron attractors than hydrogen; substituents with negative σ values attract electrons more weakly (or repel electrons more strongly) than hydrogen. Reactions with positive ρ values are accelerated by electron withdrawal from the benzene ring, whereas those with negative ρ values are retarded by electron withdrawal.

It will now be shown that the Hammett relationships are equivalent to the existence of linear relationships between the free energies (of reaction or of activation) for different series of reactions. The free energy of activation $\Delta G^\ddagger$ is related [cf. Eq. (86) of Chap. 3] to the rate constant k by the equation

$$k = \frac{\mathbf{k}T}{\mathbf{h}} e^{-\Delta G^\ddagger/RT} \tag{84}$$

so that the logarithm of the rate constant is given by

$$\log k = \log \frac{\mathbf{k}T}{\mathbf{h}} - \frac{\Delta G^\ddagger}{2.303RT} \tag{85}$$

Equation (82) may therefore be written as

$$\Delta G^\ddagger = \Delta G_0{}^\ddagger - 2.303RT\rho\sigma \tag{86}$$

This equation, with a particular value of ρ, applies to any reaction involving a reactant having a series of substituents. For a second series of homologous reactions, having the reaction constant ρ',

$$\Delta G'^\ddagger = \Delta G_0'^\ddagger - 2.303RT\rho'\sigma \tag{87}$$

Equations (86) and (87) may be written as

$$\frac{\Delta G^\ddagger}{\rho} = \frac{\Delta G_0{}^\ddagger}{\rho} - 2.303RT\sigma \tag{88}$$

and

$$\frac{\Delta G'^\ddagger}{\rho'} = \frac{\Delta G_0'^\ddagger}{\rho'} - 2.303RT\sigma \tag{89}$$

Subtraction gives

$$\frac{\Delta G^\ddagger}{\rho} - \frac{\Delta G'^\ddagger}{\rho'} = \frac{\Delta G_0{}^\ddagger}{\rho} - \frac{\Delta G_0'^\ddagger}{\rho'} \tag{90}$$

which may be written as

$$\Delta G^\ddagger - \frac{\rho}{\rho'} \Delta G'^\ddagger = \text{const} \tag{91}$$

There is thus a linear relationship between the free energies of activation for one homologous series of reactions and those for another. An equivalent relationship applies to free energies for the overall reactions.

A large number of examples of linear free-energy relationships have been observed; one is shown in Fig. 56. The correlations are not very

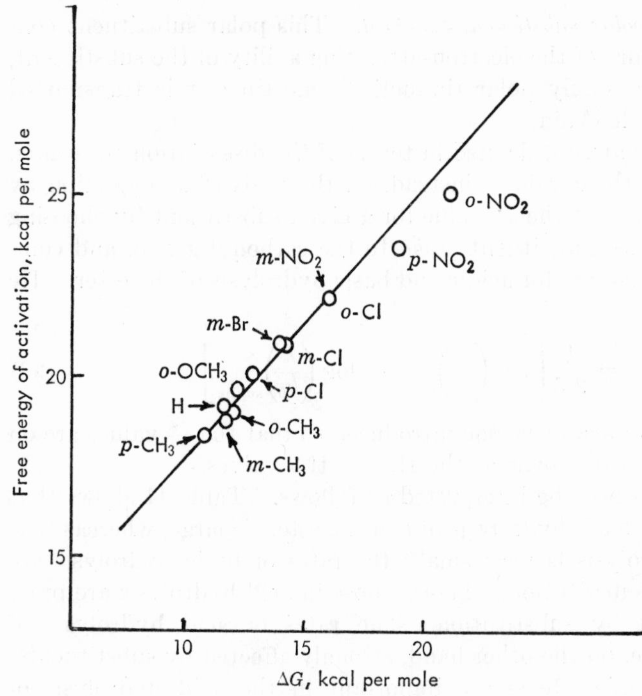

Fig. 56. A linear free-energy relationship: a plot of the free energy of activation, for the benzoylations of substituted anilines, against the free energy of dissociation of the aniline ΔG. [*Data of F. J. Stubbs and C. N. Hinshelwood, J. Chem. Soc.,* S71 (1949).]

close in some instances, such as when the reactions are very different from one another. The applicability of the linear relationships is usually quite poor for ortho substituents; the reason is that these exert not only an electron-attracting or electron-repelling effect but also a steric effect. This steric effect usually leads to a decrease in the rate of reaction, and is referred to as *steric hindrance.*

The Taft Equation. The Hammett equation does not apply very well to the reactions of aliphatic compounds, partly because there is usually some steric interference between the substituent and the reaction site. Taft[1] has proposed that for aliphatic compounds

$$\log k = \log k_0 + \sigma^* \rho^* \qquad (92)$$

where k is the rate or equilibrium constant for a particular member of the reaction series, and k_0 is the value for the parent compound (usually the methyl compound). ρ^* is the *reaction constant,* analogous to Hammett's

[1] R. W. Taft, *J. Am. Chem. Soc.,* **74,** 2729, 3120 (1952); **75,** 4231 (1953).

ρ, and σ^* is the *polar substituent constant.* This polar substituent constant σ^* is a measure of the electron-attracting ability of the substituent, the effect being a purely polar (inductive) one since it is transmitted through an aliphatic chain.

The σ^* values are not defined in terms of the dissociation constants, as was done with the σ values; instead, on the basis of a suggestion by Ingold,[1] Taft arrived at the σ^* value for a given substituent by choosing an ester having the substituent *alpha* to the carbonyl group, and comparing the rate constants for acidic and basic hydrolysis of the ester. He then defined σ^* as

$$\sigma^* = \frac{1}{2.5}\left[\log\left(\frac{k}{k_0}\right)_{\text{basic}} - \log\left(\frac{k}{k_0}\right)_{\text{acidic}}\right] \tag{93}$$

The factor 2.5 is an arbitrary one introduced so that the σ^* values are on approximately the same scale as the Hammett σ values.

The σ^* values may be interpreted as follows. Table 41 shows that the ρ value for the basic hydrolysis of benzoic esters is large, whereas that for the acid hydrolysis is very small; the rates of basic hydrolysis are very sensitive to substitution, whereas those in acid hydrolysis are practically unaffected by substitution. The rates of acid hydrolysis of aliphatic esters are, on the other hand, strongly affected by substituents; it follows that steric effects are important in the acid hydrolysis of aliphatic esters. The inductive and resonance effects are concluded to be negligible in this reaction, just as they are in the aromatic series, and the ratio k/k_0 in the acid hydrolysis of aliphatic esters is taken to be a measure of the steric effect of the substituent. As will be discussed in Chap. 10, the activated complexes for the acid and base hydrolyses of esters are very similar to each other, differing only by the presence of two additional protons in the acidic case:

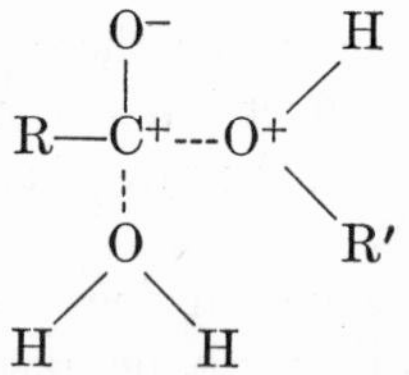

```
     O⁻        H                  O⁻
     |        /                   |
R—C⁺---O⁺                   R—C---O
     ⋮        \                   ⋮     \
     O         R'                 O      R'
    / \                          /
   H   H                        H
(acid hydrolysis)          (base hydrolysis)
```

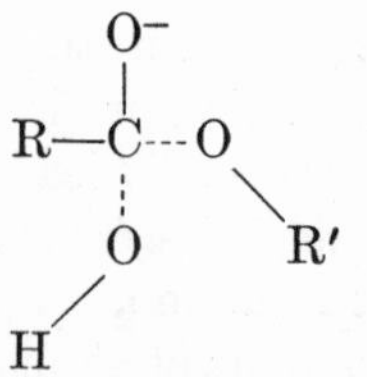

Taft assumed because of this that the steric effects in the two types of hydrolysis should be very similar to each other. In the base-catalysed hydrolyses both the inductive and steric effects are important, and the ratio k/k_0 for the base hydrolysis is thus a measure of both effects. The contribution to the free energy of activation arising from steric effects alone is therefore proportional to $\log (k/k_0)_{\text{acid}}$; that arising from both

[1] C. K. Ingold, *J. Chem. Soc.*, 1032 (1930).

steric and inductive effects is proportional to log $(k/k_0)_{\text{basic}}$. The resonance effect is unimportant, and the difference is therefore a measure of the inductive effect alone, as stated in the Taft equation (93).

Some values of Taft's σ^* values are given in Table 42, and of ρ^* values in Table 43. As in the Hammett equation, a positive ρ^* value indicates that the reaction is facilitated by electron withdrawal.

Table 42 TAFT σ^* (POLAR) VALUES

Group	σ^*
CH_3	0.00
C_2H_5	−0.10
iso-C_3H_7	−0.19
tert-C_4H_9	−0.30
H	0.49
C_6H_5	0.60
$C_6H_5CH_2$	0.22
CH_3CO	1.65
Cl_3C	2.65

Table 43 TAFT ρ^* (REACTION) CONSTANTS

Reaction	ρ^*
$RCOOH + H_2O \rightleftharpoons RCOO^- + H_3O^+$ (eq.)	1.72
$RCH_2OH + H_2SO_4 \rightarrow RCH_2OSO_3H + H_2O$ (rate)	4.60
$C_6H_5COCHR_2 + Br_2 \xrightarrow{OH^-} C_6H_5COCR_2Br + Br^-$ (rate)	1.59
$RCH{-}CH_2$ (epoxide, bridged by O) $+ H_2O \xrightarrow{HClO_4} RCHOHCH_2OH$ (rate)	−1.83

Compensation Effect.[1] It has sometimes been argued that linear free-energy relationships such as those of Hammett and Taft are associated with the existence of linear relationships between energies of activation and energies of reaction, the entropies remaining constant within a homologous series. It has now become apparent, on the contrary, that free energies are much simpler functions than energies, which are more sensitive to external factors, such as those brought about by the solvent. Examples are now known in which free energies show linear relationships, and exhibit additivity, but in which the corresponding energy and enthalpy changes show no such relationship. This is possible because there is a general tendency in processes in solution for heats and entropies to compensate each other, so that the changes in free energy are much smaller.

[1] K. J. Laidler, *Trans. Faraday Soc.*, **55**, 1725 (1959).

In a considerable number of instances plots of $T\,\Delta S^{\ddagger}$ against $\Delta H^{\ddagger}$ have been found to be straight lines of approximately unit slope. This is frequently the case for a given reaction investigated in a series of solvents, and also for homologous reactions in which substituents are introduced into a reactant. An example of such a correlation is seen in Fig. 57.

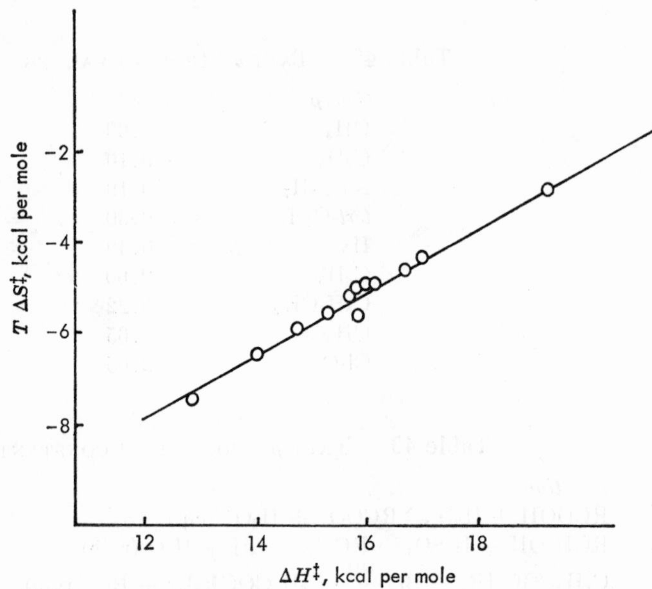

Fig. 57. The compensation effect: a plot of $T\,\Delta S^{\ddagger}$ against $\Delta H^{\ddagger}$ for the alkaline hydrolysis of ethyl benzoate in alcohol-water mixtures. [*Data of R. A. Fairclough and C. N. Hinshelwood, J. Chem. Soc.*, 1573 (1937).]

The free energy of activation $\Delta G^{\ddagger}$ is equal to $\Delta H^{\ddagger} - T\,\Delta S^{\ddagger}$, and it follows that if there is an exact linear relationship between $\Delta H^{\ddagger}$ and $T\,\Delta S^{\ddagger}$, with unit slope, there will be no variation of $\Delta G^{\ddagger}$. If the relationship is only an approximate one, it means that the dependence of $\Delta G^{\ddagger}$ on solvent or substituent is much smaller than that of $\Delta H^{\ddagger}$ or $T\,\Delta S^{\ddagger}$.

A similar compensation effect has frequently been found between ΔH and $T\,\Delta S$ for overall processes in solution; one cannot therefore explain the compensation between $\Delta H^{\ddagger}$ and $T\,\Delta S^{\ddagger}$ in terms of purely kinetic effects. The true explanation must lie in terms of solvent-solute interactions. Any effect that, for example, leads to a stronger binding between a solute molecule and the solvent molecules will lower the enthalpy; it will also, by restricting the freedom of vibration and of rotation of the solvent molecules, lower the entropy. Application of more exact theories to these effects leads to the result that they will generally give rise to a fairly exact compensation between ΔH and $T\,\Delta S$, and therefore to a very small effect on ΔG.

Although changes of substituent and solvent frequently exert their influence on $\Delta H^{\ddagger}$ in a rather complex manner, the partial compensation between $\Delta H^{\ddagger}$ and $T\,\Delta S^{\ddagger}$ is of such a nature that their influence on $\Delta G^{\ddagger}$ is of a much simpler nature. It is for this reason that relatively simple concepts have been very successful in explaining the effects of solvents and substituents on rates, i.e., on $\Delta G^{\ddagger}$. Much more complicated explanations, involving detailed considerations of solvent-solute interactions, must be invoked to explain the effects on heats and entropies. Relatively little progress has as yet been made in this field.

PROBLEMS

1. The second-order rate constant for the reaction between pyridine and methyl iodide in benzene solution at 60°C is 1.46×10^{-4} liter mole^{-1} sec^{-1}, and the activation energy is 14.3 kcal. Calculate the frequency factor and the entropy of activation.

2. The rate constant for the reaction

$$H^+ + OH^- \rightarrow H_2O$$

has been given by Eigen and de Maeyer[1] as 1.3×10^{11} liters mole^{-1} sec^{-1}. Calculate the half period for the neutralization of a strong acid by a strong base, both at concentrations of 10^{-4} N.

3. Predict the effect of (**a**) increasing the dielectric constant, (**b**) increasing the ionic strength, and (**c**) increasing the hydrostatic pressure, on the rates of the following reactions:

$$CH_2ClCOO^- + OH^- \rightarrow CH_2OHCOO^- + Cl^-$$
$$Co(NH_3)_5Br^{2+} + NO_2^- \rightarrow Co(NH_3)_5NO_2^+ + Br^-$$
$$CH_2BrCOOCH_3 + S_2O_3^{2-} \rightarrow CH_2(S_2O_3^-)COOCH_3 + Br^-$$
$$CH_3Br + 2H_2O \rightarrow CH_3OH + H_3O^+ + Br^-$$
$$CH_3Br + OH^- \rightarrow CH_3OH + Br^-$$

Estimate the sign of the entropy of activation in each case.

4. The rate constant for the reaction between persulfate ions and iodide ions varies with the ionic strength as follows:

u, moles per liter	*k, liters mole^{-1} sec^{-1}*
0.00245	1.05
0.00365	1.12
0.00445	1.16
0.00645	1.18
0.00845	1.26
0.01245	1.39

[1] M. Eigen and L. de Maeyer, *Z. Elektrochem.*, **59**, 986 (1955).

Estimate the value of $z_A z_B$. If the rate-controlling step is reaction between a persulfate ion and an iodide ion (I^-), what is the charge on the persulfate ion?

5. Make an estimate of the volumes of activation in cubic centimeters per mole for the results plotted in Fig. 53.

6. The following results were obtained for reactions between substituted dimethyl anilines and methyl iodide in nitrobenzene solution:

	$k \times 10^5$, liters mole^{-1} sec^{-1}				
Amine	15.0°C	24.8°C	40.1°C	60.0°C	80.1°C
Dimethyl-*p*-anisidine	34.7	71.9	183	560	
Dimethyl-*p*-toluidine	—	28.4	79.6	253	759
Dimethylaniline	—	8.39	21.0	77.2	238
p-Chlorodimethylaniline	0.926	2.11	5.97	25.6	
p-Bromodimethylaniline	0.824	1.80	5.55	21.3	

Show that the influence of the substituent is mainly on the energy of activation.

7. Using the values given in Tables 40 and 41, estimate the ratio of rate constants for each of the following pairs of reactions:

(a) Alkaline hydrolysis in 60 percent acetone of methyl-*p*-hydroxybenzoate and methyl-*m*-chlorobenzoate.
(b) Benzoylation in benzene of *p*-nitroaniline and *m*-chloroaniline.

8. Using the values given in Tables 42 and 43 estimate the ratio of the rate constants for the following reactions:

$$tert\text{-}C_4H_9CH_2OH + H_2SO_4 \rightarrow tert\text{-}C_4H_9CH_2OSO_3H + H_2O$$
$$iso\text{-}C_3H_7CH_2OH + H_2SO_4 \rightarrow iso\text{-}C_3H_7CH_2OSO_3H + H_2O$$

***9.** The rate constant for the reaction

$$[CoBr(NH_3)_5]^{2+} + OH^- \rightarrow [Co(NH_3)_5OH]^{2+} + Br^-$$

is given as 1.52 liters mole^{-1} sec^{-1} at 15°C. This value was obtained in an experiment in which the reactants were present at the following concentrations:

$[CoBr(NH_3)_5]^{2+}2Br^-$	$5.0 \times 10^{-4}M$
NaOH	$7.95 \times 10^{-4}M$

Make an estimate of the rate constant of the reaction at zero ionic strength.

Calculate the rate constants corresponding to the following concentrations of reactants and sodium chloride, and compare with the experimental values:[1]

Concentration, moles per liter			
$[CoBr(NH_3)_5]^{2+}2Br^-$	NaOH	NaCl	Experimental rate constant, liters mole^{-1} sec^{-1}
5.96×10^{-4}	1.004×10^{-3}	—	1.45
6.00×10^{-4}	0.696×10^{-3}	0.005	1.23
6.00×10^{-4}	0.696×10^{-3}	0.020	0.97
6.00×10^{-4}	0.691×10^{-3}	0.030	0.91

10. The fading of bromophenol blue in alkaline solution is a second-order reaction between hydroxide ions and the quinoid form of the dye:

$$\text{Quinoid form (blue)} + OH^- \rightarrow \text{carbinol form (colorless)}$$

The following results show the variation of the second-order rate constant k with the hydrostatic pressure p:

Pressure, lb per sq in.	*Rate constant, liters mole^{-1} sec^{-1}*
14.7	9.30×10^{-4}
4,000	11.13×10^{4}
8,000	13.1×10^{-4}
12,000	15.3×10^{-4}
16,000	17.9×10^{-4}

Calculate the volume of activation for the reaction.

[1] J. N. Brønsted and R. S. Livingston, *J. Am. Chem. Soc.*, **49**, 435 (1927).

chapter

6 Reactions on Surfaces and in the Solid State

THE RATES OF a great many chemical reactions are influenced by solid surfaces. This fact is frequently a serious complication to the study of homogeneous gas reactions, in that an appreciable amount of reaction may occur on the surface of the reaction vessel and must be allowed for if the homogeneous reaction is the one of special interest. In experiments of this kind the amount of surface reaction can be determined by measuring reaction rates under conditions in which the area of the surface is varied over as wide a range as possible.

In addition to investigations in which there is incidental catalysis by the walls of the vessel, a great many experiments have been made on the kinetics of reactions occurring on surfaces that are deliberately introduced into the system. As a result of such work, it has been found that many processes can be made to occur much more rapidly by the introduction of a suitable surface upon which the reaction proceeds; the solid material is then said to catalyze the reaction. In particular, a number of processes that do not occur homogeneously at an appreciable rate can be made to occur on surfaces. The subject of catalysis by solid surfaces is therefore of very great technical importance. The majority of investigations of surface reactions have, in fact, been carried out with the object of finding a suitable substance to catalyze a technical gas reaction, and have not been carried out under conditions suitable for an elucidation of the fundamental processes concerned. In this chapter primary attention will be devoted to a consideration of investigations of a more fundamental nature, the essential criteria of such being that they include specification of the surface used, in particular its smoothness and area, and that absolute rates and activation energies of the reactions have been measured accurately.

The most important result that has emerged from such investigations is that catalysis by surfaces involves specific chemical interaction between the surface and the reacting gas molecules, which must become adsorbed on the surface before reaction can occur. This view was first proposed in 1825 by Faraday, who studied the nature of adsorption on surfaces, and considered that reaction occurred in adsorbed films. The original idea was that the main effect of the catalyst was to cause the molecules to be present in much higher concentrations than in the main body of the gas. This concept is, however, shown to be false by the fact that in certain cases different surfaces give rise to different products of reaction; e.g., ethyl alcohol decomposes primarily into ethylene and water on an alumina catalyst, and mainly into acetaldehyde and hydrogen on copper. This result, along with many others, clearly indicates that specific chemical forces are involved at surfaces. In view of the importance of adsorption forces in connection with surface catalysis, some discussion will now be devoted to modern views on this subject.

ADSORPTION[1]

It is now recognized that two main types of adsorption may be clearly distinguished. In the first type the forces are of a physical nature, and the adsorption is relatively weak; the forces correspond to those assumed in the van der Waals equation of state of gases and are consequently known as *van der Waals* forces. These play only a very unimportant part in connection with surface reactions (except for certain atomic processes), since they are not sufficiently strong to influence appreciably the reactivity of the molecules adsorbed. The second type of adsorption

[1] For reviews see J. K. Roberts, "Some Aspects of Adsorption," Cambridge University Press, New York, 1939; S. Brunauer, "Physical Adsorption," Princeton University Press, Princeton, N.J., 1943; A. R. Miller, "The Adsorption of Gases on Solids," Cambridge University Press, New York, 1949; K. J. Laidler, Chemisorption, in P. H. Emmett (ed.), "Catalysis," vol. 1, Reinhold Publishing Corporation, New York, 1954; B. M. W. Trapnell, in W. E. Garner (ed.), "Chemisorption," Butterworth & Co. (Publishers), Ltd., London, 1955.

is considerably stronger; according to Langmuir's original concept of it,[1] the adsorbed molecules are held to the surface by valence forces of the same type as those occurring between bound atoms in molecules. The heat evolved in this type of adsorption, known as *chemisorption*, should be of the same order as that found with chemical reactions and, in agreement with this idea, values of 10 to 100 kcal have been observed. By contrast, the heat changes found with van der Waals adsorption are usually less than 5 kcal per mole.

An important consequence of this concept of chemisorption, regarded by Langmuir as an essential part of his theory, is that after a surface has become covered with a single layer of adsorbed molecules it is essentially saturated; additional adsorption can occur only on the layer already formed, and this usually takes place only with some difficulty. This idea of the *unimolecular layer* is capable of direct experimental test, and a number of investigations have shown that a definite adsorption limit occurs, beyond which further molecules cannot be adsorbed readily. When the surface area is known, this limit is found to correspond to the existence of a unimolecular layer.[2] This result is good evidence for the theory that chemical forces are involved in chemisorption.

It was suggested by Taylor[3] that chemisorption is frequently associated with an appreciable activation energy and may therefore be a relatively slow process; for this reason it is now frequently referred to as *activated adsorption*. The energies of activation are often of the order of 20 kcal, and consequently the adsorption is extremely slow at low temperatures; under these conditions, van der Waals adsorption, which requires no activation energy, will predominate.

It must not be assumed that all surfaces are smooth and that adsorbed molecules are arranged on them in simple layers. In reality surfaces are never smooth from the molecular standpoint, and the kind of behavior to be expected on rough surfaces was discussed by Taylor,[4] Constable,[5] and others.[6] Some surface sites will be more active than others, and chemical processes will occur predominantly on the most

[1] I. Langmuir, *J. Am. Chem. Soc.*, **38**, 2221 (1916).

[2] I. Langmuir, *ibid.*, **40**, 1361 (1918); F. A. Paneth and W. Vorwerk, *Z. Physik. Chem.*, **101**, 445, 480 (1922); J. K. Roberts, *Proc. Roy. Soc.* (*London*), **A152**, 445 (1935); cf. Miller, *op. cit.*, pp. 16–18.

[3] H. S. Taylor, *J. Am. Chem. Soc.*, **53**, 578 (1931); *Chem. Rev.*, **9**, 1 (1931).

[4] H. S. Taylor, *Proc. Roy. Soc.* (*London*), **A108** (1925); *J. Phys. Chem.*, **30**, 145 (1926); cf. N. P. Keier and S. Z. Roginsky, *Dokl. Akad. Nauk., SSSR*, **57**, 151 (1947); *J. Phys. Chem. USSR*, **23**, 897 (1949); J. T. Kummer and P. H. Emmett, *J. Am. Chem. Soc.*, **73**, 2886 (1951); P. H. Emmett and J. T. Kummer, *J. Chim. Phys.*, **47**, 67 (1950); H. S. Taylor and S. C. Liang, *J. Am. Chem. Soc.*, **69**, 1306 (1947); H. Sadek and H. S. Taylor, *ibid.*, **72**, 1168 (1950).

[5] F. H. Constable, *Proc. Roy. Soc.* (*London*), **A108**, 355 (1925)

[6] E. Cremer and G. M. Schwab, *Z. Physik. Chem.*, **A144**, 243 (1929); G. M. Schwab, *ibid.*, **B5**, 406 (1929).

active sites, which Taylor referred to as *active centers.* It was originally thought that atoms present on surface peaks would be the most active, but it has later become clear that the matter is more complicated than this; active centers may actually correspond to certain types of lattice defect. This question of the nature of active centers is considered in more detail later in this chapter.

Another complication that exists in connection with chemisorption is that there are interactions, usually of a repulsive nature, between atoms or molecules adsorbed side by side on a surface. The first evidence for this was obtained by Roberts,[1] who measured heats of adsorption of hydrogen on a tungsten surface that was considered to be quite smooth. The heat was found to fall from about 45 kcal per mole for a bare surface to 15 kcal for what was believed to be a fully covered surface; later evidence,[2] however, indicated that the surface was only 70 percent covered, and that the heats of adsorption become close to zero when the surface is actually fully covered. If the surface is really homogeneous, this change in heat of adsorption must be due to repulsive interactions between the adsorbed molecules; when the surface is sparsely covered, the molecules are sufficiently far apart so as not to interact with each other, but the repulsive interactions become more important as the coverage increases. Additional evidence for repulsive interactions has been obtained by Emmett and Kummer[3] using an isotope method, and by Weber and Laidler[4] on the basis of measurements of rates of desorption.

ADSORPTION ISOTHERMS

Work on chemisorption has been concerned with equilibria and with rates. The amount of gas adsorbed after equilibrium is established depends on various factors, including the nature of the surface and the absorbate, the temperature, and the pressure. If for a given system one keeps the temperature constant and studies the amount of adsorption as a function of pressure, the resulting relationship is known as an *adsorption isotherm.* A number of such isotherms have been suggested, some being empirical and others obtained theoretically. Of the theoretical equations the simplest is that of Langmuir,[5] whose isotherm has the special significance of being the one that applies to the ideal case of chemisorption

[1] J. K. Roberts, *Proc. Roy. Soc. (London)*, **A152**, 445 (1935); cf. W. G. Frankenburg, *J. Am. Chem. Soc.*, **66**, 1827 (1944); O. Beeck, *Rev. Mod. Phys.*, **17**, 61 (1945).

[2] E. K. Rideal and B. M. W. Trapnell, *J. Chim. Phys.*, **47**, 126 (1950); B. M. W. Trapnell, *Proc. Roy. Soc. (London)*, **A206**, 39 (1951).

[3] P. H. Emmett and J. T. Kummer, *J. Chim. Phys.*, **47**, 67 (1950); J T. Kummer and P. H. Emmett, *J. Am. Chem. Soc.*, **73**, 2886 (1951).

[4] J. Weber and K. J. Laidler, *J. Chem. Phys.*, **18**, 1418 (1950); **19**, 1089 (1951).

[5] Langmuir, *J. Am. Chem. Soc.*, **38**, 2221 (1916); **40**, 1361 (1918).

on a perfectly smooth surface with no interactions between adsorbed molecules. The Langmuir isotherm therefore has an importance in adsorption theory which is equivalent to that of the ideal-gas laws, and it is convenient to speak of adsorption that obeys Langmuir's isotherm as *ideal adsorption*. The equations for ideal adsorption play an important role in surface kinetics, and they will now be derived from different points of view and for several different situations.

The Langmuir Adsorption Isotherm. The simplest situation exists when the gas atoms or molecules occupy single sites on the surface, and are not dissociated; the adsorption and desorption processes may then be represented as

$$\mathrm{G} + \text{—}\overset{|}{\mathrm{S}}\text{—} \rightleftharpoons \text{—}\underset{}{\overset{\overset{\mathrm{G}}{|}}{\mathrm{S}}}\text{—}$$

Langmuir's well-known kinetic derivation[1] of the isotherm is briefly as follows. Let θ be the fraction of surface that is covered and $1 - \theta$ the fraction that is bare. The rate of adsorption is then $k_1p(1 - \theta)$, where p is the gas pressure and k_1 a constant; the rate of desorption is $k_{-1}\theta$. At equilibrium the rates are equal, so that

$$\frac{\theta}{1 - \theta} = \frac{k_1}{k_{-1}}\, p = Kp \tag{1}$$

where K, equal to k_1/k_{-1}, is a constant. This equation can be written as

$$\theta = \frac{Kp}{1 + Kp} \tag{2}$$

Figure 58 shows the type of behavior that corresponds to this equation, and gives the behavior at the limits of low and high pressures.

Adsorption with Dissociation. In certain cases there is evidence that the process of adsorption is accompanied by the dissociation of the molecule on the surface. It is found, for example, that hydrogen is adsorbed on the surfaces of many metals in the form of atoms, each of which occupies a surface site. Similarly methane adsorbed on metals is usually dissociated into CH_3, CH_2, and hydrogen atoms. In the case of the dissociation of a molecule into two species (e.g., of H_2 into 2H) the process may be represented as

$$\mathrm{G_2} + \text{—}\overset{|}{\mathrm{S}}\text{—}\overset{|}{\mathrm{S}}\text{—} \rightleftharpoons \text{—}\overset{\overset{\mathrm{G}}{|}}{\mathrm{S}}\text{—}\overset{\overset{\mathrm{G}}{|}}{\mathrm{S}}\text{—}$$

The process of adsorption must be considered to be a reaction between the gas molecule and two surface sites, and the rate of adsorption may

[1] Langmuir, *loc. cit.*

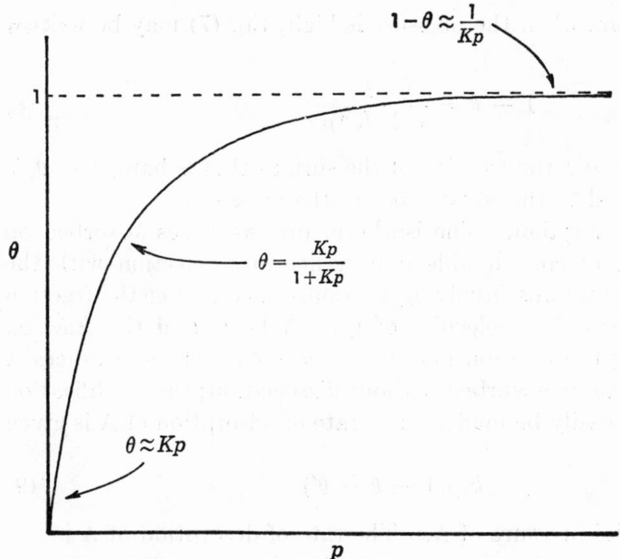

Fig. 58. The relationship between the fraction of surface covered θ and the pressure, for the case of absorption without dissociation in which the Langmuir equation (2) applies. The rate varies with pressure in exactly the same manner for both a unimolecular reaction [Eq. (29)] and a bimolecular reaction proceeding by a Langmuir-Rideal mechanism [Eq. (54)].

therefore be written as

$$v_1 = k_1 p(1 - \theta)^2 \tag{3}$$

The desorption process involves reaction between *two* adsorbed atoms, and the rate is therefore proportional to the square of the fraction of surface covered,

$$v_{-1} = k_{-1}\theta^2 \tag{4}$$

At equilibrium the rates are equal, whence

$$\frac{\theta}{1 - \theta} = \left(\frac{k_1}{k_{-1}}\, p\right)^{\frac{1}{2}} \tag{5}$$

$$= K^{\frac{1}{2}}p^{\frac{1}{2}} \tag{6}$$

where K is equal to k_1/k_{-1} This equation can be written as

$$\theta = \frac{K^{\frac{1}{2}}p^{\frac{1}{2}}}{1 + K^{\frac{1}{2}}p^{\frac{1}{2}}} \tag{7}$$

When the pressure is sufficiently small so that $K^{\frac{1}{2}}p^{\frac{1}{2}}$ is much smaller than unity, the fraction covered is proportional to $p^{\frac{1}{2}}$. Another case of special interest occurs when the pressure is high; Eq. (7) may be written as

$$1 - \theta = \frac{1}{1 + K^{1/2}p^{1/2}} \tag{8}$$

so that when $K^{1/2}p^{1/2} \gg 1$ the fraction of the surface that is bare, $1 - \theta$, is inversely proportional to the square root of the pressure.

Competitive Adsorption. The isotherm for two gases adsorbed on the same surface is of considerable importance in connection with the kinetics of surface reactions involving two substances. Let the fraction of the surface covered by molecules of type A be θ, and the fraction covered by B be θ'; the fraction bare is $1 - \theta - \theta'$. The substances A and B are assumed to be adsorbed without dissociation; the modification for dissociation can easily be made. The rate of adsorption of A is given by

$$v_1 = k_1 p(1 - \theta - \theta') \tag{9}$$

where p is the partial pressure of A. The rate of desorption of A is

$$v_{-1} = k_{-1}\theta \tag{10}$$

At equilibrium these rates are equal, whence

$$\frac{\theta}{1 - \theta - \theta'} = Kp \tag{11}$$

where K is equal to k_1/k_{-1}. In the same way it can be shown that for the equilibrium of the gas B,

$$\frac{\theta'}{1 - \theta - \theta'} = K'p' \tag{12}$$

where p' is the partial pressure of B, and K' is the equilibrium constant for the adsorption of B. Equations (11) and (12) are two simultaneous equations, the solution of which gives, for the fractions covered by A and B,

$$\theta = \frac{Kp}{1 + Kp + K'p'} \tag{13}$$

and

$$\theta' = \frac{K'p'}{1 + Kp + K'p'} \tag{14}$$

Equation (13) reduces to (2) in the event that $p' = 0$ (gas B is not present) or that $K' = 0$ (gas B is not adsorbed). It is seen from Eqs. (13) and (14) that the fraction of the surface covered by one gas is reduced if the pressure of the other gas is increased; this is due to the fact that the molecules are competing with one another for a limited number of surface sites, and one may speak in this case of *competitive chemisorption.* There is an indication that in some special cases two gases may become adsorbed on two different sets of surface sites, in which case there is no competition. The isotherms would then be the same as if two completely separate surfaces were involved; i.e., Eq. (2) will apply to each gas.

Statistical Treatment of Ideal Adsorption.[1] By the methods of statistical mechanisms it is possible to derive equations that are equivalent to the isotherms given above, but which express the constants in terms of partition functions. The case of adsorption without dissociation will be considered first. Let the volume of the gas be V cc, and the area of the surface be S sq cm. At equilibrium the number of bare sites may be written as N_s, and the number of adsorbed molecules as N_a; the total number of molecules in the gas phase is N_g. It is now convenient to define concentrations as follows:

Concentration in gas phase: $c_g = N_g/V$ molecules per cc
Concentration of bare sites: $c_s = N_s/S$ sites per sq cm
Concentration of adsorbed molecules: $c_a = N_a/S$ molecules per sq cm

The equilibrium constant for the adsorption process is

$$K_c = \frac{c_a}{c_g c_s} = \frac{N_a}{(N_g/V)N_s} \tag{15}$$

By the use of the procedures explained in Chap. 3, the equilibrium constant can be written as

$$K_c = \frac{F_a}{F_g F_s} e^{\epsilon/\mathbf{k}T} \tag{16}$$

where the F's are the partition functions per unit volume, and ϵ is the energy released, per molecule, at 0°K. This can more conveniently be expressed as

$$\frac{c_a}{c_g c_s} = \frac{f_a}{F_g f_s} e^{\epsilon/\mathbf{k}T} \tag{17}$$

where f_a and f_s are the total partition functions (rather than those per unit volume or unit area). If θ is the fraction covered,

$$\frac{c_a}{c_g} = \frac{\theta}{1-\theta} \tag{18}$$

so that

$$\frac{\theta}{1-\theta} = c_g \frac{f_a}{F_g f_s} e^{\epsilon/\mathbf{k}T} \tag{19}$$

The concentration c_g is equal to $p/\mathbf{k}T$, and F_g may be written as

$$F_g = \frac{(2\pi m\mathbf{k}T)^{3/2}}{\mathbf{h}^3} b_g \tag{20}$$

[1] R. H. Fowler, *Proc. Cambridge Phil. Soc.*, **31**, 260 (1935); R. H. Fowler and E. A. Guggenheim, "Statistical Thermodynamics," p. 426, Cambridge University Press, New York, 1939.

where b_g represents the rotational and vibrational factors in the partition function. The adsorption sites have very little freedom of motion so that the partition function f_s may be taken as unity. The partition function for the adsorbed molecules also involves only internal factors, which may be written as b_a. The adsorption isotherm thus becomes

$$\frac{\theta}{1-\theta} = p\,\frac{\mathbf{h}^3}{(2\pi m)^{3/2}(\mathbf{k}T)^{5/2}}\,\frac{b_a}{b_g}\,e^{\epsilon/\mathbf{k}T} \tag{21}$$

This equation has the same form as Eq. (2), but now the constant K is given in explicit form.

In a similar way it can be shown that for adsorption with dissociation the isotherm is

$$\frac{\theta}{1-\theta} = p^{1/2}\,\frac{\mathbf{h}^{3/2}}{(2\pi m)^{3/4}(\mathbf{k}T)^{5/4}}\,\frac{b_a}{b_g^{1/2}}\,e^{\epsilon/\mathbf{k}T} \tag{22}$$

where ϵ is the energy liberated at 0°K when one molecule is adsorbed. For the adsorption of two gases on the same surface Eqs. (13) and (14) apply, with K given by

$$K = \frac{\mathbf{h}^3}{(2\pi m)^{3/2}(\mathbf{k}T)^{5/2}}\,\frac{b_a}{b_g}\,e^{\epsilon/\mathbf{k}T} \tag{23}$$

A corresponding expression holds for K'.

The equations above apply only to the situation in which the adsorbed molecules are localized on the surface; that is to say, they have no translational freedom. At the other extreme is the situation in which the adsorbed molecules can move perfectly freely in two dimensions. The isotherm that then applies is

$$\theta = p\,\frac{\mathbf{h}}{L(2\pi m)^{1/2}(\mathbf{k}T)^{3/2}}\,\frac{b_a}{b_g}\,e^{\epsilon/\mathbf{k}T} \tag{24}$$

where L is the total number of molecules that are adsorbed on 1 sq cm when the surface is fully covered. This relationship only applies for sparse coverage, since when there is a greater degree of coverage there can no longer be a free movement of the molecules on the surface.

Deviations from Ideal Behavior.[1] It is beyond the scope of this book to consider the treatments that apply to inhomogeneous surfaces, and to the case of interactions between adsorbed molecules. Brief reference should, however, be made to two isotherms that are applicable to certain kinetic problems. The first is that of Freundlich,[2] which relates the volume v of gas adsorbed to the pressure p as follows:

$$v = kp^{1/n} \qquad (n > 1) \tag{25}$$

[1] For a review see K. J. Laidler, Chemisorption, in P. H. Emmett (ed.), "Catalysis," vol. 1, pp. 98–114, Reinhold Publishing Corporation, New York, 1954.

[2] H. Freundlich, "Kapillarchemie" Leipzig, 1909.

The theoretical significance of this equation has been considered by a number of authors, and it has been shown[1] that an equation of the same form as Eq. (25) is obtained if there is adsorption on a variety of sites that have a certain type of statistical distribution. The isotherm may alternatively be explained in terms of repulsive forces between adsorbed molecules.

Another isotherm that has frequently been applied to kinetic problems is that of Slygin and Frumkin,[2] which is

$$\theta = \frac{1}{f} \ln ap \tag{26}$$

where f and a are constants. This isotherm can be interpreted theoretically on the assumption that heat of adsorption is a function of the fraction of surface covered.

CHEMICAL REACTIONS ON SURFACES

Mechanisms of Surface Reactions. A reaction occurring on a surface may usually be regarded as involving five consecutive steps, as follows:

1. Diffusion of the reacting molecules to the surface
2. Adsorption of the gases on the surface
3. Reaction on the surface
4. Desorption of the products
5. Diffusion of the desorbed products into the main body of the gas

At one time it was fairly generally believed that one of the diffusion processes, 1 or 5, was the slowest process, and, therefore, determined the overall rate. More detailed investigations of surface reactions showed, however, that this could not be the case, except perhaps in certain technical processes involving porous catalysts. This is evident from the fact that heterogeneous processes nearly always involve appreciable activation energies, whereas diffusion in the gaseous state involves no activation energy; the diffusion process is, therefore, much more rapid than the overall process and cannot constitute its slow step. Langmuir[3] presented the same type of argument in a somewhat different form when he showed that, in order for diffusion to be the slow step, it would be necessary to postulate such a thick diffusion layer on the surface that it would be visible. Since diffusion is slower in solution than in the gas

[1] J. Zeldowitch, *Acta Physicochim. URSS*, **1**, 961 (1935); G. D. Halsey and H. S. Taylor, *J. Chem. Phys.*, **15**, 624 (1947); R. Sips, *ibid.*, **18**, 1024 (1950); F. C. Tompkins, *Trans Faraday Soc.*, **46**, 569 (1950).

[2] A. Slygin and A. Frumkin, *Acta Physicochim. URSS*, **3**, 791 (1935).

[3] I. Langmuir, *J. Am. Chem. Soc.*, **38**, 1145 (1916).

phase, it may sometimes be the rate-determining step in solid-liquid reactions.

The processes of adsorption or desorption are much more likely to be the slow steps in heterogeneous reactions, since both may involve appreciable energies of activation. The activation energies for desorption are particularly high, and it is likely that in very many reactions the desorption of the products is the rate-determining step. In practice, however, it is not always convenient to separate steps 3 and 4 because one usually does not know the rate of desorption of the products; it is usual, therefore, to regard the reaction on the surface, giving the gaseous products, as a single step. This concept is in fact the basis of the usual modern treatment of surface reactions, due to Langmuir[1] and Hinshelwood.[2] This treatment involves, first, obtaining an expression for the concentrations of reactant molecules on the surface, and then expressing the rate of formation of gaseous products in terms of these surface concentrations; the rate is then expressible in terms of the concentrations of the gaseous reactants. If there is a single reactant, the surface process is a simple unimolecular change; if there are two, A and B, reaction may take place between two molecules adsorbed on neighboring surface sites, and the probability of this happening is proportional to the individual concentrations of adsorbed A and adsorbed B. The Langmuir-Hinshelwood mechanism for a reaction between A and B may be formulated as follows.

$$
\mathrm{A} + \mathrm{B} + \begin{array}{c} | \\ \text{—S—} \end{array} \rightleftharpoons \begin{array}{c} \mathrm{A}\quad\mathrm{B} \\ |\quad\;| \\ \text{—S—S—} \end{array} \rightleftharpoons \begin{array}{c} \text{A—B} \\ |\quad\;| \\ \text{—S—S—} \end{array} \rightleftharpoons \begin{array}{c} |\quad\;| \\ \text{—S—S—} \end{array} + \text{products}
$$

(adsorption) (activated complex)

Another type of mechanism for surface reactions was also considered by Langmuir. According to this mechanism the reaction occurs between a gas molecule and an adsorbed molecule, so that only one of the reactants has to be adsorbed. This mechanism may be represented as

$$
\mathrm{A} + \begin{array}{c} \mathrm{B} \\ | \\ \text{—S—} \end{array} \rightarrow \begin{array}{c} | \\ \text{—S—} \end{array} + \text{products}
$$

It is not necessary that A is not at all adsorbed; it is simply postulated, in this mechanism, that an adsorbed A molecule does not react. Interest in these mechanisms was revived by Rideal[3] and, as will be seen, they probably do apply to certain atom and radical combinations. They may also play a role in other reaction systems, but on the whole the Langmuir-

[1] I. Langmuir, *Trans. Faraday Soc.*, **17**, 621 (1921).

[2] C. N. Hinshelwood, "Kinetics of Chemical Change," Clarendon Press, Oxford, p. 145, 1926; p. 187, 1940.

[3] E. K. Rideal, *Proc. Cambridge Phil. Soc.*, **35**, 130 (1939); *Chem. Ind.* (*London*), **62**, 335 (1943).

Rideal mechanisms do not appear to be as common as the Langmuir-Hinshelwood ones, in which reaction occurs between two adsorbed molecules.

In connection with the mechanisms of surface reactions, an important concept is the *molecularity*, which is the number of molecules that come together during the course of reaction; it is convenient not to count the surface sites. The molecularity of a surface reaction is deduced from the kinetics on the basis of the experimental results and of theoretical considerations. The actual relationships between molecularity and order will be considered in the following sections, in which reactions are classified according to their molecularity. One or two examples may here be mentioned briefly. Reactions involving a single reacting substance are usually, but not invariably, unimolecular. The mechanism of the surface-catalyzed ammonia decomposition (cf. p. 271) is, for example, usually unimolecular. On the other hand, the kinetics of the decomposition of acetaldehyde on various surfaces[1] can only be interpreted on the hypothesis that two acetaldehyde molecules, adsorbed on neighboring surface sites, undergo a bimolecular reaction. Reactions involving two reacting substances, such as the reaction between nitric oxide and oxygen on glass,[2] are usually bimolecular. When reactant molecules are dissociated on the surface, the reaction may involve interaction between an atom or radical and a molecule; for example, the exchange reaction between ammonia and deuterium on iron[3] must be regarded as a bimolecular interaction between a deuterium *atom* and an ammonia molecule (cf. p. 283).

UNIMOLECULAR SURFACE REACTIONS

The simplest treatment of surface reactions involving one molecule of a reactant is in terms of the Langmuir adsorption isotherm [Eq. (2)], according to which the fraction θ of the surface covered is related to the pressure p by

$$\theta = \frac{Kp}{1 + Kp} \tag{27}$$

The rate of reaction is proportional to θ and may therefore be written as

$$v = k_2\theta \tag{28}$$

$$= \frac{k_2Kp}{1 + Kp} \tag{29}$$

where k_2 is the proportionality constant. This formulation is based on the assumption that the adsorption equilibrium is not disturbed by the occurrence of the reaction, a condition that is generally satisfied.

[1] P. C. Allen and C. N. Hinshelwood, *Proc. Roy. Soc.* (*London*), **A121**, 141 (1928).
[2] M. Temkin and V. Pyzhev, *Acta Physicochim. URSS*, **2**, 473 (1935).
[3] J. Weber and K. J. Laidler, *J. Chem. Phys.*, **19**, 1089 (1951).

The relationship given in Eq. (29) between the rate and the pressure has exactly the same form as that in Fig. 58, which relates surface coverage and pressure. At sufficiently high pressures the rate is independent of the pressure, which means that the kinetics are zero order. Under these conditions $Kp \gg 1$, so that Eq. (29) reduces to

$$v = k_2 \tag{30}$$

At low pressures, when $Kp \ll 1$, Eq. (29) reduces to

$$v = k_2Kp \tag{31}$$

and the kinetics are first order. Some examples of both cases, and of intermediate cases where the order is between unity and zero, are considered later.

Inhibition. One complication that frequently exists in surface reactions is that a substance other than the reactant is adsorbed on the surface; the result is that the effective surface area, and therefore the rate, is reduced. Suppose that a substance A is undergoing a unimolecular reaction on a surface and that a nonreacting gaseous substance I (referred to as an *inhibitor* or *poison*) is also adsorbed. If the fraction of the surface covered by A is θ, and that covered by I is θ_i, the fraction covered by A can be expressed by [cf. Eq. (13)]

$$\theta = \frac{Kp}{1 + Kp + K_ip_i} \tag{32}$$

where p_i is the partial pressure of the inhibitor and K_i its adsorption constant. The rate of reaction, equal to $k_2\theta$, is therefore

$$v = \frac{k_2Kp}{1 + Kp + K_ip_i} \tag{33}$$

In the absence of inhibitor this reduces to Eq. (29).

A case of special interest occurs when the pressure of the reactant is sufficiently low so that the available surface is only sparsely covered by the reactant. The term Kp is then negligible in comparison with $1 + K_ip_i$, and the rate of the inhibited reaction is

$$v = \frac{k_2Kp}{1 + K_ip_i} \tag{34}$$

If the inhibitor is very strongly adsorbed, K_ip_i is large compared with unity, so that

$$v = \frac{k_2Kp}{K_ip_i} \tag{35}$$

The reaction is therefore first order in reactant, and the rate is inversely proportional to the inhibitor pressure. Special cases of the above equations arise when the inhibitor I is a product of the reaction; some examples of this are considered later.

Activation Energies. The rate constant k_2 appearing in Eq. (29) will obey the Arrhenius law, which may be expressed as

$$\frac{d \ln k_2}{dT} = \frac{E}{RT^2} \tag{36}$$

The temperature variation of the equilibrium constant K follows the analogous van't Hoff relationship

$$\frac{d \ln K}{dT} = -\frac{\lambda}{RT^2} \tag{37}$$

where λ is the heat evolved, per mole of reactant gas, in the adsorption process. The temperature dependence of the rate may now be considered with reference to the two limiting cases.

If the pressure is low, the rate is given by Eq. (31), so that the first-order rate constant k^I is given by

$$k^I = k_2 K \tag{38}$$

Using Eqs. (36) and (37), it follows that

$$\frac{d \ln v}{dT} = \frac{d \ln k^I}{dT} = \frac{d \ln k_2}{dT} + \frac{d \ln K}{dT} \tag{39}$$

$$= \frac{E - \lambda}{RT^2} \tag{40}$$

The *apparent activation energy* E_a is therefore given by $E - \lambda$; it is the "true" activation energy E reduced by the heat of adsorption of the reactant.

If the pressure is sufficiently high, Eq. (30) applies, and the apparent activation energy is now equal to the true activation energy E.

These relationships may be considered with reference to the potential-energy diagram shown in Fig. 59. Reaction first involves the passage of the system over an initial energy barrier to give the adsorbed state, the energy of which is lower by λ than that of the initial state. The system then passes over a second barrier of height E. If the pressure is low, most of the reactant molecules are in the unadsorbed state, and to pass to the activated state they only have to acquire the energy $E - \lambda$. At high pressures, however, the equilibrium favors the adsorbed state, and the system has to acquire the energy E in order to pass to the activated state.

When a reaction is inhibited, the activation energy is modified by the energy of adsorption of the inhibitor. There are several possibilities, the simplest of which is that corresponding to Eq. (35), for which the reactant

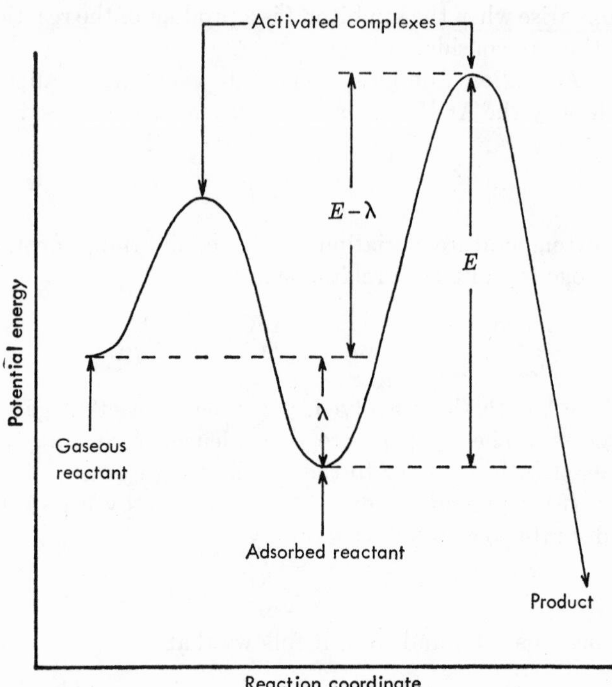

Fig. 59. Potential-energy diagram for a unimolecular surface reaction.

is weakly and the inhibitor strongly adsorbed. The inhibition constant K_i varies with temperature according to the equation

$$\frac{d \ln K_i}{dT} = -\frac{\lambda_i}{RT^2} \tag{41}$$

where λ_i is the heat of adsorption of the poison. It follows that

$$\frac{d \ln v}{dT} = \frac{d \ln k_2}{dT} + \frac{d \ln K}{dT} - \frac{d \ln K_i}{dT} \tag{42}$$

$$= \frac{E - \lambda + \lambda_i}{RT^2} \tag{43}$$

The apparent activation energy is therefore given by

$$E_a = E - \lambda + \lambda_i \tag{44}$$

The reason that the activation energy is increased by λ_i is that it is necessary for a molecule of the inhibitor to be desorbed in order for a molecule of reactant to become adsorbed and undergo reaction.

A few examples of unimolecular surface reactions will now be discussed.

Decomposition of Ammonia. Ammonia decomposes into nitrogen and hydrogen on a number of metal surfaces, and several kinetic investigations have been carried out. A study of the decomposition on tungsten and platinum surfaces was made by Hinshelwood and Burk.[1] In their work with tungsten they used a commercial tungsten-filament lamp as a reaction vessel. The vessel was kept in melting ice and the filament heated electrically to a constant temperature, which was measured by determining its resistance. The course of the reaction was followed manometrically.

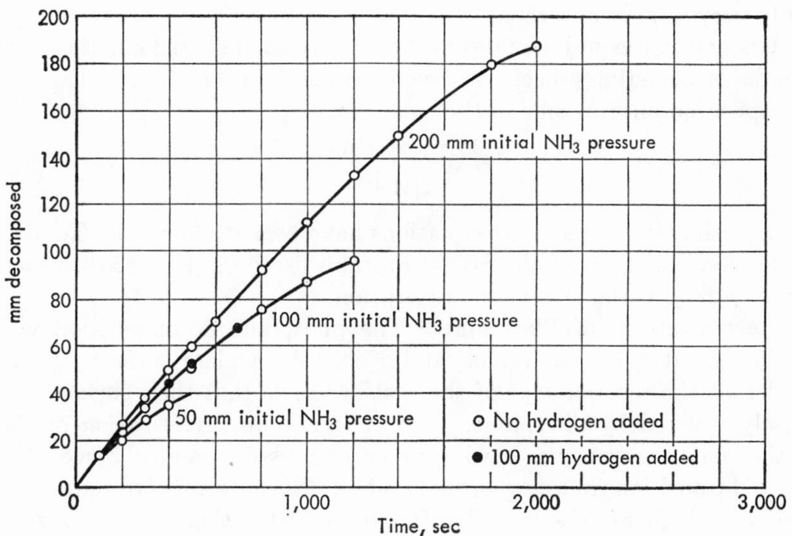

Fig. 60. Pressure-time curves obtained in the decomposition of ammonia on a heated tungsten surface. (*Hinshelwood and Burk.*) Added hydrogen is seen to have no effect on the rate.

Some of their results, obtained at 856°C, are plotted in Fig. 60. It is to be noted that the initial slopes are all the same, in spite of differences in the initial concentrations; this indicates that the reaction is of zero order under the conditions of the experiments. The same conclusion is indicated by the fact that the pressure-time curves are linear over the initial range of pressures; deviations from linearity occur at later times, since the kinetics approach first-order behavior at lower partial pressures of ammonia. It is clear that under conditions of the experiments

[1] C. N. Hinshelwood and R. E. Burk, *J. Chem. Soc.*, **127**, 1051, 1114 (1925).

of Hinshelwood and Burk the tungsten surface is largely covered by ammonia. Barrer[1] made a careful study of the zero-order reaction on tungsten, and found the activation energy to be 42.4 kcal per mole.

Hinshelwood and Burk also made a study of the decomposition of ammonia on platinum. They found that the reaction was inhibited by the hydrogen produced in the reaction, and by added hydrogen, the rate law being

$$v = \frac{k[NH_3]}{[H_2]} \tag{45}$$

This equation is of the same form as Eq. (35); evidently the ammonia is weakly, and the hydrogen strongly, adsorbed under the conditions of their experiments. There is no inhibition by nitrogen, which apparently is only very weakly adsorbed.

Under other experimental conditions more complicated kinetic equations have sometimes been observed. Thus Winter[2] found that the decomposition on iron follows the equation

$$v = \frac{k[NH_3]}{[H_2]^{3/2}} \tag{46}$$

This and similar complex rate equations have been explained by Temkin and Pyzhev[3] in terms of the Slygin-Frumkin isotherm [Eq. (26)], which corresponds to variable heats of adsorption.

Decomposition of Phosphine. The phosphine decomposition was first investigated by van't Hoff and Kooij[4] on a glass surface. They found that the reaction was of the first order, so that their surface was sparsely covered by phosphine. Barrer[5] made an investigation of the reaction on tungsten over a wide range of pressures and observed the expected transition from first-order kinetics at low pressures to zero-order kinetics at higher pressures. He found the activation energy to vary from 26.5 kcal at low pressures to 31.3 at high pressures; the difference, 4.8 kcal, is to be regarded, according to Eq. (40), as the heat of adsorption of phosgene on the surface. A similar change from first-order to zero-order kinetics with increasing pressure was observed on a molybdenum surface by Melville and Roxburgh.[6] The activation energy fell by 7.2 kcal over the pressure range, and this may be approximately the heat of adsorption.

[1] R. M. Barrer, *Trans. Faraday Soc.*, **32**, 490 (1936).

[2] E. Winter, *Z. Physik. Chem.*, **B13**, 401 (1931).

[3] M. Temkin and V. Pyzhev, *Acta Physicochim. URSS*, **12**, 327 (1940); for a review see K. J. Laidler, Kinetic Laws in Surface Catalysis, in P. H. Emmett (ed.), "Catalysis," vol. 1, Reinhold Publishing Corporation, New York, 1954.

[4] J. H. van't Hoff and D. M. Kooij, *Z. Physik. Chem.*, **12**, 155 (1893).

[5] Barrer, *loc. cit.*

[6] H. W. Melville and H. L. Roxburgh, *J. Chem. Soc.*, 586 (1933).

Decompositions of Other Hydrides. Arsine was found by van't Hoff[1] to decompose on glass according to a first-order law, and the same type of behavior has been found in the decomposition of selenium hydride on selenium[2] and of methane on carbon.[3] For the decomposition of stibine on an antimony surface[4] the behavior is more complex, but is consistent with Eq. (29). Hinshelwood and Prichard[5] found the decomposition of hydrogen iodide on gold to be zero order, while Hinshelwood and Burk[6] found the same reaction on platinum to be first order.

Decomposition of Nitrous Oxide. A number of investigations[7] have been made of the decomposition of nitrous oxide into nitrogen and oxygen, and several different surfaces have been used. Most of the rate laws obtained are special cases of the general law

$$v = \frac{k[N_2O]}{1 + a[N_2O] + b[O_2]} \tag{47}$$

This indicates that both nitrous oxide and the product oxygen are adsorbed to an appreciable extent.

Decomposition of Formic Acid. Hinshelwood and coworkers[8] studied the kinetics of the decomposition of formic acid on a number of surfaces, including glass, platinum, silver, gold, and titanium dioxide. The first-order law was obeyed under the conditions of all of their experiments. On the glass the reaction proceeds partly as a dehydration,

(1) $$HCOOH \rightarrow CO + H_2O$$

and partly as a dehydrogenation,

(2) $$HCOOH \rightarrow CO_2 + H_2$$

The activation energy for the dehydration was found to be 16.0 kcal, and that for the dehydrogenation was 28.0 kcal. On metals the dehydrogenation predominated, whereas on titanium dioxide the dehydration was more important.

[1] J. H. van't Hoff, "Études de dynamique chimique," p. 83, F. Muller and Company, Amsterdam, 1884.

[2] M. Bodenstein, *Z. Physik. Chem.*, **29**, 429 (1899).

[3] G. M. Schwab and E. Pietsch, *ibid.*, **12**, 155 (1893).

[4] A. Stock and M. Bodenstein, *Ber.*, **40**, 570 (1907).

[5] C. N. Hinshelwood and C. R. Prichard, *J. Chem. Soc.*, **127**, 1552 (1925).

[6] C. N. Hinshelwood and R. E. Burk, *J. Chem. Soc.*, **127**, 2896 (1925).

[7] E.g., C. N. Hinshelwood and C. R. Prichard, *J. Chem. Soc.*, **127**, 327 (1925); *Proc. Roy. Soc.* (*London*), **A108**, 211 (1925); G. M. Schwab, R. Stager, and H. H. von Baumbach, *Z. Physik. Chem.*, **B21**, 65 (1933); E. W. R. Steacie and H. O. Folkins, *Can. J. Res.*, **B15**, 237 (1937).

[8] C. N. Hinshelwood, H. Hartley, and B. Topley, *Proc. Roy. Soc.* (*London*), **A100**, 575 (1922); H. C. Tingey and C. N. Hinshelwood, *J. Chem. Soc.*, **121**, 1668 (1922); C. N. Hinshelwood and B. Topley, *J. Chem. Soc.*, **123**, 1014 (1923).

Schwab and his coworkers[1] have made extensive studies of the decomposition of formic acid on a variety of alloy surfaces. Under the conditions of their experiments the kinetics were generally of zero order. These investigations were mainly concerned with the relationship between catalytic activity and the nature of the surface, and are considered again later in this chapter.

BIMOLECULAR SURFACE REACTIONS

Reaction between Two Adsorbed Molecules. It appears, as has been mentioned, that most surface reactions between two substances occur by reaction between two molecules that are adsorbed on neighboring surface sites; this is conveniently referred to as a Langmuir-Hinshelwood mechanism. The rate of such a reaction between A and B is proportional to the probability that A and B are adsorbed on neighboring sites, and this is proportional to the fractions of the surface, θ and θ', covered by A and B. These fractions were given by Eqs. (13) and (14), and the rate of reaction is therefore

$$v = k_2\theta\theta' \tag{48}$$

$$= \frac{k_2KK'pp'}{(1 + Kp + K'p')^2} \tag{49}$$

If the pressure p' is kept constant, and p is varied, the rate varies in accordance with Fig. 61; the rate first increases, passes through a maximum, and then decreases. There is a similar variation with p' if p is held constant. The physical explanation of the falling off of the rate at high pressures is that one reactant displaces the other as its pressure is increased. The maximum rate corresponds to the existence of the maximum number of neighboring A-B pairs on the surface.

Two special cases of the general equation (49) may now be considered.

1. *Sparsely Covered Surfaces.* If the pressures p and p' are both sufficiently low that Kp and Kp' may be neglected in comparison with unity, the rate equation becomes

$$v = k_2KK'pp' \tag{50}$$

The reaction is therefore second order, being first order in both A and B. A number of reactions obey this law: examples are the reaction between nitric oxide and oxygen on glass and that between ethylene and hydrogen under certain circumstances (cf. p. 278).

[1] G. M. Schwab, *Trans. Faraday Soc.*, **42,** 689 (1946); G. M. Schwab and S. Permatjoglou, *J. Phys. Colloid Chem.*, **52,** 1046 (1948); G. M. Schwab, *Discussions Faraday Soc.*, **8,** 166 (1950).

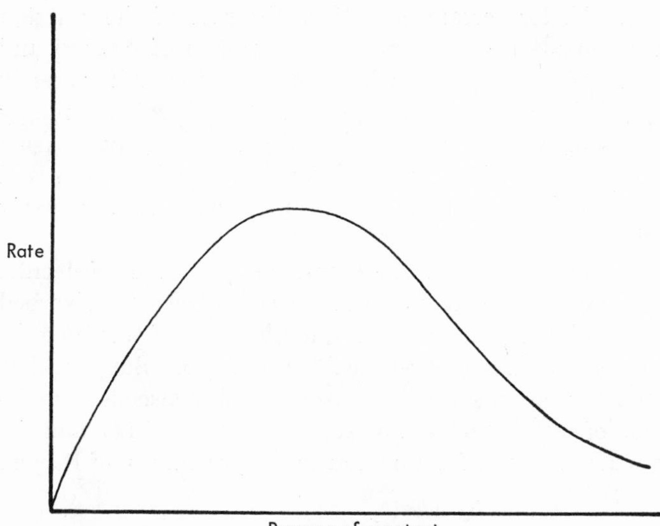

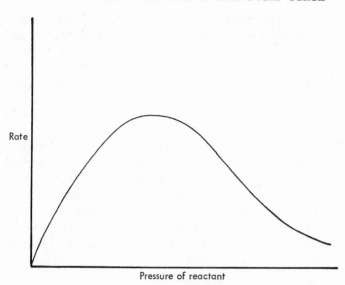

Fig. 61. Schematic representation of the variation of rate with the pressure of one reactant (the other being held constant) for a bimolecular reaction proceeding by a Langmuir-Hinshelwood mechanism [Eq. (49)].

2. *One Reactant Very Weakly Adsorbed.* If reactant A is very weakly adsorbed, the term Kp in the denominator of Eq. (49) may be neglected, and the rate equation becomes

$$v = \frac{k_2KK'pp'}{(1 + K'p')^2} \tag{51}$$

The rate is now proportional to the pressure of A, but as the pressure of B increases, the rate first increases, passes through a maximum, and then decreases (Fig. 61). Such a maximum in the rate has been observed in the reaction between hydrogen and carbon dioxide on platinum,[1] in the exchange reaction between deuterium and ammonia on iron (p. 283), and in the reaction between hydrogen and ethylene (p. 278).

If reactant B is sufficiently strongly adsorbed so that $K'p'$ is much greater than unity, the rate equation becomes

$$v = \frac{k_2Kp}{K'p'} \tag{52}$$

The rate is now inversely proportional to the pressure of the strongly adsorbed reactant B, and the order of the reaction with respect to B may

[1] C. R. Prichard and C. N. Hinshelwood, *J. Chem. Soc.*, **127**, 806 (1925).

be said to be -1. Under certain conditions the rate of the reaction between carbon monoxide and oxygen on the surfaces of quartz[1] and platinum[2] is directly proportional to the pressure of oxygen and inversely proportional to that of carbon monoxide; the latter is therefore strongly adsorbed, and as its pressure is increased, it displaces the oxygen from the surface. Another example is the reaction between hydrogen and oxygen on platinum (p. 278); the rate under certain conditions is inversely proportional to the oxygen pressure.

Reaction between a Gas Molecule and an Adsorbed Molecule. There is also the possibility that the reaction is between an adsorbed molecule and a molecule from the gas phase; mechanisms of this type are conveniently referred to as Langmuir-Rideal mechanisms. Suppose that reaction occurs between an adsorbed A molecule and a gaseous B molecule. The fraction of surface covered by A is given by Eq. (13), and the rate is now proportional to this fraction and to the pressure p' of B, viz.,

$$v = k_2\theta p \tag{53}$$

$$= \frac{k_2 K p p'}{1 + Kp + K'p'} \tag{54}$$

It is not assumed, in this mechanism, that B is not at all adsorbed, since the term $K'p'$ in the denominator corresponds to the adsorption of B; adsorbed B molecules do not enter directly into reaction, but they affect the rate by occupying surface that might otherwise be occupied by A.

Equation (54) is to be contrasted with Eq. (49) for the Langmuir-Hinshelwood mechanism. There is now no maximum in the rate as the pressure p (or p') increases; instead the rate varies with the pressure of either reactant in exactly the manner shown in Fig. 58. A decision between the two types of mechanism may therefore be made by seeing whether the rate passes through a maximum with increase in the pressure of either reactant; if it does, the Langmuir-Rideal mechanism can be excluded.

There are few well-defined examples of reactions occurring by a Langmuir-Rideal mechanism. Allen and Hinshelwood[3] studied the decomposition of acetaldehyde into methane and carbon monoxide on various surfaces; at low pressures the kinetics are second order and at high pressures first order. There seems to be no tendency for the reaction to become zero order at high pressures, which would occur if there were reaction between two adsorbed molecules. The results therefore appear to favor a Langmuir-Rideal mechanism, but more work is desirable. The reaction between ethylene and hydrogen has frequently been interpreted as occurring by a Langmuir-Rideal mechanism, and a careful investiga-

[1] M. Bodenstein and F. Ohlmer, *Z. Physik. Chem.*, **53**, 166 (1905).

[2] I. Langmuir, *Trans. Faraday Soc.*, **17**, 621 (1922).

[3] P. C. Allen and C. N. Hinshelwood, *Proc. Roy. Soc.* (*London*), **A121**, 141 (1928).

tion of the reaction on evaporated films in fact suggested that it occurs by a combination of the two mechanisms (p. 279).

The surface combinations of atoms and free radicals appear definitely to occur by Langmuir-Rideal mechanisms; these reactions are discussed later (p. 284).

Adsorption of Two Gases without Mutual Displacement. A third possibility, which occurs in one or two cases, is that there is reaction between two molecules which are adsorbed on two different types of surface site, so that they do not displace each other from the surface. The isotherm for the adsorption of gas A on sites of type 1 is

$$\frac{\theta}{1-\theta} = Kp \tag{55}$$

Similarly, for the adsorption of B on sites of type 2,

$$\frac{\theta'}{1-\theta'} = K'p' \tag{56}$$

The rate is proportional to $\theta\theta'$, so that

$$v = \frac{k_2 K K' p p'}{(1 + Kp)(1 + K'p')} \tag{57}$$

This dependence of rate on p and p' is quite different from that of Eqs. (49) and (54), and this case is readily distinguished by measuring rates over a wide range of pressures.

Equation (57) has been found to be applicable to the reaction between hydrogen and nitrous oxide on gold,[1] and to the reaction between hydrogen and carbon dioxide on tungsten.[2]

Inhibition of Bimolecular Surface Reactions. Inhibition equations for reactions of this type may readily be derived, and only a few simple cases need be considered. Consider a reaction between A and B occurring by a Langmuir-Hinshelwood mechanism and inhibited by a gaseous substance of partial pressure p_i. The fractions covered by A and B are easily shown to be

$$\theta = \frac{Kp}{1 + Kp + K'p' + K_i p_i} \tag{58}$$

and

$$\theta' = \frac{K'p'}{1 + Kp + K'p' + K_i p_i} \tag{59}$$

The rate is therefore

$$v = k_2 \theta\theta' \tag{60}$$

$$= \frac{k_2 K K' p p'}{(1 + Kp + K'p' + K_i p_i)^2} \tag{61}$$

[1] W. H. Hutchison and C. N. Hinshelwood, *J. Chem. Soc.*, **129**, 1556 (1926).

[2] C. R. Prichard and C. N. Hinshelwood, *J. Chem. Soc.*, **127**, 1546 (1925).

If the inhibitor is a diatomic molecule that is adsorbed atomically, the corresponding equation is

$$v = \frac{k_2 K K' p p'}{(1 + Kp + K'p' + K_i^{1/2} p_i^{1/2})^2} \tag{62}$$

If there is sparse coverage by reactant molecules and large coverage by inhibitor, the equation becomes

$$v = \frac{k_2 K K' p p'}{K_i p_i} \tag{63}$$

A few examples of bimolecular surface reactions will now be considered.

Hydrogen-Oxygen Reaction. The reaction between hydrogen and oxygen has been investigated under a wide variety of conditions, and very different types of behavior have been observed. On a porcelain surface Bodenstein[1] found that the rate was proportional to the pressures of both hydrogen and oxygen, which means that the surface is sparsely covered by both reactants. On a variety of surfaces including silver, gold, copper, and nickel the reaction has been found[2] to be first order in hydrogen and zero order in oxygen, and therefore to be consistent with a Langmuir-Rideal mechanism. On a platinum surface inhibition by oxygen has been detected,[3] while on silver[3] there is inhibition by water, the product of reaction.

Ethylene-Hydrogen Reaction. A considerable amount of kinetic work has been done on the hydrogenation of ethylene, on a variety of surfaces, and there has been much uncertainty both as to the facts and to the mechanisms involved. Quite different behavior is observed under different conditions, and it appears that reaction may occur by two or more mechanisms at the same time.

An investigation by Pease[4] of the reaction on a copper surface indicated that the rate is proportional to the hydrogen pressure and that it passes through a maximum as the ethylene pressure is increased, the rate ultimately becoming inversely proportional to the ethylene pressure. The rate law is, to a good approximation,

$$v = \frac{k[H_2][C_2H_4]}{(1 + K[C_2H_4])^2} \tag{64}$$

[1] M. Bodenstein, *Z. Physik. Chem.*, **29**, 665 (1899).

[2] W. A. Bone and R. V. Wheeler, *Phil. Trans.*, **A206**, 1 (1906); R. N. Pease and H. S. Taylor, *J. Am. Chem. Soc.*, **43**, 2179 (1921); **44**, 1637 (1922); A. F. Benton and P. H. Emmett, *ibid.*, **48**, 632 (1926); cf. also R. P. Donnelly, *J. Chem. Soc.*, **132**, 2438 (1929).

[3] I. Langmuir, *Trans. Faraday Soc.*, **17**, 621 (1922).

[4] R. N. Pease, *J. Am. Chem. Soc.*, **45**, 1196 (1923).

which is of the same form as Eq. (51). This result is consistent with a Langmuir-Hinshelwood mechanism, with the ethylene more strongly adsorbed than the hydrogen.

The facts regarding the reaction on a nickel surface have been a matter of some controversy. Several workers[1] have obtained results that are consistent with the rate equation,

$$v = \frac{k[H_2][C_2H_4]}{1 + K[C_2H_4]} \tag{65}$$

This type of behavior is consistent with a Langmuir-Rideal mechanism, and Beeck[2] and Jenkins and Rideal[3] have suggested that reaction occurs between a pair of adsorbed hydrogen atoms and a gaseous ethylene molecule:

$$\begin{array}{c}\mathrm{H}\;\;\mathrm{H}\\ |\;\;\;|\\ \text{—S—S—}\end{array} + C_2H_4 \rightarrow \begin{array}{c}|\;\;\;|\\ \text{—S—S—}\end{array} + C_2H_6$$

Toyama,[4] on the other hand, obtained definite evidence that the rate fell at high ethylene pressures, a fact that requires that the Langmuir-Hinshelwood mechanism play a role. A similar result was obtained by Laidler and Townshend[5] in an investigation, using an evaporated nickel surface, that was primarily concerned with distinguishing between the two mechanisms. They found that the kinetic behavior depended to a considerable extent upon which gas was first admitted to the surface (or whether both were admitted together). Laidler and Townshend interpreted their and other results on the basis of the hypothesis that two mechanisms are taking place simultaneously. One mechanism, favored by prior addition of ethylene or by the presence of excess of ethylene, is the Langmuir-Hinshelwood one. The second, favored by prior addition of hydrogen or excess of hydrogen, is the Langmuir-Rideal mechanism between adsorbed hydrogen and gaseous ethylene. These conclusions throw light on apparent discrepancies among the results of previous workers, who used a variety of experimental conditions and usually did not specify how the gases were introduced to the reaction vessel.

On the basis of much evidence[6] regarding the way in which hydrogen and ethylene are adsorbed, Laidler and Townshend concluded that a molecular mechanism previously proposed by Markham, Wall, and

[1] E. K. Rideal, *J. Chem. Soc.*, **121**, 309 (1922); H. Zur Strassen, *Z. Physik. Chem.*, **A169**, 81 (1934); A. Farkas, L. Farkas, and E. K. Rideal, *Proc. Roy. Soc.* (*London*), **A171**, 55 (1939); O. Beeck, *Rev. Mod. Phys.*, **17**, 61 (1945).

[2] Beeck, *ibid.*, **20**, 127 (1948); *Discussions Faraday Soc.*, **8**, 118, 126, 193 (1956).

[3] G. I. Jenkins and E. K. Rideal, *J. Chem. Soc.*, 2490, 2496 (1955).

[4] O. Toyama, *Rev. Phys. Chem. Japan*, **11**, 153 (1937).

[5] K. J. Laidler and R. E. Townshend, *Trans. Faraday Soc.*, **57**, 1590 (1961).

[6] E.g., Jenkins and Rideal, *loc. cit.*; C. Kemball, *J. Chem. Soc.*, 735 (1956).

Laidler[1] was applicable to the reactions. According to this scheme, ethylene may become "associatively" adsorbed on a pair of bare surface sites,

$$\text{(1)} \qquad C_2H_4 + -\overset{|}{S}-\overset{|}{S}- \rightleftharpoons \begin{array}{c} CH_2-CH_2 \\ | \qquad | \\ -S-\!-\!-S- \end{array}$$

In addition, an ethylene molecule from the gas phase may add on to an adsorbed hydrogen atom to form an alkyl radical,

$$\text{(2)} \qquad C_2H_4 + \begin{array}{c} H \\ | \\ -S- \end{array} \rightleftharpoons \begin{array}{c} CH_3 \\ / \\ CH_2 \\ | \\ -S- \end{array}$$

Adsorbed alkyl radicals may also be formed from adsorbed ethylene molecules and neighboring adsorbed hydrogen atoms. Ethane is produced in the gas phase either by interaction between two neighboring adsorbed alkyl radicals,

$$\text{(3)} \qquad \begin{array}{cc} CH_3 & CH_3 \\ | & | \\ CH_2 & CH_2 \\ | & | \\ -S- & -S- \end{array} \rightleftharpoons \begin{array}{c} CH_2-CH_2 \\ | \qquad | \\ -S-\!-\!-S- \end{array} + CH_3CH_3$$

or by interaction between an adsorbed alkyl radical and an adsorbed hydrogen atom,

$$\text{(4)} \qquad \begin{array}{cc} CH_3 & \\ | & \\ CH_2 & H \\ | & | \\ -S- & -S- \end{array} \rightleftharpoons -\overset{|}{S}-\overset{|}{S}- + CH_3CH_3$$

This mechanism is of the Langmuir-Hinshelwood type; the Rideal mechanism is shown on page 279.

Ethylene-Deuterium Exchange Reaction. Some kinetic studies have been made[2] of the exchange reaction between ethylene and deuterium on a nickel surface. The results are not clear-cut, but Laidler, Wall, and Markham[3] have shown that the rate is probably proportional to the first power of the ethylene pressure and to the square root of the

[1] M. C. Markham, M. C. Wall, and K. J. Laidler, *J. Chem. Phys.*, **20**, 1331 (1952); **21**, 949 (1953).

[2] G. H. Twigg and E. K. Rideal, *Proc. Roy. Soc.* (*London*), **A171**, 55 (1939); G. K. T. Conn and G. H. Twigg, *Proc. Roy. Soc.* (*London*), **A171**, 70 (1939); C. Kemball, *J. Chem. Soc.*, 735 (1956).

[3] K. J. Laidler, M. C. Wall, and M. C. Markham, *J. Chem. Phys.*, **21**, 949 (1953).

deuterium pressure. The mechanism proposed by them[1] involves the formation of mixed ethyl radicals by reaction between adsorbed deuterium atoms and ethylene molecules,

$$\text{(1)} \qquad C_2H_4 + \begin{array}{c} D \\ | \\ -S- \end{array} \rightleftharpoons \begin{array}{l} \quad CH_2D \\ \ / \\ CH_2 \\ \ | \\ -S- \end{array}$$

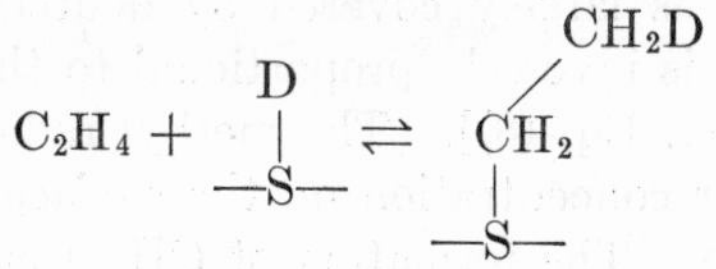

or

$$\text{(2)} \qquad \begin{array}{ccccc} CH_2 & - & CH_2 & & D \\ | & & | & & | \\ -S & - & S & - & S \end{array} \rightleftharpoons \begin{array}{l} \quad CH_2D \\ \ / \\ CH_2 \\ \ | \qquad | \quad | \\ -S - S - S \end{array}$$

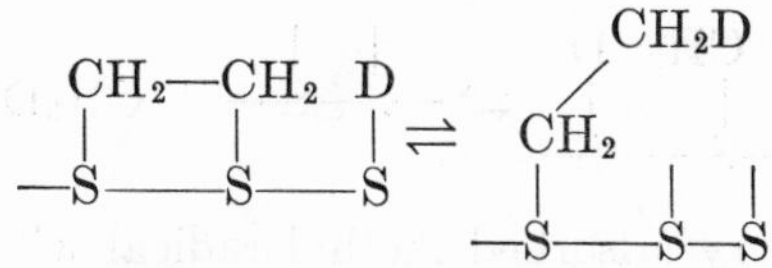

Surface exchange may occur by interaction between adsorbed alkyl radicals and adsorbed ethylene molecules,

$$\text{(3)} \qquad \begin{array}{ccc} CH_2D & & \\ | & & \\ CH_2 & CH_2 - & CH_2 \\ | & | & | \\ S - & S - & S \end{array} \rightleftharpoons \begin{array}{ccc} & & CH_3 \\ & & | \\ CH_2 - & CH_2D & CH_2 \\ | & | & | \\ -S - & S - & S- \end{array}$$

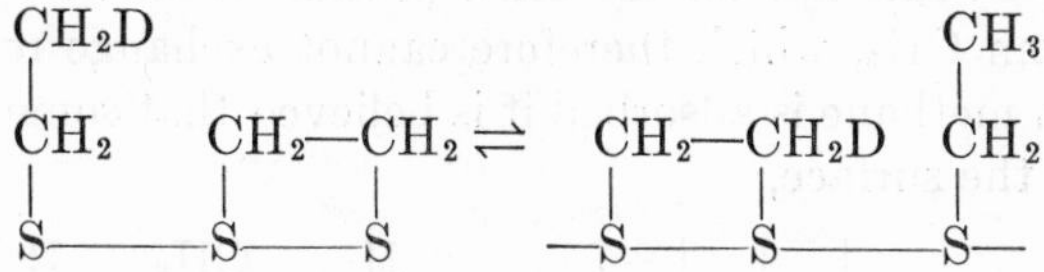

Species such as C_2HD_3 and C_2D_4 are obtained in the initial stages of the reaction,[2] and this is explained if reactions (2) and (3) occur very rapidly; the evidence, in fact, suggests that there is a complete mixing of the H and D atoms on the surface. Since the concentration of adsorbed D atoms is proportional to the square root of the pressure, the exchange rate will be proportional to the square root of the pressure, as is believed to be the case.

Methane-Deuterium Exchange Reactions. The exchange reactions between methane and deuterium have been studied by Kemball,[3] who used evaporated nickel surfaces. He found that all the products, CH_3D, CH_2D_2, CHD_3, and CD_4, were produced in the initial stages of the reaction; this behavior is to be contrasted with that found with ammonia (p. 282), where the products are formed by consecutive reactions. The rates of formation of all of the methanes are proportional to the first power of the methane pressure. The rate of formation of CH_3D is inversely proportional to the square root of the deuterium pressure, whereas the rates of formation of CH_2D_2, CHD_3, and CD_4 are inversely proportional to the first power of the deuterium pressure.

These results suggest that two different exchange mechanisms are involved, one leading to the production of CH_3D, and the other to the

[1] Cf. also Laidler and Townshend, *loc. cit.*

[2] C. Kemball, *J. Chem. Soc.*, 735 (1956).

[3] C. Kemball, *Proc. Roy. Soc.* (*London*), **A207**, 539 (1951).

production of CH_2D_2, CHD_3, and CD_4. Kemball suggested that CH_3D is formed from adsorbed CH_3 radicals, and the other products from adsorbed CH_2 radicals which rapidly exchange with adsorbed deuterium atoms. The surface is largely covered by deuterium atoms, and the number of bare sites is inversely proportional to the square root of the deuterium pressure [cf. Eq. (8)]. The methyl radicals are adsorbed on single sites, and their concentration on the surface is therefore proportional to $[CH_4]/[D_2]^{1/2}$. The formation of CH_3D is explained as due to the reaction

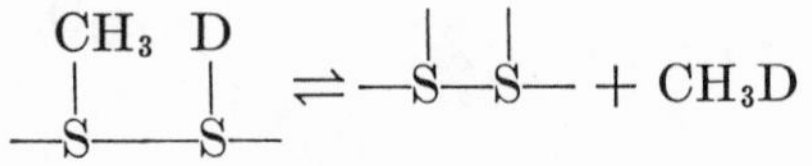

$$\begin{array}{cc} CH_3 & D \\ | & | \\ -S- & -S- \end{array} \rightleftharpoons \begin{array}{cc} | & | \\ -S- & S- \end{array} + CH_3D$$

Since practically every adsorbed methyl radical will have a deuterium atom as a near neighbor, the rate of production of CH_3D is proportional to $[CH_4]/[D_2]^{1/2}$.

The different rate law for the other products indicates that they are not formed from CH_3, which therefore cannot exchange readily with D atoms. When methane is adsorbed it is believed that some CH_2 radicals are formed on the surface,

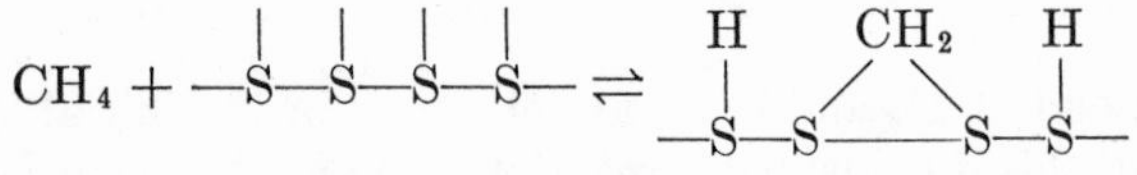

$$CH_4 + \begin{array}{cccc} | & | & | & | \\ -S- & S- & S- & S- \end{array} \rightleftharpoons \begin{array}{ccccc} H & & CH_2 & & H \\ | & / & & \backslash & | \\ -S- & S- & & -S- & S- \end{array}$$

Since these are adsorbed on a pair of sites, their concentration will be proportional to the square of the number of bare sites, i.e., to $1/[D_2]$. The adsorbed CH_2 radicals are assumed to exchange readily with neighboring D atoms, so that CH_2, CHD, and CD_2 radicals are present on the surface in amounts that depend on statistical factors. Their concentrations will be proportional to $[CH_4]/[D_2]$. The rates of production of CH_2D_2, CHD_3, and CD_4, by reactions such as

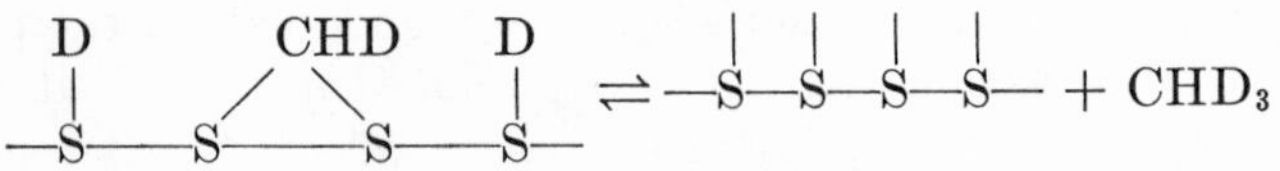

$$\begin{array}{ccccc} D & & CHD & & D \\ | & / & & \backslash & | \\ -S- & S- & & -S- & S- \end{array} \rightleftharpoons \begin{array}{cccc} | & | & | & | \\ -S- & S- & S- & S- \end{array} + CHD_3$$

will therefore also be proportional to $[CH_4]/[D_2]$.

Ammonia-Deuterium Exchange Reaction. The exchange reaction between ammonia and deuterium, with the formation of NH_2D, NHD_2, and ND_3, offers an interesting contrast in that, on a number of surfaces (including nickel and platinum), the products are formed in consecutive reactions.[1] The initial product is NH_2D, and NHD_2 is formed from it in a subsequent independent reaction; finally ND_3 is formed from NHD_2. These results are most simply explained on the assumption that ammonia on adsorption is dissociated only into NH_2 and H, and that the former

[1] C. Kemball, *ibid.*, **A217**, 376 (1953).

can merely add on a deuterium atom,

$$\underset{\text{—S——S—}}{\overset{\text{NH}_2\quad\text{D}}{|\qquad|}} \rightleftharpoons \text{—}\overset{|}{\text{S}}\text{—}\overset{|}{\text{S}}\text{—} + NH_2D$$

The adsorbed radical NH_2 apparently cannot undergo exchange with an adsorbed deuterium atom.

A number of studies have been made of the dependence of the exchange rate on the concentrations of ammonia and deuterium. Farkas[1] used a pure iron surface and found that the rate was proportional to the square root of the deuterium pressure and independent of the ammonia pressure. Weber and Laidler[2] worked with an activated iron surface and also observed the square-root dependence on deuterium pressure. They found, however, that the rate passed through a maximum as the ammonia pressure was increased, and could be fitted to the Langmuir-Hinshelwood equation,

$$v = \frac{k[D_2]^{1/2}[NH_3]}{(1 + K[NH_3])^2} \tag{66}$$

The conclusion is that the surface is rather heavily covered by NH_2 radicals, and only sparsely by D atoms, and that reaction occurs between these two adsorbed species.

Somewhat different results were obtained by Singleton, Roberts, and Winter,[3] who used evaporated films of iron, tungsten, and nickel. Their results are consistent with the hypothesis that the Langmuir-Hinshelwood mechanism applies at lower pressures of ammonia. At higher pressures of ammonia the rate does not fall toward zero, but only to a constant level, and the rate is then proportional to the first power of the deuterium pressure. It appears that under these conditions a Langmuir-Rideal mechanism predominates, reaction being between an adsorbed NH_2 radical and a gaseous deuterium molecule:

$$\underset{\text{—S—}}{\overset{NH_2}{|}} + D_2 \rightleftharpoons \underset{\text{—S—}}{\overset{D}{|}} + NH_2D$$

SOME SPECIAL TYPES OF REACTIONS

Certain reactions are not conveniently classified as either unimolecular or bimolecular, and are now considered separately.

The Parahydrogen Conversion. Parahydrogen becomes converted into the equilibrium mixture of the ortho and para forms by being brought

[1] A. Farkas, *Trans. Faraday Soc.*, **32**, 416 (1936).

[2] J. Weber and K. J. Laidler, *J. Chem. Phys.*, **19**, 1089 (1951).

[3] J. H. Singleton, E. R. Roberts, and E. R. S. Winter, *Trans. Faraday Soc.*, **47**, 1318 (1951).

into contact with metal surfaces, especially those of the transition metals which are particularly effective in adsorbing hydrogen. The reaction probably occurs[1] by a mechanism originally proposed by Bonhoeffer and Farkas.[2] This mechanism may be represented as

$$p\text{-H}_2 + \begin{array}{c}|\quad|\\ \text{—S—S—}\end{array} \rightleftharpoons \begin{array}{c}\text{H}\quad\text{H}\\ |\quad\ |\\ \text{—S—S—}\end{array} \rightleftharpoons \begin{array}{c}|\quad|\\ \text{—S—S—}\end{array} + o\text{-H}_2$$

The hydrogen becomes adsorbed on the surface and is then desorbed; since adsorption involves dissociation, the desorption process leads to the equilibrium mixture. The order of the reaction is close to zero,[3] a result that can be reconciled with the Bonhoeffer-Farkas mechanism.

Surface Combination of Atoms and Radicals. Atoms and free radicals combine on most surfaces, and kinetic studies have been made of a number of systems. In almost all the cases investigated the reactions are first-order processes[4] which become second order at higher temperatures.[5] One mechanism that is consistent with this behavior is that reaction occurs between a gaseous atom or radical and an adsorbed one; thus, for the recombination of hydrogen atoms this mechanism would be

$$\text{H} + \begin{array}{c}\text{H}\\ |\\ \text{—S—}\end{array} \rightarrow \begin{array}{c}|\\ \text{—S—}\end{array} + \text{H}_2$$

If the surface is fully covered by atoms, the rate is proportional to the pressure of the atoms; i.e., the kinetics are first order. At higher temperatures the surface becomes sparsely covered, and the fraction covered is proportional to the atomic concentration; the kinetics are then second order.

The kinetic equations for this mechanism may be formulated as follows: The fraction covered depends on the atomic pressure p according to the isotherm

$$\frac{\theta}{1-\theta} = Kp \tag{67}$$

[1] For a detailed discussion of the mechanism, which involves some complex features, see K. J. Laidler, *J. Phys. Chem.*, **57**, 320 (1953); also K. J. Laidler, in P. H. Emmett (ed.), "Catalysis," vol. 1, pp. 178–180, Reinhold Publishing Corporation, New York, 1954.

[2] K. F. Bonhoeffer and A. Farkas, *Z. Physik. Chem.*, **B12**, 231 (1931); K. F. Bonhoeffer, A. Farkas, and K. W. Rummel, *ibid.*, **B21**, 225 (1933).

[3] D. D. Eley and E. K. Rideal, *Proc. Roy. Soc.* (*London*), **A178**, 429 (1941).

[4] L. von Muffling, "Handbuch der Katalyse," vol. VI, p. 94, J. Springer, Vienna, 1943; W. V. Smith, *J. Chem. Phys.*, **11**, 110 (1941).

[5] W. Buben and A. Schechter, *Acta Physicochim. URSS*, **10**, 371 (1939); F. Paneth, W. Hofeditz, and A. Wunsch, *J. Chem. Soc.*, 372 (1935); F. Paneth and W. Lautsch, *Ber.*, **64B**, 2708 (1931).

The rate is proportional to θ and to p, whence

$$v = kp\theta \tag{68}$$

$$= \frac{kKp^2}{1 + Kp} \tag{69}$$

At lower temperatures the surface may be fully covered, which means that $Kp \gg 1$; in this case

$$v = kp \tag{70}$$

and the kinetics are first order. At higher temperatures, on the other hand, $Kp \ll 1$, so that

$$v = kKp^2 \tag{71}$$

and the kinetics are second order. It is to be noted that this mechanism is of the Langmuir-Rideal type.

Doubt as to whether this is the correct mechanism is, however, cast by some work on the reverse reaction, as will now be considered.

The Production of Atoms at Hot Surfaces. It was first shown by Langmuir[1] that hydrogen atoms are produced from hydrogen molecules at a hot tungsten surface, and Bryce[2] showed that the rate of reaction is approximately proportional to the square root of the hydrogen pressure. Roberts and Bryce[3] proposed a mechanism in which a hydrogen molecule strikes a bare site, whereupon one atom is adsorbed and the other passes into the gas phase,

$$\text{H—H} + \underset{}{\overset{|}{\text{—S—}}} \rightarrow \underset{\text{—S—}}{\overset{\text{H}}{|}} + \text{H}$$

This mechanism is the reverse of that considered above, for the combination reactions. It accounts for the pressure dependence of the rate, provided that the surface is fully covered; the fraction of surface bare is then inversely proportional to the square root of the pressure, so that the rate, being proportional both to the pressure and the fraction bare, is proportional to the square root of the pressure. Laidler[4] has discussed the mechanism in some detail and concluded that this mechanism is the correct one.

A more recent experimental investigation by Brennan and Fletcher[5] has, however, led to results that were different from those previously obtained, and has cast doubt on the Roberts-Bryce mechanism. As an alternative they propose that the hydrogen becomes adsorbed in the

[1] I. Langmuir, *J. Am. Chem. Soc.*, **34**, 1310 (1912); **37**, 417 (1915).
[2] G. Bryce, *Proc. Cambridge Phil. Soc.*, **32**, 648 (1936).
[3] J. K. Roberts and G. Bryce, *ibid.*, 653.
[4] K. J. Laidler, *J. Phys. Colloid Chem.*, **55**, 1067 (1951).
[5] D. Brennan and P. C. Fletcher, *Proc. Roy. Soc.* (*London*), **A250**, 389 (1959).

atomic form,

$$\mathrm{H_2} + \underset{|}{\text{—S}}\underset{|}{\text{—S—}} \rightleftharpoons \begin{matrix}\mathrm{H} & \mathrm{H}\\ | & |\\ \text{—S} & \text{—S—}\end{matrix}$$

and that hydrogen atoms become desorbed,

$$\begin{matrix}\mathrm{H}\\ |\\ \text{—S—}\end{matrix} \rightarrow \text{—}\overset{|}{\mathrm{S}}\text{—} + \mathrm{H}$$

They further conclude that at the temperatures of their experiments the adsorbed atoms have full translational motion on the surface. It is likely that different mechanisms apply under different experimental conditions.

ABSOLUTE RATES OF SURFACE REACTIONS

Attention has so far been confined, in this chapter, to the question of the influence of concentrations on rates, without regard to the absolute rates of the reactions. The treatment of this latter problem involves, as with all reactions, two types of consideration. The first is a calculation by quantum-mechanical methods of the energy of activation; the second is the evaluation of the partition functions for the initial and activated states. The first problem is a very difficult one; approximate methods have to be used, and good agreement with experiment has never yet been achieved. In addition to the usual complications of such calculations, there is the difficulty that relatively little is known about the exact nature of the surfaces that are involved in catalysis.

The second type of procedure, the calculation of absolute rates using partition functions, use being made of experimental energies of activation, has been carried out much more successfully. The application of absolute-rate theory to surface reactions was first done in any detail by Laidler, Glasstone, and Eyring,[1] and a number of different types of reactions have been treated,[2] all with comparative success. Since this whole question has been reviewed in considerable detail,[3] only a very brief discussion is given here.

It should be noted that the theory can only be profitably applied to investigations in which the surface area is known, and in which the

[1] K. J. Laidler, S. Glasstone, and H. Eyring, *J. Chem. Phys.*, **8**, 667 (1940); cf. B. Topley, *Nature*, **128**, 115 (1931); R. E. Burk, *J. Am. Chem. Soc.*, **56**, 1279 (1935).

[2] K. J. Laidler, *J. Phys. Chem.*, **57**, 320 (1953); M. C. Markham, M. C. Wall, and K. J. Laidler, *ibid.*, 321; K. J. Laidler, M. C. Wall, and M. C. Markham, *J. Chem. Phys.*, **21**, 149 (1953).

[3] K. J. Laidler, Absolute Rates of Surface Reactions, in P. H. Emmett (ed.), "Catalysis," chap 5, Reinhold Publishing Corporation, New York, 1954.

surface is reasonably smooth; only if these conditions are satisfied can one make a reliable estimate of the number of surface sites.

Absolute Rates of Adsorption. The process of adsorption is a bimolecular reaction between surface sites and gas molecules; the case of the localized activated complex will be considered first. Let N_s, N_g, and $N_\ddagger$ be the numbers of bare sites, gas molecules, and activated complexes, respectively, and let the corresponding concentrations be $c_s(= N_s/S)$, $c_g(= N_g/V)$, and $c_\ddagger(= N_\ddagger/S)$. The usual assumption of equilibrium between the activated complexes and the reactants then gives rise to the equation

$$\frac{c_\ddagger}{c_g c_s} = \frac{f^\ddagger}{F_g f_s} e^{-\epsilon_1/\mathbf{k}T} \tag{72}$$

As in Eq. (17), the partition functions $f^\ddagger$ and f_s relate to unit surface area, and F_g relates to unit volume. The energy ϵ_1 is the energy of the complexes with reference to the reactants, at the absolute zero, and is therefore the activation energy per molecule at that temperature.

As pointed out in Chap. 3, the partition function F_g can be factorized into translational, rotational, and vibrational factors. If the activated complex is localized on the surface, it has no translational or rotational motion, but it undergoes various types of vibrational motion. As previously (p. 76), one of the vibrational factors in the partition function corresponds to a very loose vibration, and may be expressed as $\mathbf{k}T/\mathbf{h}\nu$, where ν is the frequency of the vibration. Equation (72) may therefore be expressed as

$$\frac{c_\ddagger}{c_g c_s} = \frac{f_\ddagger(\mathbf{k}T/\mathbf{h}\nu)}{F_g f_s} e^{-\epsilon_1/\mathbf{k}T} \tag{73}$$

where the partition function $f_\ddagger$ lacks the contribution for the one degree of freedom. Equation (73) rearranges to

$$\nu c_\ddagger = c_g c_s \frac{\mathbf{k}T}{\mathbf{h}} \frac{f_\ddagger}{F_g f_s} e^{-\epsilon_1/\mathbf{k}T} \tag{74}$$

The frequency ν is the frequency of vibration of the activated complexes in the degree of freedom corresponding to their transformation into adsorbed molecules. The expression on the left-hand side of Eq. (74) is thus the product of the concentration $c_\ddagger$ of complexes and the frequency of their transformation; it is therefore the rate of the adsorption process, which is thus given by the expression on the right-hand side of the equation, viz.,

$$v_1 = c_g c_s \frac{\mathbf{k}T}{\mathbf{h}} \frac{f_\ddagger}{F_g f_s} e^{-\epsilon_1/\mathbf{k}T} \tag{75}$$

The partition functions may now be evaluated in the same manner as in the equilibrium equations. There are no translational and rotational factors in $f_\ddagger$, and the remainder, due to vibration, will be represented by $b_\ddagger$. The function f_s is taken as unity since the surface atoms can undergo only very restricted vibration, while F_g will be written as $(2\pi m\mathbf{k}T)^{3/2}b_g/\mathbf{h}^3$, where b_g represents the vibrational and rotational factors. Substitution of these values gives

$$v_1 = c_g c_s \frac{\mathbf{k}T}{\mathbf{h}} \frac{b_\ddagger}{[(2\pi m\mathbf{k}T)^{3/2}/\mathbf{h}^3]b_g} e^{-\epsilon_1/\mathbf{k}T} \tag{76}$$

If the gas is diatomic, factor b_g contains the rotational factor $8\pi^2 I\mathbf{k}T/\sigma\mathbf{h}^2$, where σ is the symmetry number,[1] and in addition contains a vibrational factor. At ordinary temperatures the latter is close to unity, and therefore can be omitted. Similarly $b_\ddagger$ is very close to unity, apart from a symmetry factor $1/\sigma_\ddagger$; the rate expression can therefore be written as

$$v_1 = c_g c_s \frac{\mathbf{k}T}{\mathbf{h}} \frac{1/\sigma_\ddagger}{\frac{(2\pi m\mathbf{k}T)^{3/2}}{\mathbf{h}^3} \frac{8\pi^2 I\mathbf{k}T}{\mathbf{h}^2}} e^{-\epsilon_1/\mathbf{k}T} \tag{77}$$

$$= c_g c_s \frac{\sigma}{\sigma_\ddagger} \frac{\mathbf{h}^4}{8\pi^2 I(2\pi m\mathbf{k}T)^{3/2}} e^{-\epsilon_1/\mathbf{k}T} \tag{78}$$

In the above it has been assumed that in the formation of the activated state the gas molecule becomes attached to only one adsorption site. In many cases two adjacent sites, i.e., a dual site, are necessary for adsorption. If this is so, Eq. (78) still gives the rate of adsorption provided that c_s is replaced by c_{s_2}, the concentration of such dual sites. If the surface is bare, the number of dual sites is related to the number of single sites as follows. Each single site has a certain number s of adjacent sites; s is known as the coordination number of the surface and depends upon the particular type of surface lattice. If the number of dual sites were evaluated by counting s for each single site, the result would be sc_s, but in this procedure each pair is counted twice; the actual number of dual sites is $\frac{1}{2}sc_s$. The rate of adsorption on dual sites is thus given by replacing c_s in the above expression by $\frac{1}{2}sc_s$,

$$v_1 = \frac{1}{2} s c_g c_s \frac{\sigma}{\sigma_\ddagger} \frac{\mathbf{h}^4}{8\pi^2 I(2\pi m\mathbf{k}T)^{3/2}} e^{-\epsilon_1/\mathbf{k}T} \tag{79}$$

This expression is, however, only valid for adsorption on an initially bare surface; in other words, it applies only to initial rates of adsorption on dual sites. If the fraction of surface already covered is θ, the average number of bare sites adjacent to any given site is, assuming random distribution, $s(1 - \theta)$. The total number of bare dual sites is therefore

[1] As discussed on page 84, this treatment requires modification under certain circumstances.

now $\frac{1}{2}c_s s(1 - \theta)$. If the concentration of covered single sites is c_a, θ is given by

$$\theta = \frac{c_a}{c_a + c_s} \tag{80}$$

so that the concentration of bare dual sites is

$$c_{s_2} = \frac{\frac{1}{2}c_s{}^2 s}{c_a + c_s} \tag{81}$$

$$= \frac{\frac{1}{2}sc_s{}^2}{L} \tag{82}$$

where $L = c_a + c_s$ is the total concentration of single sites when the surface is completely bare. The rate of adsorption on dual sites is thus generally given by replacing c_s in Eq. (78) by c_{s_2}, using Eq. (82), and the expression obtained is

$$v_1 = \frac{sc_g c_s{}^2}{2L} \frac{\sigma}{\sigma_\ddagger} \frac{\mathbf{h}^4}{8\pi^2 I(2\pi m\mathbf{k}T)^{3/2}} e^{-\epsilon/_1\mathbf{k}T} \tag{83}$$

This reduces to Eq. (79) if $L = c_s$, which is so if the surface is completely bare.

The rate equations are quite different if the molecules are not localized in the adsorbed state, and hence presumably in the activated state. The equilibrium between initial and activated states may now be represented by

$$K_c = \frac{c_\ddagger}{c_g} = \frac{N_\ddagger/S}{N_g/V} = \frac{F^\ddagger}{F_g} \tag{84}$$

where F_g and $F^\ddagger$ are the partition functions for unit volume of gas and per square centimeter of activated complex, respectively. By exactly the same methods as used previously it can easily be shown that the rate of adsorption is given by

$$v_1 = c_g \frac{\mathbf{k}T}{\mathbf{h}} \frac{F_\ddagger}{F_g} e^{-\epsilon_1/\mathbf{k}T} \tag{85}$$

where $F_\ddagger$ differs from $F^\ddagger$ in lacking the $\mathbf{k}T/\mathbf{h}\nu$ factor corresponding to reaction. The activated complexes now differ from the reactants by having translational freedom in only two dimensions, and the ratio $F_\ddagger/F_g$ is thus simply $\mathbf{h}/(2\pi m\mathbf{k}T)^{1/2}$. The rate of adsorption thus becomes

$$v_1 = c_g \frac{\mathbf{k}T}{\mathbf{h}} \frac{\mathbf{h}}{(2\pi m\mathbf{k}T)^{1/2}} e^{-\epsilon_1/\mathbf{k}T} \tag{86}$$

Replacement of $c_g\mathbf{k}T$ by the pressure p, for the special case of zero activation energy, gives

$$v_1 = \frac{p}{(2\pi m\mathbf{k}T)^{1/2}} \tag{87}$$

This equation is the classical Hertz-Knudsen equation for the number of gas molecules striking 1 sq cm of surface in unit time. Equation (87) is often used for calculating rates of adsorption when there is no activation energy, but it should be emphasized that it is only applicable when the adsorbed molecules are not localized on the surface, and this is by no means always the case. For a localized layer Eq. (78) or (83) should be used; these expressions correspond to very much lower rates of adsorption than does Eq. (87).

Equations for absolute rates of adsorption can also be formulated for adsorption with dissociation; they will not be derived here.

Absolute Rates of Desorption. The process of desorption of undissociated molecules held in a localized layer will be considered first. Desorption from such a layer involves an activated state in which the molecule has acquired the necessary configuration and activation energy to escape from the surface. If N_a and $N_\ddagger$ are the numbers of adsorbed molecules and activated complexes, and c_a and $c_\ddagger$ are the corresponding concentrations, in molecules per square centimeter, the equilibrium between the initial and activated states may be written as

$$K_c = \frac{c_\ddagger}{c_a} = \frac{N_\ddagger/S}{N_a/S} = \frac{f^\ddagger}{f_a} e^{-\epsilon_{-1}/\mathbf{k}T} \tag{88}$$

where ϵ_{-1} is the activation energy for desorption at the absolute zero. The concentration of activated complexes is therefore given by

$$c_\ddagger = c_a \frac{f^\ddagger}{f_a} e^{-\epsilon_{-1}/\mathbf{k}T} \tag{89}$$

Application of the methods employed earlier gives rise to the rate expression

$$v_{-1} = c_a \frac{\mathbf{k}T}{\mathbf{h}} \frac{f_\ddagger}{f_a} e^{-\epsilon_{-1}/\mathbf{k}T} \tag{90}$$

where $f_\ddagger$ differs from $f^\ddagger$ in no longer including the partition function $(\mathbf{k}T/\mathbf{h}\nu)$ for passage across the potential-energy barrier.

Unimolecular Reactions. The absolute rates of ordinary chemical reactions can be formulated in a very similar way to those of adsorption processes. Unimolecular reactions will be considered first: these involve reaction between a gas molecule and a surface site, to give an activated complex at the surface.

Consider a reaction involving one molecule of the gaseous reactant A, which is undergoing reaction on the surface. If the process occurs on a single site S, it may be written as

$$\mathrm{A} + S \rightleftharpoons \mathrm{A}S^\ddagger \rightarrow \text{products}$$

and the equilibrium between initial and activated states is

$$\frac{c_\ddagger}{c_g c_s} = \frac{f^\ddagger}{F_g f_s} e^{-\epsilon_0/\mathbf{k}T} \tag{91}$$

where ϵ_0 is the energy of activation at the absolute zero. The rate of reaction is therefore given by

$$v = c_g c_s \frac{\mathbf{k}T}{\mathbf{h}} \frac{f_\ddagger}{F_g f_s} e^{-\epsilon_0/\mathbf{k}T} \tag{92}$$

The expression is formally identical with that for the rate of adsorption [Eq. (75)], but the activated states are different in the two cases. However, in both cases the value of the partition function $f_\ddagger$ may be taken as unity, since the activated state consists of a molecule immobilized on the surface.

Two limiting cases of Eq. (92) are of interest, according to whether c_s is large or small. If the surface is only sparsely covered by adsorbed molecules, the concentration of bare surface sites c_s is approximately equal to L, the number of sites per square centimeter of completely bare surface. Under these conditions c_s is therefore approximately independent of c_g, so that the rate of reaction is directly proportional to c_g; the process is therefore kinetically of the first order.

If a reaction of this type occurs on a dual surface site, the concentration c_s in Eq. (92) must be replaced by c_{s_2}. For a bare surface c_{s_2} is equal to $\frac{1}{2}sc_s$, i.e., to $\frac{1}{2}sL$, so that the rate is

$$v = \tfrac{1}{2}sc_g L \frac{f_\ddagger}{F_g f_s} e^{-\epsilon_0/\mathbf{k}T} \tag{93}$$

If the reaction involves a diatomic molecule, the rate equation becomes

$$v = c_g L \frac{\sigma}{\sigma_\ddagger} \frac{\frac{1}{2}s\mathbf{h}^4}{8\pi^2 I(2\pi m\mathbf{k}T)^{3/2}} e^{-\epsilon_0/\mathbf{k}T} \tag{94}$$

where σ and $\sigma_\ddagger$ are the symmetry numbers of the molecules of reactant and activated complex, respectively, and I and m are the moment of inertia and the mass of the reacting molecule. For a nonlinear polyatomic molecule the rate is

$$v = c_g L \frac{\sigma}{\sigma_\ddagger} \frac{\frac{1}{2}s\mathbf{h}^5}{8\pi^2(8\pi^3 ABC)^{1/2}(2\pi m)^{3/2}(\mathbf{k}T)^2} e^{-\epsilon_0/\mathbf{k}T} \tag{95}$$

where A, B, and C are the three moments of inertia of the reactant.

The application of these equations to the experimental results has been considered by Laidler, Glasstone, and Eyring[1] and more recently

[1] Laidler, Glasstone, and Eyring, *loc. cit.*; S. Glasstone, K. J. Laidler, and H. Eyring, "The Theory of Rate Processes," chap. 7, McGraw-Hill Book Company, New York, 1941.

by Robertson.[1] There is agreement that Eq. (95) applies to data of van't Hoff and Kooij[2] on the decomposition of phosphine on glass. For the decompositions of hydrogen iodide on platinum[3] and of nitrous oxide on gold,[4] Robertson has shown that the experimental values are higher by several powers of 10 than the calculated ones. Robertson also adduces additional data, obtained in his own laboratories, in which a similar discrepancy exists. His interpretation of these anomalies is that the activated complexes actually form a mobile layer on the surface, in which case an equation of the form of Eq. (85) applies; this equation is capable of giving much higher values of the preexponential factor than does (93).

This explanation is not, however, completely satisfying. It is difficult to see what type of activation a surface could confer upon an adsorbed molecule if the latter were free to move over the surface. Furthermore, in other classes of reactions, including zero-order unimolecular reactions and bimolecular reactions of all types, the results are satisfactorily explained in terms of an immobile layer. It is possible that in the reactions considered by Robertson there are abnormalities due to the roughness of the surfaces; this might cause the observed activation energies to be quite different from the true ones. A reinvestigation of some of the reactions in question would be well worthwhile.

When the surface is almost completely covered by adsorbed molecules, the concentration c_g varies with the pressure of the gas, and the kinetic law may be obtained by combining the rate equation (92) with the isotherm,

$$\frac{c_a}{c_s} = c_g \frac{f_a}{F_g f_s} e^{\epsilon/\mathbf{k}T} \tag{96}$$

The law obtained is

$$v = c_a \frac{\mathbf{k}T}{\mathbf{h}} \frac{f_\ddagger}{f_a} \exp\left(-\frac{\epsilon_0 + \epsilon}{\mathbf{k}T}\right) \tag{97}$$

When the surface is almost completely covered by adsorbed molecules, c_a may be taken as constant, so that the rate is independent of the pressure of the reactant; the kinetics are therefore zero order.

Since both $f_\ddagger$ and f_a may be taken as unity, the rate law may be written as

$$v = c_a \frac{\mathbf{k}T}{\mathbf{h}} e^{-E/RT} \tag{98}$$

where E is the activation energy per mole at the absolute zero. An equa-

[1] A. J. B. Robertson, *J. Colloid Sci.*, **11**, 308 (1956).

[2] J. H. van't Hoff and D. M. Kooij, *Z. Physik. Chem.*, **12**, 155 (1893).

[3] C. N. Hinshelwood and R. E. Burk, *J. Chem. Soc.*, **127**, 2896 (1925).

[4] C. N. Hinshelwood and C. R. Prichard, *Proc. Roy. Soc. (London)*, **A108**, 211 (1925).

tion of this general form, with a frequency factor of 10^{12} sec^{-1} in place of $\mathbf{k}T/\mathbf{h}$, was first proposed by Topley.[1]

In Table 44 are given some of the calculated and observed rates, expressed as molecules cm^{-2} sec^{-1}, for reactions which exhibit zero-order kinetics; in all cases the value of c_a was taken to be 10^{15}. The agreement is seen to be satisfactory except for the decomposition of hydrogen iodide on gold; the discrepancy here is presumably due to the fact that the reaction occurs on a small fraction of the surface.

Table 44 OBSERVED AND CALCULATED RATES FOR ZERO-ORDER REACTIONS

Decomposition of	Surface	E., kcal	Temp., °K	Rate Calc.	Rate Obs.	Ref.
NH_3	W	38.0	904	8.0×10^{18}	4×10^{17}	*a*
NH_3	W	41.5	1316	3.4×10^{21}	2×10^{19}	*b*
NH_3	Mo	53.2	1228	8.5×10^{18}	$5\text{–}20 \times 10^{18}$	*c*
HI	Au	25.0	978	5.2×10^{22}	1.6×10^{17}	*d*
$HCOOCH(CH_3)_2$	Glass	35.0	714	7.5×10^{17}	5.8×10^{16}	*e*

[a] C. N. Hinshelwood and R. E. Burk, *J. Chem. Soc.*, **127**, 1051 (1925).
[b] C. H. Kunsman, E. S. Lamar, and W. E. Deming, *Phil. Mag.*, **10**, 1015 (1930).
[c] R. E. Burk, *Proc. Natl. Acad. Sci.*, **13**, 67 (1927).
[d] C. N. Hinshelwood and C. R. Prichard, *J. Chem. Soc.*, **127**, 1552 (1925).
[e] G. M. Schwab, *J. Phys. Chem.*, **50**, 427 (1946).

Bimolecular Reactions

A bimolecular reaction occurring by a Langmuir-Hinshelwood mechanism may be formulated as

$$A + B + S_2 \rightleftharpoons \begin{array}{cc} A & B \\ | & | \\ -S- & S- \end{array} \rightarrow \text{products}$$

where A and B are the reacting molecules, and S_2 is a dual site. The rate of reaction is then given by

$$v = c_g c'_g c_{s_2} \frac{\mathbf{k}T}{\mathbf{h}} \frac{f_\ddagger}{F_g F'_g f_{s_2}} e^{-\epsilon_0/\mathbf{k}T} \tag{99}$$

[1] B. Topley, *Nature*, **128**, 115 (1931).

where c_g and c_g' are the gas-phase concentrations of A and B, and F_g and F_g' are the corresponding partition functions per unit volume. The concentration of bare dual sites is related to the concentration of bare single sites by Eq. (82), so that the rate may be formulated as

$$v = \tfrac{1}{2}s \frac{c_g c_g' c_s^2}{L} \frac{\mathbf{k}T}{\mathbf{h}} \frac{f_\ddagger}{F_g F_g' f_{s_2}} e^{-\epsilon_0/\mathbf{k}T} \tag{100}$$

This equation may be put into a more general form, using the isotherms

$$\frac{c_a}{c_g c_s} = K \tag{101}$$

and

$$\frac{c_a'}{c_g' c_s} = K' \tag{102}$$

where c_a and c_a' are the concentrations of adsorbed A and adsorbed B. Since in addition

$$c_a + c_a' + c_s = L \tag{103}$$

it is found that

$$c_s = \frac{L}{1 + Kc_g + K'c_g'} \tag{104}$$

Insertion of this expression into Eq. (100) gives

$$v = \frac{\tfrac{1}{2}s c_g c_g' L}{(1 + Kc_g + K'c_g')^2} \frac{\mathbf{k}T}{\mathbf{h}} \frac{f_\ddagger}{F_g F_g' f_{s_2}} e^{-\epsilon_0/\mathbf{k}T} \tag{105}$$

as the general equation for a bimolecular reaction. The equation is best applied to the data in its various limiting forms, as follows.

When the surface is sparsely covered, Kc_g and $K'c_g'$ can be neglected in comparison with unity; the rate equation is then

$$v = \tfrac{1}{2}s c_g c_g' L \frac{\mathbf{k}T}{\mathbf{h}} \frac{f_\ddagger}{F_g F_g' f_{s_2}} e^{-\epsilon_0/\mathbf{k}T} \tag{106}$$

so that the kinetics are second order.

This equation has been applied to the reaction between nitric oxide and oxygen on a glass surface. This reaction has been found experimentally to be of the second order; the rate at 85°K is given by[1]

$$v = 9.4 \times 10^{-27} c_{NO} c_{O_2} e^{-\epsilon_0/\mathbf{k}T} \qquad \text{molecules cm}^{-2}\ \text{sec}^{-1}$$

if the concentrations of the reacting gases are in molecules per cubic centimeter. The rate has been calculated assuming $f_\ddagger/f_{s_2}$ to be unity, L to be 10^{15} sites per sq cm, and s to be 4. The result was

$$v = 14.8 \times 10^{-27} c_{NO} c_{O_2} e^{-\epsilon_0/\mathbf{k}T} \qquad \text{molecules cm}^{-2}\ \text{sec}^{-1}$$

in satisfactory agreement with the experimental value.

[1] M. Temkin and V. Pyzhev, *Acta Physicochim. URSS*, **3**, 473 (1935).

If B is only weakly adsorbed, but A is not necessarily weakly adsorbed, $K'c'_g$ may be neglected, but not Kc_g; the rate equation is thus

$$v = \tfrac{1}{2}s \frac{Lc_g c'_g}{(1 + Kc_g)^2} \frac{\mathbf{k}T}{\mathbf{h}} \frac{f_\ddagger}{F_g F'_g f_{s_2}} e^{-\epsilon_0/\mathbf{k}T} \tag{107}$$

The rate will therefore pass through a maximum as c_g is increased, the maximum occurring when $Kc_g = 1$.

If A is strongly adsorbed, Kc_g is large compared with unity, and the equation becomes

$$v = \tfrac{1}{2}s \frac{L}{K^2} \frac{c'_g}{c_g} \frac{\mathbf{k}T}{\mathbf{h}} \frac{f_\ddagger}{F_g F'_g f_{s_2}} e^{-\epsilon_0/\mathbf{k}T} \tag{108}$$

If K is expressed in terms of partition functions, Eq. (108) becomes

$$v = \tfrac{1}{2}sL \frac{c'_g}{c_g} \frac{\mathbf{k}T}{\mathbf{h}} \frac{F_g f_\ddagger f_{s_2}}{F'_f f_a^2} \exp\left(-\frac{\epsilon_0 + 2\epsilon}{\mathbf{k}T}\right) \tag{109}$$

The activation energy will be greater by 2ϵ than the value for a sparsely covered surface; the reason for this is that two molecules of A must be desorbed before the activated complex is formed.

Equation (109) has been applied quantitatively to the reaction between carbon monoxide and oxygen on a platinum surface. The observed rate at 572°K was found[1] to be equal to

$$v = 7.10 \times 10^{14} \frac{c_{O_2}}{c_{CO}} \qquad \text{molecules cm}^{-2}\text{ sec}^{-1}$$

the activation energy being 33.3 kcal at this temperature. The calculated rate was found to be

$$v = 4.33 \times 10^{15} \frac{c_{O_2}}{c_{CO}} \qquad \text{molecules cm}^{-2}\text{ sec}^{-1}$$

in satisfactory agreement with experiment.

When both reacting molecules are the same, the general rate equation (105) becomes

$$v = \tfrac{1}{2}s \frac{c_g^2 c_s^2}{L} \frac{\mathbf{k}T}{\mathbf{h}} \frac{f_\ddagger}{F_g^2 f_s} e^{-\epsilon_0/\mathbf{k}T} \tag{110}$$

If the surface is sparsely covered, Eq. (110) reduces to

$$v = \tfrac{1}{2}sc_g^2 L \frac{\mathbf{k}T}{\mathbf{h}} \frac{f_\ddagger}{F_g^2 f_s} e^{-\epsilon_0/\mathbf{k}T} \tag{111}$$

The general rate equation is

$$v = \tfrac{1}{2}s \frac{Lc_g^2}{(1 + Kc_g)^2} \frac{\mathbf{k}T}{\mathbf{h}} \frac{f_\ddagger}{F_g^2 f_s} e^{-\epsilon_0/\mathbf{k}T} \tag{112}$$

[1] I. Langmuir, *Trans. Faraday Soc.*, **17**, 621 (1922).

When the surface is almost completely covered

$$v = \tfrac{1}{2}s \frac{L}{K^2} \frac{\mathbf{k}T}{\mathbf{h}} \frac{f_\ddagger}{F_g{}^2 f_s} e^{-\epsilon_0/\mathbf{k}T} \tag{113}$$

$$= \tfrac{1}{2}sL \frac{\mathbf{k}T}{\mathbf{h}} \frac{f_\ddagger f_s}{f_a{}^2} \exp\left(-\frac{\epsilon_0 + 2\epsilon}{\mathbf{k}T}\right) \tag{114}$$

Absolute-rate equations have also been derived in a similar manner for the Langmuir-Rideal mechanism,[1] and for more complex types of reactions.[2]

Comparison of Homogeneous and Heterogeneous Reactions.[3] Calculations of the kind outlined above can readily be used for making a comparison between the rates of heterogeneous and homogeneous reactions between the same reactants. The reaction rate per square centimeter of surface for a second-order heterogeneous reaction between A and B may be written as [cf. Eq. (99)]

$$v_{\text{het}} = c_A c_B c_{s_2} \frac{\mathbf{k}T}{\mathbf{h}} \frac{1}{F_A F_B} e^{-E_{\text{het}}/RT} \tag{115}$$

The partition functions of the activated complex and of the reaction centers have been taken as unity. For the corresponding homogeneous process, the rate, according to the theory of absolute reaction rates, is

$$v_{\text{hom}} = c_A c_B \frac{\mathbf{k}T}{\mathbf{h}} \frac{F_\ddagger}{F_A F_B} e^{-E_{\text{hom}}/RT} \tag{116}$$

It follows, therefore, that

$$\frac{v_{\text{het}}}{v_{\text{hom}}} = \frac{c_{s_2}}{F_\ddagger} e^{\Delta E/RT} \tag{117}$$

where ΔE is equal to $E_{\text{hom}} - E_{\text{het}}$. For 1 sq cm of surface, c_{s_2} is about 10^{15}, whereas for 1 cc of gas $F_\ddagger$ is frequently about 10^{27}; hence

$$\frac{v_{\text{het}}}{v_{\text{hom}}} \approx 10^{-12} e^{\Delta E/RT} \tag{118}$$

The heterogeneous rate refers to 1 sq cm of surface and to a volume of 1 cc, and the homogeneous rate to 1 cc of reactants. It is evident that for the two rates to be comparable either a very large surface must be employed or the activation energy of the heterogeneous reaction must be much lower than that of the gas-phase reaction; alternatively, a combination of these two factors may make the rates comparable. At a temperature of 300°K the rates will be comparable for 1 sq cm of surface if the activation energy of the surface reaction is about 16.5 kcal lower

[1] K. J. Laidler, *Discussions Faraday Soc.*, **8**, 47 (1950); *J. Phys. Colloid Chem.*, **55**, 1067 (1951).

[2] M. C. Markham, M. C. Wall, and K. J. Laidler, *ibid.*, **57**, 321 (1953).

[3] K. J. Laidler, S. Glasstone, and H. Eyring, *J. Chem. Phys.*, **8**, 667 (1940).

Table 45 ACTIVATION ENERGIES FOR HETEROGENEOUS AND HOMOGENEOUS REACTIONS

Reaction	Surface	Activation energy, kcal per mole	Reference
Decomposition of HI	None	44.0	*a*
	Gold	25.0	*b*
	Platinum	33.8	*c*
Decomposition of N_2O	None	~60	*d*
	Gold	29.0	*e*
	Platinum	32.5	*f*
	Calcium oxide	34.8	*g*
	Aluminum oxide	29.3	*g*
Decomposition of NH_3	None	>80	*h*
	Tungsten	38.7	*i*
	Molybdenum	32–43	*j*
	Osmium	47.6	*k*
Parahydrogen conversion	None	60.8	*l*
	Gold	5–20	*m*
	Copper	10–12	*m*
	Palladium	4	*n*

[a] M. Bodenstein, *Z. Physik. Chem.*, **13,** 56 (1894); **22,** 1 (1897); **29,** 295 (1899).
[b] C. N. Hinshelwood and C. R. Prichard, *J. Chem. Soc.*, **127,** 1552 (1925).
[c] C. N. Hinshelwood and R. E. Burk, *ibid.*, 2896.
[d] H. S. Johnston, *J. Chem. Phys.*, **19,** 663 (1951).
[e] C. N. Hinshelwood and C. R. Prichard, *Proc. Roy. Soc.* (*London*), **A108,** 211 (1925).
[f] C. N. Hinshelwood and C. R. Prichard, *J. Chem. Soc.*, **127,** 327 (1925).
[g] G. M. Schwab, R. Stager, and H. H. von Baumbach, *Z. Physik. Chem.*, **B21,** 65 (1933).
[h] No data are apparently available; the lower limit of 80 kcal per mole is deduced from the known thermal stability of ammonia.
[i] C. N. Hinshelwood and R. E. Burk, *J. Chem. Soc.*, **127,** 1105 (1925).
[j] C. H. Kunsman, *J. Am. Chem. Soc.*, **50,** 2100 (1928).
[k] E. A. Arnold and R. E. Burk, *ibid.*, **54,** 23 (1932).
[l] R. E. Weston, *J. Chem. Phys.*, **31,** 892 (1959).
[m] D. D. Eley and D. R. Rossington, in W. E. Garner (ed.), "Chemisorption," p. 137, Butterworth & Co. (Publishers), Ltd., London, 1957.
[n] A. Couper and D. D. Eley, *Discussions Faraday Soc.*, **8,** 172 (1950).

than that of the homogeneous reaction. At higher temperatures a larger difference is necessary, the difference required being proportional to the absolute temperature.

In view of this result, it is clearly necessary for a reaction which proceeds at an appreciable rate on a surface of comparatively small size to have a much smaller activation energy on the surface than in the gas phase. An examination of the data reveals that in a number of instances this is the case; some values are given in Table 45.

The way in which the activation energy of the surface reaction may be less than that of the homogeneous reaction may be considered with reference to the potential-energy diagram shown in Fig. 62. The solid

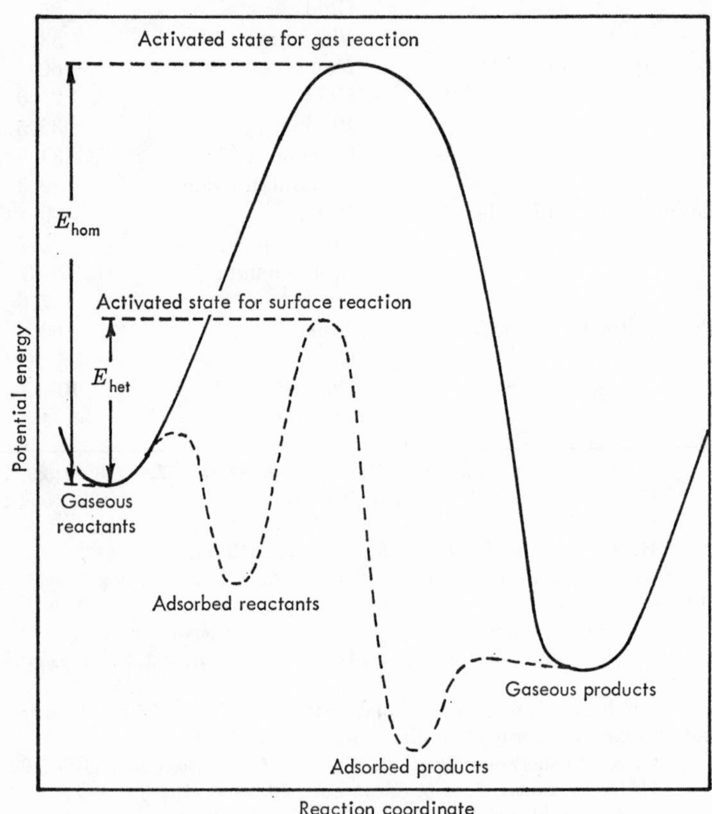

Fig. 62. Potential-energy diagram for a reaction occurring homogeneously (solid curve) and heterogeneously (dashed curve).

curve in this figure represents the variation in the potential energy as the homogeneous reaction proceeds, and the dashed curve represents the corresponding change for the surface reaction. In general, the system passes over an energy barrier to reach the adsorbed state, and then a second barrier is surmounted to give products in the adsorbed state. The height of this second barrier with reference to the initial level is

E_{het}. The difference between E_{hom} and E_{het} is the difference between the energy of the gaseous activated complex and that of the adsorbed activated complex. A good surface catalyst is therefore one on which the activated complex can be strongly adsorbed.

SURFACE HETEROGENEITY

Active Centers. In the above discussion of the kinetics of surface reactions, it has been tacitly assumed that all the surface sites are of the same character. However, as has already been mentioned, H. S. Taylor has laid stress on the improbability of a perfectly smooth surface such as would be necessary for consistency with the idea of uniformity of the sites. Some of the kinetic evidence for variations in surface activity will now be discussed.

Experiments on the retarding influence of gases on reactions frequently provide evidence of this kind. For instance, the decomposition of ammonia on molybdenum[1] is retarded by nitrogen, but as the surface becomes saturated with nitrogen, the rate of the decomposition does not fall to zero. This suggests that the reaction can occur on certain adsorption sites upon which the nitrogen cannot be adsorbed. A further conclusion that can be drawn is that one type of active center can be most active for the adsorption of one species and another type for the adsorption of another type of molecule. An additional example leading to the same conclusion is the fact that a platinum surface that has been poisoned by carbon dioxide with respect to reaction between it and hydrogen remains unpoisoned with respect to the decomposition of nitrous oxide.[2]

Further evidence of the same kind comes from studies on the amounts of reactants adsorbed in surface reactions. When hydrogen and carbon dioxide react on the surface of platinum, the total adsorption of hydrogen is very much greater than that of carbon dioxide, although the reaction rate varies inversely with the pressure of the latter; it is evident that the reaction occurs only on certain sites upon which the carbon dioxide is much more strongly adsorbed; the hydrogen molecules adsorbed on other sites play no part in the reaction.

Support to the idea of active centers is also given by the fact that raising the temperature of a metal results in a decreased activity for adsorption and catalysis; this is explained as due to sintering of the surface, resulting in a decrease in the number of atoms constituting the most active centers.

Kinetics on Nonuniform Surfaces. When a reaction takes place on a surface on which there is a variation of activity, the overall rate is the sum of the rates on the various types of sites. Suppose for simplicity

[1] R. E. Burk, *Proc. Natl. Acad. Sci. U.S.*, **13**, 67 (1927).

[2] C. N. Hinshelwood and C. R. Prichard, *J. Chem. Soc.*, **127**, 445 (1925).

that there are only two kinds of sites: atoms having a constant high activity, and atoms having a constant low activity. If the concentrations of the two kinds of sites are c_1 and c_2 and the activation energies are E_1 and E_2, and if it is assumed that both types of sites are sparsely covered, the rate of reaction involving a single reactant is given by

$$v = c_g \frac{\mathbf{k}T}{\mathbf{h}} \frac{1}{F_g} (c_1 e^{-E_1/RT} + c_2 e^{-E_2/RT}) \tag{119}$$

The sites of type 1 have been supposed to be the more active, which means that E_1 is less than E_2. If c_1 and c_2 are of comparable magnitude, this implies that the first term in Eq. (119) is more important than the second, or that the overall activation energy is closer to the lower value E_1 than to the higher value E_2. This result is also to be expected if there is a variety of types of sites, in which case the overall rate is given by

$$v = c_g \frac{\mathbf{k}T}{\mathbf{h}} \frac{1}{F_g} \sum_i c_i e^{-E_i/RT} \tag{120}$$

Unless the distribution of the numbers of sites is a very unusual one, it is again to be expected that the reaction will occur mainly on the most active sites, and that the energy of activation of the overall process will approach the value which corresponds to these sites. This has been shown to be the case by Constable[1] for a particular and probable distribution of numbers of sites.

This simple conclusion, that on a nonuniform surface the kinetics will approximately correspond to the occurrence of the reaction on the most active sites, may require modification in certain cases. In the above discussion it was assumed that all types of sites were sparsely covered, and that the rate was controlled by interaction between gas molecules and sites. There is also the possibility that the rate-controlling step is not the same on all types of sites; thus, it might be interaction between gas molecule and site on some types, and desorption of the products on others. If this is the case, the reaction will not show the simple kinetics that would be expected if the surface were uniform.

It may first be demonstrated that adsorption processes themselves may show complex behavior on nonuniform surfaces.[2] Suppose that a surface consists of two types of sites, and that the activation energies for chemisorption are E_1 and E_2 and the heats of adsorption ϵ_1 and ϵ_2. If gas is gradually admitted to the system at sufficiently low temperatures, and E_1 is less than E_2, the sites of type 1 will be covered more rapidly than

[1] F. H. Constable, *Proc. Roy. Soc.* (*London*), **A108**, 355 (1925); see also E. Cremer and G. M. Schwab, *Z. Physik. Chem.*, **A144**, 243 (1929); G. M. Schwab, *ibid.*, **B5**, 406 (1929).

[2] Cf. H. S. Taylor and S. C. Liang, *J. Am. Chem. Soc.*, **69**, 1306 (1947).

those of type 2, and may be completely covered before the latter are more than sparsely covered. The relationship between total coverage and gas pressure will clearly be more complex than corresponds to the Langmuir isotherm. Further complexities will be revealed when the temperature is raised. Suppose that this occurs when sites of type 1 are practically fully covered and those of type 2 are sparsely covered. If $E_2 + \epsilon_2$ is larger than $E_1 + \epsilon_1$, the rate of desorption from sites of type 2 will be less than that from sites of type 1, so that raising the temperature may bring about complete coverage of sites of type 2 and sparse coverage of the other sites. It is clear that the temperature coefficient of the overall rate of adsorption would not have a simple significance.

If the degree of adsorption may vary with pressure and temperature in a complex manner on nonuniform surfaces, the rates of surface reactions, which depend on surface coverage, will also do so. Suppose that E_1 is the activation energy for reaction to give adsorbed products on sites of type 1, and E_1' is the activation energy for desorption of products on sites of type 1; similarly let E_2 and E_2' be the corresponding quantities for reaction on sites of type 2. If E_1 is greater than E_1', the rate-controlling step on sites of type 1 is the formation of the adsorbed products. If the product is more strongly adsorbed on sites of type 2, this will have the effect of reducing the activation energy for the formation of the adsorbed products (i.e., E_2 is less than E_1), but at the same time the activation energy for desorption, E_2', will be raised. The net effect may be that the desorption controls the rate on the sites of type 2. It is thus possible for the rate of the reaction to be controlled by different processes on different types of surface sites. The surfaces upon which the desorption is the slow process will be more covered than the others, and there will clearly be no simple relationship between the rate and the gas pressure or temperature.

Some special cases of this type of behavior have been treated quantitatively by Halsey.[1] With certain simplifying assumptions, which are probably approached in certain cases, it was found that a reaction which obeys the law

$$v = \frac{ap}{1 + bp} \tag{121}$$

on a smooth surface, may obey

$$v = \left(\frac{ap}{1 + bp}\right)^{1/2} \tag{122}$$

on a nonuniform one. This result is a particularly interesting one since it throws light on the fractional orders frequently found in surface

[1] G. D. Halsey, *J. Chem. Phys.*, **17**, 758 (1949).

reactions. The decomposition of ammonia on doubly promoted iron catalysts was discussed by Halsey in terms of his treatment.

It should be emphasized that this type of kinetic complexity will not necessarily arise on a rough surface; in order for the rate to be controlled by different processes on the different types of sites, the distribution of surface activities must be sufficiently broad. If this condition is not satisfied, the reaction will occur most rapidly on the most active sites, as envisaged by Constable. This offers an interpretation of an apparent discrepancy that has frequently been noticed when kinetic results are compared with adsorption measurements on the same system. The adsorption results often indicate a wide range of activity of the surface sites, while the kinetic results may be consistent with the assumption that reaction occurs on sites all of which have the same activity. The explanation of the anomaly is that on any catalytic surface there is one group of sites that are more active than the remainder, and that reaction occurs almost entirely on this group. Reaction on the less active sites therefore does not introduce any complexity into the kinetic laws. Calculations of absolute rates suggest that in the case of smooth metal surfaces this group of most active sites constitutes a large fraction of the total, but that with oxides and composite catalysts the active sites may comprise only a thousandth or less of the total number.

Variation in Interatomic Distances. Another idea that has been of great practical importance in connection with surface activity was that of Burk,[1] that the adsorption of a molecule sometimes takes place on more than one site; this is often referred to as "multiple adsorption." It follows from this that adsorption must depend upon the lattice spacing at the surface, a concept that was developed by Balandin[2] in his so-called "multiplet hypothesis." Balandin postulated that catalysis frequently arises as the result of the action of more than one surface site, and considered that if two atoms become adsorbed on a single site, a bond will be formed between them. For example, the dehydration of ethyl alcohol was envisaged as involving the attachment of two carbons to one site, and of a hydrogen and oxygen atom to a neighboring one, the situation being represented as follows, the asterisks denoting sites:

$$
\begin{array}{ccc}
H_2C & \overset{*}{—} & CH_2 \\
| & & | \\
H & * & OH
\end{array}
$$

Since the hydrogen atom of the methyl group and the oxygen atom are attached to the same site, there is a tendency for them to unite, so that the splitting off of water is facilitated by the catalyst. In the dehydro-

[1] R. E. Burk, *J. Phys. Chem.*, **30**, 1134 (1926).

[2] A. A. Balandin, *Z. Physik. Chem.*, **B2**, 289 (1929); **B3**, 167 (1929).

genation of alcohol, on the other hand, the adsorption would be

$$\begin{array}{ccc} CH_3CH & \overset{*}{—} & O \\ | & & | \\ H & * & H \end{array}$$

so that the splitting off of a hydrogen molecule would occur.

Balandin discussed the dehydrogenation of hydroaromatic compounds from the same point of view, the rings being adsorbed upon the octahedral faces, as represented in Fig. 63. The surface atoms a, b, and c

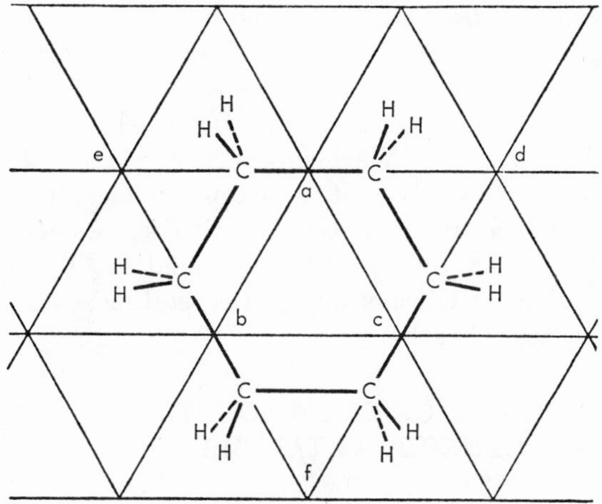

Fig. 63. Balandin's representation of the mechanism of the decomposition of a hydroaromatic compound.

are supposed to cause extension of the carbon-carbon distances, while the atoms d, e, and f attract pairs of hydrogen atoms and aid their combination. This picture of what occurs on a catalytic surface is undoubtedly too simple, but it has proved valuable in leading to qualitative predictions of the right kind.

The general conclusion from this kind of catalyst model—that catalytic activity depends upon interatomic spacing—is an important one and has received confirmation from many sources. Sherman and Eyring[1] calculated activation energies for the adsorption of hydrogen on a carbon surface and found them to be very sensitive to the carbon-carbon distance in the surface layer, a distance of 3.6 A being most favorable. It is of interest that this distance is considerably larger than the normal

[1] A. Sherman and H. Eyring, *J. Am. Chem. Soc.*, **54**, 2661 (1932).

H—H distance in molecular hydrogen. Similar results have been obtained from calculations of the activation energy for the adsorption of hydrogen on nickel.[1] Two different Ni-Ni distances are found in nickel, 2.49 and 3.52 A, and calculations were made for both; the latter separation gave a much lower energy of activation, from which the conclusion can be drawn that adsorption will occur primarily on the (100) and (110) planes of nickel, since the (111) plane contains only the 2.49-A separation. However, the calculated activation energies are much too high, the experimental values being approximately zero; the general conclusion that the activation energies depend upon the spacing is nevertheless valid. The main reason that the calculations do not yield satisfactory results is that too simple a model was assumed for the surface.

The problem of the influence of the lattice spacing on the catalytic activity of a surface has been extensively investigated, especially by Beeck and his collaborators,[2] who have studied in particular the hydrogenation of ethylene on a nickel surface. The main conclusion is that the activity on the (110) plane is five times as great as that on a nickel film in which the crystals are oriented at random; the situation is, however, very much more complicated than the theoretical calculations would imply. Studies on the selective activities of different crystal faces have also been made by Leidheiser and Gwathmey.[3]

ELECTRONIC THEORIES OF CHEMISORPTION AND HETEROGENEOUS CATALYSIS

During recent years a considerable amount of work has been devoted to the theoretical treatment of heterogeneous catalysis in terms of the structure of solids, with particular reference to surface structures. Basically such treatments deal with the nature of the chemisorptive bond. Only a very brief account can be given here.

The serious study of this problem may be said to have begun in 1928 when Roginskii and Schul'tz[4] stressed the importance of electronic factors in connection with bonds between chemisorbed species and the surface. A year later Rideal and Wansborough-Jones[5] noted that the activation

[1] G. Okamoto, J. Horiuti, and K. Hirota, *Sci. Papers Inst. Phys. Chem. Res. (Tokyo)*, **29**, 223 (1936); cf. A. Sherman, C. E. Sun, and H. Eyring, *J. Chem. Phys.*, **3**, 49 (1934).

[2] O. Beeck, A. Wheeler, and A. E. Smith, *Phys. Rev.*, **55**, 601 (1939); O. Beeck and A. Wheeler, *J. Chem. Phys.*, **7**, 631 (1939); A. E. Smith and O. Beeck, *Phys. Rev.*, **55**, 602 (1939); O. Beeck, A. E. Smith, and A. Wheeler, *Proc. Roy. Soc. (London)*, **177**, 64 (1940). Cf. G. H. Twigg and E. K. Rideal, *Trans. Faraday Soc.*, **36**, 533 (1940).

[3] H. Leidheiser and A. T. Gwathmey, *J. Am. Chem. Soc.*, **70**, 1200, 1206 (1948).

[4] S. Roginskii and E. Schul'tz, *Z. Physik. Chem.*, **A138**, 21 (1928).

[5] E. K. Rideal and O. H. Wansborough-Jones, *Proc. Roy. Soc. (London)*, **A123**, 202 (1929).

energy E for the oxidation of metals was linearly related to the work function ϕ of the metal, the relationship being

$$\phi - E = \text{const} \tag{123}$$

Later Lennard-Jones[1] presented the first detailed account of the variations in potential energy as an atom or a molecule approaches a surface. According to his concept, which is illustrated in Fig. 64, the van der

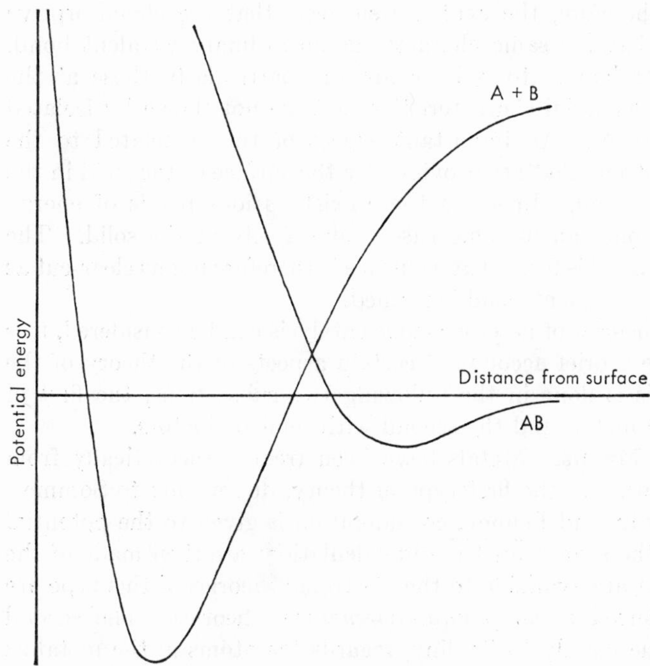

Fig. 64. Potential-energy changes in the adsorption of a species AB, which is chemisorbed with dissociation into A + B. In the case shown there is an activation energy for chemisorption.

Waals attractive forces are most important at large distances. As the adsorbed species approaches closer to the surface, there is a transition to a chemical type of adsorption. Lennard-Jones regarded the chemisorptive bond as essentially a covalent bond involving an electron from the solid and an electron from the adsorbate.

In contrast to this, a number of workers[2] have suggested that the

[1] J. E. Lennard-Jones, *Trans. Faraday Soc.*, **28**, 333 (1932).

[2] A. K. Brewer, *J. Phys. Chem.*, **32**, 1006 (1928); O. Schmidt, *Chem. Rev.*, **12**, 363 (1933); J. E. Nyrop, "The Catalytic Action of Surfaces," Ernest Benn, Ltd.–Benn Bros., Ltd., London, 1939.

chemisorptive bond is largely ionic in character. This view has, however, been criticized[1] on the basis of calculations which suggest that the formation of an ionic bond would in general be much more endothermic than the formation of a covalent bond. Measurements of surface potential[2] have indicated for several systems that there is only a small transfer of charge; in the case of hydrogen adsorbed on tungsten, for example, the dipole moment of the W—H bond is only 0.4 debye and corresponds to the transfer of about one-tenth of an electronic charge. On the whole, therefore, the evidence suggests that the chemisorptive bond has somewhat the same character as an ordinary covalent bond.

On the other hand, atoms in solids and particularly those at the surface have some special characteristics that are not shown by isolated atoms and molecules. An important aspect of this is related to the source of the electrons that are provided by the surface of the solid in the formation of the bond. In solids there exist various bands of energy levels, and electrons can in some cases move freely in the solid. The situation when a bond is formed at a surface is therefore not as clear-cut as when an ordinary covalent bond is formed.

Before the theories of heterogeneous catalysis can be considered, it is necessary to give a brief account of certain aspects of the theory of the solid state. This is done in the following two subsections, the first of which deals with metals and the second with semiconductors.

Theories of Metals. Metals have been treated theoretically from two points of view. In the first type of theory, due mainly to Sommerfeld, Bloch, Krönig, and Penney, consideration is given to the potential fields set up by the atomic nuclei, and calculations are then made of the energy levels that are available to the electrons; theories of this type are conveniently referred to as *quantum-mechanical* theories. The second point of view, due mainly to Pauling, regards the atoms in the metal as held together by ordinary localized bonds, and considers the possible resonance states existing between them. This theory is conveniently known as the *resonating-bond* theory.

In the quantum-mechanical theories the potential energy is taken as varying periodically through the metal, owing to the presence of the atomic nuclei, and the Schrödinger equation is set up and solved on that basis. The equation can be solved easily for the case of rectangular

[1] P. H. Emmett and E. Teller, "Twelfth Report of the Commission on Contact Catalysis," p. 68, New York, 1940; A. Couper and D. D. Eley, *Discussions Faraday Soc.*, **8**, 172 (1950).

[2] A. Couper and D. D. Eley, *Trans. Faraday Soc.*, **48**, 172 (1952); R. C. L. Bosworth and E. K. Rideal, *Physika*, **4**, 925 (1937); *Proc. Roy. Soc.* (*London*), **A162**, 1 (1937); *Proc. Cambridge Phil. Soc.*, **33**, 394 (1937); C. W. Oatley, *Proc. Phys. Soc.*, **51**, 318 (1939); J. C. P. Mignolet, *Discussions Faraday Soc.*, **8**, 105 (1950); D. D. Eley, *Quart. Rev.* (*London*), **3**, 209 (1949).

barriers,[1] and it is found that certain *bands* of energy levels correspond to permitted electronic states. For a more realistic potential field, illustrated in Fig. 65, the situation is essentially the same. There are seen from the diagram to be certain permitted energy levels which are lower than the maxima, and these therefore correspond to levels occupied by localized electrons which are unable to pass from one nucleus to another.

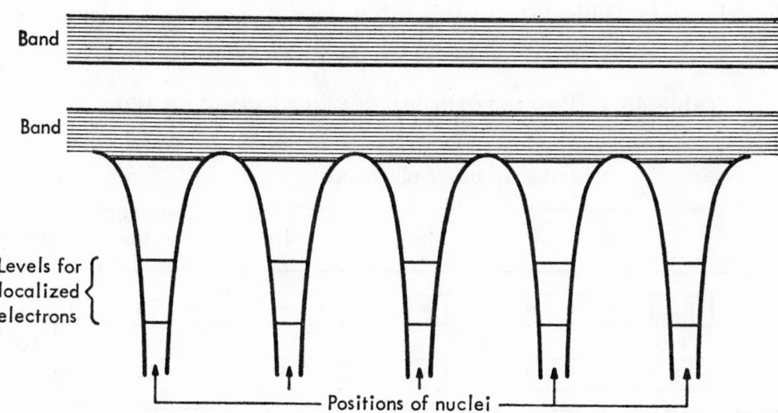

Fig. 65. Potential-energy diagram for a metal, showing the permitted electronic energy levels.

In addition, there are groups of energy levels corresponding to values higher than the maxima, and these are the bands. If these levels are incompletely filled with electrons, the application of an electric field will excite some of the electrons into higher energy levels and they may then move from one nucleus to another. If the band is filled, however, conduction can only arise if the field is sufficiently strong to excite electrons into an upper band. The electrons in a completely filled band are therefore essentially localized, and can only move under the action of very powerful forces.

In Pauling's theory of metals[2] the metallic bond is regarded as involving resonance between covalent and ionic bonds formed between the individual atoms. The theory is conveniently explained with reference to lithium metal, for which Pauling postulates resonance of the type

$$\begin{matrix} \text{Li—Li} \\ \text{Li—Li} \end{matrix} \quad \leftrightarrow \quad \begin{matrix} \text{Li—Li}^- \\ \quad\ | \\ \text{Li}^+ \ \text{Li} \end{matrix}$$

[1] Cf. C. N. Hinshelwood, "The Structure of Physical Chemistry," p. 294, Clarendon Press, Oxford, 1951.

[2] L. Pauling, *Phys. Rev.*, **54**, 899 (1938); *J. Am. Chem. Soc.*, **69**, 542 (1947); *Proc. Roy. Soc.* (*London*), **A196**, 343 (1949).

In order for this resonance to be possible, the atom in question must be capable of forming a structure similar to —Li^-—, and this means that the metal must have an available orbital, known as the *metallic* orbital. This metallic orbital consists of a vacancy into which an electron may be placed; this electron is then shared with a neighboring atom. In lithium the metallic orbital is a p orbital; in transition metals it is frequently a d orbital. In the case of iron, for example, the situation is represented by the scheme in Table 46. In this table the dots represent valence electrons which are unpaired, while the arrows represent paired electrons. The circles indicate metallic orbitals; these are unfilled spaces which may receive an additional electron which will pair with an electron from a neighboring atom. Two structures are possible; in the first (Fe A) there are three unpaired d electrons, while in the second (Fe B) there are two. According to the theory of paramagnetism each unpaired d electron contributes a value of one Bohr magneton to the magnetic saturation dipole moment. The experimental magnetic moment of iron is 2.22 magnetons, and to explain this it is necessary to assume that the atom is 78 percent in the A form and 22 percent in the B form. The valency of the A form is 6 and that of the B form is 5, so that the weighted average is 5.78. In structure A there are three d electrons, and altogether 7 orbitals are involved in the bonding; in B there are two d electrons, and 6 electrons are involved in bonding. One can therefore work out a *percentage d character* for the metal, as follows:

Table 46 THE ELECTRONIC CONFIGURATION OF IRON

Form	Number of outer electrons: 3d	4s	4p	Resonance ratio	Valency
Fe A	↑ ↑ • • •	•	• • ○	78	6 } 5.78
Fe B	↑ ↑ ↑ • •	•	• • ○	22	5

Percentage d character = $(78 \times 3/7) + (22 \times 2/6) = 39.7$

$$\% \ d \text{ character} = (78 \times 3/7) + (22 \times 2/6) = 29.7$$

Various attempts have been made to correlate chemisorption properties with the percentage d character of the metal.

Another quantity that may be of significance in connection with chemisorption is the *number of holes in the d band.* The copper atom, for example, has in its ground state the configuration

$$(1s)^2(2s)^2(2p)^6(3s)^2(3p)^6(3d)^{10}(5s)$$

The *d* shell is seen to be filled by 10 electrons, and quantum-mechanical calculations lead to the result that the 3*d* band is completely filled. Copper has no paramagnetism, from which it is also concluded that the *d* band is completely filled. Nickel has one fewer electron than copper, and the *d* band is now not completely filled. The saturation magnetic dipole moment of nickel is 0.6, and this indicates that there are on the average 9.4 electrons per atom in the *d* band; this means that the *d* band has 0.6 hole in it, and this accounts for the magnetic moment.

It is important to distinguish between Pauling's concept of percentage *d* character, and that of the number of holes in the *d* band. Values of each, for some metals of interest in connection with chemisorption, are given in Table 47. There is no simple relationship between the

Table 47 VALUES OF PERCENTAGE *d* CHARACTER, AND OF THE NUMBER OF HOLES IN THE *d* BAND

Metal	Percentage *d* character	Number of holes in *d* band
Fe	39.7	2.2
Co	39.5	1.7
Ni	40.0	0.6
Cu	36.0	0
Pt	44.0	0.6
Pd	46.0	0.55

two quantities. Attempts have been made to relate the chemisorptive power of metals to both quantities; there are no very clear-cut correlations, but on the whole it appears that the number of holes in the *d* band is of more significance.

Theories of Semiconductors.[1] Solids other than metals frequently fall into the class of semiconductors; examples are metal oxides and halides. Semiconductors are solids which are insulators in the sense that their conduction bands are completely filled, but which show some conductivity, owing to the fact that higher bands may be utilized for the movement of electrons through the solid. This may arise in two different

[1] For a general account see A. L. F. Rees, "Chemistry of the Defect Solid State," Methuen & Co., Ltd., London, 1954.

ways. In the first place, bands may be close together so that electrons may pass without difficulty from one band into another; solids of this type are known as *intrinsic semiconductors.* Another type of semiconductivity, and one that is of particular importance from the standpoint of adsorption and catalysis, arises as a result of the fact that all solids contain what are known as "defects," which may be of different types. In the first place, the solid may contain an impurity which will distort the band structure. Secondly, even solids that are perfectly pure in the chemical sense may contain lattice imperfections which will alter the band structure. Thirdly, some solids are known as *nonstoichiometric,* which means that the anions and cations are not present in equivalent amounts. Whenever in the crystal there is an excess or a deficiency of one type of atom, there results a distortion in the band structure, with a corresponding increase in conductivity.

The nonstoichiometric solids play a particularly important role in connection with catalysis, and should be considered in more detail. A well-known example of a nonstoichiometric crystal is zinc oxide, which loses oxygen on heating so that the zinc is then in excess. The oxygen is, of course, evolved as an electrically neutral substance, so that associated with each excess zinc ion in the crystal there will be two electrons which remain trapped in the solid. Solids of this type are known as *n-type semiconductors,* the n standing for negative. Sodium chloride, containing an excess of sodium ions, is also an n-type semiconductor.

A second class of nonstoichiometric solids consists of the *p-type semiconductors,* examples of which are ferrous oxide (FeO) and cuprous oxide (Cu_2O). These oxides frequently occur with an excess of oxygen, which means that certain of the cationic sites are vacant. In order for electrical neutrality to be preserved, some of the oxygen atoms must exist not as doubly charged ions but as singly charged or uncharged species. In order to preserve the analogy with the p-type semiconductors it is customary to speak of "positive holes" as existing at these oxygen atoms, a positive hole being a place where an electron is missing.

When the band theory is applied to n-type and p-type semiconductors, the situation is found to be somewhat as represented in Fig. 66. The n type is exemplified by zinc oxide in which there is an excess of zinc, and the diagram shows a region where there is a missing oxygen atom. The potential energy in this region is lower than it otherwise would be, and the bands are of the form shown in the diagram. The trapped electrons which replace the missing oxygen ion reside in the position indicated. With p-type semiconductors such as nickel oxide, also illustrated in Fig. 66, the position is different. In this case the bands become higher in the region of the defect, and the valence band now contains a vacant site.

Chemisorption. Many attempts have been made to treat chemisorption from the standpoint of the band theory, and such discussions

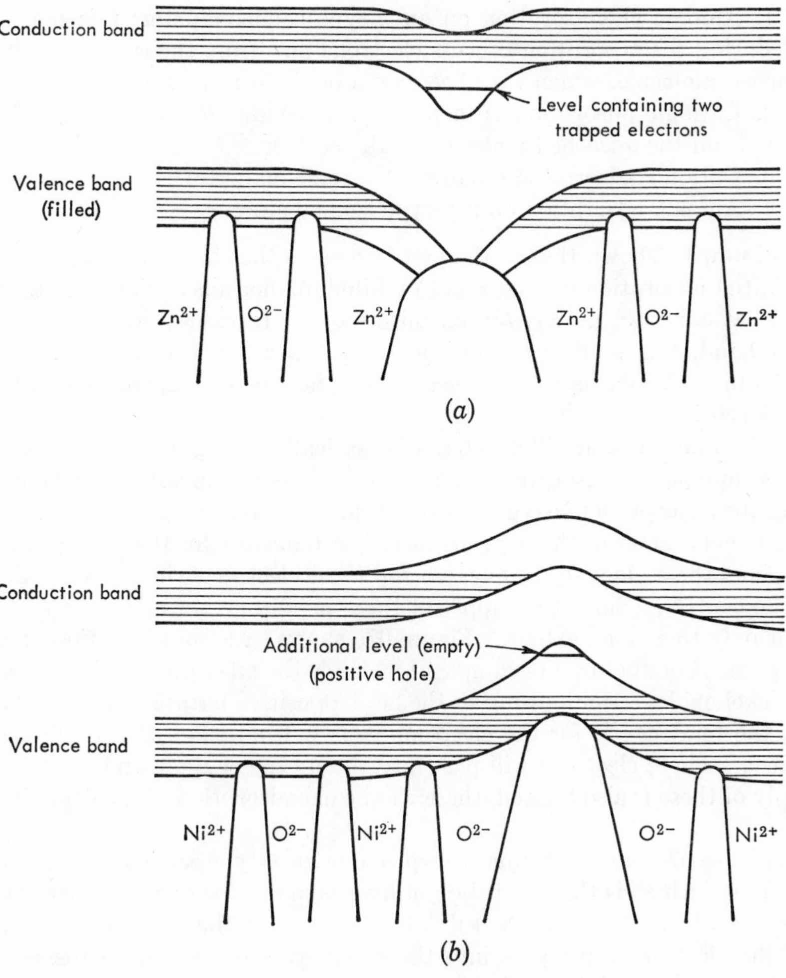

Fig. 66. Potential-energy diagrams for (*a*) zinc oxide with a missing oxygen atom (an *n*-type semiconductor), and (*b*) nickel oxide with a missing nickel atom (a *p*-type semiconductor).

have been of value in leading to an understanding of the process, and also of the mechanisms of chemical reactions on surfaces. Little of a quantitative nature, however, has arisen from such considerations. In the case of chemisorption on semiconductors it is possible to distinguish between different types of behavior. The semiconductor may be of the *n*-type or the *p*-type, and the molecule may become adsorbed with a flow of electrons either to the surface or from the surface. Four different situations may in fact arise, as follows:

1. Anionic chemisorption on an n-type semiconductor; this means that during the adsorption process electrons flow from the surface to the adsorbed molecule, which thus becomes anionic in character.
2. Cationic adsorption on a p-type semiconductor; in this case the flow is from the adsorbed molecule to the surface.
3. Cationic adsorption on an n-type semiconductor.
4. Anionic adsorption on a p-type semiconductor.

It will now be shown that in the first two cases the changes occurring on the initial adsorption are such as to inhibit further adsorption; one then has what is known as *depletive* chemisorption. In cases 3 and 4, on the other hand, this tendency does not exist, and adsorption will continue until a unimolecular layer has been formed; here one speaks of *cumulative* chemisorption.

The four cases are illustrated schematically in Fig. 67. Figure 67*a* shows anionic chemisorption on an n-type semiconductor, an example being the adsorption of oxygen on zinc oxide. Here, owing to the electronegative character of the oxygen, there is a tendency for the electrons to flow from the surface to the oxygen, and these electrons will flow from the n-type centers. Since the supply of these is limited, the adsorption will occur only to a small extent. Figure 67*b* shows cationic adsorption on a p-type semiconductor, an example of which is the adsorption of hydrogen on nickel oxide. Here, owing to the electropositive nature of the hydrogen, the tendency is for the electrons to flow from the hydrogen to the surface. These electrons will pass into the p-type centers, and since the supply of these is also limited, there will be chemisorption of the depletive type.

Figure 67*c* shows cationic adsorption on an n-type semiconductor, an example of which is the adsorption of hydrogen on zinc oxide. Electrons pass from the hydrogen to the solid, but in this case the n levels are filled, and the electrons must pass into the conduction band. Since the conduction band is capable of holding a large number of electrons, there is here no tendency for depletion. Figure 67*d* shows anionic chemisorption on a p-type semiconductor, an example being the adsorption of oxygen on nickel oxide or cuprous oxide. Electrons pass from the valence band to the adsorbed species, and since the supply of electrons in the valence band is very great, there is again no depletion.

Heterogeneous Catalysis.[1] Only a very brief account can here be given of the application of the above ideas to the mechanisms of surface reactions. During recent years a number of investigations of heterogeneous processes have been made from this point of view, and the greatest progress has been achieved in cases in which a very simple reaction,

[1] For further details see F. S. Stone, in W. E. Garner (ed.), "Chemistry of the Solid State," Butterworth & Co. (Publishers), Ltd., London, 1955.

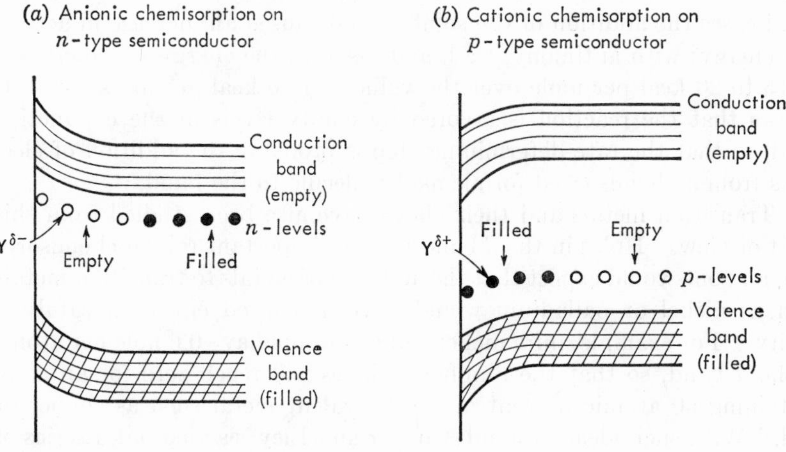

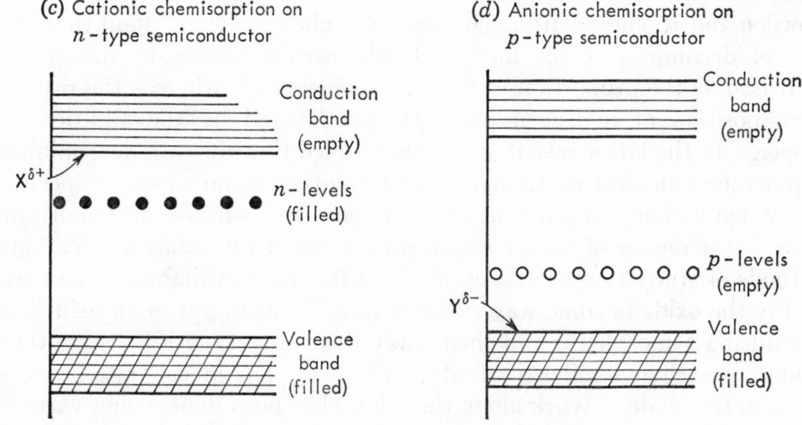

Fig. 67. Four types of chemisorption on a semiconductor.

such as the decomposition of nitrous oxide or of formaldehyde, has been chosen for study.

Some metals, such as silver, dissolve other metals to form stable alloys, and as the solute metal is added, its electrons fill up the vacant bands; the number of vacant energy levels therefore decreases. If these vacant levels are important in catalysis, one would therefore expect a systematic change in catalytic activity as the solute metal is added. A number of studies of this type have been made by Schwab and his coworkers,[1] who were concerned with the zero-order decomposition of formic acid over catalysts consisting of various metals dissolved in silver. In all cases the addition of the solute metal caused an increase in activation energy; with antimony, lead, and bismuth the energy was increased by 15 to 20 kcal per mole over the value of 17.6 kcal in pure silver. It follows that the reaction is favored by empty levels in the conduction band, so that the rate-determining step is probably the addition of electrons from a chemisorbed formic acid molecule to the band.

Transition metals and their alloys have also been studied from this point of view. Holes in the *d* band play an important role in chemisorption, and one would expect that the addition of metals to transition metals such as nickel or palladium would have a marked effect on catalytic ability. For example, pure nickel and palladium have 0.6 hole per atoms in the *d* band, so that the number of holes will reach zero for an alloy containing 60 atomic percent of a monovalent metal such as copper or gold. With such ideas in mind, Couper and Eley[2] carried out a series of experiments on the parahydrogen conversion on palladium-gold wires. They found that the activation energy increased abruptly as soon as the proportion of gold reached 60 atomic percent, which means that catalysis is favored by holes in the *d* band. Similar results were obtained by Dowden and Reynolds[3] using copper-nickel alloys. They found that the rate of decomposition of methanol into carbon monoxide and water decreased as the proportion of copper was increased, whereas the rate of decomposition of hydrogen peroxide was favored by the addition of copper. In the latter case it is to be concluded that the rate-determining step involves an electron transfer from the surface to an adsorbed species.

When a chemical reaction occurs on an oxide surface, an important factor is the degree of *n*-typeness or *p*-typeness of the catalyst. Various methods of study of catalysis on oxide surfaces are available. One may modify the oxide in some way (for example, by heating it in an oxidizing or reducing atmosphere) and then study the catalytic activity and other properties such as semiconductivity. Also, one may incorporate impurities into the oxide. Work along these lines has been done, using various oxides, with reference to the decomposition of nitrous oxide, the oxidation of carbon monoxide, and the H_2-D_2 exchange, and some of the main results will be discussed briefly.

The initial step in both the homogeneous and heterogeneous decompositions of nitrous oxide is found to be the breaking of the N—O bond:

$$N_2O \rightarrow N_2 + O$$

[1] G. M. Schwab, *Trans. Faraday Soc.*, **42,** 689 (1946); G. M. Schwab and S. Pesmatjoglou, *J. Phys. Colloid Chem.*, **52,** 1046 (1948); G. M. Schwab, *Discussions Faraday Soc.*, **8,** 166 (1950).

[2] A. Couper and D. D. Eley, *Discussions Faraday Soc.*, **8,** 172 (1950).

[3] D. A. Dowden and P. W. Reynolds, *ibid.*, 184.

On NiO Wagner and Hauffe[1] observed an increase in conductivity during the reaction at 750°C. A similar result was obtained at below 400°C by Garner, Gray, and Stone,[2] and under these conditions the equilibrium between the surface and the bulk of the solid is frozen. It follows that the reaction takes place as

$$N_2O + e \text{ (from surface)} \rightarrow N_2 + O^-_{ads}$$

and that this is followed by

$$O^-_{ads} \rightarrow \tfrac{1}{2}O_2 + e$$
$$O^-_{ads} + N_2O \rightarrow N_2 + O_2 + e \text{ (to surface)}$$

The removal of electrons from the *p*-type semiconductor brings about an increase in conductivity.

The effectiveness of oxide catalysts for the nitrous oxide decomposition is as follows:

$$Cu_2O > CoO > NiO > CuO > MgO > CaO > Al_2O_3 > ZnO > CdO > TiO_2 > Cr_2O_3 > Fe_2O_3 > Ga_2O_3$$

The *p*-type oxides are the best catalysts, insulators the next best, and the *n*-type oxides the worst. The desorption process is therefore the slow and rate-determining one. These conclusions have been confirmed by the work of Hauffe and coworkers,[3] who modified the structure of NiO by adding other ions. Similarly Dell, Stone, and Tiley[4] found that pretreatment of cuprous oxide with oxygen, which increases the number of positive holes, increases the rate of the reaction.

The H_2-D_2 exchange has been studied on zinc oxide catalysts by Molinari and Parravano,[5] who modified the catalyst by addition of Li_2O and other oxides. The incorporation of Li_2O into ZnO, which decreases the *n*-type character of the oxide, decreased the rate of the H_2-D_2 exchange, whereas the addition of Ga_2O_3 or Al_2O_3, which increases the *n*-type character, increased the catalytic activity. These results indicate that the rate-determining step is the cationic chemisorption of hydrogen. Similar conclusions may be drawn from the work of Voltz and Weller,[6] who pretreated a chromium oxide catalyst with hydrogen and oxygen and in this way modified its *p*-typeness. The degree of its *p*-typeness was determined from measurements of electrical conductivity, and they found that decreasing *p*-typeness favored the reaction.

[1] C. Wagner and K. Hauffe, *Z. Elektrochem.*, **44,** 172 (1938).

[2] W. E. Garner, T. J. Gray, and F. S. Stone, *Discussions Faraday Soc.*, **8,** 246 (1950).

[3] K. Hauffe, R. Glang, and H. J. Engell, *Z. Physik. Chem.*, **201,** 223 (1950); H. J. Engell and K. Hauffe, *Z. Elektrochem.*, **57,** 776 (1953).

[4] R. M. Dell, F. S. Stone, and P. F. Tiley, *Trans. Faraday Soc.*, **49,** 201 (1953).

[5] E. Molinari and G. Parravano, *J. Am. Chem. Soc.*, **75,** 5233 (1953).

[6] S. E. Voltz and S. Weller, *ibid.*, 5227, 5231.

As a general rule, it is found that the catalytic activation of oxygen is favored by increasing the p-typeness of the catalyst, whereas that of hydrogen is favored by increasing the n-typeness. These conclusions are of much value in connection with a study of mechanisms on oxide catalysts, but except in the simplest cases the situation is not clear-cut, and it is difficult to make predictions as to the most effective catalysts.

REACTIONS IN THE SOLID STATE[1]

A very considerable amount of work has been done on the kinetics of solid-state reactions. Space does not permit more than a very brief account, in which only the most important principles are referred to.

Lattice imperfections play a very large role in connection with reactions in the solid state. In many such reactions the diffusion of a reactant or a product is rate controlling, and diffusion is only possible by virtue of lattice defects of various types. Another factor that has an important effect on rates is lattice strain, which may arise from external pressure, from imperfections in the lattice, or from the existence of impurity atoms of such a nature as to disturb the regularity of the lattice. Such strain may act as a source of energy, and so aid the chemical process, or it may increase the ease with which imperfections are formed and hence increase the rate of diffusion. An example of the effect of strain is to be found in the work of Morrison and Nakayama[2] on the reaction between chlorine and potassium bromide.

The definition of a rate constant for a solid-state reaction gives rise to some difficulty, and the matter has been discussed briefly by Gomes.[3] The main problem is that the concept of concentration has no significance, so that the rate constant cannot be defined in the same way as for a homogeneous reaction. Special procedures can be worked out in particular cases. If, for example, the product of a reaction is formed as a layer on the surface of the solid, one can consider the change with time of the thickness of the layer.

For the same reason the activation energy of a solid-state reaction does not have the significance that it has in a homogeneous reaction. It is only in rare cases that the apparent activation energy is a simple quantity; usually the temperature dependence of a diffusion constant is involved, sometimes in a complicated way.

[1] For reviews see W. Jost, "Diffusion in Solids, Liquids and Gases," Academic Press Inc., New York, 1960; F. S. Stone, in J. H. de Boer (ed.), "Reactivity of Solids," Elsevier Publishing Company, Amsterdam, 1961; G. Parravano, *Chem. Eng. News*, **40**(12), 110 (1962); E. K. Gill and J. A. Morrison, *Ann. Rev. Phys. Chem.*, **14**, 205 (1963).

[2] J. A. Morrison and K. Nakayama, *Trans. Faraday Soc.*, **59**, 2560 (1963).

[3] W. Gomes, *Nature*, **192**, 865 (1961).

There are a number of different types of solid-state reactions, of which the following may be mentioned:

(1) Solid A + solid B $\rightarrow$ solid AB
(2) Solid A + gas B $\rightarrow$ solid AB
(3) Solid A + liquid B $\rightarrow$ solid AB
(4) Solid A + gas B $\rightarrow$ gas AB
(5) Various types of thermal decompositions, such as explosions of solids

In reactions (2) and (3) the product AB may remain as a layer around the solid reactant A, and in this case two possibilities may be distinguished:

(*a*) The molar volume of AB may be less than that of A.
(*b*) The molar volume of AB may be greater than that of A.

In case (*a*) the product layer will probably be porous so that the rate-determining step may be the chemical process occurring at the interface of A. Under these circumstances the rate is determined by the available surface area of A, and such processes are referred to as *topochemical.* In case (*b*) the product AB will usually form a protective layer around A, and the rate will probably be *diffusion controlled.*

Topochemical reactions, which include many reactions of metals with oxygen and the halogens, may be considered in an elementary way as follows. Suppose that the experiments are carried out with spherical particles, which remain spherical as reaction proceeds, and that the rate of reaction is proportional to the area S of the surface; then

$$-\frac{dV}{dt} = kS \tag{124}$$

where V is the volume of a particle at time t. Since the surface area is $4\pi r^2$, where r is the radius at time t, and V is $\frac{4}{3}\pi r^3$,

$$-\frac{dV}{dt} = 4k\pi r^2 \tag{125}$$

$$= k(26\pi)^{1/2} V^{2/3} \tag{126}$$

The reaction can thus be said to be of "two-thirds order." It can be seen from (125) that

$$-\frac{d}{dt}\left(\frac{4}{3}\pi r^3\right) = 4k\pi r^2 \tag{127}$$

so that

$$-\frac{dr}{dt} = k \tag{128}$$

The radius thus recedes at a constant rate.

The simplest treatment of a diffusion-controlled reaction between a solid and a gas proceeds as follows. If x is the thickness of the product layer, the simplest assumption is that

$$\frac{dx}{dt} = \frac{k}{x} \tag{129}$$

whence

$$x^2 = 2kt \tag{130}$$

This is known as the *parabolic* law, which is frequently observed. The constant k is proportional to the diffusion coefficient. Various deductions of this law have been given,[1] using the laws of diffusion, and in particular Mott[2] has obtained explicit expressions for the constant k on the basis of various diffusion mechanisms. Other laws have also been obtained, and various refinements of the theory have been made. For example, Eq. (130) applies only if the area is the same for the inner and outer surfaces of the layer, and a correction has to be made for spherical particles. Also, in an exact treatment a correction should be made for the difference in molar volume between the solid reactant and the product; such corrections have been made by Carter[3] in a treatment of the oxidation of nickel spheres.

A number of different kinetic equations may apply to the case of a solid undergoing thermal decomposition.[4] In some instances, for example, the extent of decomposition varies with the time in a sigmoid fashion, the rate increasing in the early stages and then falling off. This behavior may be interpreted as arising from the production of nuclei at various places in the crystal, followed by the growth of these nuclei; at later times there is a decay in the reaction as nuclei overlap, and the area of the interface between reactant and product phases decreases. An equation due to Prout and Tompkins[5] is widely used to describe processes in which the rate of formation and growth of nuclei dominates the decomposition of a solid.

PROBLEMS

1. Estimate the rate constant for the decomposition of ammonia on tungsten from the results plotted in Fig. 60.

[1] G. Tammann, *Nachr. Ges. Wiss. Göttingen, Math.-Physik. Klasse*, 225 (1919); N. B. Pilling and R. E. Bedworth, *J. Inst. Metals*, **29**, 529 (1925).

[2] N. F. Mott, *Trans. Faraday Soc.*, **35**, 1175 (1939); **36**, 472 (1940); **43**, 429 (1947).

[3] R. C. Carter, *J. Chem. Phys.*, **34**, 2010 (1961); **35**, 1137 (1961).

[4] Cf. P. W. M. Jacobs and F. C. Tompkins, in W. E. Garner (ed.), "Chemistry of the Solid State," chap. 7, Butterworth & Co. (Publishers), Ltd., London, 1955; D. Dollimore, J. Dollimore, and D. Nicholson, in J. H. de Boer (ed.), "Reactivity of Solids," p. 627, Elsevier Publishing Company, Amsterdam, 1961.

[5] E. G. Prout and F. C. Tompkins, *Trans. Faraday Soc.*, **40**, 488 (1944).

2. A first-order surface reaction is proceeding with a velocity v moles liter^{-1} sec^{-1} and a rate constant k sec^{-1}. What will be the rate and the rate constant if (**a**) the surface area is increased tenfold, (**b**) the amount of gas is increased tenfold at constant pressure and temperature, (**c**) the area and the amount of gas are both increased tenfold?

If the reaction occurs with rate v and rate constant k on the surface of a spherical vessel of radius r, what will be the rate and rate constant in a similar vessel of radius $10r$?

Define a new rate constant k' which, unlike k, is independent of the gas volume V and the area S of the catalyst surface.

How far are these conclusions valid for (**a**) a zero-order reaction, (**b**) a second-order reaction?

3. The thermal decomposition of a substance,

$$\mathrm{A} \rightarrow \mathrm{P} + \mathrm{Q}$$

takes place initially as a homogeneous first-order reaction. There is also a heterogeneous zero-order surface reaction taking place on the surface of the solid product P, which is formed as a film on the surface of the vessel. Obtain an equation for the rate of decrease of the concentration of A.

4. The activation energy for the desorption of carbon monoxide from platinum is given[1] as 32.0 kcal at 600°C. The rate may be expressed as

$$v = c_a \frac{\mathbf{k}T}{\mathbf{h}} \frac{f_{\ddagger}}{f_a} e^{-E_0/RT}$$

where c_a, taken as 10^{15} molecules per sq cm, is the number of adsorbed molecules per square centimeter, and $f_{\ddagger}$ and f_a are the partition functions for activated and adsorbed molecules, respectively. These partition functions may be assumed to be equal to each other.

Calculate E_0, the activation energy at 0°K, and then calculate the rate of desorption at 600°K, in molecules cm^{-2} sec^{-1}.

***5.** Hydrogen iodide decomposes on gold according to a zero-order law and with an activation energy of 25.0 kcal at 1000°K.[2] The mechanism required to account for the order leads to an equation identical in form with that of the preceding problem. Calculate the activation energy at 0°K and the rate at 1000°K.

***6.** Hydrogen iodide decomposes on platinum, the reaction at 826°K following a first-order law and having an activation energy of 14.0 kcal. The rate is given by Eq. (94). Calculate the activation energy at 0°K. Assuming that the number of sites is 10^{15} cm^{-2}, calculate the rate of

[1] I. Langmuir, *ibid.*, **17,** 641 (1922).
[2] C. N. Hinshelwood and C. R. Prichard, *J. Chem. Soc.*, **127,** 806 (1925).

the reaction corresponding to 1 liter of gas at 1 atm pressure and a platinum surface of 1 sq cm. The interatomic distance in hydrogen iodide is 1.604 A; the vibrational partition function may be taken as unity.

★7. The rate of the reaction between carbon monoxide and oxygen on platinum is found under certain circumstances to be directly proportional to the oxygen pressure and inversely proportional to the carbon monoxide pressure.[1] Derive a rate equation, in terms of partition functions, which is consistent with this fact. If the activation energy is 33.3 kcal at 600°K, calculate the value at 0°K. Calculate the rate of reaction at 600°K as a function of the concentrations of oxygen and carbon monoxide (expressed in molecules per cubic centimeter) and corresponding to a volume of 1 liter and a catalyst surface area of 1 sq cm. The interatomic distances in O_2 and CO are 1.208 and 1.128 A, respectively; the vibrational partition functions may be taken as unity.

★8. On the basis of absolute-rate theory, derive expressions for the rates of the following reactions in terms of the appropriate partition functions:

(a) The ethylene-deuterium exchange reactions
(b) The methane-deuterium exchange reactions
(c) The ammonia-deuterium exchange reactions

[1] I. Langmuir, *Trans. Faraday Soc.*, **17,** 621 (1922).

chapter

Complex Reactions 7

A GREAT MANY chemical processes are found, on detailed study, not to occur by a simple rearrangement of the atoms in a single stage, but to take place in a number of well-defined steps. Various kinds of evidence are available to support this conclusion in individual instances, and this chapter is concerned with a discussion of the more significant points.

The most obvious indication of complexity is when the kinetic law is inconsistent with the stoichiometric equation for the reaction. An example of this is the reaction between nitric oxide and hydrogen, the process being represented by the equation

$$2NO + 2H_2 = N_2 + 2H_2O$$

According to the stoichiometry, this reaction might be expected to be of the fourth order, with the rate proportional to the squares of the concentrations of both nitric oxide and hydrogen. In fact, in the gas phase the rate is proportional to the square of the nitric oxide concentration but only to the first power of the hydrogen concentration,[1]

$$v = k[NO]^2[H_2] \tag{1}$$

[1] C. N. Hinshelwood and T. E. Green, *J. Chem. Soc.*, **129**, 730 (1926).

This result may be interpreted as indicating that the initial step in the reaction is actually

$$2NO + H_2 \rightarrow N_2 + H_2O_2$$

and that this process is followed by

$$H_2O_2 + H_2 \rightarrow 2H_2O$$

If it is assumed that the second reaction is rapid compared with the first, the rate of the first controls the rate of the second and therefore gives rise to the kinetic behavior observed.

Another example of this type of complexity is found in the reaction between hydrogen and iodine monochloride,

$$2ICl + H_2 = I_2 + 2HCl$$

Instead of being of the third order, as the equation might indicate, this reaction obeys the law[1]

$$v = k[ICl][H_2] \tag{2}$$

i.e., is of the second order. The mechanism suggested is that there is an initial slow process,

$$ICl + H_2 \rightarrow HI + HCl$$

which is rate determining, and that this is followed by the rapid process

$$HI + ICl \rightarrow HCl + I_2$$

Because of this type of complexity, it is very frequently found that the order of a reaction is less than that which corresponds directly to the stoichiometric equation. It was seen in Chap. 4 that a reaction between three molecules is very much less probable than one between two, on account of the greater loss of entropy in the activated state; collisions between four molecules are so improbable that it is unlikely that there are any elementary reactions having a molecularity of 4 or more. A reaction whose stoichiometric equation involves more than three molecules usually may proceed much more effectively via a rate-controlling step of lower molecularity.

Rate Equations for Complex Systems.[2] In order to treat the various kinds of complex schemes that arise in kinetic problems, it is necessary to set up rate equations and, if possible, to integrate them. Table 48 gives solutions for a number of different mechanisms. The system of consecutive first-order reactions, $A \rightarrow B \rightarrow C$, is one that frequently

[1] W. D. Bonner, W. L. Gore, and D. M. Yost, *J. Am. Chem. Soc.*, **57**, 2723 (1935).

[2] For further details, with examples, see A. A. Frost and R. G. Pearson, "Kinetics and Mechanisms," 2d ed., chap. 8, John Wiley & Sons, Inc., New York, 1961.

Table 48 INTEGRATED RATE EQUATIONS FOR SOME COMPLEX REACTIONS

System	Differential equation	Integrated equation	Reference
$A \xrightarrow{k_1} P$ (first order) $A \xrightarrow{k_2} P$ (second order)	$\frac{d[P]}{dt} = k_1[A] + k_2[A]^2$	$\ln \frac{k_1[A]_0 + k_2[A]_0[A]}{(k_1 + k_2[A]_0)[A]} = k_1t$	†
$A \xrightarrow{k_1} P_1$ $A \xrightarrow{k_2} P_2$ $A \xrightarrow{k_3} P_3$ all first order	$\frac{d[P_1]}{dt} = k_1[A]$ etc.	$[P_1] = [P_1]_0 + \frac{k_1[A]_0}{k_1 + k_2 + k_3}[1 - \exp[-(k_1 + k_2 + k_3)t]$ etc.	
$A \xrightarrow{k_1} P$ $B \xrightarrow{k_2} P$ first order	$\frac{d[P]}{dt} = k_1[A] + k_2[B]$	$[A] = [A]_0e^{-k_1t}$ $[B] = [B]_0e^{-k_2t}$ $[P] = [A_0](1 - e^{-k_1t}) + [B_0](1 - e^{-k_2t})$	
$A \xrightarrow{k_1} B \xrightarrow{k_2} C$	$\frac{-d[A]}{dt} = k_1[A]$ $\frac{d[B]}{dt} = k_1[A] - k_2[B]$ $\frac{d[C]}{dt} = k_2[B]$	$[A] = [A]_0e^{-k_1t}$ $[B] = \frac{[A]_0k_1}{k_2 - k_1}(e^{-k_1t} - e^{-k_2t})$ $[C] = \frac{[A]_0}{k_2 - k_1}[k_2(1 - e^{-k_1t}) - k_1(1 - e^{-k_2t})]$	§

† R. Wegschneider, *Z. Physik. Chem.*, **41,** 52 (1902).
§ A. V. Harcourt and W. Esson, *Proc. Roy. Soc.* (*London*), **A14,** 470 (1865); *Phil. Trans.*, **156,** 193 (1866); **157,** 117 (1867).

arises, and it is of interest to consider the way in which the three concentrations vary with time, as given by the integrated equations. These variations are shown in Fig. 68. The concentration of A falls with time

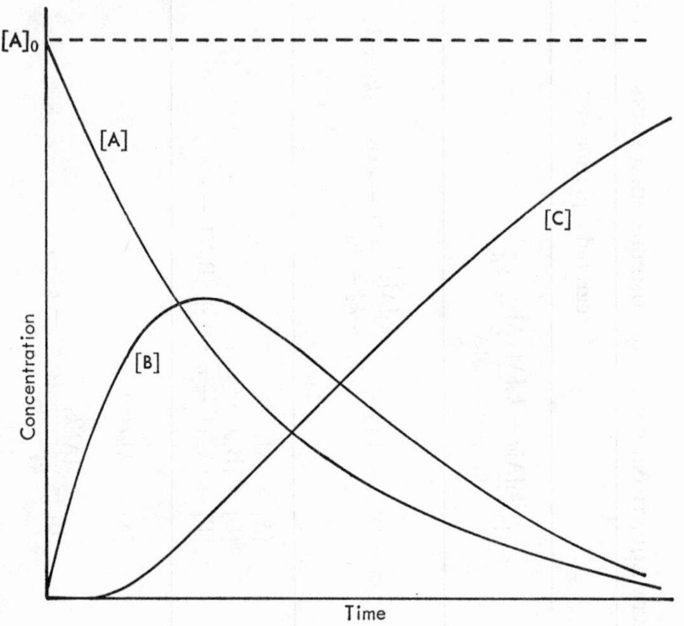

Fig. 68. Variation of the concentrations of A, B, and C with time, for a reaction of the type A → B → C.

in a simple exponential manner. That of B is initially zero, and it passes through a maximum, ending at zero since all of B is finally converted into C. The rate of formation of C is always proportional to [B]; it is therefore zero initially, passes through a maximum when [B] is a maximum, and gradually falls to zero. The curve for [C] is therefore S-shaped, and there may be said to be an *induction period* for the formation of C; during this period very little C is formed. The existence of such induction periods is an indication that a product is not formed directly, but via some intermediate.

Integrated rate equations for some more complicated kinetic systems have also been worked out, and some references to them are given in Table 49. In many cases, however, solutions in closed form cannot be obtained, and various procedures may then be followed. In some instances, to be considered later, it is permissible as a good approximation to set the rates of change of the concentrations of certain intermediates to be zero; this is known as the *steady-state treatment.* In other cases

Table 49 SOLUTIONS FOR OTHER COMPLEX REACTIONS

System	*Reference*
$A + B \rightarrow C + E$ $A + C \rightarrow D + E$	E. Abel, *Z. Physik. Chem.*, **56,** 558 (1906).
$A \rightarrow B;\ 2B \rightarrow C$ $2A \rightarrow B;\ B \rightarrow C$ $2A \rightarrow B;\ 2B \rightarrow C$ $2A \rightarrow B;\ B + D \rightarrow C$ $A \rightarrow B;\ B + D \rightarrow C$	J. Chien, *J. Am. Chem. Soc.*, **70,** 2256 (1948).
More complicated cases of the above types	S. W. Pskezhetskii and R. N. Rubinshkein, *J. Phys. Chem.* (*USSR*), **21,** 659 (1947).
Series of general first-order reactions, e.g., $A \rightleftharpoons B \rightleftharpoons C \rightleftharpoons D \cdots$ $B \rightleftharpoons B'$; $C \rightleftharpoons C' \rightleftharpoons C'' \rightarrow$	F. A. Matsen and J. L. Franklin, *J. Am. Chem. Soc.*, **72,** 3337 (1950); see also A. Skrabal, "Homogenkinetik," Theodor Steinkopff, Dresden and Leipzig, 1941; B. J. Zwolinski and H. Eyring, *J. Am. Chem. Soc.*, **69,** 2702 (1947); T. M. Lowry and W. T. John, *J. Chem. Soc.*, **97,** 2634 (1910); E. S. Lewis and M. D. Johnson, *J. Am. Chem. Soc.*, **82,** 5406 (1960).

solutions may be obtained using numerical methods, for example using a computer. Appendix A, prepared by J. L. Howland, explains the basic principles of such methods.

Chain Reactions. Another type of complexity in chemical reactions consists in the formation of free atoms and radicals as intermediates. These reactions show many features which are different from those discussed above and may be recognized on the basis of showing one or more of these characteristics.

When reactions occur by a series of processes involving atoms or radicals, it is sometimes, but by no means always, found that the kinetic laws are unusually complex. A well-known example is the reaction between hydrogen and bromine, which does not obey the simple law,

$$\frac{d[\mathrm{HBr}]}{dt} = k[\mathrm{H_2}][\mathrm{Br_2}] \tag{3}$$

analogous to that obeyed in the hydrogen-iodine reaction, but follows the equation

$$\frac{d[\mathrm{HBr}]}{dt} = \frac{k[\mathrm{H_2}][\mathrm{Br_2}]^{1/2}}{1 + [\mathrm{HBr}]/k'[\mathrm{Br_2}]} \tag{4}$$

where k and k' are constants at a given temperature. A significant feature of this law is the occurrence, in the denominator, of the concentration of the product hydrogen bromide, implying that this substance acts as an inhibitor of the reaction. It will be seen later that the existence of such inhibition is unequivocal evidence in favor of an atomic or free-radical mechanism.

The reaction scheme proposed[1] to explain the kinetics obtained was

$$Br_2 \rightarrow 2Br$$
$$Br + H_2 \rightarrow HBr + H$$
$$H + Br_2 \rightarrow HBr + Br$$
$$H + HBr \rightarrow H_2 + Br$$
$$2Br \rightarrow Br_2$$

The way in which it interprets the kinetic results will be considered later. It is seen that hydrogen and bromine atoms are postulated as intermediates and that, since in all reactions except the last they regenerate one another, one atom of bromine may be responsible for the formation of a number of molecules of hydrogen bromide. On account of this important feature, reactions of this type are spoken of as *chain reactions.*

It should be emphasized that chain reactions do not always follow complex kinetic laws. Simple laws are obeyed, for example, by certain organic decompositions which are found to be complex on the basis of other evidence to be considered later. A particular example is the decomposition of ethane, which follows first-order kinetics.

A second piece of evidence that certain reactions proceed by a chain mechanism comes from the results of photochemical investigations, for it is found that in many cases the absorption of one quantum of light is followed by the reaction of a large number of molecules. Since on theoretical grounds a molecule is not likely to absorb more than one photon at a time, it may be inferred that the initial act of absorption is followed by a chain of processes which may, under favorable circumstances, bring about a considerable amount of reaction.

The original suggestion that a chemical reaction, particularly one initiated by light, may proceed by a chain process was made in 1913 by Bodenstein,[2] and a new phase in the history of kinetics may be said to have started at that time. In 1918 Nernst[3] proposed a specific scheme for the photochemical union of hydrogen and chlorine. The chains were initiated by the light absorption, which dissociated chlorine molecules into atoms,

$$Cl_2 + \mathbf{h}\nu \rightarrow 2Cl$$

Each chlorine atom produced could then attack a hydrogen molecule,

$$Cl + H_2 \rightarrow HCl + H$$

[1] J. A. Christiansen, *Kgl. Danske Videnskab. Selskab Mat.-Fys. Medd.*, **1**, 14 (1919); K. F. Herzfeld, *Z. Elektrochem.*, **25**, 301 (1919); *Ann. Physik.*, **59**, 635 (1919); M. Polanyi, *Z. Elektrochem.*, **26**, 50 (1920).

[2] M. Bodenstein, *Z. Physik. Chem.*, **85**, 329 (1913).

[3] W. Nernst, *Z. Elektrochem.*, **24**, 335 (1918).

and the resultant hydrogen atom could react with a chlorine molecule,

$$H + Cl_2 + HCl + Cl$$

In the two last reactions two molecules of hydrogen chloride have been produced by a single chlorine atom, which has been regenerated; the process can therefore continue. If it were not for certain chain-ending processes such as $2Cl \rightarrow Cl_2$, $2H \rightarrow H_2$, and $H + Cl \rightarrow HCl$, this process could continue indefinitely. Although Nernst's general idea was correct, it is now known that his reaction scheme requires modification; this is discussed in detail later.

That reaction chains of a similar type occur in thermal reactions is evident from the strong similarity which frequently exists between thermal and photochemical reactions. With both the hydrogen-bromine and hydrogen-chlorine reactions the rates were found to depend in a complicated fashion on the concentrations of hydrogen, halogen, and oxygen (if present), the laws being very similar in the two cases. This suggests that the main difference between the processes lies in the initial formation of the halogen atoms, the subsequent radical reactions being the same in both cases.

Various other kinds of evidence have been brought forward in favor of the participation of free-radical reactions in chemical processes. The presence of radicals in reaction systems has been detected by various means. Thus the line spectra of atoms and the band spectra of radicals have been observed in reaction mixtures, and the existence of free organic radicals in organic reactions has been proved by causing them to undergo characteristic reactions, e.g., with metallic mirrors. These and other methods of studying free-radical reactions will be discussed later in this chapter.

Steady-state Treatment. The theoretical treatment of the elementary reactions which play a part in complex mechanisms follows the same lines that have been shown in the previous chapters. In order to express the overall rate of a complex reaction in terms of the individual rate constants, a special treatment is required and will be described here.

A rigorous treatment of this problem would involve writing the appropriate differential equations for the individual reactions, eliminating the concentrations of the intermediate atoms and free radicals, and solving the equations so obtained. However, such a procedure can seldom be followed, since the resulting differential equation is always extremely complicated. The procedure that is then employed is as follows. Intermediates such as atoms and free radicals, the concentrations of which are necessarily low, are assumed to have a constant concentration during the course of reaction. In this way simple expressions for their concentrations may be obtained, and hence an equation for the overall rate can be derived. The first application of this treatment to a complex reaction was made by Christiansen,[1] Herzfeld,[2] and Polanyi,[3] in 1919, the reaction treated being the hydrogen-bromine reaction. The steady-state treatment has been criticized by Skrabal,[4] but his objections were answered by Bodenstein.[5]

The treatment of the hydrogen-bromine reaction proceeds as follows. The reaction scheme proposed is

(1) $$Br_2 \rightarrow 2Br$$
(2) $$Br + H_2 \rightarrow HBr + H$$
(3) $$H + Br_2 \rightarrow HBr + Br$$
(4) $$H + HBr \rightarrow H_2 + Br$$
(5) $$Br + Br \rightarrow Br_2$$

The chain carriers, i.e., the species participating in the reaction chain, are the hydrogen and bromine atoms. The steady-state equations for these atoms are, in terms of the rate constants k_1 to k_5 for the five processes listed above,

$$\frac{d[\mathrm{Br}]}{dt} = 2k_1[\mathrm{Br_2}] - k_2[\mathrm{Br}][\mathrm{H_2}] + k_3[\mathrm{H}][\mathrm{Br_2}] + k_4[\mathrm{H}][\mathrm{HBr}] - 2k_5[\mathrm{Br}]^2 = 0 \quad (5)$$

and

$$\frac{d[\mathrm{H}]}{dt} = k_2[\mathrm{Br}][\mathrm{H_2}] - k_3[\mathrm{H}][\mathrm{Br_2}] - k_4[\mathrm{H}][\mathrm{HBr}] = 0 \quad (6)$$

These are simultaneous equations in [H] and [Br] and can be solved to give expressions for these concentrations. Addition of Eq. (5) to (6) gives rise to

$$[\mathrm{Br}] = \left(\frac{k_1}{k_5}\right)^{1/2} [\mathrm{Br_2}]^{1/2} \quad (7)$$

and insertion of this into either (5) or (6) gives

$$[\mathrm{H}] = \frac{k_2(k_1/k_5)^{1/2}[\mathrm{H_2}][\mathrm{Br_2}]^{1/2}}{k_3[\mathrm{Br_2}] + k_4[\mathrm{HBr}]} \quad (8)$$

The equation for the rate of formation of HBr is

$$\frac{d[\mathrm{HBr}]}{dt} = k_2[\mathrm{Br}][\mathrm{H_2}] + k_3[\mathrm{H}][\mathrm{Br_2}] - k_4[\mathrm{H}][\mathrm{HBr}] \quad (9)$$

and introduction of the expressions for [H] and [Br] gives, after some

[1] Christiansen, *loc. cit.*
[2] Herzfeld, *loc. cit.*
[3] Polanyi, *loc. cit.*
[4] A. Skrabal, *Ann. Physik.*, **82**, 138 (1927).
[5] M. Bodenstein, *ibid.*, 836; D. A. Frank-Kamenetsky, *J. Phys. Chem., USSR*, **14**, 695 (1940).

rearrangement,

$$\frac{d[\mathrm{HBr}]}{dt} = \frac{2k_2(k_1/k_5)^{1/2}[\mathrm{H_2}][\mathrm{Br_2}]^{1/2}}{1 + k_4[\mathrm{HBr}]/k_3[\mathrm{Br_2}]} \tag{10}$$

This equation has the same form as the one obtained experimentally [Eq. (4)], a fact that gives considerable support to the mechanism proposed. Further evidence comes from studies of the rates of the individual processes and will be considered in the next chapter.

MICROSCOPIC REVERSIBILITY

The principle of microscopic reversibility was explained in Chap. 3 (p. 110), the conclusion being that, for an elementary process, the ratio of rate constants for reactions in forward and reverse directions must be equal to an equilibrium constant.[1] In the case of a complex process this is also sometimes true. In certain circumstances, however, this relationship does not apply, and it is important to realize the conditions under which one is justified in equating k_1/k_{-1} with K.

Consider a mechanism of the type

$$\mathrm{A} \underset{k_{-1}}{\overset{k_1}{\rightleftharpoons}} \mathrm{B} \underset{k_{-2}}{\overset{k_2}{\rightleftharpoons}} \mathrm{C}$$

At complete equilibrium one can write

$$\left(\frac{[\mathrm{B}]}{[\mathrm{A}]}\right)_{\mathrm{eq}} = \frac{k_1}{k_{-1}} \quad \text{and} \quad \left(\frac{[\mathrm{C}]}{[\mathrm{B}]}\right)_{\mathrm{eq}} = \frac{k_2}{k_{-2}} \tag{11}$$

and

$$\left(\frac{[\mathrm{C}]}{[\mathrm{A}]}\right)_{\mathrm{eq}} = \frac{k_1 k_2}{k_{-1}k_{-2}} \tag{12}$$

If one makes measurements of the rate of disappearance of A at the very beginning of the reaction, before any B and C have accumulated,

$$-\frac{d[\mathrm{A}]}{dt} = k_1[\mathrm{A}] \tag{13}$$

and the first-order rate constant is k_1. Similarly if one starts with pure C and measures initial rates, the rate constant obtained is k_{-2}. The ratio k_1/k_{-2} is not in general equal to the equilibrium constant K.

The point is that the initial rate constants measured, k_1 and k_{-2}, are *not the rate constants that apply when the system is at equilibrium.* When

[1] One should say *an* equilibrium constant, since an equilibrium constant is not unique; it can be raised to any arbitrary power and still be a true equilibrium constant.

the system is at equilibrium,

$$\frac{d[\mathrm{B}]}{dt} = k_1[\mathrm{A}] - (k_{-1} + k_2)[\mathrm{B}] + k_{-2}[\mathrm{C}] = 0 \tag{14}$$

whence

$$[\mathrm{B}] = \frac{k_1[\mathrm{A}] + k_{-2}[\mathrm{C}]}{k_{-1} + k_2} \tag{15}$$

The net rate of disappearance of A is

$$-\frac{d[\mathrm{A}]}{dt} = k_1[\mathrm{A}] - k_{-1}[\mathrm{B}] \tag{16}$$

Introduction of the expression for [B] gives, with some rearrangement,

$$-\frac{d[\mathrm{A}]}{dt} = \frac{k_1k_2}{k_{-1} + k_2}[\mathrm{A}] - \frac{k_{-1}k_{-2}}{k_{-1} + k_2}[\mathrm{C}] \tag{17}$$

The first term is the rate of the reaction from left to right, and the corresponding rate constant is $k_1k_2/(k_{-1} + k_2)$. Similarly the rate constant from right to left is $k_{-1}k_{-2}/(k_{-1} + k_2)$. The ratio of these two rate constants, $k_1k_2/k_{-1}k_{-2}$, is equal to the equilibrium constant.

If the rate constants that are measured for forward and reverse directions are those that apply when the system is at equilibrium, their ratio is bound to be an equilibrium constant for the reaction. This follows from the fact that at equilibrium the rates must be the same in the two directions.

Rate constants that do not apply under the equilibrium conditions are not, however, necessarily related in this way. Great caution should therefore be used in deducing rate constants (and rate laws) in one direction from the equilibrium conditions and from the behavior in the other direction.

DETECTION AND ESTIMATION OF ATOMS AND RADICALS IN REACTION SYSTEMS[1]

In only a few cases can much information concerning the constants of elementary processes be obtained from the kinetics of the overall processes. The hydrogen-bromine reaction is, in fact, one of the few reactions for which this can be done; as will be seen in detail in the following chapter, the values of the five constants k_1 to k_5 can be determined by comparing Eq. (10) with the empirical expression for the rate, and making use of certain additional information. In most thermal reac-

[1] For reviews, see E. W. R. Steacie, "Atomic and Free Radical Reactions," chap. 2, Reinhold Publishing Corporation, New York, 1954; K. R. Jennings, *Quart. Revs.*, **15**, 237 (1961); F. Kaufman, in G. Porter (ed.), "Progress in Reaction Kinetics," vol. 1, Pergamon Press, Oxford, 1961.

tions, however, the situation is too complicated to allow an empirical kinetic expression to be deduced on the basis of an assumed mechanism, so that other methods have to be employed in order for the individual processes to be investigated. One procedure which gives some information of this type involves making detailed analyses of the reaction mixture at various stages; unfortunately, chemical methods of analysis are usually difficult to carry out. In any case these methods are applicable only to stable molecules and do not give much information concerning the detailed mechanism of the process. Methods of detecting and estimating the concentrations of the intermediate atoms and free radicals are therefore required, and a number of different systems have been developed. These include (1) spectroscopic methods, (2) the removal of metallic mirrors, a procedure particularly applicable to organic free radicals, (3) electron-spin resonance spectroscopy, (4) calorimetry, (5) methods depending on mass differences, (6) methods involving the study of reactions of the radicals, (7) trapping of radicals. These procedures will now be discussed.

Spectroscopic Methods.[1] Spectroscopic methods of detecting and estimating atoms and radicals include the study of both absorption and emission spectra and depend on the fact that the wavelengths absorbed or emitted are characteristic of each compound; moreover the intensities of the lines or bands can give a measure of the concentrations of the species present. Recently, absorption spectra in particular have been used in studies of this kind, and both the ultraviolet and infrared regions have been the subject of much investigation, the experimental techniques for the former being much simpler. Absorption spectroscopy is especially used in connection with the technique of flash photolysis (p. 47), which produces very high concentrations of radicals. Emission spectra are useful when the reaction is accompanied by a flame, but give no indication of the concentrations of unexcited molecules or radicals. These methods have been applied particularly to atoms such as H and Cl and to radicals such as OH, CH, C_2, SO, and HCO; the spectra of more complicated radicals are usually too difficult to analyze satisfactorily owing to the overlapping of a large number of bands.

Indirect spectroscopic methods are also used occasionally, the general principle being the identification of reaction products which almost certainly arise from a particular atom or radical. For example, Gaydon[2] has shown that oxygen atoms can be detected by the introduction of nitric oxide into a reaction mixture, the result being the emission of a yellow-green radiation having a characteristic spectrum, which is ascribed

[1] G. Herzberg, *Proc. Chem. Soc.*, 116 (1959); *Proc. Roy. Soc.* (*London*), **A262,** 291 (1961).

[2] A. G. Gaydon, *ibid.*, **A183,** 11 (1944); *Trans. Faraday Soc.*, **42,** 292 (1946); cf. W. H. Rodebush, *J. Phys. Chem.*, **41,** 283 (1937).

to excited NO_2 produced in the reaction

$$O + NO \rightarrow NO_2^*$$

This method has been applied successfully to a number of oxidation systems, with significant results.

Oxygen and nitrogen atom concentrations have been measured using the absorption spectrum of nitric oxide.[1] For oxygen atoms the procedure is to add just enough NO_2 to quench the faint afterglow they produce; a molecule of nitric oxide is produced for each oxygen atom present,

$$O + NO_2 \rightarrow 2NO$$

and the concentration of nitric oxide is measured spectroscopically. A number of other indirect spectroscopic procedures have been employed, most of them applicable particularly to atoms and radicals in flames.

Removal of Mirrors. The technique for detecting free radicals by causing them to remove metallic mirrors deposited on surfaces is due to Paneth and Hofeditz,[2] whose apparatus is shown schematically in Fig. 69.

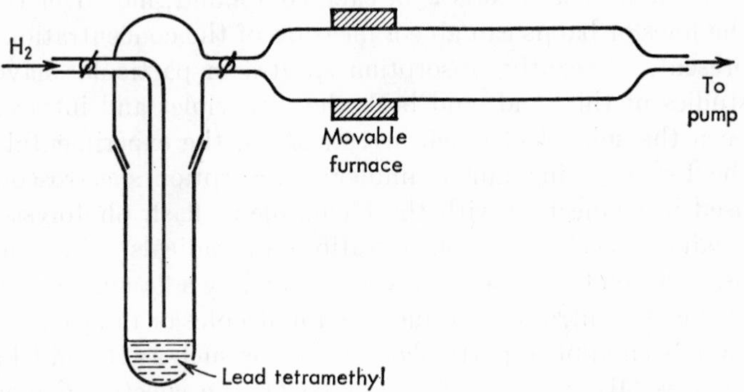

Fig. 69. Apparatus used by Paneth and Hofeditz for the detection of free organic radicals.

A stream of pure hydrogen was passed at a pressure of 1 to 2 mm through a cooled vessel, in which it was saturated with lead tetramethyl, after which it was passed through a tube one part of which was heated. The heating caused decomposition of the lead tetramethyl, and lead was

[1] H. P. Broida, H. I. Schiff, and T. M. Sugden, *Nature*, **185**, 760 (1960).

[2] F. Paneth and W. Hofeditz, *Ber.*, **B62**, 1335 (1929); cf. F. Paneth and W. Lautsch, *ibid.*, **B64**, 2702 (1931).

deposited as a mirror on the surface of the tube. It was then found that if the tube was heated upstream of the mirror, the mirror gradually disappeared, while a second mirror was deposited at the position of the second heating. This was interpreted as due to the fact that free methyl radicals produced in the hot tube reacted with the lead. It was found that the phenomenon could not be explained as due to thermal effects causing sublimation and condensation of the mirror, since the behavior was not obtained in the absence of lead tetramethyl in the hydrogen. Moreover, cooling of the tube between the position of heating and the mirror caused no change. Mirror removal could be effected by heating the tube at distances up to 30 cm from the mirror, although the rate of removal was less, the greater the distance. This is because the radicals have more chance to recombine as the distance becomes greater. Mirrors of zinc and antimony were also removed in the same manner.

The existence of methyl radicals in the gas phase in these experiments was shown by passing the gas over a zinc mirror and collecting the material formed; this was demonstrated by its melting point, boiling point, and other properties to be zinc dimethyl. The ethyl radical was identified in a similar manner.

Paneth's technique for the detection of free radicals by the removal of metallic mirrors was greatly simplified by Rice, Johnston, and Evering,[1] who used condensable gases as carriers in place of the hydrogen or helium used by Paneth; these gases could be frozen out with liquid air after they had passed over the mirror, and high-speed pumps were therefore rendered unnecessary. Water vapor, organic vapors, and carbon dioxide were employed, and as mirrors Rice and his coworkers showed that in addition to lead, zinc, and antimony, a wide variety of substances could be used. Examples are the alkali metals, mercury, tin, lead, arsenic, antimony, bismuth, selenium, and tellurium.

In a comparison of the different kinds of mirrors Rice and Glasebrook[2] discovered specificities with respect to the radicals with which reaction occurs; thus tellurium, antimony, selenium, and arsenic are attacked by the methylene radical, whereas zinc, cadmium, bismuth, thallium, and lead are not, although they are attacked by alkyl radicals. The activity of lead mirrors was found to be lessened by heating, or by cooling to 0°C, the reason apparently being that adsorption of impurities takes placed. The activity of antimony mirrors, on the other hand, is hardly affected by the temperature. Zinc sulfide screens have also been used to detect free radicals;[3] these glow when recombination occurs.

The Paneth-Rice technique has been modified by the use of radio-

[1] F. O. Rice, W. R. Johnston, and B. L. Evering, *J. Am. Chem. Soc.*, **54**, 3559 (1932).

[2] F. O. Rice and A. L. Glasebrook, *ibid.*, **55**, 4329 (1933); **56**, 2381, 2472 (1934).

[3] P. N. Kohanenko, *Acta Physicochim. URSS*, **9**, 93 (1938).

active materials. Leighton and Mortensen[1] used a lead mirror containing radium D, E, and F and followed the disappearance of the mirror by the loss of β-ray activity as measured by an electroscope. The volatile products were collected and detected by their β-ray activity. A similar procedure was employed by Burton, Ricci, and Davis,[2] who used a radium-D mirror.

In addition to organic free radicals, hydrogen atoms have been detected by the mirror-removal method. Pearson, Robinson, and Stoddart[3] found that atomic hydrogen removes arsenic, antimony, selenium, tellurium, germanium, and tin mirrors, but not lead. Burton[4] has made use of these facts to detect hydrogen atoms in photochemical processes; the reaction mixture was first passed over a lead mirror, which removes all the alkyl radicals, and then over an antimony mirror, which removes the hydrogen atoms.

The mirror method was of great importance in the early development of the subject of organic free-radical reactions, since it led to the conclusion that free radicals are important in many reaction systems. The method is, however, not widely used today since more reliable methods are now available.

Electron-spin Resonance Spectroscopy.[5] Substances such as atoms and free radicals which contain unpaired electrons produce a splitting of energy levels in a strong magnetic field. Atoms or radicals can be introduced into a quartz tube between the poles of a magnet, and at right angles to the broad face of a wave guide; the power is provided by a magnetron or klystron, and a crystal detector is used to measure the absorption of radiation. The intensity of absorption depends upon the number of unpaired electrons, and the method can therefore be used for measuring radical concentrations. The region of absorption differs for different species, so that atoms and free radicals can be identified.

A number of atoms, including N and O, and of radicals, such as CH_3, CH_2OH, and aromatic radicals, have been detected in reaction systems by the use of this technique.

Calorimetry. In a few investigations calorimetric methods have been used for estimating atom and free-radical concentrations in reaction systems, but the method presents some difficulties. Some of these have been overcome by using a "catalytic probe," and Greaves and Linnett[6]

[1] P. A. Leighton and R. A. Mortensen, *J. Am. Chem. Soc.*, **58**, 488 (1936).

[2] M. Burton, J. E. Ricci, and T. W. Davis, *ibid.*, **58**, 488 (1936).

[3] T. G. Pearson, P. L. Robinson, and E. M. Stoddart, *Proc. Roy. Soc.* (*London*), **A142**, 275 (1933).

[4] M. Burton, *J. Am. Chem. Soc.*, **58**, 692, 1645 (1936).

[5] D. J. E. Ingram, "Free Radicals as Studied by Electron Spin Resonance," Butterworth & Co. (Publishers), Ltd., London, 1958.

[6] J. C. Greaves and J. W. Linnett, *Trans. Faraday Soc.*, **55**, 1338 (1959).

have been successful in applying this method. Work has also been done using an isothermal calorimeter.[1]

Mass Spectrometry.[2] The mass spectrometer has been used to a considerable extent for the detection and estimation of free radicals in reaction systems. Early and important work in this field was carried out by Eltenton,[3] who found evidence for a number of organic free radicals in reaction systems in which organic decompositions were taking place. He detected, for example, methyl and ethyl radicals in the decomposition of ethane, and methylene in the decomposition of diazomethane. More recently a large amount of work of this kind has been carried out, and more than 60 different free radicals have been detected by this method in thermal decomposition reactions; examples are OH, CH_2, CH_3, C_2H_5, CHO, CH_3CO, and $CH_2{=}CH$. Radicals such as HO_2 have also been detected in bimolecular reaction systems. The concentrations of free radicals in thermal decompositions, under the usual conditions of kinetic experiments, are too small to allow the radicals to be detected by mass spectrometry; by working at higher temperatures, however, the concentrations can be increased sufficiently for detection to be possible.

Reactions have sometimes been caused to occur in the chamber of the mass spectrometer, and their kinetics have been studied. Thus by adding nitric oxide to a stream of methyl radicals, Lossing, Bryce, and coworkers[4] studied the reaction between these species, and identified the products NH_3, H_2O, HCN, CO, N_2, CH_3CN, and CH_3NO.

Other Methods Involving Mass Differences. Another method which depends on mass differences involves the use of a gauge originally devised by Wrede; an account of its construction and use has been given elsewhere.[5] The principle of the instrument is that the atoms or free radicals diffuse through an orifice into a small chamber, where they recombine on a catalytic surface; as a result, a pressure difference is set up across the orifice, and its value is a measure of the concentration of atoms or radicals. This method is only suitable for a pure gas.

Chemical Methods. Various methods for the detection and estimation of atoms and free radicals depend upon a study of their reactions. The introduction of metallic oxides into reaction systems has, for example,

[1] E. L. Tollefson and D. J. LeRoy, *J. Chem. Phys.*, **11**, 1057 (1948); L. Elias, E. A. Ogryzlo, and H. I. Schiff, *Can. J. Chem.*, **37**, 1680 (1959).

[2] F. P. Lossing, *Ann. N.Y. Acad. Sci.*, **67**, 499 (1957); J. Cuthbert, *Quart. Rev.* (*London*), **13**, 215 (1959).

[3] G. C. Eltenton, *J. Chem. Phys.*, **10**, 403 (1942); **15**, 455 (1947); *J. Phys. Colloid Chem.*, **52**, 463 (1948); *Rev. Inst. Franc. Petrole Ann. Combust.*, **4**, 468 (1949).

[4] F. P. Lossing, K. U. Ingold, and A. W. Tickner, *Discussions Faraday Soc.*, **14**, 34 (1953); W. A. Bryce and K. U. Ingold, *J. Chem. Phys.*, **23**, 1968 (1956).

[5] Greaves and Linnett, *loc. cit.*

been used frequently for the detection of hydrogen atoms. Iodine vapor has been employed in a similar way; this forms hydrogen iodide with hydrogen atoms, and alkyl iodide with free alkyl radicals.

Concentrations of hydrogen atoms have also been determined[1] by introducing parahydrogen into the reaction system and following the rate of its conversion into the equilibrium mixture,

$$H + p\text{-}H_2 \rightarrow o\text{-}H_2 + H$$

A disadvantage of the method is that the conversion is also catalyzed by paramagnetic substances such as other radicals that may be present in the reaction system. The exchange reactions

$$H + D_2 \rightarrow HD + D$$

and

$$D + H_2 \rightarrow HD + H$$

have been used in a similar manner for measuring H and D concentrations.[2]

Atomic oxygen concentrations have been measured by making use of the reaction

$$O + NO_2 \rightarrow O_2 + NO \qquad (1)$$

From the amount of nitric oxide produced in a given time, using an excess of NO_2, the concentration of oxygen atoms can be estimated. A similar method[3] makes use also of the reaction

$$O + NO \rightarrow NO_2 + h\nu \qquad (2)$$

If a little NO_2 is added to a stream of atomic oxygen, nitric oxide is formed by reaction (1), and reacts by reaction (2) to form a yellow-green afterglow. If the amount of NO_2 is slowly increased, more nitric oxide is produced, but fewer oxygen atoms remain to react with it; finally a point is reached at which the glow is just extinguished, the flow rate of the nitrogen dioxide then being equal to that of the oxygen atoms. Procedures such as this are commonly referred to as *gas-phase titrations.* A similar titration procedure has been used for determining nitrogen atom concentrations.

Nitric oxide has also been used to detect organic free radicals, the procedure being to study the inhibiting effect of this substance on organic decompositions. This procedure involves some difficulties of interpretation, and is discussed later (p. 393).

[1] L. Farkas and H. Sachsse, *Z. Physik. Chem.*, **B27**, 111 (1935); F. Patat and H. Sachsse, *Z. Elektrochem.*, **41**, 493 (1935).

[2] N. R. Trenner, K. Morikawa, and H. S. Taylor, *J. Chem. Phys.*, **5**, 203 (1937).

[3] F. Kaufman, *Proc. Roy. Soc. (London)*, **A247**, 123 (1958).

Trapping of Free Radicals.[1] During recent years a considerable amount of work has been done on the "trapping" of free radicals, the procedure being to pass a reaction system over a surface that has been cooled, for example, by liquid nitrogen. The solid that condenses is frequently of a vivid color, and by the use of various techniques for detecting radicals—such as mass spectrometry and electron-spin resonance spectroscopy—can be shown to contain free radicals.

Work of this kind has been done on a number of atoms and free radicals, including H, O, N, NH, NH_2, OH, HO_2, HNO, CH_3, and other small organic radicals. So far this technique has not been used for determining radical concentrations.

PRODUCTION OF FREE ATOMS AND RADICALS

These methods for detecting and estimating atoms and radicals give valuable information concerning reaction mechanisms, but in the majority of cases must be supplemented by more direct studies on the elementary reactions which constitute steps in the overall processes. In order to make such studies, it is useful to be able to cause elementary processes to occur to the exclusion of other reactions. It is difficult to achieve this, since side reactions nearly always occur; in some cases data have been obtained, but there is often some uncertainty in their interpretation.

If such a procedure is employed, and it is known that a certain reaction is occurring to the exclusion of all others, the rate constant can be determined, provided that one knows the initial concentrations of the reactants and either the rate of disappearance of a reactant or the rate of appearance of a product. For the determination of the activation energy the rate should also be known at more than one temperature; in some cases, however, the activation energy has been obtained from the rate at only one temperature by making an assumption about the magnitude of the frequency factor.

Since an important part of an investigation of this type is the production of the necessary atoms or free radicals to undergo reaction, this section will be devoted to a consideration of methods for this production.[2] The methods may be classified as (1) thermal, (2) photochemical, (3) radiochemical, and (4) electrical.

Thermal Methods. Appreciable concentrations of atoms and free radicals may, particularly at elevated temperatures, exist in thermal

[1] H. P. Broida, *Ann. N.Y. Acad. Sci.*, **67**, 530 (1957); *Endeavour*, **17**, 208 (1958); T. L. Franklin and H. P. Broida, *Ann. Rev. Phys. Chem.*, **10**, 145 (1959); G. T. Minkoff, "Frozen Free Radicals," Interscience Publishers, New York, 1960.

[2] For further details see E. W. R. Steacie and D. J. LeRoy, *Chem. Rev.*, **31**, 227 (1942); E. W. R. Steacie, "Atomic and Free Radical Reactions," chap. 2, Reinhold Publishing Corporation, New York, 1954.

equilibrium with molecules, which may therefore be introduced directly into a reaction system. The method is not, however, used very frequently, since at the temperatures necessary to produce an appreciable concentration of the active substance the situation is usually complicated by the occurrence of side reactions.

The method is best used with certain molecules that are readily dissociated, such as iodine. Sodium is also appreciably dissociated, even at room temperature, and the reactions of atomic sodium can be investigated simply using sodium vapor; the work of M. Polanyi and his collaborators on certain inorganic reactions involving atomic sodium will be considered later.

A more useful method of producing atoms or radicals by thermal methods involves passing the substance producing them through a heated tube. In this procedure the reacting substances, on reaching the reaction system, are no longer in equilibrium with the substance from which they are produced.

Since substances that decompose thermally to give free radicals frequently increase the rates of reactions, they are known as *sensitizers.* Certain metal alkyls decompose thermally to give organic free radicals and therefore act as sensitizers in many organic reactions. Sensitized reactions of this type were first investigated by Taylor and Jones,[1] who studied the influence of mercury and lead methyls on the polymerization of ethylene in the presence of hydrogen. The metal alkyls decompose into alkyl radicals and the metal, e.g.,

$$Hg(CH_3)_2 \rightarrow Hg + 2CH_3$$

and the radicals react with ethylene to form addition products, which may polymerize further:

$$CH_3 + C_2H_4 \rightarrow C_3H_7$$

In addition to the metal alkyls, ethylene oxide and azomethane have also been used as sensitizers. With sensitizers of this type, both methods, i.e., equilibrium and nonequilibrium, have been used. When these methods are employed, it is usual to determine the reaction rates by studying the rate of formation of the products.

Active species are also produced thermally in reaction systems at the surfaces of heated filaments, a method first used by Langmuir,[2] who worked mainly with hydrogen and oxygen. By measuring the heat loss from such filaments he demonstrated the formation of the atoms; at sufficiently low pressures these were able to reach the walls of the vessel and in the case of hydrogen atoms, for example, could be detected by

[1] H. S. Taylor and W. H. Jones, *J. Am. Chem. Soc.*, **52,** 1111 (1930).

[2] I. Langmuir, *ibid.*, **34,** 1310 (1912); **37,** 417 (1915); A. E. Freeman, *ibid.*, **35,** 927 (1913); I. Langmuir and G. M. J. Mackay, *ibid.*, **36,** 1708 (1914).

their reducing action on metallic oxides. The method was applied by Storch[1] to the production of methyl radicals from methane, and has been used by Belchetz and Rideal[2] in the study of various kinds of elementary reactions. The gas was passed at high velocity and low pressure over a heated platinum or carbon filament, and the radicals formed were caused to come into contact with a target which was cooled by water. Mirrors were deposited on the target, and their removal constituted evidence of the participation of radicals in the reactions. From the study of the formation of the radicals, the rates and activation energies of the radical-forming processes were inferred; however, the processes considered in this work are almost certainly not homogeneous ones but are catalyzed on the surface.

Photolysis.[3] In many chemical systems atoms and free radicals are conveniently produced by the action of radiation. There are many different types of radiation, and they all fall into two main classes:

1. Electromagnetic radiation, which includes the visible, ultraviolet, X-ray, and infrared regions
2. Particle radiations, including beams of electrons and protons

Chemical processes brought about by the action of particle radiations are usually spoken of as *radiolytic* processes, and are considered in a later section. Processes brought about by electromagnetic radiation may be either *photochemical* or *radiolytic* processes. A distinction frequently made between these two types of processes is that if ions, as well as atoms and radicals, are involved, the process is called a radiolytic one; if ions are not involved, the term photochemical is used. What this means in practice is that photochemical processes are brought about by electromagnetic radiations in the visible and near ultraviolet regions, the energies being too small for there to be ionization. Ions are, however, produced by most particle radiations and by high-energy electromagnetic radiations such as X rays, and the chemical processes are then classed as radiolytic ones.

A further distinction can be made as far as photochemical processes

[1] H. H. Storch, *ibid.*, **54**, 4188 (1932).

[2] L. Belchetz, *Trans. Faraday Soc.*, **30**, 170 (1934); L. Belchetz and E. K. Rideal, *J. Am. Chem. Soc.*, **57**, 1168 (1935). See in addition Tollefson and LeRoy, *loc. cit.*; A. J. B. Robertson, *Proc. Roy. Soc.* (*London*), **A199**, 394 (1949).

[3] For detailed treatments of photochemical reactions see W. A. Noyes and P. A. Leighton, "The Photochemistry of Gases," Reinhold Publishing Corporation, New York, 1941; G. K. Rollefson and M. Burton, "Photochemistry and the Mechanism of Chemical Reactions," Prentice-Hall, Inc., Englewood Cliffs, N.J., 1939; E. J. Bowen, "The Chemical Aspects of Light," Clarendon Press, Oxford, 1946; H. Staude, "Photochemie," Bibliographisches Institut, Mannheim, 1962. General principles are considered in K. J. Laidler, "The Chemical Kinetics of Excited States," Clarendon Press, Oxford, 1955.

are concerned. If the radiation directly produces excited species, atoms or radicals that play a part in the main reaction, the process is a photochemical one in the strict sense of the word. In some cases, however, the molecules that absorb the radiation do not themselves participate in the main reaction, but pass on their energy to other molecules that do. In such situations, discussed further in the next section, one speaks of *photosensitization*, and of the absorbing substance as a *photosensitizer*. The absorbing substance is actually a kind of photochemical catalyst for the reaction.

As examples of photochemical processes may be mentioned reactions in which alkyl radicals are produced by the absorption of radiation, and undergo subsequent reactions. Acetone, for example, absorbs radiation in the neighborhood of 2,800 A to give CH_3CO and CH_3, and at higher temperatures the acetyl radical further decomposes into CH_3 and CO; the overall process is therefore

$$CH_3COCH_3 + \mathbf{h}\nu \rightarrow 2CH_3 + CO$$

where $\mathbf{h}\nu$ represents the photon. The photolysis of the mercury alkyls has also been used as a source of free radicals,

$$Hg(CH_3)_2 + \mathbf{h}\nu \rightarrow Hg + 2CH_3$$

Methylene is conveniently produced by the photolysis of ketene,

$$CH_2CO + \mathbf{h}\nu \rightarrow CH_2 + CO$$

and of diazomethane,

$$CH_2N_2 + \mathbf{h}\nu \rightarrow CH_2 + N_2$$

A number of important principles are associated with the production of excited molecules and of atoms and radicals by the absorption of electromagnetic radiations. In the first place, in order for the light to have any effect, it must be absorbed by the system; all the radiation that is absorbed is, however, by no means able to cause dissociation. There are certain ranges of wavelength where there is absorption, and certain narrower ranges within these correspond to the formation of atoms and free radicals.

The excitation of molecules by radiation is governed by the Franck-Condon principle, according to which the most probable transitions are those corresponding to the least change in the internuclear distances in the molecules. The nature of the photoexcitation is determined by this principle, by the energy of the radiation, and by the relative positions of the potential-energy surfaces. Radiation of frequency ν can only be absorbed by a molecule provided that the energy $\mathbf{h}\nu$ is equal to the energy difference between a quantized energy level in the excited state and a quantized energy level in the initial state. The probability of the transition will be small if the two states correspond to very different interatomic distances, since a considerable rearrangement would have to accompany the absorption. The probability is also small if certain selection rules are not satisfied; this is the case, for example, if the two states correspond to different spectroscopic multiplicities.

Figure 70 shows a number of possible arrangements of potential-energy surfaces for a diatomic molecule, and indicates transitions that can occur from the ground state of the molecule. In this state the molecule

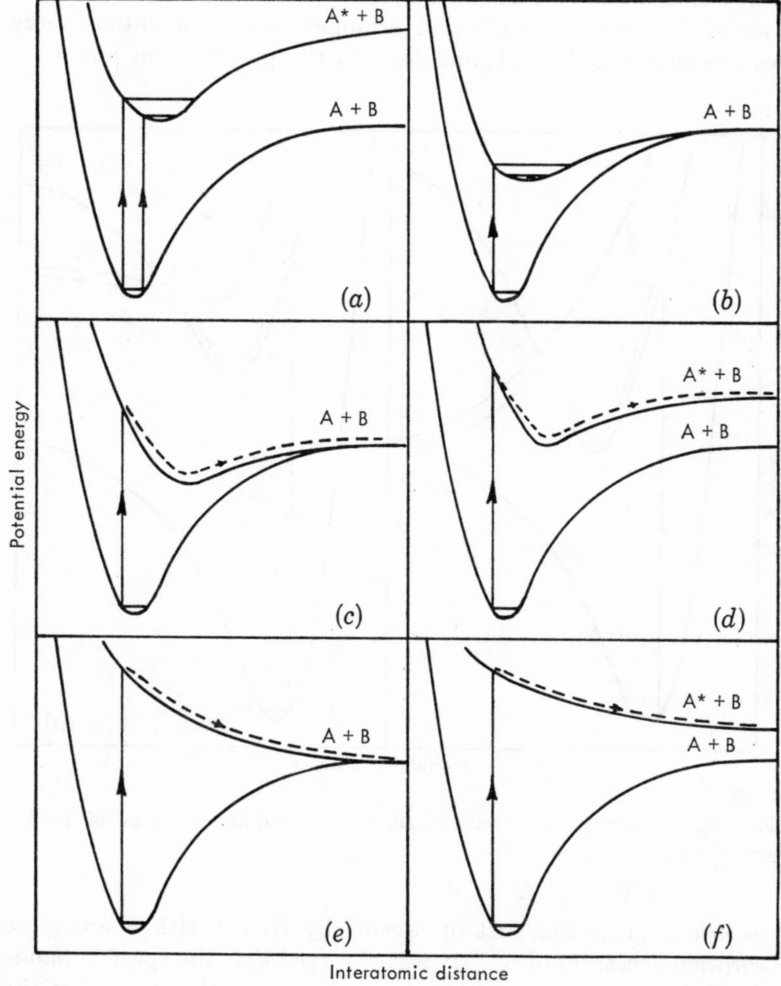

Fig. 70. Potential-energy curves for a triatomic molecule AB, showing a number of processes that can occur when radiation is absorbed by AB in its ground state.

exists at its zero-point vibrational level, and it spends most of its time at the extremities of its vibrations, since here the relative atomic velocities are low. In (*a*) and (*b*) in Fig. 70 the absorption of the radiation results in an excited molecule which is stable with respect to dissociation; it does not give rise to atoms and radicals, but it may nevertheless play an important role in photochemical processes. In (*c*) excitation results in a molecule which at once dissociates to give the atoms in their ground electronic states. In (*d*) there is again dissociation, but one or both of the atoms are now in an excited electronic state. In (*e*) and (*f*) there is again the production of atoms, the excited states now being repulsive ones.

Two slightly more complicated arrangements of potential-energy surfaces are shown in Fig. 71, and lead to the phenomenon known as

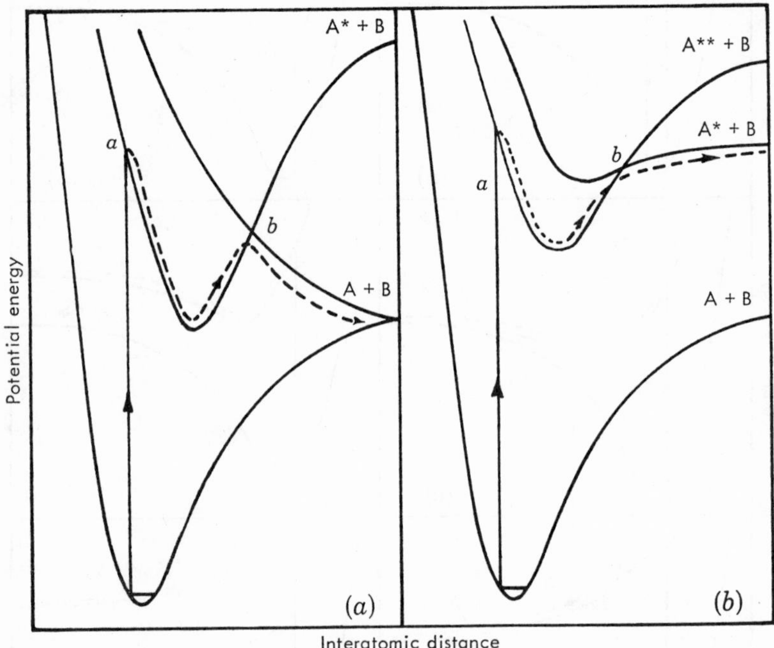

Fig. 71. Potential-energy curves showing two different cases of predissociation.

predissociation. This was first discovered by Henri[1] with reference to the absorption spectrum of S_2. It was observed that the spectral bands corresponding to certain transitions were diffuse, in the sense that the

[1] V. Henri, *Compt. Rend.*, **177**, 1037 (1923); V. Henri and M. C. Teves, *ibid.*, **178**, 894 (1924).

rotational fine structure was not well defined. Henri's explanation was that there is a transition to an excited state, the molecule then dissociating into atoms. This process of dissociation must take place within a longer period of time than the period of a molecular vibration, but a shorter time than that required for a rotation; consequently the vibrational energy, which determines the overall structure of the band system, is quantized; the rotational energy, however, is not quantized, so that the rotational fine structure is not observed. In both of the cases shown in Fig. 71 the initial absorption process may lead to the production of the excited molecule at an energy corresponding to point a, and there can then be a transition to curve B at the crossing point b; the result is the production of atoms.

The situation with polyatomic molecules is the same in principle as described above. The curves in Figs. 70 and 71 for the diatomic molecules may, in fact, be regarded as sections through the multidimensional potential-energy curves for polyatomic molecules.

Radiation is absorbed by a molecule in the form of a photon of energy $\mathbf{h}\nu$. Since for most of the wavelengths employed in photochemistry the energy of the photon is considerably greater than the average thermal energy of the absorbing molecule, there is little variation in the effectiveness of a photon from molecule to molecule in the reacting system. On changing the frequency, there is therefore a fairly sharp transition from a region in which no absorption and no chemical reaction occurs, to a region in which a considerable amount of chemical reaction occurs. Many examples of such photochemical "thresholds" have been observed; reaction occurs on the higher-frequency, or lower-wavelength, side of the threshold.

Since the lifetime of an electronically excited species is very small, often about 10^{-8} sec, it is very unlikely for a molecule that has absorbed one photon to absorb another before it has become deactivated. There is therefore a one-to-one relationship between the number of photons absorbed by the system and the number of excited molecules produced. If, for example, light is absorbed with the production of an excited species that dissociates into two radicals, as in the process

$$CH_3COCH_3 + \mathbf{h}\nu \rightarrow CH_3COCH_3^* \rightarrow CO + 2CH_3$$

the rate of production of methyl radicals is twice the rate of absorption of photons. This principle, which is due to Einstein and is known as the *law of photochemical equivalence*, has been of great value in photochemical studies, since it enables the rate of production of radicals to be calculated from optical measurements. It is convenient to speak of a mole of photons as an *einstein;* the rate of production of methyl radicals in the photolysis of acetone would then be, in moles cc^{-1} sec^{-1}, twice the number of einsteins absorbed per cubic centimeter per second.

In photochemical experiments it is often found that the number of molecules that are transformed chemically differs markedly from the number of photons absorbed. In such cases it is customary to state that Einstein's law is not obeyed, although the violation is only an apparent one. There are two main reasons for failure of the law. In the first place, radicals that are produced initially may recombine before they can undergo reaction; as will be seen, this very commonly occurs in solution. In this case the rate of reaction is less than expected if the Einstein law applies. In other systems the radicals produced may initiate chain reactions, in which case the rate of reaction may be much larger than expected. Deviations from the Einstein law obviously provide valuable information about reaction mechanisms, and examples will be considered in later chapters. The ratio of the number of molecules undergoing reaction in a given time to the number of photons absorbed is known as the *quantum yield*.

Photosensitization. Photosensitization has been used very extensively for the production of atoms and free radicals in reaction systems. The importance of the method lies in the fact that definite amounts of light energy can conveniently be transferred to certain molecules that do not absorb at the appropriate wavelength. For example, the production of hydrogen atoms from a hydrogen molecule requires 103.2 kcal of energy per mole, and this corresponds to a wavelength of 2,776 A. However the lowest excited state of hydrogen requires considerably more energy than this, corresponding to a much lower wavelength. Working at such low wavelengths is difficult, so that alternative methods are valuable. Mercury has been very widely used as a sensitizer for this and other processes; mercury vapor is normally in a 6^1S_0 state and is raised to the 6^3P_1 level by illumination with the mercury resonance line at 2,537 A, which corresponds to an energy of 112 kcal. On collision with a hydrogen molecule, dissociation into atoms may occur, the process actually being very efficient. The experimental technique is very simple; the mercury vapor is mixed with the hydrogen, and the mixture illuminated with light of the appropriate wavelength. Many bonds having strengths of less than 112 kcal can be split in this way.

Photosensitization was first discovered by Cario and Franck,[1] who demonstrated the formation of hydrogen atoms from hydrogen molecules and excited mercury, detecting them by their chemical reactivity. They described a collision between the excited mercury atom and the molecule as a "Stoss zweiter Art" ("collision of the second kind"). Later Taylor and his coworkers[2] used the method to investigate the reactions of atomic

[1] G. Cario and J. Franck, *Z. Physik.*, **11**, 161 (1922).

[2] H. S. Taylor and J. R. Bates, *Proc. Natl. Acad. Sci. U.S.*, **12**, 714 (1926); H. S. Taylor and D. G. Hill, *J. Am. Chem. Soc.*, **51**, 2927 (1929); *Z. Physik. Chem.*, **B2**, 449 (1929); H. S. Taylor and A. L. Marshall, *J. Phys. Chem.*, **29**, 1140 (1925).

hydrogen, which they caused to react with carbon monoxide, nitrous oxide, hydrocarbons, and other substances.

The mechanism of the reaction between excited mercury and hydrogen has been the subject of some investigation. The reaction is sometimes written in two stages,

$$(1) \qquad Hg(^3P_1) + H_2 \rightarrow HgH + H$$
$$(2) \qquad HgH \rightarrow Hg(^1S_0) + H$$

and it is clear that the first reaction is more exothermic than the process

$$(3) \qquad Hg(^3P_1) + H_2 \rightarrow 2H + Hg(^1S_0)$$

by the dissociation energy of HgH, which is 8.5 kcal. The presence of HgH in these systems was investigated spectroscopically by Olsen,[1] who found that it was not present in the normal state, but only in an excited state, presumably having been produced by secondary processes. It is therefore concluded that either process (3) occurs in one stage[2] or the HgH produced in reaction (1) is so excited vibrationally that it dissociates at once.[3] It may be mentioned here that the purely quenching type of process,

$$Hg(^3P_1) + H_2 \rightarrow Hg(^1S_0) + H_2$$

in which electronic energy is converted into translational, rotational, and vibrational energy, cannot readily occur, since it violates the spin-conservation rule.

Excited mercury has also been caused to react directly with other molecules, such as the hydrocarbons. With the saturated hydrocarbons the main primary process that takes place is

$$Hg(^3P_1) + HR \rightarrow H + R + Hg(^1S_0)$$

where R is a free radical, such as ethyl in the case of ethane. With unsaturated hydrocarbons the same type of process may occur, but in addition an excited molecule can be formed and can undergo subsequent reaction.

Work has also been done using mercury in its singlet-excited 6^1P_1 state, which corresponds to a wavelength of 1,849 A and an energy of 153.9 kcal per mole. Zinc and cadmium, in both singlet- and triplet-excited states, have been used in photosensitization experiments, particularly by Steacie and his coworkers.[4] The amounts of energy liberated

[1] L. O. Olsen, *J. Chem. Phys.*, **6**, 307 (1938).

[2] Cf. J. Franck and H. Sponer, *Nachr. Ges. Wiss. Göttingen*, 241 (1928); H. Beutler and E. Rabinowitch, *Z. Physik. Chem.*, **B8**, 403 (1930).

[3] K. J. Laidler, *J. Chem. Phys.*, **10**, 43 (1942).

[4] For reviews see E. W. R. Steacie, "Atomic and Free Radical Reactions," Reinhold Publishing Corporation, New York, 1954.

Table 50 AMOUNTS OF ENERGY LIBERATED BY EXCITED ATOMS

Metal	Line, A	Transition	Energy of excited atom, kcal	Total energy available if hydride is formed, kcal
Mercury	2,537	6^3P_1–6^1S_0	112.2	120.7
	1,849	6^1P_1–6^1S_0	153.9	162.4
Cadmium	3,261	5^3P_1–5^1S_0	87.3	102.8
	2,288	5^1P_1–5^1S_0	124.4	139.9
Zinc	3,076	4^3P_1–4^1S_0	92.5	115.6
	2,139	4^1P_1–4^1S_0	133.4	156.5

in each case are given in Table 50, the values with and without the formation of the hydride being included. By using these and other excited states the energy available for transfer to the reacting molecule can be varied over a convenient range. In some cases there is ambiguity as to whether the hydride is formed or not, although it appears that when the reacting molecule requires the additional energy, the hydride will be formed in order to make it available. This may be illustrated by comparing the reactions of triplet mercury and cadmium. Triplet mercury has sufficient energy to split the H—H bond without hydride formation and, as has been seen, the hydride is not formed as a final product. With triplet cadmium, on the other hand, the energy available is only just about sufficient if the hydride is formed. The fact that the reaction proceeds readily therefore requires that the hydride be a final product, and this has been found spectroscopically to be the case by Bender.[1] The overall process is therefore

$$Cd(^3P_1) + H_2 \rightarrow CdH + H$$

and other reactions proceed in the same way. Thus Steacie and LeRoy[2] have detected CdH in the cadmium-photosensitized reactions of propane.

Radiolysis.[3] The field of *radiation chemistry* includes the study of

[1] P. Bender, *Phys. Rev.*, **36**, 1535 (1930); cf. Olsen, *loc. cit.*

[2] E. W. R. Steacie and D. J. LeRoy, *J. Chem. Phys.*, **12**, 34 (1944).

[3] For general reviews of the subject of radiation chemistry see S. C. Lind, C. J. Hochanadel, and T. A. Ghormley, "Radiation Chemistry of Gases," Reinhold Publishing Corporation, New York, 1961; A. O. Allen, "The Radiation Chemistry of Water and Aqueous Solutions," D. Van Nostrand Company, Inc., Princeton, N.J.,

chemical processes brought about by radiations of sufficiently high energy that ionization is produced in the reaction systems. It is convenient to use the term *radiolysis* to describe the primary processes, analogous to those in photochemical initiation, that occur when ionizing radiations come into contact with chemical substances. A considerable amount of investigation has been carried out along these lines over the past several years, particularly as a result of the construction of a number of different kinds of particle-accelerating machines. This development of the subject began about 1935. An additional reason for the enhanced interest at about that time was the realization[1] that atoms and free radicals are important products of the initiation steps. The field of radiation chemistry was thus brought into close relationship with that of photochemistry, and with the study of thermal reactions.

The most important radiations that produce ions, in addition to atoms and free radicals, are α and β rays (beams of helium nuclei and electrons, respectively), beams of positive ions such as protons and deuterons, and X and γ rays. The X and γ rays consist of electromagnetic radiation of lower wavelengths (and higher frequencies and energies) than the ultraviolet radiation used in photochemistry. The other radiations mentioned are beams of charged particles. A matter of importance in an experimental study of a reaction induced by ionizing radiations is the rate of absorption of energy by the reaction system; this quantity is commonly measured in electron volts (ev) per liter per second. The energy absorbed may be measured directly by studying the absorption coefficient for the reaction system, although this procedure is somewhat difficult. The method is greatly simplified if it is possible to arrange matters in such a way that all the radiation is absorbed. A second method, more widely used, is to measure the amount of ionization produced by the radiation when it passes through the reaction vessel containing a gas such as air. The rate of production of ions is determined by applying to the system a sufficiently high electrical potential that the current reaches a limiting value (the *saturation current*); when this is done, the ions are swept out of the system as rapidly as they are produced by the radiation, and the rate of production of the ions can therefore be calculated from the saturation current. In order to convert the rate of ion production into the energy absorbed per second, it is necessary to

---

1961; E. J. Hart and R. J. Platzman, in "Mechanisms of Radiobiology," vol. 1, chap. 2, Academic Press Inc., New York, 1961; J. W. T. Spinks and R. J. Woods, "An Introduction to Radiation Chemistry," John Wiley & Sons, Inc., New York, 1964. Initiation by ionizing radiations is also discussed in K. J. Laidler, "The Chemical Kinetics of Excited States," chap. 4, Clarendon Press, Oxford, 1955; cf. also J. D. Craggs and C. A. McDowell, *Rept. Progr. Phys.*, **18**, 375 (1955).

[1] H. Eyring, J. O. Hirschfelder, and H. S. Taylor, *J. Chem. Phys.*, **4**, 479, 570 (1937).

know what energy is dissipated in creating an ion pair; for air the value usually employed is 32.5 ev per ion pair for electrons, and 35 ev per ion pair for other types of radiation.

A third method for determining the rate of energy absorption, and the one most commonly used, involves allowing the radiation to pass into a reaction vessel which contains reactants, the reaction rate of which is easily followed and is related in a known manner to the radiation absorbed. The oxidation of ferrous sulfate in 0.8 *N* sulfuric acid is sometimes used for this purpose.

In both photolytic and radiolytic processes it is convenient to refer to the initial act of absorption of the radiation as the primary process, and the subsequent reactions as secondary processes. In a photochemical process the primary process usually occurs in only two stages, the first of which is the production of an electronically excited species, and the second the dissociation of this species into atoms and free radicals. In radiation chemistry, on the other hand, a number of steps usually occur between the original interaction of the radiation with the substance and the formation of free radicals. All these processes are usually regarded as being included in the primary process. The usual modern convention is to write the primary act using an arrow of the form $\rightsquigarrow$ and to indicate the type of radiation as a superscript above the arrow. Thus when α radiation interacts with hydrogen, the primary act results in the production of hydrogen atoms, and the process is written as

$$H_2 \overset{\alpha}{\rightsquigarrow} 2H$$

The processes that occur when radiations interact with matter vary considerably with the type of radiation and with the substance involved. The situation is complicated, and the details have only been worked out in a few cases. One important result that has emerged is that the radiation usually produces atoms and free radicals directly, and also produces ions that are later converted by neutralization into atoms and radicals. One indication that this is so is that the energy W used in the production of an ion pair is always considerably larger than the ionization potential; W is usually about 35 ev, and only about half of this is usually required for ionization. Another argument is that *ion yields* (the number of molecules transformed for each ion pair produced) are frequently greater than photochemical quantum yields (p. 344). Since an ion pair can in general not produce more than a pair of radicals, this fact can only be explained if atoms and free radicals are produced as well as ions.

Further evidence for the same point of view is provided by the work of Essex and his collaborators,[1] who measured rates of radiation-chemical

[1] C. Smith and H. Essex, *ibid.*, **6**, 188 (1938); A. D. Kolumban and H. Essex, *ibid.*, **8**, 450 (1940); N. T. Williams and H. Essex, *ibid.*, **16**, 1153 (1948); **17**, 995 (1949).

reactions when saturation currents (p. 347) were passed through reaction systems. If the atoms and free radicals were all produced from the ions formed in the primary process, the saturation current, by completely sweeping out the ions, would reduce the reaction rate to zero. In fact, the rates were generally reduced by a factor of about 2 by passing the saturation current. This suggests that about half of the reaction is brought about by atoms and free radicals that are produced directly, and not from the neutralization of ions.

When a high-energy electron interacts with a molecule, an important process is frequently the production of a positive ion,

$$e + \mathrm{M} \rightarrow \mathrm{M}^+ + 2e$$

Since there is an increase in the number of electrons, a single initial electron may bring about the formation of a large number of positive ions. Eventually, however, an electron is slowed down to a velocity at which it can no longer eject an electron from a molecule, and one of several things may then happen to it. In the case of some molecules, slow electrons may become attached to them with the formation of the negative ion,

$$e + \mathrm{M} \rightarrow \mathrm{M}^-$$

A second possible process is electron capture associated with the dissociation of the molecule,

$$e + \mathrm{R}_2 \rightarrow \mathrm{R}^- + \mathrm{R}$$

A third possibility is that the electron may neutralize a positive ion,

$$e + \mathrm{M}^+ \rightarrow \mathrm{M}$$

Frequently this neutralization is accompanied by dissociation,

$$e + \mathrm{R}_2^+ \rightarrow \mathrm{R} + \mathrm{R}$$

In a few cases some of these processes can be interpreted in terms of potential-energy curves. The formation of positive ions from the hydrogen molecule, for example, is explained[1] in terms of the curves shown in Fig. 72. As with photons, the process of excitation by electrons obeys the Franck-Condon principle, the most probable transitions being those in which there is little change in internuclear separation. It is to be seen from the figure that electrons with energy of about 16 ev may bring about excitation to the lowest, $^2\Sigma_g^+$, state of the H_2^+ ion; the most probable transitions, in fact, are to vibrationally excited states. There is also a certain probability of a transition to a point on the left-hand limb of the $^2\Sigma_g^+$ curve that corresponds to an energy in excess of the dissociation energy; in this case dissociation occurs within the period of the first

[1] J. L. Magee and M. Burton, *J. Am. Chem. Soc.*, **72**, 1965 (1950).

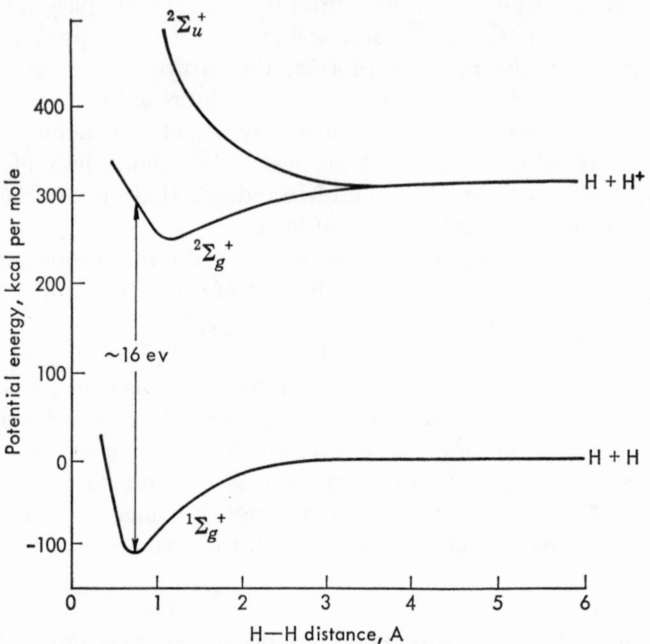

Fig. 72. Potential-energy curves for H_2 and H_2^+, showing how positive ions are formed by electron impact.

vibration. The overall process can then be written as

$$e + H_2 \rightarrow H + H^+ + 2e$$

Electrons having an energy of about 26 ev can also produce molecules in the repulsive ${}^2\Sigma_u^+$ state of H_2^+; the result is the production of H + H^+ having high kinetic energies.

Other processes occurring with hydrogen, and the various primary radiolytic reactions of oxygen,[1] water,[2] and methane[3] have also been considered from a similar point of view.

Positively charged ions, such as α particles, also interact with molecules, mainly by ejecting electrons; for example,

$$\alpha + M \rightarrow M^+ + e + \alpha$$

[1] K. J. Laidler and E. K. Gill, *Trans. Faraday Soc.*, **54,** 633 (1958); D. C. Frost and C. A. McDowell, *J. Am. Chem. Soc.*, **80,** 6183 (1958).

[2] K. J. Laidler, *J. Chem. Phys.*, **22,** 1740 (1954); F. Fiquet-Fayard, *J. Chim. Phys.*, 274 (1957).

[3] C. A. McDowell, *Trans. Faraday Soc.*, **50,** 423 (1954).

The positive ion continues on its way with little deflection and ionizes other molecules. The ejected electron frequently has sufficient energy to bring about ionization of additional molecules, by the mechanism described above.

Photons differ from the material particles in that they are usually absorbed and annihilated in a single elementary act, instead of undergoing a stepwise loss of energy. Three distinct processes are of importance in reactions brought about by photons:

1. Formation of an excited molecule, which may dissociate into atoms and radicals:

$$M + \mathbf{h}\nu \rightarrow M^* \rightarrow 2R$$

This is the type of process occuring in *photo*chemical initiation.

2. Electromagnetic radiations having energy sufficient to cause ionization but not greater than about 0.5 mev (500,000 ev), which lead to the ejection of an electron with the formation of the positive ion

$$M + \mathbf{h}\nu \rightarrow M^+ + e$$

There is complete transfer of the energy of the radiation to the electron, which is therefore ejected with an energy equal to that of the photon minus the ionization potential.

3. At energies between about 10 kev (10,000 ev) and 1 mev (1,000,000 ev) Compton scattering of the photon with ejection of the electron and the formation of a positive ion,

$$M + \mathbf{h}\nu \rightarrow M^+ + e + \mathbf{h}\nu'$$

The difference between this process and that of mechanism 2 is that the photon is not annihilated, but continues on its way with a different frequency. The scattered photon is liable to be absorbed by subsequent molecules in its path.

In spite of the fact that the details of radiolytic initiation processes are somewhat complex, the overall result is usually fairly simple. In hydrogen, for example, the initiation process with most types of radiation is largely the production of atoms,

$$H_2 \rightsquigarrow 2H$$

Similarly, with hydrogen iodide the main process is

$$HI \rightsquigarrow H + I$$

In all cases the production of ions must, however, also be taken into consideration.

In the study of overall reactions initiated by ionizing radiations there are two quantities that are frequently quoted and that lead to important information about mechanisms. The first is the *ion-pair yield*, or *ionic yield*, which is denoted as M/N; this is the ratio of the rate of production of product molecules to the rate of formation of ion pairs. The second is the *G value*, which is the number of product molecules produced per 100 ev input. Both these quantities give some idea of chain lengths.

Discharge-tube Methods. Atoms and free radicals are produced in electrical discharges in gases and may be used to give rise to chemical reaction. Not much information has come from work in which the reacting substances are subjected to a discharge, because a large variety of atoms and radicals are formed, and the processes taking place are therefore very complicated. Of more importance is the technique by which the products from a discharge through a single gas, such as hydrogen atoms from hydrogen gas, are carried into the reaction system.

Wood[1] first demonstrated in 1920 that hydrogen atoms produced by a glow discharge in hydrogen could be pumped out of the system and transported for a considerable distance before they recombined. He found that it was necessary for the walls of the tube to be poisoned, e.g., by a film of water or phosphoric acid, in order for the recombination of the atoms on the walls to be inhibited.

Bonhoeffer[2] made modifications of Wood's apparatus and carried out a number of investigations of the reactions of atomic hydrogen. A suitable piece of apparatus for work of this kind is shown in Fig. 73. The glow discharge is produced by an emf of several thousand volts across the electrodes, and a very rapid stream of hydrogen at low pressure (0.2 to 0.5 mm) is passed through. In this way an appreciable concentration of atoms is produced in the reaction vessel, into which the other reactants are introduced. To prevent recombination of atoms, the walls of the discharge tube and reaction vessel are poisoned by a film of water vapor, or better by coating with such materials as potassium chloride or syrupy phosphoric acid.

A great many reactions of hydrogen atoms have been investigated by the Wood-Bonhoeffer method. Geib and Harteck,[3] for example, studied the reaction

$$H + p\text{-}H_2 \rightarrow o\text{-}H_2 + H$$

using the apparatus shown schematically in Fig. 74. It is not usual to determine activation energies by employing this method over a range of temperatures, since the measurements of the atom concentrations are not

[1] R. W. Wood, *Proc. Roy. Soc.* (*London*), **A97**, 455 (1920); **A102**, 1 (1922); *Phil. Mag.*, **42**, 729 (1921); **44**, 538 (1922).

[2] K. F. Bonhoeffer, *Z. Physik. Chem.*, **113**, 119, 492 (1924); **116**, 391 (1925); *Z. Elektrochem.*, **31**, 521 (1925); *Ergeb. Exakt. Naturw.*, **6**, 201 (1927). Cf. H. S. Taylor and A. L. Marshall, *Nature*, **112**, 937 (1923).

[3] K. H. Geib and P. Harteck, *Z. Physik. Chem.*, Bodenstein-Festband, 849 (1931).

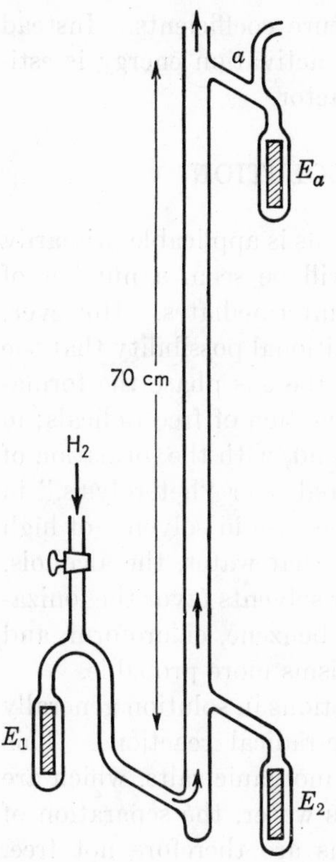

Fig. 73. Apparatus used by Bonhoeffer, and by Geib and Harteck, for producing atomic hydrogen by the silent-discharge method.

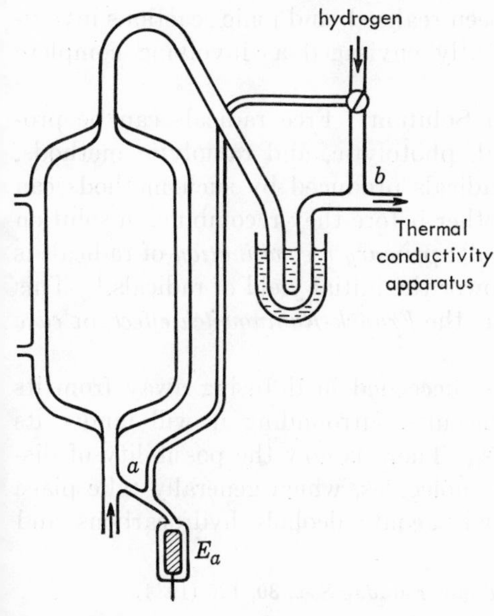

Fig. 74. Schematic view of apparatus used by Geib and Harteck for the study of the reaction $H + p\text{-}H_2 \rightarrow o\text{-}H_2 + H$. Hydrogen enriched with parahydrogen was introduced into the reaction vessel, which was maintained at constant temperature, either at position *a* or position *b*. Hydrogen atoms, produced by the silent-discharge method, entered at point *a*, and after passing through the reaction vessel, were removed by passage through a U tube immersed in liquid air. The proportion of the para and ortho forms of hydrogen was determined by measurement of the thermal conductivity. The experiments with the parahydrogen admitted at point *b* were measured using a Wrede gauge.

sufficiently accurate to give reliable temperature coefficients. Instead the work is done at one temperature, and the activation energy is estimated on the basis of an assumed frequency factor.

COMPLEX REACTIONS IN SOLUTION

The preceding discussion of complex reactions is applicable primarily to reactions in the gas phase, although, as will be seen, a number of reactions in solution involve free radicals as intermediates. However, in the case of solution reactions there is the additional possibility that the reaction proceeds by an ionic mechanism. In the gas phase the formation of ions is much less probable than the formation of free radicals; in solution, on the other hand, "homolysis" of a bond, with the formation of free atoms or radicals, is not necessarily favored over "heterolysis," in which ions are formed. This is particularly the case in solvents of high dielectric constant. In general, it can be said that water, the alcohols, nitrobenzene, pyridine, acetone, and some other solvents favor the ionization of bonds, but that such solvents as ether, benzene, chloroform, and carbon tetrachloride make free-radical mechanisms more probable.

Ionic Mechanisms in Solution. Ionic reactions in solution generally have quite different characteristics from free-radical reactions. This arises from the fact that except in the case of inorganic salts, which are extensively ionized in suitable solvents such as water, the separation of charges is usually not complete, and the ions are therefore not free. Ionic reactions therefore do not in general proceed by well-defined reaction steps but rather by a smooth transition accompanied by a shift of electrons. This has not always been realized, and ionic reactions involving organic molecules are frequently envisaged as involving complete ionization.

Free-radical Mechanisms in Solution. Free radicals can be produced in solution by the thermal, photolytic, and radiolytic methods. Whereas in the gas phase free radicals produced by such methods can usually migrate away from each other before they recombine, in solution such diffusion is much more difficult; *primary recombination* of radicals is therefore probable and tends to lower the initial yield of radicals.[1] This phenomenon is often referred to as the *Franck-Rabinowitch effect*, or *cage effect*.

However, once a radical has succeeded in diffusing away from its partner, the cage of solvent molecules surrounding it will hinder its recombination with other radicals. There is now the possibility of displacement reactions with solvent molecules, which generally take place readily; radicals are found to dehydrogenate alcohols, hydrocarbons, and

[1] J. Franck and E. Rabinowitch, *Trans. Faraday Soc.*, **30**, 120 (1934).

other molecules and to remove halogen atoms from solvents such as carbon tetrachloride. In aqueous solution hydroxyl radicals are generally released.

Reactions involving free radicals in solution are, on this account, in general not specific reactions of the radicals produced initially but are more characteristic of the solvent. For example, free-radical reactions in aqueous solution are usually reactions involving the hydroxyl radical. By choosing the appropriate solvent, however, this difficulty can generally be avoided; hydroxyl radicals, for example, regenerate themselves in water by the reaction

$$HO + H_2O \rightarrow H_2O + OH$$

whereas chlorine atoms persist in carbon tetrachloride solution owing to the reversible change

$$Cl + CCl_4 \rightleftharpoons Cl_2 + CCl_3$$

chapter

Some Complex Reactions in the Gas Phase 8

THIS CHAPTER WILL consider the mechanisms that have been proposed for some complex reactions occurring in the gas phase. A number of inorganic processes will be considered first, and some organic reactions, particularly decompositions, will be discussed later; the separation of the two types is somewhat arbitrary but may be justified by the fact that different types of free radicals are involved. In succeeding chapters will be treated, from essentially the same point of view, catalyzed reactions and reactions in solution.

REACTION BETWEEN HYDROGEN AND BROMINE

The formation of hydrogen bromide from hydrogen and bromine is a reaction the mechanism of which is well understood. The thermal reaction was first studied by Bodenstein and Lind[1] over the temperature range from 205 to 302°C, and at pressures of the order of 1 atm. They

[1] M. Bodenstein and S. C. Lind, *Z. Physik. Chem.*, **57**, 168 (1907).

found empirically that their results could be fitted to the equation

$$\frac{d[\mathrm{HBr}]}{dt} = \frac{k[\mathrm{H_2}][\mathrm{Br_2}]^{1/2}}{1 + [\mathrm{HBr}]/m[\mathrm{Br_2}]} \tag{1}$$

where k and m are constants, the latter having the value of about 10 and being independent of temperature. This equation shows that hydrogen bromide inhibits the reaction, and it was found that iodine exerted an even more powerful inhibition; water, air, and carbon tetrachloride on the other hand had no inhibiting action.

Bodenstein and Lind suggested that the appearance of the bromine concentration as a square root probably indicated that bromine atoms play an important part in the reaction; however, the results were not properly explained until 1919, when Christiansen, Herzfeld, and Polanyi independently proposed the mechanism

(1) $Br_2 \rightarrow 2Br$
(2) $Br + H_2 \rightarrow HBr + H$
(3) $H + Br_2 \rightarrow HBr + Br$
(4) $H + HBr \rightarrow H_2 + Br$
(5) $Br + Br \rightarrow Br_2$

It was shown on page 328 that the use of the steady-state treatment gives rise to the kinetic law

$$\frac{d[\mathrm{HBr}]}{dt} = \frac{2k_2(k_1/k_5)^{1/2}[\mathrm{H_2}][\mathrm{Br_2}]^{1/2}}{1 + k_4[\mathrm{HBr}]/k_3[\mathrm{Br_2}]} \tag{2}$$

This is of the same form as the empirical equation (1), with

$$k = 2k_2\left(\frac{k_1}{k_5}\right)^{1/2}$$

and $m = k_3/k_4$.

The inhibition by hydrogen bromide is accounted for by reaction (4), in which hydrogen atoms are removed by reaction with hydrogen bromide. It was originally thought[1] that the inhibition by iodine could analogously be explained by the reaction

$$H + I_2 \rightarrow HI + I$$

The hydrogen atoms so reacting would be lost to the reaction since the step

$$I + H_2 \rightarrow HI + H$$

is much too endothermic to take place readily. However Müller[2] later

[1] M. Bodenstein and W. Müller, *Z. Elektrochem.*, **30,** 416 (1924).
[2] W. Müller, *Z. Physik. Chem.*, **123,** 1 (1926).

found that at least part of the effect of the iodine was to reduce the concentration of bromine by forming IBr.

The individual rate constants k_1 to k_5 for the elementary reactions have all been evaluated, and the methods by which this has been done will now be indicated. The experimentally determined constant k is equal to $2k_2(k_1/k_5)^{1/2}$, and the ratio k_1/k_5 is the equilibrium constant for the dissociation of bromine into atoms, the value for which has been determined by Bodenstein and Cramer;[1] the rate constant k_2 can therefore be calculated. According to Jost,[2] the best value for it is given by

$$\log k_2 = 12.30 + 0.5 \log T - \frac{17{,}600}{2.303RT} \tag{3}$$

The activation energy is thus 17.6 kcal, and since the reaction is endothermic to the extent of 16.4 kcal, it follows that the activation energy for the reverse reaction (4) is equal to 1.2 kcal.

The value of m, equal to k_3/k_4, is found experimentally to be independent of the temperature; the two reactions (3) and (4) therefore have the same activation energy, so that the activation energy of (3) is also about 1.2 kcal. Since the value of m is about 10, reaction (3) proceeds about 10 times as fast as (4), in spite of the fact that the activation energies are the same. The difference in rates must be accounted for in terms of frequency factors, that for (4) being one-tenth of that for (3).

The evaluation of the rates of reactions (1) and (5) involves a comparison of the kinetics of the thermal reaction with those of the corresponding photochemical reaction. Bodenstein and Lutkemeyer[3] found that the photochemical reaction proceeds according to the empirical equation

$$\frac{d[\mathrm{HBr}]}{dt} = \frac{k'[\mathrm{H_2}]I^{1/2}}{1 + [\mathrm{HBr}]/m'[\mathrm{Br_2}]} \tag{4}$$

where k' and m' are constants, and I is the intensity of the light absorbed. The similarity between this equation and that for the thermal reaction suggests that the mechanisms are very similar, the essential difference being that in the photochemical reaction the bromine atoms are produced by the absorption of a photon by a bromine molecule:

$$\mathrm{Br_2} + \mathbf{h}\nu \rightarrow 2\mathrm{Br}$$

This process is followed by the same series of reactions as before, i.e., reactions (2) to (5). The steady-state equation for bromine atoms is,

[1] M. Bodenstein and F. Cramer, *Z. Elektrochem.*, **22**, 327 (1916).
[2] W. Jost, *Z. Physik. Chem.*, **B3**, 95 (1929).
[3] M. Bodenstein and H. Lutkemeyer, *ibid.*, **114**, 208 (1924).

according to this scheme,[1]

$$\frac{d[\mathrm{Br}]}{dt} = 2I - k_2[\mathrm{Br}][\mathrm{H_2}] + k_3[\mathrm{H}][\mathrm{Br_2}] + k_4[\mathrm{H}][\mathrm{HBr}] - 2k_5[\mathrm{Br}]^2 = 0 \quad (5)$$

while Eq. (6) on page 328 still holds for the concentration of hydrogen atoms. The solution of these equations gives, for the rate of formation of hydrogen bromide,

$$\frac{d[\mathrm{HBr}]}{dt} = \frac{k_2(2/k_5)^{1/2}[\mathrm{H_2}]I^{1/2}}{1 + k_4[\mathrm{HBr}]/k_3[\mathrm{Br_2}]} \quad (6)$$

which is of the same form as Eq. (4) with $k' = k_2(2/k_5)^{1/2}$ and $m' = k_3/k_4$.

Under the conditions employed by Bodenstein and Lutkemeyer, the rate of the photochemical reaction was found to be about 300 times that of the thermal reaction at the same temperature, which means that in the photochemical reaction the stationary concentration of bromine atoms is about 300 times that in the dark reaction, all other stages in the two reactions being identical. Since the concentration of bromine atoms in the thermal reaction is known from the thermal dissociation constant of molecular bromine, the concentration of bromine atoms in the photochemical reaction is also known, i.e., is about 300 times as great.

In both reactions the rate of production of bromine atoms is equal to the rate of their removal. The rate of formation of bromine atoms in the photochemical reaction can be calculated using Einstein's law of photochemical equivalence (p. 343), according to which one molecule of bromine is dissociated for each quantum of light absorbed. The number of bromine atoms combining in unit time in the photochemical reaction is therefore known, and since the stationary concentration is known, the rate constant can be calculated. In this way it was found that on the assumption that the combination of bromine atoms is a simple two-body process, and with reasonable values for the atomic diameters, the recombination occurs in 1 out of every 800 collisions. On theoretical grounds it is known that the recombination must involve three-body collisions, the factor of $1/800$ corresponding to the necessity for the presence of a third body. In agreement with this, it was found that there was a variation of the rate of combination with the total pressure.

From the rate of reaction (5) and the equilibrium constant, the rate of (1) can be calculated. It was found that the rate of thermal dissociation can be expressed very approximately by a first-order rate constant k_1 given by

$$k_1 = 10^{13}e^{-45,200/RT} \quad \mathrm{sec}^{-1} \quad (7)$$

[1] In Eq. (5), and in similar steady-state expressions for photochemical reactions, I must be expressed in the units mole-quanta per unit volume per second; a mole-quantum, sometimes known as an einstein, is N photons or quanta of light absorbed (cf. p. 343).

the activation energy of 45.2 kcal being equal to the heat of dissociation of bromine.

A point of some importance concerns the nature of the initiating and chain-ending steps. It is seen from Eq. (7) on page 328 that the bromine atom concentration in this reaction is the same as it would be in the absence of hydrogen, because k_1/k_5 is simply the equilibrium constant for the dissociation $Br_2 \rightleftharpoons 2Br$. This is by no means a necessary feature of chain reactions, in which atom and radical concentrations are frequently very different from their equilibrium values. In the ethane decomposition, for example, the concentration of ethyl radicals is considerably higher than if they were simply produced by the establishment of the equilibrium $C_2H_6 \rightleftharpoons H + C_2H_5$.

Since the bromine atoms are at equilibrium with the bromine molecules, the concentration of bromine atoms (and hence the concentration of hydrogen atoms and the rate of reaction) will be unaffected by any catalysts that affect the *rate* of production of bromine atoms; such catalysts cannot affect the equilibrium concentration. A change in the nature of the surface, or in its area, cannot therefore affect the rate of the reaction, and this has been found to be the case. Furthermore the presence of third bodies, which may accelerate the formation of atoms, cannot affect their concentration. For a molecule as simple as bromine, with only one degree of vibrational freedom, the dissociation will certainly be in the second-order region, and the reaction should have been represented as

$$(1') \qquad Br_2 + M \xrightarrow{k_1'} 2Br + M$$

where M is a third body that may be a bromine molecule. Similarly reaction (5) should be written as a third-order reaction,

$$(5') \qquad 2Br + M \xrightarrow{k_5'} Br_2 + M$$

In deriving the steady-state equations k_1 should therefore have been written as $k_1'[M]$, and k_5 as $k_5'[M]$. The constants k_1 and k_5 only appear in the rate equation as the ratio k_1/k_5, which now becomes k_1'/k_5'; no change is involved, since this ratio is still the equilibrium constant. The rate expression derived above is therefore valid, and foreign gases can have no effect on the rate. This prediction is confirmed by experiment.

REACTION BETWEEN HYDROGEN AND CHLORINE

The reaction between hydrogen and chlorine shows some points of resemblance to that between hydrogen and bromine but is considerably more complicated, owing to the larger number of elementary processes that play a significant part in it. Both the thermal and photochemical reactions have been the subject of much study, particularly the photochemical reaction, the details of which are now fairly well understood. This reaction will therefore be considered first.

The Photochemical Reaction. A striking feature of the photochemical reaction between hydrogen and chlorine is the extremely large quantum yield that is obtained under suitable conditions, values as high as 10^6 having been reported.[1] This is in marked contrast to the situation with hydrogen and bromine, where the quantum yield is usually less than unity. The reason for this difference is that the chain-propagating reactions are more rapid with chlorine than with bromine, as will be discussed in more detail later.

It has been established beyond question that the initial step in the photochemical reaction is the dissociation of a chlorine molecule into atoms. It is known from the spectral evidence that chlorine is dissociated by wavelengths of less than 4,785 A, and it is at such wavelengths that most of the absorption takes place. More direct evidence was given by Jost and Schweizer,[2] who exposed chlorine to radiation immediately before mixing it with hydrogen, the radiation being prevented from reaching the hydrogen; reaction was found to take place.

A large number of investigations have been carried out with the object of determining the dependence of the rate of reaction on the concentrations of reacting molecules. Many of the earlier conclusions are now known to be in error owing to the existence of certain complications that were not at first recognized. There may, for example, be a long induction period during which no reaction occurs; this was shown by Burgess and Chapman[3] to be due to the presence of nitrogenous impurities such as ammonia and organic compounds. Later Griffiths and Norrish[4] found that the real inhibitor is nitrogen trichloride, which is formed from the impurities present. Other impurities, such as chlorine dioxide, ozone, and oxygen, also act as inhibitors.

The effect of oxygen is not only to contribute to the induction period but to influence markedly the rate of the reaction after it has started. To a good approximation the rate of the reaction is inversely proportional to the concentration of oxygen,[5] and as the gases are purified from oxygen the rate becomes extremely high. Since minute traces of oxygen have such a strong effect on the rate, some erroneous conclusions were reached

[1] M. Bodenstein, *Z. Physik. Chem.*, **85**, 329 (1913).

[2] W. Jost and H. Schweizer, *ibid.*, **B13**, 373 (1931).

[3] C. H. Burgess and D. L. Chapman, *J. Chem. Soc.*, **89**, 1399 (1906).

[4] J. G. A. Griffiths and R. G. W. Norrish, *Proc. Roy. Soc.* (*London*), **A135**, 69 (1932); **A147**, 140 (1934).

[5] D. L. Chapman and P. S. MacMahon, *J. Chem. Soc.*, **95**, 959 (1909); M. Bodenstein and W. Dux, *Z. Physik. Chem.*, **85**, 297 (1913).

by the earlier workers, and various contradictory expressions for the rate of reaction were put forward.

On the basis of a survey of the experimental work that had been carried out before 1926, Thon[1] proposed that the rate of the reaction could best be represented by

$$\frac{d[\mathrm{HCl}]}{dt} = \frac{kI[\mathrm{H_2}][\mathrm{Cl_2}]}{[\mathrm{O_2}]([\mathrm{H_2}] + [\mathrm{Cl_2}]/10)} \tag{8}$$

where I is the intensity of the light absorbed. This expression implies an infinite rate in the complete absence of oxygen, and Cremer[2] pointed out that the expression is obeyed only down to an oxygen pressure of about 0.04 mm. A more accurate expression for the rate, valid down to much lower pressures, was given by Bodenstein and Unger;[3] this is

$$\frac{d[\mathrm{HCl}]}{dt} = \frac{kI[\mathrm{H_2}][\mathrm{Cl_2}]}{m[\mathrm{Cl_2}] + [\mathrm{O_2}]([\mathrm{H_2}] + [\mathrm{Cl_2}]/10)} \tag{9}$$

At oxygen pressures higher than 0.04 mm the first term in the denominator can be neglected, so that Eq. (8) is obeyed. At extremely low oxygen concentrations, the rate approximates to

$$\frac{d[\mathrm{HCl}]}{dt} = \frac{kI}{m}[\mathrm{H_2}] \tag{10}$$

so that the rate is then independent of the concentration of chlorine.

A number of alternative chain mechanisms have been proposed to account for this behavior; that of Nernst was considered on page 326, but it is inadequate to explain the results. The most satisfactory mechanism would appear to be the following, which was proposed in 1921 by Göhring:[4]

(1) $\mathrm{Cl_2} + h\nu \rightarrow 2\mathrm{Cl}$
(2) $\mathrm{Cl} + \mathrm{H_2} \rightarrow \mathrm{HCl} + \mathrm{H}$
(3) $\mathrm{H} + \mathrm{Cl_2} \rightarrow \mathrm{HCl} + \mathrm{Cl}$
(4) $\mathrm{H} + \mathrm{O_2} \rightarrow \mathrm{HO_2}$
(5) $\mathrm{Cl} + \mathrm{O_2} \rightarrow \mathrm{ClO_2}$
(6) $\mathrm{Cl} + \mathrm{X} \rightarrow \mathrm{ClX}$

Here X may be any substance which removes chlorine atoms. This reaction scheme will later be compared with that for the hydrogen-bromine reaction.

The rate of formation of the chlorine atoms by reaction (1) is $2I$, where I is the intensity of light absorbed. The rate of formation of

[1] N. Thon, *ibid.*, **124**, 327 (1926).
[2] E. Cremer, *ibid.*, **128**, 285 (1927).
[3] M. Bodenstein and W. Unger, *ibid.*, **B11**, 253 (1930).
[4] R. Göhring, *Z. Elektrochem.*, **27**, 511 (1921).

chlorine atoms is

$$\frac{d[\text{Cl}]}{dt} = 2I - k_2[\text{Cl}][\text{H}_2] + k_3[\text{H}][\text{Cl}_2] - k_5[\text{Cl}][\text{O}_2] - k_6[\text{Cl}][\text{X}] = 0 \quad (11)$$

and the rate of formation of hydrogen atoms is

$$\frac{d[\text{H}]}{dt} = k_2[\text{Cl}][\text{H}_2] - k_3[\text{H}][\text{Cl}_2] - k_4[\text{H}][\text{O}_2] = 0 \quad (12)$$

Equation (11) gives for the concentration of chlorine atoms

$$[\text{Cl}] = \frac{2I + k_3[\text{H}][\text{Cl}_2]}{k_2[\text{H}_2] + k_5[\text{O}_2] + k_6[\text{X}]} \quad (13)$$

while Eq. (12) gives

$$[\text{Cl}] = \frac{k_3[\text{H}][\text{Cl}_2] + k_4[\text{H}][\text{O}_2]}{k_2[\text{H}_2]} \quad (14)$$

If these expressions are equated, the result is

$$k_2[\text{H}_2](2I + k_3[\text{H}][\text{Cl}_2]) = (k_2[\text{H}_2] + k_5[\text{O}_2] + k_6[\text{X}])(k_3[\text{H}][\text{Cl}_2] + k_4[\text{H}][\text{O}_2]) \quad (15)$$

Omission of the very small term $k_4k_5[\text{H}][\text{O}_2]^2$ gives, for the concentration of hydrogen atoms,

$$[\text{H}] = \frac{2Ik_2[\text{H}_2]}{k_3k_6[\text{Cl}_2][\text{X}] + [\text{O}_2](k_2k_4[\text{H}_2] + k_3k_5[\text{Cl}_2] + k_4k_6[\text{X}])} \quad (16)$$

It can be shown (see p. 367) that reaction (3) is much faster than reaction (2); consequently, the rate of formation of hydrogen chloride is given fairly exactly by

$$\frac{d[\text{HCl}]}{dt} = k_3[\text{H}][\text{Cl}_2] \quad (17)$$

Introduction of expression (16) for [H] into this gives

$$\frac{d[\text{HCl}]}{dt} = \frac{2k_2k_3[\text{H}_2][\text{Cl}_2]I}{k_3k_6[\text{Cl}_2][\text{X}] + [\text{O}_2](k_2k_4[\text{H}_2] + k_3k_5[\text{Cl}_2] + k_4k_6[\text{X}])} \quad (18)$$

$$= \frac{(2k_3/k_4)I[\text{H}_2][\text{Cl}_2]}{\dfrac{k_3k_6}{k_2k_4}[\text{Cl}_2][\text{X}] + [\text{O}_2]\left([\text{H}_2] + \dfrac{k_3k_5}{k_2k_4}[\text{Cl}_2] + \dfrac{k_6}{k_2}[\text{X}]\right)} \quad (19)$$

Apart from the final term in the denominator, this expression is of the form of the empirical equation (9), the constants being related by

$$k = \frac{2k_3}{k_4} \qquad m = \frac{[\text{X}]k_3k_6}{k_2k_4} \qquad \frac{1}{10} = \frac{k_3k_5}{k_2k_4}$$

The scheme of reactions therefore gives a kinetic law which is essentially in agreement with the experimental rate equation.

The species HO_2 which appears in reaction (4) is, of course, unstable. It is eventually converted into water and oxygen by reactions such as

$$2HO_2 \rightarrow H_2O_2 + O_2$$

and

$$HO_2 + H_2 \rightarrow H_2O_2 + H$$

followed by the decomposition of the hydrogen peroxide molecule.

The Thermal Reaction. Hydrogen and chlorine react thermally at temperatures above about 200°C, and the kinetics have been studied by many workers.[1] The results are not conclusive, although it appears in general that the reaction proceeds in a manner similar to the photochemical process. In place of the intensity of light absorbed, which appears in Eq. (9), the chlorine concentration appears as the square in the numerator,

$$\frac{d[\mathrm{HC}]}{dt} = \frac{k'[\mathrm{H_2}][\mathrm{Cl_2}]^2}{m'[\mathrm{Cl_2}] + [\mathrm{O_2}]([\mathrm{H_2}] + k''[\mathrm{Cl_2}])} \tag{20}$$

This can be explained in terms of the Göhring scheme if the initial reaction is the thermal dissociation of chlorine,

$$(1') \qquad Cl_2 + M \rightarrow 2Cl + M$$

The thermal reaction is complicated by the fact that the initial thermal decomposition of a molecule of chlorine may take place on the surface, so that different results are obtained with different sizes and shapes of vessels and with different types of surface. In the photochemical case the species X could be part of the surface, so that the theory allows for the surface removal of chlorine atoms; however, the photochemical formation of the atoms must take place entirely in the gas phase. It has been seen that this surface complication does not arise in the thermal formation of hydrogen bromide, since the rate of this reaction depends on the equilibrium concentration of bromine atoms, which are removed by the reverse of the reaction by which they are formed.

Pease[2] carried out experiments with the object of elucidating the wall effect in the thermal hydrogen-chlorine reaction. These for the most part consisted of comparing the rates of reaction in packed and unpacked vessels. If the chains are started on the surface but end largely in the gas phase, increasing the surface will increase the rate, but if they start in the gas phase and end on the surface, the rate will be decreased by increasing the surface. On the other hand, if both formation and recombination of atoms take place in the gas phase, or if both take place on the

[1] H. Sirk, *Z. Physik. Chem.*, **61**, 545 (1908); K. H. A. Melander, *Arkiv. Kemi.*, **5**, No. 12 (1913–1915); J. A. Christiansen, *Z. Physik. Chem.*, **B2**, 405 (1929); R. N. Pease, *J. Am. Chem. Soc.*, **56**, 2388 (1934); G. Kornfeld and S. Khodschaian, *Z. Physik. Chem.*, **B35**, 403 (1937).

[2] Pease, *loc. cit.*

surface, changing the amount or nature of the surface may have little or no effect on the kinetics. In fact, changing the surface-volume ratio had little effect on the rate. This result alone cannot allow a decision as to whether the chains both start and stop in the gas phase, or start and stop at the surface. However, in the presence of oxygen in excess, it is to be expected that more chain ending will take place in the gas phase, by the collision of hydrogen atoms with oxygen molecules, and Pease therefore investigated the effect of packing the vessels in the presence of 10 percent of oxygen. Under these conditions packing gave a large increase in the rate, from which it is concluded that chains start on the surface. With little oxygen present they therefore end primarily at the surface. This conclusion that chains are initiated on the surface is further confirmed by quantitative arguments. The energy of activation for a homogeneous dissociation of a chlorine molecule must be at least 57 kcal, the energy of dissociation, and the rate of this process can be shown to be too slow to account for the overall rate of the reaction. If the dissociation takes place on the surface, the activation energy may be as low as one-half the energy of dissociation, and the rate may then be sufficient to account for the rate of the formation of hydrogen chloride.

Influence of Water Vapor on the Reaction. A considerable amount of difficulty was created by an observation of Coehn and Jung[1] that hydrogen and chlorine do not combine at all in the complete absence of water vapor. The photochemical reaction was studied, and it was reported that the rate increases with increasing partial pressure of water vapor and reaches a limiting value at a pressure of 10^{-5} mm. This result led to the temporary abandonment of the scheme of reactions suggested by Göhring, since it was found to be impossible to explain the effect in terms of a modification of his mechanism. Several alternative proposals were put forward,[2] some involving the participation of termolecular reactions.

It now appears, however, that the results of Coehn and Jung were erroneous, and the Göhring scheme, or a simple modification of it, may be accepted. Rodebush and Klingelhoefer[3] showed directly that the reaction $Cl + H_2 \rightarrow HCl + H$ proceeds in the complete absence of moisture, and later Bodenstein and Bernreuther[4] found no effect of intensive drying on the photochemical reaction as a whole. They attributed the result of Coehn and Jung to contamination of the reaction mixture with gold

[1] A. Coehn and G. Jung, *Z. Physik. Chem.*, **110**, 705 (1924).

[2] J. Franck and E. Rabinowitsch, *Z. Elecktrochem.*, **36**, 794 (1930); M. Bodenstein, *Trans. Faraday Soc.*, **27**, 413 (1931); G. K. Rollefson and H. Eyring, *J. Am. Chem. Soc.*, **54**, 170 (1932).

[3] W. H. Rodebush and W. C. Klingelhoefer, *ibid.*, **55**, 130 (1933).

[4] F. Bernreuther and M. Bodenstein, *Sitzber. preuss. Akad. Wiss. Physik.-Math. Klasse*, **6**, 333 (1933).

chloride, used in the preparation of the chlorine; this gave a long induction period after the manner of the other inhibitors mentioned previously.

Individual Rate Constants. On the basis of the overall rates of the thermal and photochemical reactions, and from the results of other experiments, conclusions have been reached concerning the individual rate constants and activation energies for some of the elementary processes. The arguments and conclusions have been reviewed by Morris and Pease,[1] whose discussion will be largely followed here. The values obtained for the activation energies are summarized in Table 51, which includes also the results for bromine and iodine (cf. also Table 52).

Table 51 ACTIVATION ENERGIES FOR ELEMENTARY PROCESSES OCCURRING IN THE HYDROGEN-HALOGEN REACTIONS

	Activation energy, kcal, with Y equal to		
Reaction	Cl	Br	I
$Y + H_2 \rightarrow HY + H$	6.0	17.2	33.4
$H + Y_2 \rightarrow HY + Y$	2–3.6	1.2	0
$H + HY \rightarrow H_2 + Y$	5.0	1.2	1.5

The activation energy for the reaction $Cl + H_2 \rightarrow HCl + H$ has been determined directly by Rodebush and Klingelhoefer[2] by passing atomic chlorine into hydrogen. The activation energy was calculated from the temperature coefficient of the rate of formation of hydrogen chloride and also from the rate at one temperature, simple collision theory being assumed to apply; the agreement was very good, the activation energy obtained by the two methods being 6.0 kcal. The activation energy can also be determined from the results of the overall photochemical reaction on the basis of the Göhring mechanism. In the complete absence of oxygen the rate equation (19) reduces to

$$\frac{d[\mathrm{HCl}]}{dt} = \frac{(2k_2/k_6)I[\mathrm{H_2}]}{[\mathrm{X}]} \tag{21}$$

in agreement with the experimental result of Bodenstein and Unger [Eq. (10)]. The temperature coefficient of the overall rate in the absence

[1] J. C. Morris and R. N. Pease, *J. Chem. Phys.*, **3**, 796 (1935).
[2] Rodebush and Klingelhoefer, *loc. cit.*

of oxygen is therefore that of k_2/k_6, and thus of k_2, since it may be supposed that reaction (6) has no activation energy. The activation energy of the overall process in the absence of oxygen was found to be 5.8 to 5.9 kcal,[1] in excellent agreement with the result of the direct method.

The activation energy of the reverse reaction, $H + HCl \rightarrow Cl + H_2$, is found from the above value and the heat of the reaction, which is 1.0 kcal; the activation energy of the reaction is therefore 5 kcal.

The energy of activation for the reaction $H + Cl_2 \rightarrow HCl + Cl$ cannot be arrived at with the same degree of precision. The reaction is so rapid that direct measurement is difficult, and the value must be obtained from an analysis of the overall rate. The rate of formation of hydrogen chloride in the presence of excess of oxygen is given approximately by [cf. Eq. (19)]

$$\frac{d[HCl]}{dt} = \frac{(2k_3/k_4)[Cl_2]I}{[O_2]} \tag{22}$$

so that the activation energy under these circumstances is a measure of $E_3 - E_4$. This gives a value of about 2 kcal,[2] so that (since E_4 cannot be negative) a lower limit of 2 kcal can be assumed for E_3. A similar lower limit was given by Krauskopf and Rollefson[3] on the basis of a determination of the relative amount of water formed in experiments with oxygen present.

An upper limit for the activation energy may be determined from the experimental fact that there is no measurable inhibition of the reaction by hydrogen chloride, in contrast with the situation with the hydrogen-bromine reaction. This implies that the reaction $H + HCl \rightarrow H_2 + Cl$ proceeds at least 100 times as slowly as $H + Cl_2 \rightarrow HCl + H$, from which, assuming equal frequency factors, it can be concluded that the activation energies differ by at least 1.4 kcal. Since the activation energy for the former reaction is 5.0 kcal, it follows that that for $H + Cl_2 \rightarrow HCl + Cl$ is less than 3.6 kcal. The value must therefore be between 2 and 3.6 kcal.

The rate of the chain-ending process $H + O_2$ has also been investigated. The activation energy of the process is certainly very small; it has been seen to be 2 kcal less than that of the reaction $H + Cl_2 \rightarrow HCl + Cl$, the energy for which must be less than 3.6 kcal; consequently the energy of activation for $H + O_2$ is not greater than 1.6 kcal. Since this reaction has an activation energy of 2 kcal less than that of $H + Cl_2$ it might be

[1] E. Hertel, *Z. Physik. Chem.*, **B15**, 325 (1931); J. C. Potts and G. K. Rollefson, *J. Am. Chem. Soc.*, **57**, 1027 (1935).

[2] Hertel, *loc. cit.;* M. Padoa and C. Butironi, *Atti Linc.*, **25**, 215 (1916); *Gazz. Chim. Ital.*, **47**, 6 (1917); F. Porter, D. C. Bardwell, and S. C. Lind, *J. Am. Chem. Soc.*, **48**, 2603 (1926).

[3] K. B. Krauskopf and G. K. Rollefson, *ibid.*, **56**, 327 (1934).

expected to proceed about fifty times as fast, but Bodenstein and Schenck[1] found experimentally that it actually occurs with about one-twentieth of the speed. This implies that only 1 collision in 1,000 of the collisions with sufficient energy of activation is effective, and this suggests that a third body is necessary; as has been seen, the ratio of trimolecular to bimolecular collisions is, on the basis of collision theory (which is probably applicable to these simple reactions), of the order of 1:1,000. That the process involves a third body has been shown directly by Bates and his coworkers,[2] who studied the inhibition of the photodecomposition of HI in the presence of oxygen.

Comparison of the Hydrogen-Halogen Reactions. The reaction scheme proposed for the hydrogen-chlorine reaction differs in several important respects from that for the hydrogen-bromine reaction. Now that the activation energies are known, the reason for the differences can easily be seen; reference may be made to Table 51, in which the activation energies are compared, and to pages 357 and 362, where the reaction schemes are given. The main differences are seen to be (1) the inclusion of the reaction $H + HBr \rightarrow H_2 + Br$ and the exclusion of $H + HCl \rightarrow H_2 + Cl$, and (2) the different chain-terminating steps, $Br + Br \rightarrow Br_2$ being assumed for bromine and the three processes $H + O_2$, $Cl + O_2$, and $Cl + X$ in the chlorine reaction.

The reason for neglecting the reaction $H + HCl \rightarrow H_2 + Cl$ is seen from the activation energies given in Table 51. The reaction will proceed at a negligible speed in comparison with $H + Cl_2 \rightarrow HCl + Cl$, the activation energy being 2 to 3 kcal greater; the fact that there is no inhibition by HCl was in fact used to obtain a value for this activation-energy difference. In the bromine reaction, on the other hand, $H + Br_2$ and $H + HBr$ proceed at comparable speeds, so that the latter reaction is significant, and hydrogen bromide inhibits the reaction.

The reaction $H + O_2$ is significant in the chlorine reaction because its speed is one-twentieth of that of $H + Cl_2$. Since the reaction $H + Br_2$ is appreciably faster than $H + Cl_2$, the activation energy being 1 to 2 kcal less, the $H + O_2$ reaction is negligible compared with $H + Br_2$. The same applies to the other chain-ending processes $Cl + O_2$ and $Cl + X$, which are also probably three-body reactions. On the other hand $Br + Br$ is the only significant chain-ending process in the bromine reaction. It is as a result of this fact that the photochemical rate is proportional to the square root of the light intensity, the concentration of bromine atoms being proportional to this.

Under certain circumstances the reaction $Cl + Cl \rightarrow Cl_2$ becomes

[1] M. Bodenstein and P. W. Schenck, *Z. Physik. Chem.*, **B20**, 420 (1933).

[2] J. R. Bates and G. I. Lavin, *J. Am. Chem. Soc.*, **55**, 81 (1933); G. A. Cook and J. R. Bates, *ibid.*, **57**, 1775 (1935).

the most important chain-breaking process. Thus Ritchie and Norrish,[1] working with oxygen-free mixtures, found a dependence of the rate on the 0.6 power of the light intensity, and an exponent of 0.5 was found by Potts and Rollefson[2] and by Kramer and Moignard.[3] Another variation found by Ritchie and Norrish was inhibition by hydrogen chloride in oxygen-free mixtures, and this may be due to the occurrence of the reaction H + HCl on the surface of the vessel.

It is clear that the rather marked differences between the reactions of chlorine, bromine, and iodine with hydrogen are due to differences between activation energies of elementary processes, and a theoretical treatment of the problem[4] has contributed toward an understanding of it; in particular, it explains why the hydrogen-iodine reaction is elementary while the others are not. In Table 52 the values of the activation energies of the relevant elementary processes are collected.

Table 52 CALCULATED ACTIVATION ENERGIES OF THE HYDROGEN-HALOGEN REACTIONS

Reaction	Activation energy, kcal, with Y equal to		
	Cl	Br	I
$H_2 + Y_2 \rightarrow 2HY$	50†	45†	40.7§
$\frac{1}{2}Y_2 \rightarrow Y$	28	23	17
$Y + H_2 \rightarrow YH + H$	6.0	17.6	33.4§
$H + Y_2 \rightarrow HY + Y$	2–3.6	1.2	0
Sum of three last values	37	41	50.4

† Calculated by A. Wheeler, B. Topley, and H. Eyring, *J. Chem. Phys.*, **4,** 178 (1936).

§ J. H. Sullivan, *ibid.*, **30,** 1292 (1959).

Consider first the reaction between hydrogen and iodine; the experimental value for the activation energy of the molecular reaction is 40.7 kcal. In order for reaction to proceed by a radical mechanism, the initial step would be $\frac{1}{2}I_2 \rightarrow I$, which requires 17 kcal, for the production

[1] M. Ritchie and R. G. W. Norrish, *Proc. Roy. Soc.* (*London*), **A140,** 112, 713 (1933).

[2] Potts and Rollefson, *loc. cit.*

[3] W. J. Kramer and L. A. Moignard, *Trans. Faraday Soc.*, **45,** 903 (1949).

[4] A. Wheeler, B. Topley, and H. Eyring, *J. Chem. Phys.*, **4,** 178 (1936).

of 1 mole of iodine atoms, and this would have to be followed by the third and fourth reactions for the production of 2 moles of hydrogen iodide. The activation energy for the overall process is therefore

$$33 + 17 + 0 = 50 \text{ kcal}$$

and since this is higher than that for the molecular mechanism, the latter will predominate, as is found to be the case.

The situation is otherwise with chlorine and bromine. With chlorine the calculated activation energy for the elementary molecular process is 50 kcal, whereas that for the production of two molecules of hydrogen chloride by the atomic mechanisms is $28 + 6 + 3 = 37$ kcal. The atomic mechanism will therefore predominate; the reaction therefore involves free atoms, and the kinetics are relatively complicated, owing to the number of stages involved. The atomic mechanism also predominates in the hydrogen-bromine reaction, the activation energy being $23 + 18 + 1 = 42$ kcal, as compared with 45 kcal for the molecular process.

FORMATION AND DECOMPOSITION OF PHOSGENE

Another reaction whose mechanism is fairly well understood is that represented by the overall equation

$$CO + Cl_2 = COCl_2$$

The rates of formation and decomposition of phosgene have been investigated by Christiansen[1] and more accurately by Bodenstein and Plaut,[2] who obtained results in essential agreement.

The rate of formation of phosgene was found to obey the equation

$$\frac{d[COCl_2]}{dt} = k[Cl_2]^{3/2}[CO] \tag{23}$$

and the rate of its decomposition obeyed the equation

$$-\frac{d[COCl_2]}{dt} = k'[Cl_2]^{1/2}[COCl_2] \tag{24}$$

Equating these rates gives the expression for the equilibrium constant,

$$K = \frac{k}{k'} = \frac{[COCl_2]}{[CO][Cl_2]} \tag{25}$$

the value of which was determined as a function of the temperature. The rate constants and activation energies of both reactions were also determined.

[1] J. A. Christiansen, *Z. Physik. Chem.*, **103**, 99 (1922).
[2] M. Bodenstein and H. Plaut, *ibid.*, **110**, 399 (1924).

The expressions for the rates show that the mechanisms are complex, and in particular the presence of the concentration of chlorine molecules to the one-half and three-halves powers indicates that chlorine atoms play a part in the reactions. Bodenstein and Plaut pointed out that the observed results can be explained equally well in terms of two alternative mechanisms, one of which involves the intermediate formation of COCl and the other of Cl_3. The first scheme may be represented by

(1) $$Cl_2 \rightleftharpoons 2Cl$$
(2) $$Cl + CO \rightleftharpoons COCl$$
(3) $$COCl + Cl_2 \rightleftharpoons COCl_2 + Cl$$

Processes (1) and (2) are supposed to be rapid in both directions, and in addition process (2) involves a third body. The equilibria expressed in reactions (1) and (2) may be written as

$$\frac{[Cl]^2}{[Cl_2]} = K_1 \tag{26}$$

and

$$\frac{[COCl]}{[CO][Cl]} = K_2 \tag{27}$$

Solving for [COCl] and [Cl] gives

$$[COCl] = K_1^{1/2}K_2[CO][Cl_2]^{1/2} \tag{28}$$

and

$$[Cl] = K_1^{1/2}[Cl_2]^{1/2} \tag{29}$$

Since the rate of formation of phosgene is controlled by reaction (3), the rate constant for which may be written as k_3, the overall rate is given by

$$\frac{d[COCl_2]}{dt} = k_3[COCl][Cl_2] \tag{30}$$

$$= k_3K_1^{1/2}K_2[CO][Cl_2]^{3/2} \tag{31}$$

which is of the same form as Eq. (23). The rate of decomposition of phosgene is similarly given by

$$-\frac{d[COCl_2]}{dt} = k_{-3}[COCl_2][Cl] \tag{32}$$

$$= k_{-3}K_1^{1/2}[COCl_2][Cl_2]^{1/2} \tag{33}$$

which agrees with Eq. (24).

The alternative scheme for the reaction may be represented by

(1) $$Cl_2 \rightleftharpoons 2Cl$$
(2) $$Cl + Cl_2 \rightleftharpoons Cl_3$$
(3) $$Cl_3 + CO \rightleftharpoons COCl_2 + Cl$$

Again the rate of reaction is supposed to be controlled by reaction (3), reactions (1) and (2) being postulated to be rapid in both directions.

The treatment is very similar to the one just given and gives rise to kinetic equations of the right form.

On the basis of the thermal reactions alone a decision cannot be made between the two possible mechanisms. However, investigations of the photochemical formation of phosgene[1] suggest that COCl is a more probable intermediate than Cl_3.

THERMAL DECOMPOSITION OF NITROGEN PENTOXIDE

The decomposition of nitrogen pentoxide

$$2N_2O_5 = 2N_2O_4 + O_2$$

was first studied kinetically by Daniels and Johnston[2] in 1921. The reaction was the first homogeneous first-order reaction to be investigated, and it was not for four years that another example of this class was found. The reaction consequently played a very important role in the development of the theory of the rates of reactions.

Since the original investigation of Daniels and Johnston a great many studies have been made on the reaction, and the main conclusions of these may be outlined briefly. The question of whether the rate of the reaction is influenced by the walls of the vessel or by the presence of impurities has been investigated very thoroughly, with the result that it appears that the decomposition is uncatalyzed. Part of the evidence for this is that excellent agreement between the results of different investigations has been obtained, in spite of the use of different types of vessels and of different methods of purifying the pentoxide.[3] Rice and Getz[4] made a special study of the possible influence of catalysts. Their rates agreed with those of Daniels and Johnston within the limits of experimental error, and they also found no change in the rate if the gases were carefully freed from dust or were thoroughly dried with phosphorus pentoxide. Various methods of preparing the pentoxide were employed in this work, with no effect on the rate. Hirst[5] found that argon had no influence, while Hunt and Daniels[6] found the same negative result with a large excess of nitrogen. Busse and Daniels[7] found that hydrogen, bromine, chlorine, and other substances were without influence. In this

[1] M. Bodenstein, S. Lenher, and C. Wagner, *ibid.*, **B3**, 459 (1959); M. Bodenstein, W. Brenschade, and H. J. Schumacher, *ibid.*, **B28**, 81 (1935); **B40**, 120 (1938).

[2] F. Daniels and E. H. Johnston, *J. Am. Chem. Soc.*, **43**, 53 (1921).

[3] H. S. Hirst, *J. Chem. Soc.*, **127**, 657 (1925); E. C. White and R. C. Tolman, *J. Am. Chem. Soc.*, **47**, 1240 (1925).

[4] F. O. Rice and D. Getz, *J. Phys. Chem.*, **31**, 1572 (1927).

[5] Hirst, *loc. cit.*

[6] J. K. Hunt and F. Daniels, *J. Am. Chem. Soc.*, **47**, 1602 (1925).

[7] W. F. Busse and F. Daniels, *ibid.*, **49**, 1257 (1927).

connection the results of the influence of various solvents, discussed on page 199, are very relevant. Lueck[1] and Eyring and Daniels[2] found very little variation in the rate in a variety of solvents; this is a much more stringent test of the effect of foreign molecules, owing to the high concentrations involved. On the whole, it may therefore be said that foreign substances have little or no influence on the kinetics of the reaction.

Ozone is one substance that does influence the kinetics, and its effect was at one time not clear. Ozone ensures the complete absence of lower oxides of nitrogen by oxidizing them rapidly to nitrogen pentoxide; consequently it was expected that in the presence of ozone there should be no net decomposition until the ozone had been used up, after which the reaction should proceed normally. However, Daniels, Wulf, and Karrer[3] reported that no decomposition proceeds even after the ozone is used up, a result which suggests that pure nitrogen pentoxide cannot decompose but that a lower oxide must be present initially. On the other hand, Hirst[4] and White and Tolman[5] found the opposite result that after the ozone was used up, the decomposition took place at the same rate as in the original experiments of Daniels and Johnston; the results of Daniels, Wulf, and Karrer therefore seem to be in error. Schumacher and G. Sprenger[6] further clarified the influence of ozone, showing that it oxidizes nitrogen dioxide to nitrogen trioxide, which reacts with another nitrogen dioxide molecule to give nitrogen pentoxide. When the ozone is exhausted, they, too, found that the reaction proceeded normally.

The kinetics of the decomposition at very low pressures have been investigated carefully by a number of workers. The importance of this study is in connection with the theory of unimolecular reactions, according to whether the order of the reaction should become 2 at very low pressures; at such pressures there should be a falling off of the first-order rate "constant." Hirst and Rideal,[7] who were the first to investigate this experimentally, reported that the rate constant *increased* at low pressures, but Hibben[8] found no change in the constant down to 0.0018 mm pressure. H. C. Sprenger,[9] on the other hand, reported that the reaction stopped completely at 0.01 mm pressure. This confused situation later became clarified on the experimental side by exhaustive studies carried

[1] R. H. Lueck, *ibid.*, **44,** 757 (1922).

[2] H. Eyring and F. Daniels, *ibid.*, **52,** 1472, 1486 (1930).

[3] F. Daniels, O. R. Wulf, and S. Karrer, *ibid.*, **44,** 2402 (1922).

[4] Hirst, *loc. cit.*

[5] White and Tolman, *loc. cit.*

[6] H. J. Schumacher and G. Sprenger, *Z. Physik. Chem.*, **A140,** 281 (1929).

[7] H. S. Hirst and E. K. Rideal, *Proc. Roy. Soc.* (*London*), **A109,** 526 (1925).

[8] J. H. Hibben, *Proc. Natl. Acad. Sci. U.S.*, **13,** 626 (1927); *J. Am. Chem. Soc.*, **50,** 940 (1928).

[9] H. C. Sprenger, *Z. Physik. Chem.*, **136,** 49 (1928).

out in a number of laboratories. Ramsperger, Nordberg, and Tolman[1] found that the high-pressure rate constant was maintained down to 0.05 mm but fell at lower pressures and reached about half its value at 0.005 mm. This result was approximately confirmed in a later investigation by Schumacher and G. Sprenger,[2] who failed to find the stopping of the reaction previously reported by H. C. Sprenger. Hodges and Linhorst[3] also found a falling off of the rate at 0.06 mm and reported that below 0.004 mm the reaction approximately obeys a second-order law. The investigations at very low pressures are complicated by adsorption of the nitrogen pentoxide on the walls of the vessel, but on the whole it seems to have been established that a falling off really occurs. Another complication reported by Ramsperger and Tolman is that the ratio of final to initial pressures is, in the low-pressure experiments, less than 2.5, which corresponds to the change $2N_2O_5 = 4NO_2 + O_2$; this is probably due to the greater importance of the dissociation $N_2O_5 = NO_2 + NO_3$ at these pressures.

The fact that there is a falling off of the rate constant at low pressures does not, however, constitute evidence for the Lindemann theory, since the falling off takes place at much too low a pressure. As has been seen, the pressure at which the falling off occurs depends on the molecular diameter and the number of degrees of freedom contributing to the vibration of the molecule. Even the most favorable assumption as to the values of these quantities led to the conclusion that an appreciable change in the constant should have occurred at a pressure of 0.1 mm, and this is certainly not the case. All attempts to explain this result by modifying the theory or stretching the experimental data ended in failure.

The stoichiometric equation for the decomposition

$$2N_2O_5 = 2N_2O_4 + O_2$$

involves two molecules of N_2O_5 on the left-hand side and therefore cannot represent the mechanism of the process, which is first order. Various initial steps involving only one molecule of N_2O_5 have been considered, and the process

$$N_2O_5 \rightarrow N_2O_3 + O_2$$

first proposed by Busse and Daniels,[4] was accepted for some time. However, this reaction, which involves a change in spin angular momentum, would occur very slowly (cf. p. 166), and an alternative step is necessary.

[1] H. C. Ramsperger, M. E. Nordberg, and R. C. Tolman, *Proc. Natl. Acad. Sci. U.S.*, **15**, 453 (1929); H. C. Ramsperger and R. C. Tolman, *ibid.*, **16**, 6 (1930).

[2] H. J. Schumacher and G. Sprenger, *ibid.*, 129.

[3] J. H. Hodges and E. F. Linhorst, *ibid.*, **17**, 28 (1931); *J. Am. Chem. Soc.*, **56**, 836 (1934).

[4] Busse and Daniels, *loc. cit.*

Two other possibilities are

$$N_2O_5 \rightarrow N_2O_4 + O$$

and

$$N_2O_5 \rightarrow NO_2 + NO_3$$

of which the first can be excluded on energetic grounds. The second has been accepted by Ogg[1] as the basis of a mechanism which has the additional advantage of explaining the failure of the rate to fall off at low pressures in the manner predicted by a simple application of the Lindemann theory. The existence of NO_3 as an intermediate is also suggested from an analysis of other reactions.

The mechanism suggested by Ogg is as follows:

(1) $N_2O_5 \rightarrow NO_2 + NO_3$

(2) $NO_2 + NO_3 \rightarrow N_2O_5$

(3) $NO_2 + NO_3 \rightarrow NO_2 + O_2 + NO$

(4) $NO + N_2O_5 \rightarrow 3NO_2$

According to this scheme NO_2 and NO_3 react to give the alternative products N_2O_5 and $NO_2 + O_2 + NO$. The activation energy for reaction (2) is probably zero or very small, as it resembles a radical-recombination reaction, but reaction (3) is endothermic and consequently has an activation energy. It follows that k_3 is very much less than k_2, and consequently reaction (3) controls the rate of the decomposition. Calculation of the steady concentration of NO_3, and substitution of the value in the expression for the rate of (3), gives the rate of the overall reaction.

The steady-state treatment for NO_3 gives

$$\frac{d[NO_3]}{dt} = k_1[N_2O_5] - k_2[NO_3][NO_2] - k_3[NO_3][NO_2] = 0 \qquad (34)$$

whence

$$[NO_3] = \frac{k_1[N_2O_5]}{(k_2 + k_3)[NO_2]} \qquad (35)$$

Every time a molecule of NO_3 reacts with one of NO_2 to give $NO_2 + O_2 +$ NO, two molecules of N_2O_5 are decomposed, since the NO molecule produced decomposes an extra N_2O_5 molecule by reaction (4); consequently

$$-\frac{d[N_2O_5]}{dt} = 2k_3[NO_3][NO_2] \qquad (36)$$

$$= \frac{2k_1k_3[N_2O_5]}{k_2 + k_3} \qquad (37)$$

or approximately

$$-\frac{d[N_2O_5]}{dt} = \frac{2k_1k_3[N_2O_5]}{k_2} \qquad (38)$$

since $k_2 \gg k_3$. The theory thus accounts for the fact that the reaction is of the first order, in spite of the fact that the rate-controlling step is the

[1] R. A. Ogg, *J. Chem. Phys.*, **15**, 337 (1947); **18**, 572 (1950).

second-order reaction (3). Moreover, the apparent first-order rate constant $2k_1k_3/k_2$ is the product of an equilibrium constant k_1/k_2 and a second-order rate constant k_3. The Lindemann theory would therefore not apply to it, so that the fact that the constant does not fall off at the pressure predicted by this theory is explained. The actual falling may be explained in terms of Eq. (37); k_2 falls off at low pressures, and ultimately becomes unimportant compared with k_3, the rate expression then being $v = 2k_1[N_2O_5]$. This falling off has been discussed quantitatively by Mills and Johnston.[1]

The mechanism proposed is consistent with the known thermochemical values. The energy of activation of the reaction is clearly $E_1 + E_3 - E_2$, and the observed value is 24.6 kcal. Therefore

$$E_1 + E_3 - E_2 = 24.6 \text{ kcal} \tag{39}$$

Addition of the reactions (1) and (3) gives

$$N_2O_5 = NO_2 + O_2 + NO$$

so that $E_1 + E_3$ must be not less than the total energy change in this reaction, known to be 24.3 kcal, i.e.,

$$E_1 + E_3 \geqslant 24.3 \text{ kcal} \tag{40}$$

Assuming, as is probable, that $E_2 \approx 0$, it follows from (39) that

$$E_1 + E_3 \approx 24.6 \text{ kcal} \tag{41}$$

which is consistent with (40). The value of E_1 is probably about 20 kcal, so that E_3 is about 5 kcal; since E_2 is close to zero, these values are consistent with the fact that reaction (3) is very slow compared with (2).

Confirmation of Ogg's mechanism has been provided in various ways. His hypothesis that reactions (1) and (2) occur rapidly leads to the conclusion that it should be possible to demonstrate isotopic exchange in a mixture of, for example, $N_2{}^{15}O_5$ and $N^{14}O_2$:

$$N_2{}^{15}O_5 + N^{14}O_2 \rightleftharpoons N_2{}^{14}O_5 + N^{15}O_2$$

Such an exchange was demonstrated by Ogg[2] in the gas phase and in carbon tetrachloride solution; in the latter case he used $N_2{}^{13}O_5$. The rate constant of this exchange reaction should be equal to k_1, and the exchange should be first order in nitrogen pentoxide (at sufficiently high pressures) and zero order in nitrogen dioxide. Ogg found that at 27°C the rate fell by a factor of about 5 when the total pressure was reduced from 500 to

[1] R. L. Mills and H. S. Johnston, *J. Am. Chem. Soc.*, **73**, 938 (1951).

[2] Ogg, *J. Chem. Phys.*, **18**, 573 (1950).

50 mm. This is the kind of behavior to be expected for a molecule of the size of nitrogen pentoxide.

Further evidence for the mechanism has been provided by studies of the decomposition of nitrogen pentoxide in the presence of nitric oxide.[1] The mechanism is

(1) $N_2O_5 \rightarrow NO_2 + NO_3$
(2) $NO_2 + NO_3 \rightarrow N_2O_5$
(3) $NO + NO_3 \rightarrow 2NO_2$

Application of the steady-state treatment leads to

$$-\frac{d[NO]}{dt} = -\frac{d[N_2O_5]}{dt} = \frac{k_1k_3[N_2O_5][NO]}{k_3[NO] + k_2[NO_2]} \tag{42}$$

The initial rate (when $[NO_2]$ is zero), and any rate at a high concentration of nitric oxide, is equal to $k_1[N_2O_5]$; an experimental study under these conditions therefore provides information about k_1 and its falling off at low pressures. In the investigation of Mills and Johnston the reaction between N_2O_5 and NO was studied over a 100,000-fold range of total pressure, and included studies with various inert gases. The results fully confirmed the mechanism, and were consistent with the isotope exchange studies.

DECOMPOSITION OF OZONE

The elucidation of the mechanism of the decomposition of ozone has proved a matter of considerable difficulty. One of the complications has been that a wall reaction occurs as well as a homogeneous reaction, and it is difficult to separate the two processes. There is a first-order reaction which is largely heterogeneous, and a second-order homogeneous reaction.[2]

Chapman and his coworkers[3] studied the decomposition of ozone in the presence of excess of oxygen, and found that the reaction was second order in ozone. Later Jahn[4] found that the rate was inversely proportional to the oxygen concentration, and to explain this he proposed the

[1] Mills and Johnston, *loc. cit.;* H. S. Johnston and R. L. Perrine, *J. Am. Chem. Soc.*, **73,** 4782 (1951); cf. also Ogg, *J. Chem. Phys.*, **15,** 337 (1947); **18,** 572 (1950); J. H. Smith and F. Daniels, *J. Am. Chem. Soc.*, **69,** 1735 (1947).

[2] E. H. Riesenfeld and W. Bohnholtzer, *Z. Physik. Chem.*, **130,** 241 (1927); E. H. Riesenfeld and H. J. Schumacher, *ibid.*, **138,** 268 (1928).

[3] D. L. Chapman and H. E. Clarke, *J. Chem. Soc.*, **93,** 1638 (1908); D. L. Chapman and H. E. Jones, *ibid.*, **97,** 2463 (1910); cf. E. G. Warburg, *Sitzber. kgl. presses. Acad. Wis.*, **48,** 1126 (1901).

[4] S. Jahn, *Z. Anorg. Chem.*, **48,** 260 (1906); cf. E. P. Perman and R. H. Greaves, *Proc. Roy. Soc. (London)*, **80,** 353 (1908).

mechanism

(1) $$O_3 \underset{k_{-1}}{\overset{k_1}{\rightleftharpoons}} O_2 + O$$

(2) $$O + O_3 \xrightarrow{k_2} 2O_2$$

The decomposition of a molecule as simple as ozone must, however, be in its second-order region except at extremely high pressures, and Benson and Axworthy[1] have therefore modified the Jahn mechanism as follows:

(1) $$O_3 + M \underset{k_{-1}}{\overset{k_1}{\rightleftharpoons}} O_2 + O + M$$

(2) $$O + O_3 \xrightarrow{k_2} 2O_2$$

Application of the steady-state treatment to the concentration of oxygen atoms gives

$$k_1[O_3][M] - k_{-1}[O_2][O][M] - k_2[O][O_3] = 0 \tag{43}$$

whence
$$[O] = \frac{k_1[O_3][M]}{k_{-1}[O_2][M] + k_2[O_3]} \tag{44}$$

The rate of decomposition of ozone is

$$-\frac{d[O_3]}{dt} = k_1[O_3][M] - k_{-1}[O_2][O][M] + k_2[O][O_3] \tag{45}$$

and insertion of Eq. (44) for [O] gives rise to

$$-\frac{d[O_3]}{dt} = \frac{2k_1k_2[O_3]^2[M]}{k_{-1}[O_2] + k_2[O_3]} \tag{46}$$

Benson and Axworthy obtained additional kinetic results using both concentrated ozone and ozone diluted by oxygen, and found that all the results were consistent with this kinetic equation. The equation is seen to account for the fact that the rate is inversely proportional to the oxygen concentration when sufficient oxygen is present, and for the second-order behavior when oxygen is present.

The Benson-Axworthy mechanism does not correspond to a chain reaction; there are no chain-propagating steps, the atoms instead leading directly to products by the reaction $O + O_3 \rightarrow 2O_2$. A chain reaction was suggested by Glissman and Schumacher[2] and discussed again by Schumacher;[3] it involves excited oxygen molecules which are supposed to

[1] S. W. Benson and A. E. Axworthy, *J. Chem. Phys.*, **26,** 1718 (1957).
[2] A. Glissman and H. J. Schumacher, *Z. Physik. Chem.*, **B21,** 323 (1933).
[3] H. J. Schumacher, *J. Chem. Phys.*, **33,** 938 (1960).

be involved in the following chain-propagating steps:

$$O + O_3 \rightarrow O_2 + O_2^*$$
$$O_2^* + O_3 \rightarrow 2O_2 + O$$

The suggestion is that when the reaction $O + O_3$ occurs, one out of the two oxygen molecules produced is in an excited (perhaps electronically excited) state; it may be deactivated by collisions but may also continue the propagation of the chains. It is difficult to determine the relative importance of such a mechanism, but on the basis of a critical examination of the problem Benson and Axworthy[1] conclude it to be unimportant. A similar conclusion has been reached by McKenney and Laidler[2] on the basis of a consideration of the potential-energy surfaces for the reaction.

The photochemical decomposition of ozone has also been studied in considerable detail, and there has again been some disagreement about the mechanism. The decomposition is brought about by red light, and also by light of higher frequency, such as ultraviolet light. It appears[3] that the reaction brought about by red light does not involve energy chains, like the thermal decomposition, but that the reaction in ultraviolet light does involve energy chains. The important difference is that in the thermal decomposition and the decomposition in red light the atoms produced are in their ground ^3P states, and do not have enough energy to give rise to excited oxygen molecules that are sufficiently energetic to propagate the chain. In ultraviolet light, on the other hand, $O^*(^1D)$ atoms are produced and these undergo the reaction

$$O^*(^1D) + O_3 \rightarrow O_2 + O_2^*(^3\Sigma_g^-)$$

The $O_2^*(^3\Sigma_g^-)$ molecules produced in this reaction then propagate the chain as follows:

$$O_2^*(^3\Sigma_g^-) + O_3 \rightarrow 2O_2 + O(^1D)$$

The overall mechanism for the photochemical decomposition in ultraviolet light is therefore

$$(1) \qquad O_3 + h\nu \rightarrow O_2^* + O^*(^1D)$$
$$(2) \qquad O^*(^1D) + O_3 \rightarrow O_2 + O_2^*(^3\Sigma_g^-)$$
$$(3) \qquad O_2^*(^3\Sigma_g^-) + O_3 \rightarrow 2O_2 + O^*(^1D)$$
$$(4) \qquad O + O + M \rightarrow O_2 + M$$
$$(5) \qquad O + O_2 + M \rightarrow O_3 + M$$
$$(6) \qquad O_2^* + M \rightarrow O_2 + M$$

[1] *Loc. cit.;* cf. also S. W. Benson, *J. Chem. Phys.*, **33**, 939 (1960).

[2] D. J. McKenney and K. J. Laidler, *Can. J. Chem.*, **40**, 539 (1962).

[3] Benson, *loc. cit.;* W. D. McGrath and R. G. W. Norrish, *Proc. Roy. Soc.* (*London*), **A254**, 317 (1960); McKenney and Laidler, *loc. cit.*

Reactions (2) and (3) constitute the chain-propagating steps, and (4), (5), and (6) are the chain-ending steps.

In visible (red) light the oxygen atoms are not produced in the ^1D states but in the less energetic ^3P state. These atoms have insufficient energy to produce oxygen molecules having enough energy to regenerate oxygen atoms; energy chains are therefore not involved, as in the thermal decomposition.

THERMAL PARA-ORTHO HYDROGEN CONVERSION

The conversion of parahydrogen into orthohydrogen takes place homogeneously, the rate being convenient to measure between 700 and 800°C.[1] The order of the reaction is three-halves, suggesting the mechanism

$$(1) \qquad H_2 \rightleftharpoons 2H$$

$$(2) \qquad H + p\text{-}H_2 \rightarrow o\text{-}H_2 + H$$

The concentration of hydrogen atoms is in accordance with the equilibrium equation

$$[H]^2 = K[H_2] \tag{47}$$

since there is no net change in the number of hydrogen atoms when reaction (2) occurs. The rate of the conversion is therefore

$$\frac{d[o\text{-}H_2]}{dt} = k_2[H][p\text{-}H_2] \tag{48}$$

$$= k_2K^{1/2}[H_2]^{3/2} \tag{49}$$

The activation energy of the process is seen to be given by

$$E = E_2 + \tfrac{1}{2}D \tag{50}$$

where D is the dissociation energy of hydrogen and has the value of approximately 104 kcal. Since E_2 can be shown by direct measurement to be about 9 kcal (cf. p. 352), it follows that the overall activation energy should be 61 kcal. The fact that the experimental value is close to this is strong support for the mechanism.

REACTIONS OF THE ALKALI-METAL ATOMS

One group of reactions whose mechanisms are fairly well understood are the reactions between an alkali metal and either a halogen or a halide.

[1] K. F. Bonhoeffer and P. Harteck, *Z. Physik. Chem.*, **B4**, 119 (1929); A. Farkas, *Z. Elektrochem.*, **36**, 782 (1930); *Z. Physik. Chem.*, **B10**, 419 (1930); A. Farkas and L. Farkas, *Proc. Roy. Soc.* (*London*), **A162**, 124 (1935).

Most of the work has been done with sodium, and the reactions studied fall into three classes according to the nature of the other reacting substance; this may be (1) a halogen, (2) an inorganic halide, and (3) an organic halide. The reactions in the first two classes, which will be treated in this section, are always accompanied by the emission of radiation, which in the case of sodium corresponds to the sodium D line. The reactions of the third class emit appreciable radiation only when the organic halide contains more than one halogen atom.

Highly Dilute Flames. The reactions of the first two classes have for the most part been investigated by a modification, due to Polanyi and his collaborators,[1] of the ordinary flow method; the procedure is commonly known as the method of *highly dilute flames.* The two reactants are passed into a tube from opposite ends, the pressure within the tube being kept so low that the mean free paths are greater than the tube diameter. Under these conditions the gases mix by diffusion. The products of the reaction are solids, which are deposited on the vessel walls, and as each gas reacts, its partial pressure falls to zero, as shown diagrammatically in Fig. 75, in which the reacting substances are repre-

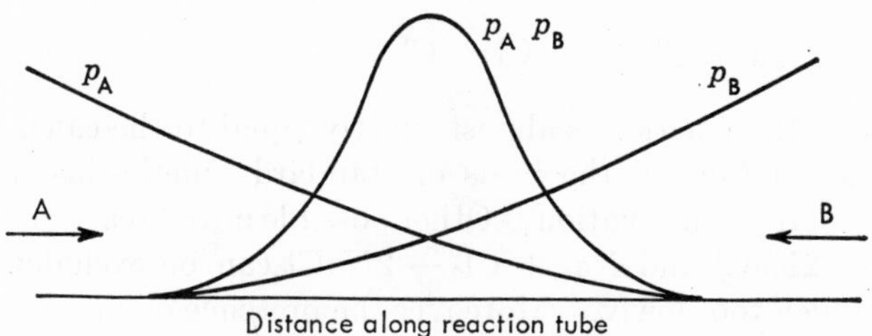

Fig. 75. The method of highly dilute flames: variation of the partial pressures of the entering gases, and of their product, with distance along the tube.

sented by A and B. If the reaction is of the first order with respect to both A and B, the rate of the reaction is proportional to the product of their pressures $p_A p_B$, which is also represented in the figure. The form of the curve $p_A p_B$ can be determined, if the product is a solid, from the thickness of the deposit at various points on the wall of the tube, and the rate constant of the reaction is related to the half-breadth of the curve. The more rapid the reaction is, the smaller will be the half-breadth: the

[1] H. Beutler, S. von Bogdandy, and M. Polanyi, *Naturwissenschaften*, **14**, 164 (1926); H. Beutler and M. Polanyi, *ibid.*, **13**, 711 (1925); *Z. Physik*, **47**, 379 (1928); S. von Bogdandy and M. Polanyi, *Z. Physik. Chem.*, **B1**, 21 (1928); M. Polanyi, "Atomic Reactions," Ernest Benn, Ltd.–Benn Bros., Ltd., London, 1932.

exact relationship is

$$k = \frac{27}{2b^3 U k_A k_B} \tag{51}$$

where k is the rate constant, b the half-breadth, U the amount of decomposition in moles per liter, and k_A and k_B are the "diffusion resistances" (low-pressure viscosities) of the two gases. By using this method, combined with studies of the luminescence accompanying the reactions, Polanyi and his coworkers obtained much information about the rates and mechanisms of these reactions. The method is directly applicable to those reactions which have zero activation energy; for those having an appreciable activation energy a further modification, known as the *method of diffusion flames*,[1] is necessary. The principle of this method is that the alkali metal is allowed to diffuse into a large excess of the other reagent. The distance that the alkali metal diffuses is measured by illumination with a suitable resonance lamp, and the rate constant is calculated from the distance and the diffusion constant of the metal.

Alkali-metal–Halogen Reactions. The reaction between sodium and chlorine will be taken as typical of the reactions of the first class. The first step is believed to be

(1) $$Na + Cl_2 \rightarrow NaCl + Cl$$

since the overall rate of the reaction is almost exactly equal to the calculated rate for such a reaction on the basis of standard kinetic-theory diameters and a zero energy of activation. Other possible initial reactions such as $2Na + Cl_2 \rightarrow 2NaCl$ and $Na_2 + Cl_2 \rightarrow 2NaCl$ can be excluded as they would occur much too slowly. Moreover the presence of chlorine atoms in the reaction has been confirmed by direct chemical evidence. Since the radiation emitted in the reaction corresponds to the D line, the sodium atoms must be excited to their ^2P states, a process which requires 48.3 kcal; the heat liberated in reaction (1) is only 40.7 kcal, so that further reactions must be involved.

The chlorine atom produced in reaction (1) may react with a sodium atom, but at an appreciable rate only in the presence of a third body, which may be the vessel wall. A more rapid process is reaction with diatomic sodium molecules, which at the temperatures involved are present in appreciable concentrations. The reaction is

(2) $$Na_2 + Cl \rightarrow NaCl + Na$$

[1] H. von Hartel and M. Polanyi, *Z. Physik. Chem.*, **B11**, 97 (1930); Polanyi, *loc. cit.;* C. E. H. Bawn, *Ann. Rept. Chem. Soc.*, **39**, 36 (1942); E. Warhurst, *Quart. Rev.* (*London*), **5**, 44 (1951); D. Garvin and G. B. Kistiakowsky, *J. Chem. Phys.*, **20**, 105 (1952); F. T. Smith and G. B. Kistiakowsky, *ibid.*, **31**, 621 (1959); D. Garvin, P. P. Gwyn, and J. W. Kokowitz, *Can. J. Chem.*, **38**, 1795 (1960).

which liberates 80 kcal of heat, sufficient to bring about excitation of a sodium atom. Further and more direct evidence for the reaction is that the intensity of the luminescence diminishes with increase of temperature, owing to the dissociation of the sodium molecules. The decrease is exponential; a plot of the logarithm of the intensity against the reciprocal of the absolute temperature gives a straight line, the slope of which gives an energy of 18.0 kcal, in excellent agreement with the directly determined value[1] of the dissociation energy of diatomic sodium. An additional piece of evidence is that the intensity varies with the square of the total sodium pressure, the concentration of Na_2 being proportional to this.

Since the energy liberated in reaction (2) is sufficient to excite a sodium atom, it might be expected that the sodium atom produced in the reaction would be excited. Quenching experiments with inert gases, particularly nitrogen, suggest, however, that this is not the case. The reduction in intensity brought about by the addition of quenching substances is much greater than that which would correspond to collisions between the added materials and the sodium atoms. It is therefore believed that the energy produced in reaction (2) does not pass into the sodium atom but goes into the sodium chloride molecule, which becomes vibrationally excited, the process being represented as

(2′) $$Na_2 + Cl \rightarrow NaCl' + Na$$

The excited NaCl molecule then transfers its additional energy to a sodium atom by collision,

(3) $$NaCl' + Na(^2S) \rightarrow NaCl + Na^*(^2P)$$

the sodium atom being excited electronically. The radiation emitted corresponds to the liberation of a photon $\mathbf{h}\nu$ by the excited ^2P sodium atom, which passes into its normal ^2S state,

(4) $$Na^*(^2P) \rightarrow Na(^2S) + \mathbf{h}\nu$$

The reason why the effect of quenching is greater than that expected if the quenching substances removed energy only from the $Na^*(^2P)$ is that the excited sodium chloride molecules exist for a considerable period of time before passing their excess energy on to a sodium atom, and are correspondingly more vulnerable.

The reactions of sodium with bromine and iodine have also been investigated, with very similar results. The rate constants for the reactions corresponding to (1) and (2) have been estimated in each case from the experimental results and are given in Table 53, the units being cc mole^{-1} sec^{-1}. Calculated constants, based on the usual kinetic-theory diameters and assuming zero activation energy, are also given. The

[1] R. Ladenburg and E. Thiele, *Z. Physik. Chem.*, **B7**, 174 (1930).

Table 53 OBSERVED AND CALCULATED RATE CONSTANTS FOR THE REACTIONS $Na + X_2$ AND $X + Na_2$

Reaction	Rate constant, cc mole^{-1} sec^{-1}		
	Observed	Calculated by collision theory	Calculated by activated-complex theory
$Na + Cl_2 \rightarrow NaCl + Cl$	4.1	0.6	4.5
$Na + I_2 \rightarrow NaI + I$	6.1	0.5	6.0
$Cl + Na_2 \rightarrow NaCl + Na$	1.5	0.56	5.1
$Br + Na_2 \rightarrow NaBr + Na$	1.5	0.46	3.0
$I + Na_2 \rightarrow NaI + Na$	0.26	0.41	2.1

reactions have also been treated theoretically by Magee[1] on the basis of the theory of absolute reaction rates. According to the treatment the interatomic distances in the activated complex are somewhat larger than those given by the kinetic theory, and the calculated rates are therefore higher; the values are included in Table 53 and are shown to be in better agreement with experiment.

Work has also been done using potassium in place of sodium.[2] The results are essentially the same, and the main reactions occurring are believed to be analogous to those with sodium; however, complications arise owing to the greater preponderance of wall reactions, which are responsible for a continuum as well as the two potassium lines which are observed. The rates of the main reactions are approximately those given by collision theory using zero activation energy.

Alkali-metal–Halide Reactions. The reactions of this class that have been investigated involve as the halides mercuric chloride and bromide; cadmium chloride; and hydrogen chloride, bromide, and iodide. The reaction with mercuric chloride may be regarded as typical of the reactions involving the metal halides,[3] and the primary process is believed to be

$$Na + HgCl_2 \rightarrow NaCl + HgCl \quad (1)$$

[1] J. L. Magee, *J. Chem. Phys.*, **8,** 687 (1940).

[2] H. Otouka, *Z. Physik. Chem.*, **B7,** 422 (1930); M. Krocsak and G. Schay, *ibid.*, **B19,** 344 (1932); E. Roth and G. Schay, *ibid.*, **B28,** 323 (1935).

[3] von Bogdandy and Polanyi, *loc. cit.;* H. Ootuka and G. Schay, *ibid.*, 68; Ootuka, *op. cit.*, 407; E. Horn, M. Polanyi, and H. Sattler, *Z. Physik. Chem.*, **B17,** 220 (1932); J. Berger and G. Schay, *ibid.*, **B28,** 332 (1935).

The energy liberated in this process, 25 kcal, is as before insufficient to excite a sodium atom. The overall rate of the reaction is of the same order as (actually, as before, a little greater than) that predicted by collision theory with zero activation energy. If these reactions were analogous to those involving the halogens themselves, the radical HgCl produced in the above reaction would react with an Na_2 molecule; however, this does not occur, since the temperature and pressure effects found with the halogen reactions are not observed here. It is therefore believed that the second stage in the process is reaction with a sodium atom,

(2) $$Na + HgCl \rightarrow NaCl' + Hg$$

which is exothermic by 63 kcal. Some of the energy liberated is carried by the NaCl molecule as vibrational energy and may be transferred on collision to a sodium atom, which becomes excited to the ^2P electronic state,

(3) $$NaCl' + Na^*(^2S) \rightarrow NaCl + Na(^2P)$$

These reactions occur with less luminescence than the reactions with the halogens.

The reactions between sodium and the hydrogen halides[1] are not so well understood. The first step in the case of hydrogen chloride appears to be

(1) $$Na + HCl \rightarrow NaCl + H - 5.2 \text{ kcal}$$

which, being endothermic, necessarily involves an activation energy. From the observed overall rate of the reaction, and using collision theory, von Hartel found an activation energy of 4.5 kcal and Bawn and Evans one of 6.1 kcal. The values are in satisfactory agreement; the activation energy must be as great as the endothermicity and appears to be approximately equal to it. Bawn and Evans also investigated the reaction between sodium and deuterium chloride and found an activation energy of 6.4 kcal.

The luminescence is assumed to be brought about by subsequent reactions of the hydrogen atoms produced, but the nature of these has not been fully elucidated. The radical NaH may be formed at the walls from H and Na and may react with a second hydrogen atom with liberation of energy

(2) $$H + NaH \rightarrow Na + H_2 + 60 \text{ kcal}$$

The energy may pass into the sodium directly, or into the hydrogen and hence by collision into a sodium atom.

[1] G. Schay, *Z. Physik. Chem.*, **B11**, 291 (1931); H. von Hartel, *ibid.*, 316; C. E. H. Bawn and A. G. Evans, *Trans. Faraday Soc.*, **31**, 1391 (1935).

ORGANIC DECOMPOSITIONS

The gas-phase reactions of organic substances have been the subject of a very considerable amount of experimental study. Homogeneous gas reactions of this type are almost invariably complex, and in many cases specific chain mechanisms have been proposed. In hardly any case is there complete agreement among investigators as to the details of the mechanism, and in arriving at an opinion as to the most probable mechanism in any given case a great many pieces of evidence have to be taken into consideration. In this section will be described some of the more significant results of the investigations of thermal, photochemical, and radiolytic decompositions of organic molecules.

Many organic reactions, including most decompositions, obey simple kinetic laws, and it was consequently assumed for some time that they are elementary processes. However, Rice and his coworkers showed that free radicals undoubtedly play an essential part in them. An important advance was made in 1934 when Rice and Herzfeld[1] pointed out that complex radical mechanisms may sometimes lead to simple overall kinetics, and proposed specific mechanisms for a number of reactions. There is no doubt that mechanisms of the type proposed by Rice and Herzfeld play an important role in organic decompositions; in many cases, however, it has been necessary to change some of the details of their proposed mechanisms.

The significant conclusion reached by Rice and Herzfeld was that the kinetic laws obeyed by many complex reactions, and the products of the reactions, can be explained on the basis of specific free-radical mechanisms; this fact had not previously been realized, since earlier free-radical mechanisms had given rise to kinetic laws that were more complicated than those usually found with organic reactions. An important fact that the mechanisms had to explain was that the kinetics were in many cases simple, the reactions frequently having orders of either unity or three-halves. Another feature of the reactions is that the production of radicals often involves the rupture of a carbon-carbon bond, which usually requires rather more than 80 kcal of energy per mole; the overall activation energy of most of the reactions is, however, considerably less than this. As will be seen, the Rice-Herzfeld mechanisms are consistent with both of these points. In particular, the experimental activation energies can be explained in terms of plausible activation energies for the individual elementary processes postulated as playing a part.

The mechanisms proposed will be discussed in a general way, and three cases will be considered, according as the order of the overall reac-

[1] F. O. Rice and K. F. Herzfeld, *J. Am. Chem. Soc.*, **56**, 284 (1934).

tion is unity, one-half, or three-halves. It will be seen later that the order is influenced largely by the nature of the initiating and of the chain-ending steps.

The mechanisms to be considered first involve *first-order* initiation processes, and termination processes of various types.

First-order Kinetics. An example of a reaction showing first-order overall kinetics is the decomposition of ethane into ethylene and hydrogen. If the initiating reaction is taken to be first order it is necessary to assume, in order to explain the overall order of unity, that the chain-ending step is a reaction between a hydrogen atom and an ethyl radical. The complete scheme is then

$$C_2H_6 \xrightarrow{k_1} 2CH_3$$
$$CH_3 + C_2H_6 \xrightarrow{k_2} CH_4 + C_2H_5$$
$$C_2H_5 \xrightarrow{k_3} C_2H_4 + H$$
$$H + C_2H_6 \xrightarrow{k_4} H_2 + C_2H_5$$
$$H + C_2H_5 \xrightarrow{k_5} C_2H_6$$

The steady-state equations for this reaction scheme are, for the methyl radicals,

$$2k_1[C_2H_6] - k_2[CH_3][C_2H_6] = 0 \tag{52}$$

for the ethyl radicals,

$$k_2[CH_3][C_2H_6] - k_3[C_2H_5] + k_4[H][C_2H_6] - k_5[H][C_2H_5] = 0 \tag{53}$$

and for hydrogen atoms,

$$k_3[C_2H_5] - k_4[H][C_2H_6] - k_5[H][C_2H_5] = 0 \tag{54}$$

Addition of (52), (53), and (54) leads to

$$[H] = \frac{k_1}{k_5}\frac{[C_2H_6]}{[C_2H_5]} \tag{55}$$

Insertion of this in (54) gives, after rearrangement,

$$k_3k_5[C_2H_5]^2 - k_1k_5[C_2H_6][C_2H_5] - k_1k_4[C_2H_6]^2 = 0 \tag{56}$$

The general solution of this quadratic equation is

$$[C_2H_5] = \left\{\frac{k_1}{2k_3} + \left[\left(\frac{k_1}{2k_3}\right)^2 + \frac{k_1k_4}{k_3k_5}\right]^{1/2}\right\}[C_2H_6] \tag{57}$$

The constant k_1 is very small, since the initiating reaction has a very high activation energy; the terms involving $k_1/2k_3$ are therefore very small in comparison with k_1k_4/k_3k_5 (which appears as the square root), and therefore

$$[C_2H_5] = \left(\frac{k_1k_4}{k_3k_5}\right)^{1/2} [C_2H_6] \tag{58}$$

The rate of production of ethylene is

$$\frac{d[C_2H_4]}{dt} = k_3[C_2H_5] \tag{59}$$

$$= \left(\frac{k_1k_3k_4}{k_5}\right)^{1/2} [C_2H_6] \tag{60}$$

The reaction is thus of the first order. If the activation energies for reactions (1), (3), (4), and (5) are E_1, E_3, E_4, and E_5, and the corresponding frequency factors are A_1, A_3, A_4, and A_5, Eq. (60) may be written as

$$\frac{d[C_2H_4]}{dt} = \left(\frac{A_1e^{-E_1/RT}A_3e^{-E_3/RT}A_4e^{-E_4/RT}}{A_5e^{-E_5/RT}}\right)^{1/2} [C_2H_6] \tag{61}$$

$$= \left(\frac{A_1A_3A_4}{A_5}\right)^{1/2} \exp\left[-\frac{E_1 + E_3 + E_4 - E_5}{2RT}\right] [C_2H_6] \tag{62}$$

The activation energy for the overall reaction is therefore

$$E = \tfrac{1}{2}(E_1 + E_3 + E_4 - E_5) \tag{63}$$

Since E_1 is usually very much larger than E_3 and E_4, the overall activation energy is usually appreciably smaller than E_1. The *chain length* of a reaction is defined as the rate of the overall reaction divided by the rate of the initiation reaction. In this case

$$\text{Chain length} = \frac{\left(\dfrac{k_1k_3k_4}{k_5}\right)^{1/2} [C_2H_6]}{k_1[C_2H_6]} \tag{64}$$

$$= \left(\frac{k_3k_4}{k_1k_5}\right)^{1/2} \tag{65}$$

Since k_1 is very small, this quantity is frequently very large. It represents the average amount of reactant transformed each time the initiating step occurs.

Three-halves-order Kinetics. In order for the overall kinetics to be of the three-halves order, for a first-order initiation reaction, the chain-terminating step must be a second-order reaction between two radicals that undergo second-order propagation reactions. As an example may be considered the mechanism originally proposed by Rice and Herzfeld for the thermal decomposition of acetaldehyde:

$$CH_3CHO \xrightarrow{k_1} CH_3 + CHO$$

$$CH_3 + CH_3CHO \xrightarrow{k_2} CH_4 + CH_3CO$$

$$CH_3CO \xrightarrow{k_3} CH_3 + CO$$

$$2CH_3 \xrightarrow{k_4} C_2H_6$$

The radical CHO also undergoes further reactions, which will be considered later (p. 409); for simplicity they will be ignored here. It will be seen later that the true situation with acetaldehyde is actually somewhat different from that represented by this mechanism.

The steady-state equations are now, for the methyl radicals,

$$k_1[CH_3CHO] - k_2[CH_3][CH_3CHO] + k_3[CH_3CO] - k_4[CH_3]^2 = 0 \quad (66)$$

and, for the CH_3CO radicals,

$$k_2[CH_3][CH_3CHO] - k_3[CH_3CO] = 0 \quad (67)$$

Addition of these equations gives rise to

$$[CH_3] = \left(\frac{k_1}{k_4}\right)^{1/2} [CH_3CHO]^{1/2} \quad (68)$$

The rate of formation of methane is

$$\frac{d[CH_4]}{dt} = k_2[CH_3][CH_3CHO] \quad (69)$$

$$= k_2 \left(\frac{k_1}{k_4}\right)^{1/2} [CH_3CHO]^{3/2} \quad (70)$$

The mechanism thus correctly explains the three-halves order. The overall activation energy is now

$$E = E_2 + \tfrac{1}{2}(E_1 - E_4) \quad (71)$$

and this is again usually much less than E_1, since E_2 is very small compared with E_1. The chain length is now

$$\text{Chain length} = k_2 \left(\frac{1}{k_1 k_4}\right)^{1/2} [CH_3CHO]^{1/2} \quad (72)$$

and depends on the concentration of reactant.

One-half-order Kinetics. When initiation is first order, one-half-order kinetics is found when the terminating step is taken to be the second-order reaction between two radicals that undergo first-order propagation reactions. In the acetaldehyde decomposition, for example, these would be the CH_3CO radicals; thus the hypothetical scheme

$$CH_3CHO \xrightarrow{k_1} CH_3 + CHO$$

$$CH_3 + CH_3CHO \xrightarrow{k_2} CH_4 + CH_3CO$$

$$CH_3CO \xrightarrow{k_3} CH_3 + CO$$

$$2CH_3CO \xrightarrow{k_4} CH_3COCOCH_3$$

will give half-order kinetics, as will now be shown. The steady-state equations are, for methyl,

$$k_1[CH_3CHO] - k_2[CH_3][CH_3CHO] + k_3[CH_3CO] = 0 \quad (73)$$

and, for CH_3CO,

$$k_2[CH_3][CH_3CHO] - k_3[CH_3CO] - k_4[CH_3CO]^2 = 0 \tag{74}$$

Addition of these equations gives

$$[CH_3CO] = \left(\frac{k_1}{k_4}\right)^{1/2} [CH_3CHO]^{1/2} \tag{75}$$

The rate of formation of carbon monoxide[1] is therefore

$$\frac{d[CO]}{dt} = k_3[CH_3CO] \tag{76}$$

$$= k_3 \left(\frac{k_1}{k_4}\right)^{1/2} [CH_3CHO]^{1/2} \tag{77}$$

The overall activation energy is now

$$E = E_3 + \tfrac{1}{2}(E_1 - E_4) \tag{78}$$

and the chain length is $k_3(1/k_1k_4)^{1/2}[CH_3CHO]^{-1/2}$

General Kinetic Schemes. The above examples show that the order of the overall reaction depends on the manner in which the chains are broken. This problem has been treated systematically by Goldfinger, Letort, and Niclause,[2] who showed that one may distinguish between two types of radicals:

1. Radicals that are involved in second-order propagation reactions; these are referred to as β radicals. In the above schemes hydrogen atoms and methyl radicals are acting as β radicals.
2. Radicals that undergo first-order reactions in the propagation steps. The radicals C_2H_5 and CH_3CO are of this type, and are referred to as μ radicals.

Goldfinger and coworkers concluded that if the initiating reaction is first order, and the termination steps do not require third bodies, the orders are as follows:

Termination	*Overall order*
$\beta\beta$	$\frac{3}{2}$
$\beta\mu$	1
$\mu\mu$	$\frac{1}{2}$

[1] In these schemes the rate of formation of carbon monoxide and methane are very close to each other, but are not identical. In the present scheme it is simpler to consider the rate of formation of carbon monoxide as the rate, whereas in the three-halves-order scheme it was better to consider the rate of formation of methane.

[2] P. Goldfinger, M. Letort, and M. Niclause, "Contribution a l'étude de la structure moléculaire," Victor Henri Commemorative Volume, p. 283, Desoer, Liège, 1948.

Their treatment also showed that if the chain-initiating reaction is second order rather than first order, the orders are higher by one-half.

Another possibility is that the chain-ending steps involve the participation of a third body, and are therefore third-order reactions. The effect of this is to reduce the order by one-half. Thus with first-order initiation and $\beta\beta$ termination requiring a third body (this may be represented by $\beta\beta$M), the order is unity.

The various possibilities are summarized in Table 54. This general

Table 54 OVERALL ORDERS OF REACTIONS FOR VARIOUS TYPES OF INITIATION AND TERMINATION REACTIONS

First-order initiation		Second-order initiation		
Simple termination	Third-body termination	Simple termination	Third-body termination	Overall order
		$\beta\beta$		2
$\beta\beta$		$\beta\mu$	$\beta\beta$M	3/2
$\beta\mu$	$\beta\beta$M	$\mu\mu$	$\beta\mu$M	1
$\mu\mu$	$\beta\mu$M		$\mu\mu$M	1/2
	$\mu\mu$M			0

The arrows show the changes that may be expected if the pressure is lowered.

type of treatment is very valuable in deciding on possible reaction mechanisms, since it avoids the necessity of working out steady-state equations in each case.

The decision as to the mechanism for a given reaction must be based on consideration of a number of factors. The order of the initiation reaction depends on the complexity of the molecule that is dissociating, the temperature of the experiment, and the pressure range. As has been seen in Chap. 4 a unimolecular reaction is more likely to be in its first-order region if

1. The number of degrees of freedom is large.
2. The pressure is high.
3. The temperature is low.

With molecules containing less than six atoms the dissociations are almost certain to be in the second-order region at the temperatures and pressures of most pyrolysis experiments. Methane and acetaldehyde, for example, probably decompose in the second-order regions under the usual experimental conditions. Butane, on the other hand, seems to have enough degrees of freedom for its decomposition to be in the first-order region.

With regard to the chain-ending step two questions are important: the first is the nature of the radicals that recombine, and the second is whether a third body is required. What radicals are involved depends upon the relative concentrations of the radicals. If β radicals are greatly predominant, $\beta\beta$ recombination will be most important, but $\mu\mu$ recombination will predominate if the concentration of μ radicals is very large compared with that of β. In intermediate cases $\beta\mu$ recombination may be most important. An additional factor is the relative rate constants of the combination reactions. Radical combinations usually occur with no activation energy, and the rate constants will thus be determined largely by the frequency factors, which depend upon the relative complexities of the molecules. On the whole, μ radicals are larger and more complex than β radicals, and the frequency factors for $\mu\mu$ recombination will thus be less than for $\beta\mu$, which in turn will be less than for $\beta\beta$. In the ethane decomposition, for example, the frequency factors are in the order

$$H + H > H + C_2H_5 > C_2H_5 + C_2H_5$$

The latter reaction is nevertheless preponderant, owing to the much higher concentration of ethyl radicals. The H-H recombination would in any case be unimportant since this reaction certainly occurs as a third-order reaction except at exceedingly high pressures.

The relative magnitudes of the radical concentrations depend on the relative rates of the chain-propagating steps. In the ethane decomposition the chain-propagating reactions are

$$C_2H_5 \xrightarrow{k_3} C_2H_4 + H$$
$$H + C_2H_6 \xrightarrow{k_4} H_2 + C_2H_5$$

The first reaction produces H and removes C_2H_5, while the second produces C_2H_5 and removes H. If k_3 were very large and k_4 very small, the concentration of H would be much greater than that of C_2H_5; conversely if k_4 is very large and k_3 very small, the concentration of C_2H_5 will predominate. Under usual conditions this second situation does apply in this case; the concentration of ethyl radicals is therefore very much greater than that of hydrogen atoms, and the predominant chain-breaking step is usually

$$C_2H_5 + C_2H_5 \rightarrow C_4H_{10}$$

For this reaction mechanism it is easily shown that the ratio of concentrations is

$$\frac{[C_2H_5]}{[H]} = \frac{k_4}{k_3}[C_2H_6] \qquad (79)$$

At sufficiently low pressures of ethane the relative concentration of ethyl radicals is therefore smaller, and the reaction

$$C_2H_5 + H \rightarrow C_2H_6$$

may then become the main terminating step. Evidence that this occurs has actually been obtained.

To summarize, the decision as to the most important terminating reaction must take account of the following factors:

1. The rate constants of the chain-propagating reactions, from which the relative radical concentrations can be deduced.
2. The frequency factors of the possible termination steps; these depend on the relative complexities of the radicals.
3. The number of degrees of freedom in the terminating reaction; if this is large a third body will be unnecessary, but otherwise it will be required.

The following is the type of procedure that might be used for establishing the mechanism of a decomposition reaction. A study may first be made of the overall order of the reaction over a wide pressure and temperature range. This limits the number of possible mechanisms to the ones corresponding to the experimental order of the reactions, as shown in Table 54. The effect of added inert gas may next be determined. An increase in the overall rate due to increase in pressure indicates a mechanism with a second-order initiation, and pressure-independent termination (column three in Table 54). A decrease of overall rate indicates a mechanism with pressure-dependent termination and first-order initiation (column two in Table 54). Both these effects, together with the overall order of the reaction, lead to a conclusion concerning the type of mechanism that applies. If no inert-gas effect is observed, the reaction may be of the type in column one or four, and it is usually necessary to decide, on the basis of further information, which of the two possibilities is correct. A useful clue may be provided by an observed change in the order of the overall reactions; the changes that are observed with decreasing pressure or increasing temperature should follow the arrows in Table 54.

Inhibition by Nitric Oxide. Evidence for the participation of free radicals in reaction systems has been provided by studies of the inhibition of reactions by nitric oxide. Staveley and Hinshelwood[1] first observed that small amounts of nitric oxide frequently reduce the rates of organic decompositions in the manner shown in Fig. 76. Since very small

[1] L. A. K. Staveley and C. N. Hinshelwood, *Proc. Roy. Soc.* (*London*), **A154**, 335 (1936); *J. Chem. Soc.*, 1568 (1937); L. A. K. Staveley, *Proc. Roy. Soc.* (*London*), **A162**, 557 (1937).

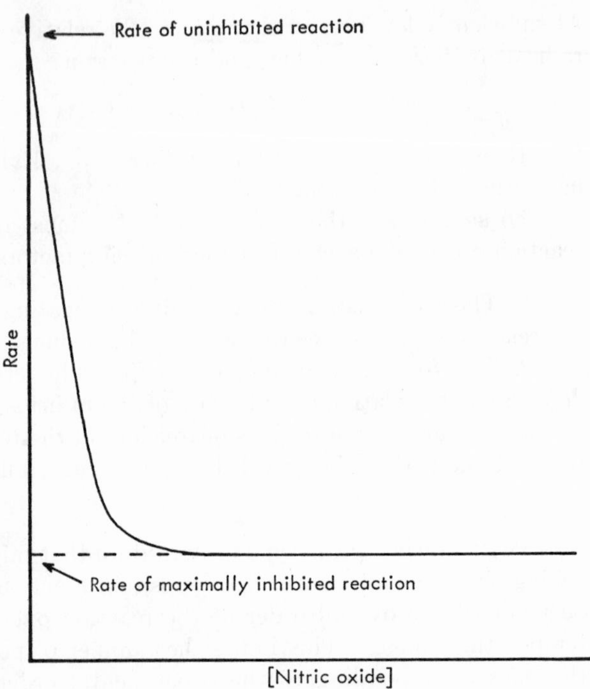

Fig. 76. Typical curve for the inhibition of an organic decomposition by nitric oxide. There is usually an increase in rate at higher inhibitor concentrations.

amounts of nitric oxide bring about inhibition to the limiting rate, it was concluded that the function of the nitric oxide is to react with and in some way destroy free radicals. It has been suggested that reactions such as

$$CH_3 + NO \rightarrow CH_3NO$$

occur, the product being converted in later steps to cyanides, ammonia, and other substances.

Since no further reduction in rate was found after a very small proportion of nitric oxide had been added, it was originally concluded that all the radicals had been removed. According to this view, the reaction that occurs after an excess of nitric oxide has been added is a purely molecular reaction; in the ethane case, for example, the limiting reaction was regarded as one in which an ethane molecule, after energization by collision, splits off a hydrogen molecule, leaving an ethylene molecule. For some time there has been considerable uncertainty with regard to this matter, but it has now become clear that the hypothesis of a molecular reaction cannot be correct for at least some of the decompositions to which it had been applied. Evidence for this has come from studies of isotopic mixing. Rice and Varnerin,[1] for example, decomposed C_2D_6 in the presence of CH_4, and investigated the rate of production of the mixed methanes, such as CH_3D.[2] They found that the ratio of CH_3D to CH_4 formed in an experiment varied linearly with the percentage of C_2H_6 that had decomposed, and moreover that a plot of $[CH_3D]/[CH_4]$ against the amount of C_2D_6 decomposed was independent of the concentration of nitric oxide. This result shows that the addition of nitric oxide reduces the rates of the mixing processes in the same ratio as it reduces the rate of the overall reaction. The concentrations of atoms and free radicals are thus not reduced to zero by the addition of nitric oxide, but are reduced in the same ratio as the overall rate is reduced. The limiting reaction must therefore still involve free-radical processes.

In order to explain these and other features of the inhibition by nitric oxide, Wojciechowski and Laidler[3] proposed that the effect of nitric oxide on an organic decomposition is to introduce a new set of free-radical processes. Nitric oxide is supposed to initiate chains by hydrogen abstraction, as well as terminating them. On the basis of such mechanisms, it is possible to explain why the rate in the presence of excess of nitric oxide is frequently independent of the nitric oxide concentration. A similar mechanism is proposed for inhibition by propylene. The mechanism proposed for the ethane decomposition, inhibited by nitric oxide, is discussed on page 404.

One important point that arises is that if such mechanisms actually take place, it is not legitimate to conclude from the absence of inhibition by nitric oxide that there are no free radicals present in the reaction system. It can be shown, for example, that a mechanism involving first-order initiation and $\beta\mu$ recombination (and therefore showing first-order kinetics) will occur at the same rate in the presence of nitric oxide as in its absence. In view of these results, nitric oxide inhibition loses its

[1] F. O. Rice and R. E. Varnerin, *J. Am. Chem. Soc.*, **76**, 324 (1954); cf. V. A. Poltorak and V. V. Voevodsky, *Dokl. Akad. Nauk. SSSR*, **91**, 589 (1953) (for propane); D. J. McKenney, B. W. Wojciechowski, and K. J. Laidler, *Can. J. Chem.*, **41**, 1993 (1963) (for dimethyl ether).

[2] CH_3D is formed by the following sequence of reactions:

$$
\begin{aligned}
C_2D_6 &\rightarrow 2CD_3 \\
CD_3 + C_2D_6 &\rightarrow CD_4 + C_2D_5 \\
C_2D_5 + CH_4 &\rightarrow C_2D_5H + CH_3 \\
CH_3 + C_2D_6 &\rightarrow CH_3D + C_2D_5, \text{ etc.}
\end{aligned}
$$

[3] B. W. Wojciechowski and K. J. Laidler, *Can. J. Chem.*, **38**, 1027 (1960); *Trans. Faraday Soc.*, **59**, 369 (1963). R. G. W. Norrish and G. L. Pratt, *Nature*, **197**, 143 (1963), have also suggested a general mechanism for inhibition; their proposals have not, however, been applied in detail to individual reactions, and appear to involve some difficulties.

usefulness as an indication of free-radical and molecular mechanisms, but still presents an interesting problem in itself.

Decomposition of Methane. Considerable confusion has existed for some time with regard to the kinetics and mechanism of the thermal decomposition of methane. The reaction is by no means typical of the hydrocarbon decompositions, and a special difficulty arises as a result of the high temperatures (over 900°C) that must be employed in order for the reaction to proceed at a measurable rate. Gordon[1] made a mass-spectrometric study to determine the main products of the reaction, and found them to be ethylene, ethane, acetylene, and hydrogen. In addition, carbon is deposited on the surface of the reaction vessel.

Early kinetic studies led to activation energies that are undoubtedly much too low. Thus Kassel[2] studied the reaction by following the pressure change in a carbon-coated vessel, at temperatures from 976 to 1113°C, and obtained an activation energy of 79 kcal. Storch[3] brought about decomposition by a hot wire, and also followed the pressure change; he reported a value of 77 kcal for the activation energy, but the experimental error was extremely large (values from 40 to 120 kcal being obtained). It is now realized that rate measurements based on pressure change are unreliable; because a variety of products is formed, the pressure change is not a good measure of the extent of reaction.

More recently, Palmer and Hirt[4] have followed the course of the reaction by observing the formation of carbon films on the surface of the reaction vessel. The methane concentration was varied over a factor of 20, and the kinetics were found to be first order. The variation of the rate constant with the temperature was represented by the equation

$$k = 10^{14.1} e^{-101{,}000/RT} \qquad \text{sec}^{-1}$$

The methane decomposition has also been studied using the shock-tube technique (cf. Chap. 2), in three independent investigations. Glick,[5] and Kevorkian, Heath, and Boudart[6] obtained an activation energy of about 85 kcal in this way. Skinner and Ruehrwein,[7] on the other hand, obtained a value of 101 kcal, in agreement with the value obtained by Palmer and Hirt. The shock-wave studies relate to a temperature range from over 1000 to nearly 2000°C, while the measurements of Palmer and Hirt were made from about 900 to 1000°C. An Arrhenius

[1] A. S. Gordon, *J. Am. Chem. Soc.*, **70,** 395 (1948).

[2] L. S. Kassel, *ibid.*, **54,** 3949 (1932).

[3] H. H. Storch, *ibid.*, 4185.

[4] H. B. Palmer and T. J. Hirt, *J. Phys. Chem.*, **67,** 709 (1963).

[5] H. S. Glick, "Seventh Symposium on Combustion," p. 98, Butterworth & Co. (Publishers), Ltd., London, 1959.

[6] V. Kevorkian, C. E. Heath, and M. Boudart, *J. Phys. Chem.*, **64,** 964 (1960).

[7] G. B. Skinner and R. A. Ruehrwein, *ibid.*, **63,** 1736 (1959).

plot of the results of Skinner and Ruehrwein and of Palmer and Hirt led to a good straight line, the rates being best represented by the equation

$$k = 10^{14.9}e^{-103,000/RT} \qquad \text{sec}^{-1}$$

The nature of the free radicals that play a part in the pyrolysis of methane has also been the subject of some controversy. Rice and his coworkers[1] used tellurium mirrors as a means of detecting and distinguishing between methyl and methylene radicals, the former giving rise to dimethyl telluride ($CH_3TeTeCH_3$) and the latter to telluroformaldehyde [$(TeCH_2)_x$]. In the decomposition of methane, they found only methyl radicals, with no trace of methylene. On the other hand, Belchetz and Rideal[2] obtained results which appear to show that the methylene radical is a primary product in the decomposition. Their procedure was to pass the reactant over a heated carbon or platinum filament and to detect the radicals by causing them to react with mirrors of tellurium and iodine. They found methylene but no trace of methyl radicals, which they concluded to be secondary products arising from reactions such as

$$CH_2 + CH_4 \rightarrow 2CH_3$$

If this were the case, the failure of Rice and others to obtain methylene would be due to the fact that under the experimental conditions employed by them all the methylene radicals had reacted. In agreement with this idea, Rice [3] confirmed the result of Belchetz and Rideal, using the same experimental technique. It is possible, however, that these results using filaments are not relevant to the homogeneous decomposition but only to that catalyzed by the surface.

The only plausible initiation reactions in the pyrolysis of methane are

$$CH_4 \rightarrow CH_3 + H$$

and

$$CH_4 \rightarrow CH_2 + H_2$$

The first of these reactions is endothermic by about 102 kcal,[4] the second by about 103 kcal.[5] If the activation energy were significantly below these values, as suggested by the earlier work, it would be necessary to postulate a chain mechanism. Various attempts to do this were in fact made, including that by Rice and Dooley.[6] It did not, however, prove

[1] F. O. Rice and A. L. Glasebrook, *ibid.*, **56**, 2472 (1934); F. O. Rice and M. D. Dooley, *ibid.*, 2747.

[2] L. Belchetz and E. K. Rideal, *Trans. Faraday Soc.*, **30**, 170 (1934); *J. Am. Chem. Soc.*, **57**, 1168 (1935).

[3] F. O. Rice, *ibid.*, **61**, 213 (1939).

[4] B. E. Knox and H. B. Palmer, *Chem. Rev.*, **61**, 247 (1961).

[5] J. A. Bell and G. B. Kistiakowsky, *J. Am. Chem. Soc.*, **84**, 3417 (1962).

[6] F. O. Rice and M. D. Dooley, *ibid.*, **56**, 2747 (1934).

possible to explain both the first-order kinetics and a low activation energy in terms of any free-radical chain mechanism.

These difficulties disappear if the activation energy is in fact about 103 kcal, as suggested by the latest work. It is then not necessary to postulate chains; the initial process is the slow step in the reaction, and the products are formed by subsequent nonchain processes. It seems likely that both initiation steps play a role in the reaction.

Methane does not absorb radiation in the visible or near-ultraviolet regions, but it does so in the "vacuum ultraviolet," and its photolysis under these conditions has been studied. Mahan and Mandal[1] have investigated the reaction using the 1,230-A resonance line of krypton, and worked with mixtures of CH_4 and CD_4. The main products are hydrogen, ethane, propane, and acetylene, and the nature of the mixed products led them to conclude that the initial absorption of light gives rise to the formation of both $CH_3 + H$ and of $CH_2 + H_2$:

$$CH_4 + h\nu \rightarrow CH_4^* \rightarrow CH_3 + H \tag{1}$$

$$CH_4 + h\nu \rightarrow CH_4^* \rightarrow CH_2 + H_2 \tag{2}$$

If initiation were entirely the first reaction, the principal subsequent processes would be

$$H + CH_4 \rightarrow H_2 + CH_3$$

and

$$2CH_3 \rightarrow C_2H_6$$

In CH_4-CD_4 mixtures, the hydrogen would appear as H_2, D_2, and HD, but it was actually found that the relative amounts of H_2 and D_2 were greater, and those of HD less, than expected on the basis of this mechanism. This clearly suggests that initiation reaction (2), which gives H_2 and D_2 but not HD, must be important also. The ethane resulting from the initiation step (1) will initially be C_2H_6, C_2D_6, and CH_3CD_3, but mixed ethanes such as CH_2DCD_3 and CHD_2CH_3 were formed in addition. The presence of these is readily understood if initiation occurs partly by reaction (2); CD_2, for example, will produce CHD_2CH_3 by reaction with CH_4:

$$CD_2 + CH_4 \rightarrow CHD_2CH_3$$

The photosensitized decomposition of methane is also of considerable interest. R. A. Back and van der Auwera[2] made a detailed study of the reaction photosensitized by triplet mercury ($^3P_1$) at temperatures ranging

[1] B. H. Mahan and R. Mandal, *J. Chem. Phys.*, **37**, 207 (1962); cf. also P. A. Leighton and A. B. Steiner, *J. Am. Chem. Soc.*, **58**, 1823 (1936); W. Groth, *Z. Physik. Chem.*, **B38**, 366 (1937).

[2] R. A. Back and D. van der Auwera, *Can. J. Chem.*, **40**, 2339 (1962); cf. also K. Morikawa, W. S. Benedict, and H. S. Taylor, *J. Chem. Phys.*, **5**, 212 (1937); G. J. Mains and A. S. Newton, *J. Phys. Chem.*, **65**, 212 (1961).

from 25 to 400°C and pressures from 100 to 1,000 mm. They worked at sufficiently low light intensities that the hydrogen-atom concentrations were very small; under these conditions the recombination reaction

$$H + H + M \rightarrow H_2 + M$$

can be neglected in comparison with the abstraction reaction

$$H + CH_4 \rightarrow H_2 + CH_3$$

They made measurements only up to very low conversions, so that secondary reactions were unimportant. Under their conditions the products were almost entirely ethane and hydrogen. Addition of sufficient ethylene was found to abolish the hydrogen production entirely; this is attributed to the fact that ethylene "scavenges" hydrogen atoms by the reaction

$$H + C_2H_4 \rightarrow C_2H_5$$

This result indicates that little or no molecular hydrogen is formed in the primary step, i.e., that

$$Hg^* + CH_4 \rightarrow CH_2 + H_2 + Hg$$

is unimportant. The results are all consistent with the hypothesis that the main primary process is

$$Hg^* + CH_4 \rightarrow CH_3 + H + Hg \tag{1}$$

the hydrogen atoms perhaps being formed from vibrationally excited HgH formed in the process

$$Hg^* + CH_4 \rightarrow CH_3 + HgH'$$

The primary process (1) is then followed by

$$H + CH_4 \rightarrow H_2 + CH_3 \tag{2}$$

and

$$2CH_3 \rightarrow C_2H_6 \tag{3}$$

This mechanism corresponds to the removal of two molecules of methane every time the initiation reaction (1) occurs. The actual quantum yields for hydrogen production were, however, small ($\sim 10^{-1}$), and this is attributed to a low efficiency for reaction (1). This result, which differs from that obtained with other hydrocarbons, has never been satisfactorily explained.

Several studies of the radiolysis of methane have been carried out. Mund and Koch[1] and Lind and Bardwell[2] exposed methane to the α rays

[1] W. Mund and W. Koch, *Bull. Soc. Chim. Belg.*, **34**, 121 (1925).
[2] S. C. Lind and D. C. Bardwell, *J. Am. Chem. Soc.*, **48**, 2335 (1926).

of radon, and observed decomposition into ethane and hydrogen. The M/N value, which is the ratio of the number of molecules of methane decomposed to the number of ion pairs formed, was approximately 2. This may be explained in terms of the mechanism

$$\begin{aligned} CH_4 &\overset{\alpha}{\rightsquigarrow} CH_4^+ \\ CH_4^+ + e &\longrightarrow CH_3 + H \\ H + CH_4 &\longrightarrow H_2 + CH_3 \\ 2CH_3 &\longrightarrow C_2H_6 \end{aligned}$$

The abstraction reaction

$$CH_3 + CH_4 \rightarrow CH_4 + CH_3$$

will also occur, but of course contributes nothing to the yield. The situation is undoubtedly much more complicated than indicated above. In particular certain ion-molecule reactions, such as

$$\begin{aligned} CH_4^+ + CH_4 &\rightarrow CH_5^+ + CH_3 \\ CH_3^+ + CH_4 &\rightarrow C_2H_5^+ + H_2 \end{aligned}$$

are known to occur in the reaction.[1]

Decomposition of Ethane. The kinetics of the pyrolysis of ethane were first investigated by Pease,[2] who used a flow system and worked at 650°C. He found the main products to be ethylene and hydrogen, the overall reaction being represented approximately by the equation

$$C_2H_6 = C_2H_4 + H_2$$

His work, and later work using the flow method,[3] indicated the reaction to be largely homogeneous and of the first order. These conclusions have been largely confirmed by later investigations[4] using static systems. Laidler and Wojciechowski[5] studied the reaction over the temperature range from 550 to 640°C, and obtained rate constants that were consistent with those of previous workers;[6] they obtained an activation energy of 73.1 kcal. At lower temperatures and higher pressures they observed a change of order from unity to $\frac{3}{2}$.

The presence of free radicals in the reaction system was demon-

[1] D. P. Stevenson and D. O. Schissler, *J. Chem. Phys.*, **23**, 1353 (1955); D. O. Schissler and D. P. Stevenson, *ibid.*, **24**, 926 (1956).

[2] R. N. Pease, *J. Am. Chem. Soc.*, **50**, 1179 (1928).

[3] F. E. Frey and D. F. Smith, *Ind. Eng. Chem.*, **20**, 948 (1928).

[4] L. F. Marek and W. B. McCluer, *ibid.*, **23**, 879 (1931); R. E. Paul and L. F. Marek, *ibid.*, **26**, 454 (1934).

[5] K. J. Laidler and B. W. Wojciechowski, *Proc. Roy. Soc.* (*London*), **A260**, 91 (1961).

[6] H. Sachsse, *Z. Physik. Chem.*, **B31**, 87 (1935); L. Küchler and H. Theile, *ibid.*, **B42**, 359 (1939); E. W. R. Steacie and G. Shane, *Can. J. Res.*, **B18**, 203 (1940).

strated by Rice and Dooley[1] using the mirror-removal method, and was confirmed by Eltenton[2] by mass spectrometry. The reaction is inhibited by nitric oxide[3] and by propylene,[4] maximal inhibition corresponding to a decrease in rate by a factor of about 10. At high nitric oxide concentrations the rate increases,[5] the rate in this region being linear in the nitric oxide concentration.

Considerable controversy has existed with regard to whether the purely molecular mechanism

$$C_2H_6 \rightarrow C_2H_4 + H_2$$

plays a significant role in the decomposition. The nitric oxide results were originally interpreted in terms of the hypothesis that the reaction uninhibitable by nitric oxide is a molecular reaction, which therefore comprises about one-tenth of the total reaction. As has been seen, however, the isotopic mixing experiments of Rice and Varnerin (p. 395) render this idea untenable, and indicate the reaction to proceed almost entirely by a free-radical mechanism. The mechanism of inhibition by nitric oxide is considered later.

There has also been uncertainty about the free-radical mechanism that applies to this reaction. There is general agreement that the chain-propagating processes, leading to the main products of reaction, are

$$C_2H_5 \rightarrow C_2H_4 + H$$
$$H + C_2H_6 \rightarrow H_2 + C_2H_5$$

There is also little doubt that the main initiation reaction is

$$C_2H_6 \rightarrow 2CH_3$$

this reaction being considerably less endothermic than the alternative split into $C_2H_5 + H$. The questions that have given rise to difficulty are the order of the initiation reaction, the order of the dissociation of C_2H_5 into $C_2H_4 + H$, and the nature and order of the chain-ending steps. The three possibilities that have been proposed for the reaction in the first-order region are shown in Table 55.

[1] F. O. Rice and M. D. Dooley, *J. Am. Chem. Soc.*, **55**, 424 (1933).

[2] G. C. Eltenton, *J. Chem. Phys.*, **10**, 403 (1942); **15**, 455 (1947).

[3] L. A. K. Staveley, *Proc. Roy. Soc.* (*London*), **A162**, 557 (1937); J. E. Hobbs and C. N. Hinshelwood, *ibid.*, **A167**, 447 (1938); J. E. Hobbs, *ibid.*; E. W. R. Steacie and G. Shane, *Can. J. Res.*, **B18**, 351 (1940); K. U. Ingold, F. J. Stubbs, and C. N. Hinshelwood, *Proc. Roy. Soc.* (*London*), **A208**, 2854 (1951); K. J. Laidler and B. W. Wojciechowski, *ibid.*, **A260**, 103 (1961).

[4] A. I. Dinzes, A. D. Stepukhovitch, D. A. Kyvatkowskii, and A. V. Frost, *J. Gen. Chem.* (*USSR*) (*Eng. Transl.*), **7**, 1754 (1937).

[5] D. R. Blackmore and C. N. Hinshelwood, *Proc. Roy. Soc.* (*London*), **A268**, 21 (1962); *ibid.*, **A271**, 34 (1963).

Table 55 MECHANISMS FOR THE ETHANE PYROLYSIS IN THE FIRST-ORDER REGION

Elementary reactions	Order		
	Rice and Herzfeld	Küchler and Theile	Quinn
$C_2H_6 \rightarrow 2CH_3$	1	2	1
$CH_3 + C_2H_6 \rightarrow CH_4 + C_2H_5$	2	2	2
$C_2H_5 \rightarrow C_2H_4 + H$	1	1	$\frac{3}{2}$†
$H + C_2H_6 \rightarrow H_2 + C_2H_5$	2	2	2
$H + C_2H_5 \rightarrow C_2H_6$	2	—	—
$2C_2H_5 \rightarrow C_4H_{10}$ and $C_2H_4 + C_2H_6$	—	2	2

† Quinn's suggestion is that the decomposition of C_2H_5 is in the intermediate region between first- and second-order kinetics, so that $v \propto [C_2H_5][C_2H_6]^{1/2}$.

The original mechanism was that of Rice and Herzfeld;[1] it involves first-order initiation and $\beta\mu$ termination. The fact that this mechanism leads to first-order kinetics was shown on page 387 (cf. also Table 54); it is convenient to describe this mechanism using the notation ${}^1\beta\mu_1$, the superscript indicating the order of the initiation reaction and the subscript the overall order. There are several difficulties about this mechanism, of which the most important are:

1. The H and C_2H_5 concentrations to which it gives rise would suggest that the chain-ending step between two ethyl radicals would be much faster than that between H and C_2H_5.
2. The mechanism gives no interpretation of the fact that the rate of the reaction is increased by the addition of foreign gases.
3. The overall activation energy calculated from the values for the elementary reactions is not in good agreement with the experimental value.

The first of these points is particularly compelling, and renders the Rice-Herzfeld mechanism untenable.

Küchler and Theile[2] studied the effect of inert gases on the reaction, and largely on this basis they rejected the Rice-Herzfeld mechanism. They argued that in order to explain the acceleration by inert gases one of the unimolecular reactions must be in its second-order region, and they proposed that this reaction was the initiation reaction. In order for the

[1] F. O. Rice and K. F. Herzfeld, *J. Am. Chem. Soc.*, **56**, 284 (1934).
[2] Küchler and Theile, *loc. cit.*

kinetics to be first order the termination step must be the reaction between two ethyl radicals; it was seen above that this choice is more satisfactory. Rice and Herzfeld[1] later accepted the Küchler-Theile proposals. Laidler and Wojciechowski[2] reexamined the matter and obtained additional evidence for the Küchler-Theile mechanism. They found, for example, that the order changes to $\frac{3}{2}$ at higher temperatures and lower pressures and showed that this is accounted for quantitatively by the Küchler-Theile mechanism, in terms of the fact that the process $H + C_2H_5 \rightarrow C_2H_6$ becomes more important under these conditions. They also showed that the overall activation energy is satisfactorily explained using the best modern values for the individual activation energies. In addition they adduced theoretical arguments in favor of the idea that under the usual experimental conditions the dissociation of ethane should be largely a second-order reaction.

Quinn[3] has studied the kinetics of formation of the minor product methane, and found the rate to be proportional to the *first* power of the ethane concentration; a similar result had previously been obtained by Danby, Spall, Stubbs, and Hinshelwood.[4] If the methane is all formed by the reaction

$$CH_3 + C_2H_6 \rightarrow CH_4 + C_2H_5$$

the kinetic order of its formation must be the same as that for the dissociation of ethane, assuming that every CH_3 radical produces a methane molecule. On this basis Quinn concluded that the initiation reaction must be first order. He accepted the fact that the main chain-ending step must be reaction between two ethyl radicals. In order to explain the overall kinetic order of unity he suggested that under the conditions of the experiments the ethyl radical decomposition is in the region intermediate between first- and second-order kinetics, the rate being approximately proportional to $[C_2H_5][C_2H_6]^{1/2}$. This is equivalent to saying that the ethyl radical is halfway between a β radical and a μ radical. It is easy to show that Quinn's mechanism corresponds to first-order overall kinetics.

More recent work by M. H. Back and Lin[5] has led to the conclusion that the mechanism is closer to that of Quinn than to either of the other mechanisms proposed. Back and Lin confirmed the result that the methane production, and therefore the dissociation of C_2H_6 into $2CH_3$, is first order under the usual pyrolysis conditions, but observed some

[1] F. O. Rice and K. F. Herzfeld, *J. Chem. Phys.*, **7**, 671 (1939).

[2] K. J. Laidler and B. W. Wojciechowski, *Proc. Roy. Soc.* (*London*), **A260,** 91 (1961).

[3] C. P. Quinn, *Proc. Roy. Soc.*, **A275,** 190 (1963); *Trans. Faraday Soc.*, **59,** 2543 (1963).

[4] C. J. Danby, B. C. Spall, F. J. Stubbs, and C. N. Hinshelwood, *Proc. Roy. Soc.* (*London*), **A218,** 450 (1953).

[5] M. H. Back and M. C. Lin, to be published.

falling off of the first-order coefficient at pressures below 100 mm. Their measurements of the rate of production of butane showed that the ethyl radical combination is the main chain-ending step, and a study of the butane production allowed them to determine the order of the dissociation of C_2H_5 radicals into C_2H_4 and H. The rate of this process was found to vary with the total pressure to a power that was 0.35 at higher pressures and lower temperatures, and 0.80 at lower pressures and higher temperatures. The situation is therefore less clear-cut than suggested by Quinn's mechanism, but of the simple proposals his is probably the nearest to the truth.

There are, however, some other complications, and work on other organic pyrolyses seems to lead to different conclusions about the order of the C_2H_6 dissociation and the methyl radical combination. The whole problem has been discussed in detail by Back, Eusuf, and Laidler.[1]

The conclusion, arrived at on the basis of isotope mixing experiments, that the reaction occurs entirely by a chain mechanism raises the question of what type of mechanism is occurring in the presence of nitric oxide. It was suggested by Wojciechowski and Laidler[2] that the effect of nitric oxide is to introduce an additional initiation reaction and an additional chain-ending step, these new processes being predominant by the time that maximal inhibition has been attained. Their mechanism is

$$C_2H_6 + NO \xrightarrow{k_1} C_2H_5 + HNO$$

$$C_2H_5 \xrightarrow{k_2} H + C_2H_4$$

$$H + C_2H_6 \xrightarrow{k_3} C_2H_5 + H_2$$

$$H + NO \xrightarrow{k_4} HNO$$

$$HNO \xrightarrow{k_5} H + NO$$

$$C_2H_5 + HNO \xrightarrow{k_6} C_2H_6 + NO$$

The nitric oxide initiates chains by the first reaction, while chain termination involves the species HNO. This species has now been identified spectroscopically[3] and has a dissociation energy (into H + NO) of about 49 kcal.

Application of the steady-state treatment to this reaction scheme gives rise to

$$\frac{d[C_2H_4]}{dt} = \left(\frac{k_1k_2k_3k_5}{k_4k_6}\right)^{1/2} [C_2H_6] \tag{80}$$

[1] M. H. Back, M. Eusuf, and K. J. Laidler, in S. Patai (ed.), "The Chemistry of Functional Groups," vol. 3, "Chemistry of the Ether Linkage," Interscience Publishers, New York, 1966.

[2] B. W. Wojciechowski and K. J. Laidler, *Can. J. Chem.*, **38**, 1027 (1960); Laidler and Wojciechowski, *Proc. Roy. Soc.* (*London*), **A260**, 103 (1961).

[3] J. L. Bancroft, J. M. Hollas, and D. A. Ramsay, *Can. J. Phys.*, **40**, 322 (1962).

In agreement with experiment, the rate of the fully inhibited reaction is first order in ethane, and there is no dependence on the nitric oxide concentration. When there is partial inhibition, the reaction occurs in part by the uninhibited mechanism and in part by the inhibited one, and there is then a decrease in rate with increasing nitric oxide concentration.

One interesting feature of this mechanism for the inhibited reaction arises from the fact that the ratio k_1k_5/k_4k_6 corresponds to the equilibrium constant for the reaction

$$C_2H_6 \rightarrow C_2H_5 + H$$

If this constant is written as K, the rate expression can be written as

$$v = (Kk_2k_3)^{1/2}[C_2H_6] \tag{81}$$

The quantity Kk_2k_3 in no way depends upon the nitric oxide, and the conclusion is therefore that any inhibitor that can give rise to the same type of mechanism will give rise to the same limiting rate. Propylene actually gives the same inhibition as nitric oxide (although a larger amount is needed), and the suggestion is made that the allyl radical C_3H_5 plays the same role as NO; it initiates chains by hydrogen-atom abstraction,

$$C_2H_6 + C_3H_5 \rightarrow C_2H_5 + C_3H_6$$

and terminates them by the reverse reaction. Propylene in fact undergoes some decomposition when it acts as an inhibitor, and allyl radicals are known to be present.[1]

The photolysis of ethane has been studied by Okabe and McNesby[2] in the vacuum ultraviolet, using xenon radiation (1,470 and 1,295 A). By working with mixtures of C_2H_6 and C_2D_6 and with CH_3CD_3 they have shown that almost all the hydrogen is formed intramolecularly, and preferentially from the same carbon atom. Methane is also formed largely by a molecular reaction. The primary processes are therefore

$$C_2H_6 + \mathbf{h}\nu \rightarrow CH_3CH + H_2$$
$$C_2H_6 + \mathbf{h}\nu \rightarrow CH_4 + CH_2$$

with a smaller contribution from

$$C_2H_6 + \mathbf{h}\nu \rightarrow C_2H_4 + H_2$$

No C_2D_6 is formed in the photolysis of CH_3CD_3, which means that processes such as

$$C_2H_6 + \mathbf{h}\nu \rightarrow 2CH_3$$

[1] K. J. Laidler and . WB. Wojciechowski, *Proc. Roy. Soc.* (*London*), **A259**, 257 (1960).

[2] H. Okabe and J. R. McNesby, *J. Chem. Phys.*, **34**, 668 (1961).

followed by free-radical reactions including

$$2CH_3 \rightarrow C_2H_6$$

are relatively unimportant.

The mercury-photosensitized decomposition of ethane has been investigated by R. A. Back,[1] whose results are consistent with the mechanism

$$\begin{aligned} Hg^*(^3P_1) + C_2H_6 &\rightarrow Hg + C_2H_5 + H \\ H + C_2H_6 &\rightarrow H_2 + C_2H_5 \\ C_2H_5 &\rightarrow H + C_2H_4 \\ 2C_2H_5 &\rightarrow C_4H_{10} \text{ and } C_2H_4 + C_2H_6 \end{aligned}$$

The decomposition of ethane under α radiation has been found[2] to give rise mainly to hydrogen, methane, propane, and butane. The M/N value is approximately 2, and the results may be explained in part by the mechanism

$$\begin{aligned} C_2H_6 &\overset{\alpha}{\rightsquigarrow} C_2H_5 + H \text{ and } 2CH_3 \\ C_2H_5 &\longrightarrow C_2H_4 + H \\ H + C_2H_6 &\longrightarrow H_2 + C_2H_5 \\ CH_3 + C_2H_6 &\longrightarrow CH_4 + C_2H_5 \\ 2C_2H_5 &\longrightarrow C_4H_{10} \text{ and } C_2H_4 + C_2H_6 \end{aligned}$$

The propane must be a secondary product, formed, for example, from butane.

Decompositions of Higher Paraffins. Methane and ethane are by no means typical of the paraffins as far as their decomposition mechanisms are concerned. The main difference arises from the fact that hydrogen atoms play a predominant role in the decompositions of methane and ethane, whereas they are less important in the decompositions of the higher paraffins. In the pyrolysis of butane, for example, hydrogen is a very minor product, the main products being methane, ethane, ethylene, and propylene. On the basis of a study of the overall kinetics the following mechanism[3] has been suggested:

$$\begin{aligned} C_4H_{10} &\rightarrow 2C_2H_5 \\ C_2H_5 + C_4H_{10} &\rightarrow C_2H_6 + C_4H_9 \\ C_4H_9 &\rightarrow CH_3 + C_3H_6 \\ C_4H_9 &\rightarrow C_2H_5 + C_2H_4 \\ CH_3 + C_4H_{10} &\rightarrow CH_4 + C_4H_9 \\ C_2H_5 &\rightarrow C_2H_4 + H \\ H + C_4H_{10} &\rightarrow H_2 + C_4H_9 \\ 2C_2H_5 &\rightarrow C_4H_{10} \text{ or } C_2H_4 + C_2H_6 \end{aligned}$$

[1] R. A. Back, *Can. J. Chem.*, **37,** 1834 (1959).

[2] S. C. Lind and D. C. Bardwell, *Science*, **60,** 364 (1924); W. Mund and W. Koch, *Bull. Soc. Chim. Belg.*, **34,** 121 (1925).

[3] N. H. Sagert and K. J. Laidler, *Can. J. Chem.*, **41,** 838 (1963).

The initiation reaction is believed to be in its first-order region. The abstraction of a hydrogen atom by C_2H_5 is much more rapid, under usual conditions, than the decomposition of C_2H_5; the hydrogen atoms are therefore present only at low concentrations and the C_2H_5 radicals are largely β radicals. First-order initiation and $\beta\beta$ termination lead (Table 54) to first-order kinetics, in agreement with experiment. A similar situation exists with the higher paraffins; propane[1] occupies an intermediate position.

In the inhibited reactions the suggested mechanisms again involve an initial abstraction. For the pyrolysis of butane inhibited by nitric oxide it is proposed[2] that initiation occurs as

$$C_4H_{10} + NO \rightarrow C_4H_9 + HNO$$

and termination by

$$C_2H_5NO + C_2H_5 \rightarrow C_4H_{10} + NO \qquad \text{or} \qquad C_2H_4 + C_2H_6 + NO$$

The propagation reactions are assumed to be the same as in the uninhibited reaction. A molecular reaction has again been found to be unimportant.[3]

The photolyses and radiolyses of the higher paraffins, in so far as they have been studied, involve the same propagation steps as the pyrolyses, and involve molecular reactions in addition. For example, Okabe and Becker[4] studied the photolysis of n-butane using the Xe resonance line at 1,470 A and the Kr line at 1,236 A. By photolyzing mixtures of n-C_4H_{10} and n-C_4D_{10} and measuring the rates of production of the mixed products, they concluded that an appreciable amount of hydrogen is produced by molecular detachment, such as

$$CH_3CH_2CH_2CH_3 + \mathbf{h}\nu \rightarrow CH_3CH{=}CHCH_3 + H_2$$

Methane and ethane are also formed partly by molecular processes, such as

$$CH_3CH_2CH_2CH_3 + \mathbf{h}\nu \rightarrow CH_4 + CH_2{=}CHCH_3$$
$$CH_3CH_2CH_2CH_3 + \mathbf{h}\nu \rightarrow CH_3CH_3 + CH_3CH$$

The formation of ethylene is concluded to be due to the processes

$$CH_3CH_2CH_2CH_3 + \mathbf{h}\nu \rightarrow CH_2{=}CH_2 + CH_3CH_3$$

and $$CH_3CH_2CH_2CH_3 + \mathbf{h}\nu \rightarrow 2C_2H_5$$

followed by $$C_2H_5 \rightarrow C_2H_4 + H$$

and $$2C_2H_5 \rightarrow C_2H_4 + C_2H_6$$

[1] K. J. Laidler, N. H. Sagert, and B. W. Wojciechowski, *Proc. Roy. Soc. (London)*, **A270**, 242 (1962).

[2] Sagert and Laidler, *loc. cit.*

[3] A. Kuppermann and L. Larson, *J. Chem. Phys.*, **33**, 1264 (1960).

[4] H. Okabe and D. A. Becker, *ibid.*, **39**, 2549 (1963); cf. also H. Okabe and J. R. McNesby, *ibid.*, **37**, 1340 (1962) (propane).

The behavior of the higher hydrocarbons, such as *n*-butane, under α radiation is very similar to that of ethane.

Decomposition of Acetaldehyde. Acetaldehyde decomposes both thermally and photochemically, the overall reaction in each case being largely

$$CH_3CHO = CH_4 + CO$$

The propagation steps are undoubtedly the same for the two reactions, namely,

$$CH_3CO \rightarrow CH_3 + CO$$
$$CH_3 + CH_3CHO \rightarrow CH_4 + CH_3CO$$

In spite of a considerable amount of work some of the features of both the thermal and photochemical reactions are still not completely understood.

There was originally some controversy with regard to the order of the thermal reaction, which is largely a homogeneous reaction. This was resolved by Letort[1] who showed that the order with respect to concentration is $\frac{3}{2}$ and the order with respect to time 2. The fact that the order with respect to time is greater than the order with respect to concentration indicates (cf. p. 16) that the reaction is inhibited by its products. The activation energy of the reaction[2] is 47.6 kcal per mole.

The presence of free radicals in the reaction system was detected using the mirror technique by Rice, Johnston, and Evering,[3] but this work was done at higher temperatures than usually employed in studying the kinetics of the reaction (~500°C). Later Burton, Ricci, and Davis,[4] using radioactive lead mirrors, were able to demonstrate the presence of free radicals at 500°C.

Numerous investigations have shown that the decomposition of acetaldehyde can be sensitized by free radicals. Thus Allen and Sickman[5] showed that azomethane, which produces methyl radicals, induces the decomposition of acetaldehyde at 300°C and that chain lengths up to 500 were obtained. Similar results were found using ethylene oxide, diethyl ether, ethyl bromide, ethyl iodide, diacetyl, and other substances as sensitizers.

The influence of foreign gases on the rate of the decomposition has been investigated very fully and throws much light on the mechanism. Certain chemically reactive substances, such as oxygen, iodine, bromine, and hydrogen sulfide, catalyze the reaction homogeneously. This they

[1] M. Letort, Thesis, University of Paris (1937); *J. Chim. Phys.*, **34,** 206 (1937).

[2] Letort, *loc. cit.;* M. Eusuf and K. J. Laidler, *Can. J. Chem.*, **42,** 1851 (1964).

[3] F. O. Rice, W. R. Johnston, and B. L. Evering, *J. Am. Chem. Soc.*, **54,** 3529 (1932).

[4] M. Burton, J. E. Ricci, and T. W. Davis, *ibid.*, **62,** 265 (1940).

[5] A. O. Allen and D. V. Sickman, *ibid.*, **56,** 2031 (1934); D. V. Sickman and A. O. Allen, *ibid.*, 1251.

do by introducing new free-radical processes; the mechanism in the case of the iodine-catalyzed reaction is discussed in the next chapter. Chemically inert substances such as inert gases, carbon dioxide, and ethane bring about a significant decrease in the rate of reaction, and increase the order of the reaction.[1]

The fact that the order of the pyrolysis of acetaldehyde is accurately $\frac{3}{2}$ over a wide range of temperatures and pressures is a good indication that the reaction occurs largely by a free-radical process; if a first-order molecular reaction occurred in addition, there would be a variation in order. The elucidation of the free-radical mechanism has presented considerable difficulty. The original mechanism of Rice and Herzfeld,[2] which has been accepted for some time, is as follows:

(1) $$CH_3CHO \rightarrow CH_3 + CHO$$
(2) $$CH_3 + CH_3CHO \rightarrow CH_4 + CH_3CO$$
(3) $$CH_3CO \rightarrow CH_3 + CO$$
(4) $$2CH_3 \rightarrow C_2H_6$$

This mechanism involves first-order initiation and $\beta\beta$ termination, and therefore leads correctly to three-halves-order kinetics. If the fate of the CHO radical produced in reaction (1) is ignored, the steady-state treatment leads to

$$v = k_2 \left(\frac{k_1}{k_4}\right)^{1/2} [CH_3CHO]^{3/2} \tag{82}$$

The CHO radical in fact leads to the following reactions:

$$CHO \rightarrow CO + H$$
$$H + CH_3CHO \rightarrow H_2 + CH_3CO$$

The effect of this is simply to increase the rate by a factor of 2; i.e.,

$$v = 2k_2 \left(\frac{k_1}{k_4}\right)^{1/2} [CH_3CHO]^{3/2} \tag{83}$$

At first sight this mechanism appears satisfactory, but unfortunately there are certain facts that seem to render it untenable:

1. The mechanism gives no interpretation of the result that inert gases decrease the rate and increase the order. The fact that there is a decrease in rate can only be explained on the basis of the hypothesis that inert gases increase the rate of radical recombination. The chain-ending step cannot, therefore, be a second-order process, but must be either third order or in the intermediate region.

[1] Eusuf and Laidler, *loc. cit.*

[2] F. O. Rice and K. F. Herzfeld, *J. Am. Chem. Soc.*, **56**, 284 (1934).

2. Trenwith[1] has shown that the production of the minor product hydrogen is second order in acetaldehyde. The rate of production of hydrogen must be equal to the rate of the initiation step, which is therefore second order and not first order.

3. The rate of production of ethane, in the chain-ending step, is also second order in acetaldehyde.[2] The rate of the chain-ending step must be equal to that of initiation, which therefore must be second order in acetaldehyde.

The mechanism proposed by Rice and Herzfeld must therefore be modified in two ways; reaction (1) must be in its second-order region, and the termination step (4) must be third order. In order to explain the fact that inert gases have little effect on the initiation reaction Eusuf and Laidler have suggested that the process occurs as

$$CH_3CHO + CH_3CHO \rightarrow CH_3CO + CH_3CHOH$$

followed by

$$CH_3CHOH \rightarrow CH_3CHO + H$$

Initiation therefore only occurs when two acetaldehyde molecules come together, and not when an inert-gas molecule is involved. The conclusion that for the acetaldehyde pyrolysis the methyl radical combination is third order is to be contrasted with the conclusion that in the ethane pyrolysis the reaction $C_2H_6 \rightarrow 2CH_3$ is in its first-order region. The explanation may lie in the different conditions; the situation is by no means clear.

The effect of nitric oxide on the acetaldehyde pyrolysis is somewhat different from that on the ethane decomposition. At high acetaldehyde pressures the effect of the nitric oxide is to accelerate the reaction at all nitric oxide pressures. At lower concentrations of acetaldehyde there is inhibition by small amounts of nitric oxide and acceleration by larger amounts. Eusuf and Laidler[3] studied the behavior in some detail, and explained the results in terms of a mechanism that involves hydrogen abstraction as one of the initiation processes,

$$CH_3CHO + NO \rightarrow CH_3CO + HNO$$

and the reaction

$$CH_3 + CH_2{=}NOH \rightarrow C_2H_6 + NO$$

as one of the termination processes.

Decomposition of Dimethyl Ether. The pyrolysis of dimethyl ether

[1] A. B. Trenwith, *J. Chem. Soc.*, 4426 (1963).
[2] Eusuf and Laidler, *loc. cit.*
[3] Eusuf and Laidler, *Can. J. Chem.*, **42**, 1861 (1964).

was first studied by Askey and Hinshelwood,[1] who concluded that the reaction was first order with respect to the ether. The formation of product could be represented approximately by the equation

$$CH_3OCH_3 \rightarrow CH_4 + CH_2O \rightarrow CH_4 + CO + H_2$$

The formaldehyde builds up in the system, and its concentration goes through a maximum when the reaction is about half complete. The reaction is quite sensitive to the state of the surface of the vessel, and it is somewhat difficult to obtain reproducible results. That the reaction proceeds at least in part by a free-radical mechanism is suggested by the fact that there is considerable inhibition by nitric oxide[2] and by propylene;[3] the mechanisms of the inhibited reactions are considered later. The decomposition has been sensitized by various substances which give rise to methyl radicals. Thus Leermakers[4] photolyzed acetone to produce methyl radicals in the presence of dimethyl ether, and studied the rate of its decomposition.

It was pointed out by Benson[5] that the kinetic data on the dimethyl ether pyrolysis were more consistent with three-halves-order than with first-order kinetics. This conclusion was supported by later experiments of Benson and Jain,[6] Imai and Toyama,[7] and McKenney and Laidler.[8] The activation energy is about 60 kcal per mole.

In spite of a considerable amount of work on this reaction it is difficult to be certain as to the mechanism. McKenney et al. have considered their results and those of other workers and concluded that the reaction is most satisfactorily interpreted in terms of the mechanism

(1) $$M + CH_3OCH_3 \rightarrow CH_3 + CH_3O + M$$
(2) $$CH_3 + CH_3OCH_3 \rightarrow CH_4 + CH_2OCH_3$$
(3) $$CH_2OCH_3 \rightarrow CH_2O + CH_3$$
(4) $$M + CH_3O \rightarrow CH_2O + H + M$$
(5) $$H + CH_3OCH_3 \rightarrow H_2 + CH_2OCH_3$$
(6) $$CH_3 + CH_3 + M \rightarrow C_2H_6 + M$$

M is a third body which in the decomposition of pure ether is the ether

[1] P. J. Askey and C. N. Hinshelwood, *Proc. Roy. Soc. (London)*, **A115**, 215 (1927).

[2] L. A. K. Staveley and C. N. Hinshelwood, *ibid.*, **A154**, 335 (1936); **A159**, 192 (1937); D. J. McKenney, B. W. Wojciechowski, and K. J. Laidler, *Can. J. Chem.*, **41**, 1993 (1963).

[3] F. O. Rice and O. L. Polly, *J. Chem. Phys.*, **6**, 273 (1938); McKenney, Wojciechowski, and Laidler, *loc. cit.*

[4] J. A. Leermakers, *J. Am. Chem. Soc.*, **56**, 1899 (1934).

[5] S. W. Benson, *J. Chem. Phys.*, **25**, 27 (1956).

[6] S. W. Benson and D. V. S. Jain, *ibid.*, **31**, 1008 (1959).

[7] N. Imai and O. Toyama, *Bull. Chem. Soc. Japan*, **34**, 328 (1961).

[8] D. J. McKenney and K. J. Laidler, *Can. J. Chem.*, **41**, 1984 (1963).

molecule itself. This scheme is of the $^2\beta\beta M_{3/2}$ type, and the rate expression is

$$v = k_2 \left(\frac{2k_1}{k_7}\right)^{1/2} [CH_3OCH_3]^{3/2} \tag{84}$$

Other chain-ending steps are believed to play minor roles.

The effect of small amounts of nitric oxide[1] is to reduce the rate to a value of somewhat less than 10 percent of the uninhibited rate, and over a range of nitric oxide concentrations the rate is independent of the nitric oxide concentration. At higher nitric oxide concentrations the rate rises again. The behavior after enough nitric oxide has been added to give maximal inhibition can be represented by the equation

$$v = k[CH_3OCH_3]^{3/2} + k'[CH_3OCH_3][NO] \tag{85}$$

and the activation energies corresponding to k and k' are 64.6 and 43.4 kcal per mole, respectively.

The results are explained in terms of the following mechanism, which is analogous to that suggested for other pyrolyses inhibited by nitric oxide:

(1) $CH_3OCH_3 + NO \rightarrow HNO + CH_2OCH_3$
(2) $CH_2OCH_3 \rightarrow CH_2O + CH_3$
(3) $CH_3 + CH_3OCH_3 \rightarrow CH_4 + CH_2OCH_3$
(4) $M + HNO \rightarrow H + NO + M$
(5) $H + CH_3OCH_3 \rightarrow H_2 + CH_2OCH_3$
(6) $M + CH_3 + NO \rightleftharpoons CH_3NO + M$
(7) $CH_3NO \rightleftharpoons CH_2NOH \rightarrow$ products (HCN, etc.)
(8) $CH_3 + CH_2NOH \rightarrow CH_3CH_2NOH \rightarrow C_2H_6 + NO$

The main difference between this mechanism and that proposed for ethane (p. 404) is that in the ethane pyrolysis hydrogen atoms play a predominant role, so that HNO is present in fairly large concentrations and is involved in chain termination. In the decomposition of dimethyl ether, however, hydrogen atoms are not chain carriers, and their concentration, and that of HNO, will be low. The species HNO will therefore not be involved in chain termination. The methyl radicals, however, are chain carriers, so that their concentration and that of CH_3NO will be fairly high. The suggestion therefore is that CH_3NO, or its isomer formaldoxime ($CH_2{=}NOH$), is the species that is involved in chain termination.

The mechanism proposed gives rise to the rate equation

$$v = k_3 \left(\frac{k_1 k_{-6} k_{-7}}{k_6 k_7 k_8}\right)^{1/2} [CH_3OCH_3]^{3/2} + 2k_1[CH_3OCH_2][NO] \tag{86}$$

[1] McKenney, Wojciechowski, and Laidler, *loc. cit.*

in agreement with experiment. A similar mechanism involving as the initiation reaction

$$CH_3OCH_3 + C_3H_5 \rightarrow CH_2OCH_3 + C_3H_6$$

has been proposed for the inhibition by propylene.

In order to decide whether a molecular reaction is involved in the dimethyl ether pyrolysis, McKenney et al. pyrolyzed a mixture of CH_3OCH_3 and CD_3OCD_3 with enough nitric oxide to ensure maximal inhibition. The CD_3H/CD_4 ratio was found to be essentially the same as in the uninhibited decomposition. The conclusion is therefore that a molecular mechanism is unimportant, the reaction proceeding almost entirely by a chain mechanism.

By an interesting contrast the diethyl ether pyrolysis does have a molecular component.[1] There are two decomposition paths:

$$C_2H_5OC_2H_5 \rightarrow C_2H_5OH + C_2H_4$$

and

$$C_2H_5OC_2H_5 \rightarrow CH_3CHO + C_2H_6$$

The alcohol formation is not inhibited by nitric oxide, and this and other evidence indicates that the first process is molecular. The second, however, occurs by a free-radical mechanism in which the propagation steps are

$$CH_3CHOC_2H_5 \rightarrow CH_3CHO + C_2H_5$$

$$C_2H_5 + CH_3CH_2OC_2H_5 \rightarrow C_2H_6 + CH_3CHOC_2H_5$$

THE HALOGENATION OF ORGANIC COMPOUNDS

During recent years there has been considerable interest in the kinetics and mechanisms of such reactions as the chlorination and bromination of hydrocarbons and other organic substances. These reactions have been studied extensively, attention being paid to both thermal and photochemical processes. The chlorination reactions have recently been reviewed.[2] Discussion will here be confined to some older work on the photochemical bromination of methane,[3] which was important in providing a value for the energy of dissociation of the C—H bond in methane.

The reaction was studied from 150 to 230°C, and the main products

[1] C. J. Danby and G. R. Freeman, *Proc. Roy. Soc.* (*London*), **A245,** 40 (1958); cf. G. R. Freeman, C. J. Danby, and C. N. Hinshelwood, *ibid.*, 28; G. R. Freeman, *ibid.*, 49; K. J. Laidler and D. J. McKenney, *ibid.*, **A278,** 505 (1964).

[2] G. Chiltz, P. Goldfinger, G. Huybrechts, G. Martens, and G. Verbeke, *Chem. Rev.*, **63,** 355 (1963); cf. P. Goldfinger, *Pure Appl. Chem.*, **5,** 423 (1962).

[3] G. B. Kistiakowsky and E. R. Van Artsdalen, *J. Chem. Phys.*, **12,** 469 (1944); cf. H. G. Anderson, G. B. Kistiakowsky, and E. R. Van Artsdalen, *ibid.*, **10,** 305 (1942).

were hydrogen bromide and methyl bromide; in addition, some methylene bromide was formed by the bromination of methyl bromide. The rate of reaction was found to obey the law

$$\frac{d[CH_3Br]}{dt} = \frac{kI^{1/2}[CH_4][Br_2]^{1/2}(1/P)^{1/2}}{1 + m[HBr]/[Br_2]} \tag{87}$$

where k and m are constants, I is the intensity of light absorbed, and P is the total pressure in the system. This law is seen to be closely analogous to that established by Bodenstein and his coworkers for the hydrogen-bromine reaction (cf. p. 357).

The dependence of the rate of reaction on the concentrations, light intensity, and total pressure establishes the mechanism

(1) $Br_2 + \mathbf{h}\nu \rightarrow 2Br$
(2) $Br + CH_4 \rightarrow CH_3 + HBr$
(3) $CH_3 + Br_2 \rightarrow CH_3Br + Br$
(4) $CH_3 + HBr \rightarrow CH_4 + Br$
(5) $Br + Br + M \rightarrow Br_2 + M$

where M is a third body. This scheme gives rise to the law

$$\frac{d[CH_3Br]}{dt} = \frac{ak_2I^{1/2}[CH_4][Br_2]^{1/2}(1/P)^{1/2}}{1 + k_4[HBr]/k_3[Br_2]} \tag{88}$$

where a is a temperature-independent apparatus constant; the $1/P$ term arises from the fact that the rate of reaction (5) is proportional to the total pressure in the system.

The temperature dependence of the constant k in Eq. (87) corresponds to an activation energy of 17.8 kcal, which applies to reaction (2). Since reaction (4) is the reverse of (2), the energy change in the reaction (2) is the difference between the activation energies of the two reactions, i.e.,

$$Br + CH_4 \rightarrow CH_3 + HBr - (17.8 - E_4) \text{ kcal}$$

Together with the thermochemical relationship

$$HBr \rightarrow H + Br - 85.8 \text{ kcal}$$

this result gives rise to

$$CH_4 \rightarrow CH_3 + H - (103.6 - E_4) \text{ kcal}$$

The activation energy of reaction (4) may be presumed to be very small by analogy with the reaction between hydrogen atoms and hydrogen bromide, the activation energy for which is about 1 kcal. This was supported by the fact that the temperature coefficient of the constant m in Eq. (87) was 2 kcal, indicating that $E_4 - E_3$ has this value; since E_3 is almost certainly zero, this gives a value of 2 kcal for E_4. This value was confirmed by the photolysis of mixtures of methyl iodide and hydrogen bromide, the yield of methane, attributable to reaction (4), showing that E_4 is about 0.8 kcal greater than the activation energy of $CH_3 + I_2 \rightarrow CH_3I + I$, which almost certainly has an activation energy of zero.

If the value of 1.5 kcal for E_4 is accepted, the energy of dissociation of methane into a methyl radical and a hydrogen atom is 103.6 − 1.5, i.e., approximately 102 kcal. At 0°K this value becomes 101 kcal.

A similar study of the photobromination of ethane led to a value of 98 kcal for the dissociation energy of the carbon-hydrogen bond.

GAS-PHASE AUTOXIDATIONS[1]

Reactions between molecular oxygen and other substances are referred to as *autoxidations*. Such reactions have certain special features when they occur in the gas phase; these features are a result of the fact that molecular oxygen is a "diradical" in that it has two unpaired electrons. An example of a reaction involving molecular oxygen is

$$H + O_2 \rightarrow HO + O$$

where one atom (H) has given rise to two radicals (O and OH). A reaction of this type, in which there is an increase in the number of radicals, is known as a *branching* reaction. Another example is

$$O + H_2 \rightarrow OH + H$$

When reactions of this type occur to a significant extent, the total number of free radicals in the system may increase rapidly, so that steady-state conditions no longer hold. The reaction therefore occurs with very high velocity, and since energy is released, the result is an explosion.

Branching Chains. A reaction mechanism that involves branching reactions is known as a *branching chain process*. The theory of such reactions was worked out mainly by Semenoff[2] and Hinshelwood.[3] The main principles of such processes can be understood in terms of the following schematic and simplified reaction mechanism:

(1)	$? \rightarrow R$	Chain initiation
(2)	$R \rightarrow \alpha R$	Chain branching
(3)	$R \rightarrow P + R$	Reaction to give final products
(4)	$R \rightarrow ?$	Chain ending at surface
(5)	$R \rightarrow ?$	Chain ending in gas phase

[1] For detailed treatments see G. J. Minkoff and C. F. H. Tipper, "Chemistry of Combustion Reactions," Butterworth & Co. (Publishers), Ltd., London, 1962; J. H. Knox, *Ann. Rept. Chem. Soc.*, **59**, 18 (1962).

[2] N. Semenoff, *Z. Physik*, **46**, 109 (1927); "Chemical Kinetics and Chain Reactions," Clarendon Press, Oxford, 1935.

[3] C. N. Hinshelwood, "Kinetics of Chemical Change," Clarendon Press, Oxford, 1940. (1st edition, 1926.)

The first reaction is the initiation reaction which produces free radicals; an example is the process $H_2 \rightarrow 2H$, which may be the initiation reaction in the hydrogen-oxygen reaction. Reaction (2) is a reaction in which the radical R undergoes an elementary process with the production of more than one radical. Reaction (3) is the reaction by which the product is formed; it may involve reaction between a radical and a molecule, and usually produces a radical in addition to the final product. An example of such a process is

$$HO_2 + H_2 \rightarrow H_2O + OH$$

Reactions (4) and (5) are chain-ending processes; for simplicity they will be treated as first order in R.

The rates of the five reactions may be written as follows:

(1) $$v_i \equiv \frac{d[\mathrm{R}]}{dt} \tag{89}$$

(2) $$v_b \equiv \frac{d[\mathrm{R}]}{dt} = f_b(\alpha - 1)[\mathrm{R}] \tag{90}$$

(3) $$v_p \equiv \frac{d[\mathrm{P}]}{dt} = f_p[\mathrm{R}] \tag{91}$$

(4) $$v_s \equiv \frac{-d[\mathrm{R}]}{dt} = f_s[\mathrm{R}] \tag{92}$$

(5) $$v_g \equiv \frac{-d[\mathrm{R}]}{dt} = f_g[\mathrm{R}] \tag{93}$$

The coefficients f_b, f_p, f_s, and f_g may be functions of concentrations of reactants, products, and other substances present. The steady-state equation for R is

$$v_i + f_b(\alpha - 1)[\mathrm{R}] - (f_s + f_g)[\mathrm{R}] = 0 \tag{94}$$

whence
$$[\mathrm{R}] = \frac{v_i}{f_s + f_g - f_b(\alpha - 1)} \tag{95}$$

The overall rate is therefore

$$v = \frac{d[\mathrm{P}]}{dt} = f_p[\mathrm{R}] \tag{96}$$

$$= \frac{f_p v_i}{f_s + f_g - f_b(\alpha - 1)} \tag{97}$$

In the branching reaction α is greater than unity (it is generally 2), so that the last term in the denominator is positive. It is therefore possible for the denominator to be zero, and under these circumstances the rate in principle becomes infinite. In reality it becomes very large rather than infinite, since steady-state conditions no longer apply when the radical concentration becomes very large. The condition that $f_b(\alpha - 1)$ is equal to $f_s + f_g$ may, nevertheless, be used as a condition for reaching the explosion limit.

The relative magnitudes of $f_s + f_g$ and of $f_b(\alpha - 1)$ depend upon the concentrations of the various species; the denominator of Eq. (97) may therefore be positive under certain conditions, and become zero at certain special values of the concentrations. At any set of concentrations for which $f_s + f_g - f_b(\alpha - 1)$ is equal to zero there is an *explosion limit;* as the concentration is changed, a steady reaction may suddenly change into an explosion. Several examples of such explosion limits are known; the hydrogen-oxygen reaction will now be briefly considered.

Upper and Lower Explosion Limits. Reaction between hydrogen and oxygen occurs at a conveniently measurable velocity between 450 and 600°C; above this range all mixtures explode. If a stoichiometric

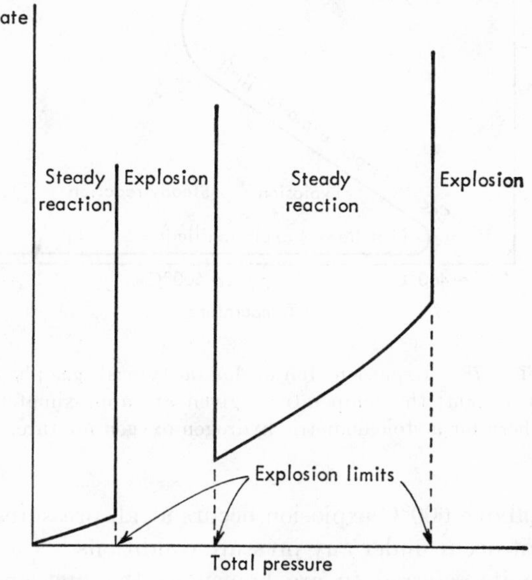

Fig. 77. The rate of the hydrogen-oxygen reaction as a function of the total pressure.

mixture of hydrogen and oxygen is maintained at 550°C and at a pressure of about 2 mm, a steady homogeneous reaction occurs. If the pressure is gradually increased, the rate increases, as shown in Fig. 77. At a certain critical pressure of a few millimeters (the exact value depends on the size and shape of the vessel), the reaction mixture explodes. If the mixture is initially maintained at 200 mm pressure, there is again a steady reaction, and if the pressure is reduced, the mixture explodes at about 100 mm pressure. There is thus, at this temperature, a pressure region within which there is explosion, but above and below which there is steady reaction. This is shown schematically in Fig. 77. The way in which the explosion limits vary with the temperature is shown in Fig. 78. It is

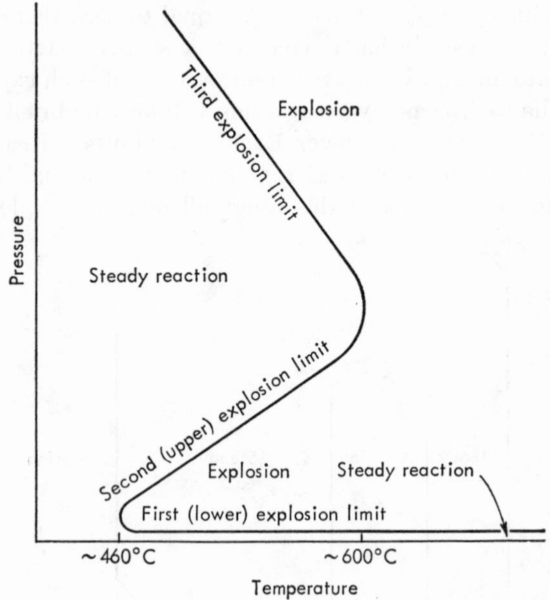

Fig. 78. Explosion limits for a typical gas-phase oxidation; the temperatures given are approximately those for a stoichiometric hydrogen-oxygen mixture.

seen from this figure that above 600°C explosion occurs at all pressures, but below 460°C it does not occur under any pressure conditions.

The two explosion limits referred to are known as the first and second, or lower and upper, limits. There is also a third limit, at still higher pressures. It appears that often this high-pressure limit is simply a thermal limit; the reaction rates become so high that the conditions are no longer isothermal. Such explosions, arising from a rise in temperature of the reaction system, are known as thermal explosions. There is some evidence,[1] however, that in the hydrogen-oxygen system the explosion

[1] C. N. Hinshelwood, *Proc. Roy. Soc.* (*London*), **A188,** 1 (1946).

occurring at the third limit is not a thermal one, but is due to a sudden increase in the concentration of free radicals.

The reason for the first and second limits is as follows. The removal of radicals by recombination may occur primarily at the surface or primarily in the gas phase. At very low pressures the radicals have easy access to the surface and do not meet many gas-phase molecules; surface recombination is therefore predominant. An increase in pressure, however, reduces the rate with which radicals can reach the walls and be removed; f_s therefore decreases and may do so to the extent that $f_s + f_g$ becomes as small as $f_p(\alpha - 1)$; explosion will then occur. At higher pressures, on the other hand, the removal of radicals occurs primarily in the gas phase, since there are sufficient molecules for gas-phase recombination to be important, and to hinder radicals from diffusing to the walls. Under these circumstances a decrease in pressure will lead to a decrease in the rate of removal of radicals; f_g thus decreases, and $f_s + f_g$ may become equal to $f_p(\alpha - 1)$, with resulting explosion.

It follows from the above considerations that since the lower limit depends on surface recombination, it will be very sensitive to the nature of the surface and to its area. Coating the surface with material that inhibits recombination will therefore increase the explodability and result in a lowering of the lower explosion limit. The same effect will be obtained by increasing the size of the vessel; the radicals then have to diffuse further to the walls, and recombine less rapidly. This phenomenon has been observed for several reaction systems, including the hydrogen-oxygen one.[1] Roughly speaking, the product of the pressures of the two gases at the lower limit varies inversely with the square of the diameter of the vessel. Foreign gases also lower the lower limit by hindering diffusion to the surface.

As expected, the second limit is not sensitive to the shape and size of the vessel. Foreign gases contribute to gas-phase deactivation and inhibit explosion, which means that they lower the second limit.

The Hydrogen-Oxygen Reaction. The detailed mechanism for the reaction between hydrogen and oxygen is very complicated, a great many elementary reactions being involved.[2] The main features of the reaction may, however, conveniently be explained in terms of the following simplified mechanism due to Hinshelwood:[3]

[1] C. N. Hinshelwood and E. A. Moelwyn-Hughes, *ibid.*, **A138**, 311 (1932).

[2] For details reference should be made to chap. 1 of the book by Minkoff and Tipper (*op. cit.*) and to the many papers by R. R. Baldwin et al. [e.g., *Trans. Faraday Soc.*, **56**, 80, 103 (1960); **58**, 2410 (1962); "Eighth International Symposium on Combustion," p. 110, The Williams & Wilkins Company, Baltimore, 1962]; cf. also M. A. A. Clyne and B. A. Thrush, *Proc. Roy. Soc.* (*London*), **A275**, 544, 559 (1963).

[3] Hinshelwood, *loc. cit.*

(1)	$H_2 \rightarrow 2H$
(2)	$H + O_2 \rightarrow OH + O$
(3)	$O + H_2 \rightarrow OH + H$
(4)	$H + O_2 + M \rightarrow HO_2 + M$
(5)	$HO_2 \rightarrow$ removal at surface
(6)	$HO_2 + H_2 \rightarrow H_2O + OH$
(7)	$OH + H_2 \rightarrow H_2O + H$
(8)	$H \rightarrow$ removal at surface
(9)	$OH \rightarrow$ removal at surface

Reactions (2) and (3) are both chain-branching processes. Reaction (4) forms the fairly stable radical HO_2 which can diffuse to the surface and be removed; it can also react with hydrogen [reaction (6)], this reaction becoming particularly important at higher pressures in the neighborhood of the third limit. The radicals are supposed not to be removed readily by gas-phase reactions, even at higher pressures; this is a somewhat special feature of this reaction system.

At the lower limit the most important radical-removing processes are (8) and (9); reactions (4), (5), and (6) are unimportant. The steady-state equations at low pressures are, therefore, for hydrogen atoms,

$$v_i - k_2[H][O_2] + k_3[O][H_2] + k_7[OH][H_2] - f_8[H] = 0 \tag{98}$$

for oxygen atoms,

$$k_2[H][O_2] - k_3[O][H_2] = 0 \tag{99}$$

and for hydroxyl radicals,

$$k_2[H][O_2] + k_3[O][H_2] - k_7[OH][H_2] - f_9[OH] = 0 \tag{100}$$

In these equations v_i is the rate of reaction (1), which certainly requires a third body, and f_8 and f_9 are rate coefficients, involving concentration terms, for reactions (8) and (9). Elimination of [H] between these equations gives rise to

$$[OH] = \frac{2v_i k_2[O_2]}{k_7 f_8[H_2] + f_8 f_9 - 2k_2 k_7[H_2][O_2]} \tag{101}$$

The rate of formation of water under these conditions is therefore

$$v = k_7[OH][H_2] = \frac{2v_i k_2 k_7[H_2][O_2]}{k_7 f_8[H_2] + f_8 f_9 - 2k_2 k_7[H_2][O_2]} \tag{102}$$

The sum $k_7 f_8[H_2] + f_8 f_9$ is related to the surface-removal processes; increasing the pressure reduces this sum by inhibiting diffusion of the radicals to the surface, and may therefore cause the denominator to become zero and the rate to become infinite.

At somewhat higher pressures, reactions (8) and (9) become unimportant, as few radicals reach the walls. Reaction (4) is now more important, and the HO_2 radicals formed either are removed at the walls [reaction (5)] or react further by reaction (6). The latter reaction is more important at very high pressures, and its occurrence accounts for the existence of the third limit. The second limit corresponds to the pressure at which the third-order process (4) becomes sufficiently rapid to balance the branching processes.

Oxidation of Hydrocarbons. A large number of investigations have been made of the oxidation of hydrocarbons. These reactions have some features in common with reactions such as that between hydrogen and oxygen, but show one additional feature; under certain circumstances a special type of flame, a "cool" flame, is observed. Such flames have been explained in terms of a hypothesis, due to Semenoff, of *degenerate branching.*

The hydrocarbon oxidations frequently show an induction period, followed by very rapid reaction. Traces of aldehydes are formed during this induction period, which is shortened or eliminated by the addition of aldehydes. Peroxides are also formed in hydrocarbon oxidations, but their formation may be suppressed by coating the vessel with potassium chloride.

The main emitter in cool flames has been found to be electronically excited formaldehyde.[1] The temperature and pressure limits for the occurrence of cool flames and explosions have been studied by Townend and his coworkers;[2] typical results are shown in Fig. 79. For all the hydrocarbons the temperature limits for the flames are about 280 and 410°C. Explosion occurs at higher temperatures and pressures, and it is seen from Fig. 79 that there is an explosion peninsula between two temperature limits; this is to be contrasted with the situation in reactions such as that between hydrogen and oxygen, for which the explosion region is confined by two *pressure* limits.

The main kinetic features of the hydrocarbon oxidations are explained by Semenoff's hypothesis[3] of *degenerate branching.* His proposal was essentially that branching is due not, as in the oxidation of hydrogen, to the reactions of radicals with the fuel or the oxygen, but to the presence of a relatively stable intermediate M that has a lifetime of the order of seconds. M is formed by a nonbranching chain process and is then able to react in two ways: it can produce inert products, or by a branching reaction can produce two radicals that can lead to the formation of more

[1] Cf. A. G. Gaydon, *Quart. Rev. (London)*, **4**, 1 (1950).

[2] D. T. A. Townend, *Chem. Revs.*, **21**, 259 (1937); M. Maccormac and D. T. A. Townend, *J. Chem. Soc.*, 238 (1938).

[3] N. Semenoff, *Z. Physik. Chem.*, **B11**, 464 (1930); cf. N. Semenoff, "Chemical Kinetics and Chain Reactions," p. 68, Clarendon Press, Oxford, 1935.

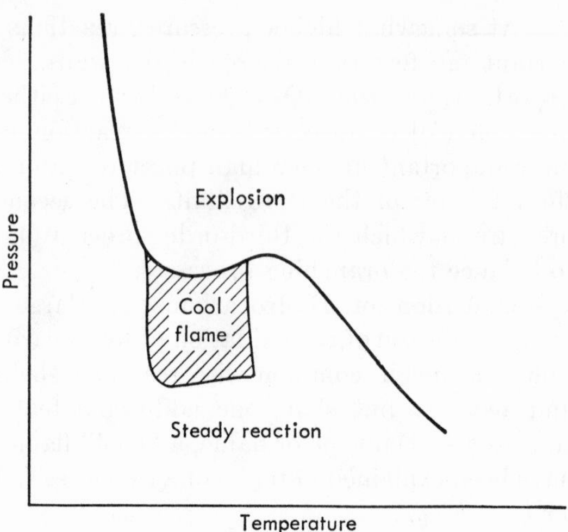

Fig. 79. Explosion and cool-flame limits for a typical hydrocarbon-oxygen reaction.

of the intermediate. This can be represented schematically as

$$M \begin{cases} \rightarrow \text{stable products} \\ \rightarrow \text{free radicals} \end{cases}$$

In the oxidation of methane, for example, it appears[1] that the role of M is played by formaldehyde, which is formed by the reaction

$$CH_3 + O_2 \rightarrow CH_2O + OH$$

The formaldehyde can undergo a nonbranching reaction, such as

$$OH + CH_2O \rightarrow CHO + H_2O$$

or it can undergo a branching process,

$$CH_2O + O_2 \rightarrow CHO + HO_2$$

Both the radicals formed in the latter reaction can regenerate formaldehyde; CHO does so by the reactions

$$CHO + O_2 \rightarrow CO + HO_2$$
$$HO_2 + CH_4 \rightarrow H_2O_2 + CH_3$$
$$CH_3 + O_2 \rightarrow CH_2O + OH$$

and HO_2 by the second and third of the above reactions.

[1] R. G. W. Norrish, *Proc. Roy. Soc.* (*London*), **A150,** 36 (1935); L. V. Karmilova, N. S. Enikolopyan, A. B. Nalbandyan, and N. N. Semenoff, *Zhr. fiz. Khim.*, **34,** 1176 (1960).

Since intermediate M has a fairly long life, branching is delayed; this explains the slow increase in the number of radicals, which gives rise to an induction period. In the hydrocarbon oxidations the number of radicals increases so slowly that before explosion can occur, the effect of the removal of radicals is significant, and the reaction has become slower. The cool flames are in fact degenerate explosions in which the rate is high, but not as high as in an ordinary explosion. The true explosions that occur with hydrocarbons are believed to be of the thermal type, due to self-heating.[1]

The explanation of the upper and lower temperature limits of explosion is as follows. The lower limit occurs because degenerate branching becomes less important as the temperature is lowered and eventually becomes too slow to allow the number of radicals to increase. The upper limit is due to the existence of some chain-breaking process which competes with the delayed branching, and becomes relatively more important as the temperature is raised. It is because of this that rates of oxidation have negative temperature coefficients under certain conditions.

Detailed mechanisms for the oxidations of hydrocarbons and related substances have been proposed in a number of cases. For the methane oxidation, for example, Karmilova et al.[2] have proposed the following mechanism:

(1) $CH_4 + O_2 \rightarrow HO_2 + CH_3$

(2) $CH_3 + O_2 \rightarrow CH_2O + OH$

(3) $OH + CH_4 \rightarrow CH_3 + H_2O$

(4) $OH + CH_2O \rightarrow CHO + H_2O$

(5) $CH_2O + O_2 \rightarrow CHO + HO_2$

(6) $CHO + O_2 \rightarrow CO + HO_2$

(7) $HO_2 + CH_4 \rightarrow CH_3 + H_2O_2$

(8) $HO_2 + CH_2O \rightarrow CHO + H_2O_2$

(9) $OH \rightarrow$ removal at walls

This mechanism predicts that the reaction should be second order in methane and first order in oxygen, in reasonable agreement with experiment. It also accounts in a satisfactory quantitative way for the acceleration of the reaction during the induction period, and for many other features of the reaction.

During recent years a number of investigations of oxidation reactions have been carried out in shock tubes. Sometimes the kinetics under these conditions are simpler than those of the reaction at lower temperatures; the reason is that because of the higher rates the slow degenerate-

[1] R. G. W. Norrish and S. G. Foord, *Proc. Roy. Soc.* (*London*), **A157,** 503 (1936).

[2] *Loc. cit.*

branching reactions do not occur. Kistiakowsky[1] has studied the oxidation of methane and of acetylene using the shock-tube technique.

POLYMERIZATION REACTIONS

There are several types of polymerization reactions. Sometimes a molecule of water is eliminated each time a pair of molecules combines, and in such cases the polymerization is said to be of the *condensation* type. In other cases there is simple addition of molecules to each other, and the process is then known as *addition* polymerization.

Gas-phase polymerizations occur by complex mechanisms that either may be of the molecular type or may involve free-radical processes. The kinetic features of these two types of reactions will now be considered. In solution or in the liquid phase, polymerizations frequently occur by ionic mechanisms, and these will be discussed in Chap. 10.

Molecular Mechanisms. An example of a polymerization occurring by a molecular mechanism is the reaction between a glycol and a dicarboxylic acid; with ethylene glycol and succinic acid the mechanism is

(1) $HOOC(CH_2)_2COOH + HO(CH_2)_2OH \rightarrow HOOC(CH_2)_2COO(CH_2)_2OH + H_2O$

(2) $HOOC(CH_2)_2COO(CH_2)_2OH + HOOC(CH_2)_2COOH \rightarrow HOOC(CH_2)_2COO(CH_2)_2OOC(CH_2)_2COOH + H_2O$

(3) $HOOC(CH_2)_2COO(CH_2)_2OOC(CH_2)_2COOH + HO(CH_2)_2OH \rightarrow HOOC(CH_2)_2COO(CH_2)_2OOC(CH_2)_2COO(CH_2)_2OH + H_2O$

and so on. If the rate of each reaction is simply proportional to the concentrations of glycol and acid (this will be the case in the presence of a constant amount of acid catalyst), the treatment is as follows. Let c be the concentration, at any time t, of functional groups (either OH or COOH); then

$$-\frac{dc}{dt} = kc^2 \tag{103}$$

For simplicity the rate constant k is assumed to be the same for each reaction. This equation, using the boundary condition $c = c_0$ when $t = 0$, integrates to

$$\frac{c_0 - c}{cc_0} = kt \tag{104}$$

If f is the fraction of functional groups that are esterified at time t,

$$f = \frac{c_0 - c}{c_0} \tag{105}$$

[1] For a general account see G. B. Kistiakowsky, *Proc. Chem. Soc.*, 289 (1962).

and elimination of c gives

$$\frac{1}{1-f} - 1 = c_0kt \tag{106}$$

A plot of $1/(1-f)$ against t should therefore be linear, provided that the assumption of constant k is correct. Flory[1] has verified this relationship for a number of reactions.

A more general treatment of the kinetics of molecular polymerization has been given by Dostal and Raff.[2] The individual reactions occurring may all be written as

$$M_m + M_n \rightarrow M_{m+n}$$

where M_m and M_n represent a chain containing m and n monomers, respectively; m and n can have any value from unity upward. The monomer M_1 may be removed by reaction with itself and with any other molecule present; its net rate of disappearance is therefore

$$-\frac{d[M_1]}{dt} = k[M_1]^2 + k[M_1][M_2] + \cdots \tag{107}$$

This may be written as

$$\frac{d[M_1]}{dt} = -k[M_1]\sum_{n=1}^{\infty}[M_n] \tag{108}$$

A molecule containing two monomer molecules may be formed by reaction between two monomers, and disappears by reaction with a molecule of any length; the net rate of production of dimer is therefore

$$\frac{d[M_2]}{dt} = \tfrac{1}{2}k[M_1]^2 - k[M_2]\sum_{n=1}^{\infty}[M_n] \tag{109}$$

The factor ½ is required because the formation of one dimer requires the reaction of two monomers.

The net rate of formation of n-mers is given in general by

$$\frac{d[M_n]}{dt} = \tfrac{1}{2}k\sum_{s=1}^{s-n-1}[M_s][M_{n-s}] - k[M_n]\sum_{s=1}^{\infty}[M_n] \tag{110}$$

Addition of all these equations gives

$$\frac{d\sum_{n=1}^{\infty}[M_n]}{dt} = -\tfrac{1}{2}k\left(\sum_{n=1}^{\infty}[M_n]\right)^2 \tag{111}$$

[1] P. J. Flory, *J. Am. Chem. Soc.*, **61,** 3334 (1939).

[2] H. Dostal and R. Raff, *Monatsch.*, **68,** 188 (1936); *Z. Physik. Chem.*, **B32,** 11 (1936).

If $[M_1]_0$ represents the total concentration of monomers at the beginning of the reaction, and $\sum_{n=1}^{\infty} [M_n]$ that of all the molecules at time t, the fraction of reaction that has occurred at time t is given by

$$f = \frac{[M_n]_0 - \sum_{n=1}^{\infty} [M_n]}{[M_1]_0} \tag{112}$$

Equations (111) and (112) give rise to

$$\frac{df}{dt} = \tfrac{1}{2}[M_1]_0 k(1 - f)^2 \tag{113}$$

which integrates to

$$f = \frac{[M_1]_0 kt}{2 + [M_1]_0 kt} \tag{114}$$

This is equivalent to Eq. (106). The concentration of n-mers is given by

$$[M_n] = [M_1]_0 f^{n-1}(1 - f)^2 \tag{115}$$

This equation is useful in that it gives the distribution of polymers corresponding to any extent of reaction.

Free-radical Mechanisms.[1] Olefinic substances, such as ethylene and styrene, usually polymerize by free-radical mechanisms. The reactions sometimes occur in the gas phase and sometimes in solution or in the liquid phase; the free-radical processes are similar in all cases. The nature of the initiation reaction varies with the conditions. Sometimes, as with ethylene, the initiation may be of the thermal type, the molecule forming the diradical —CH_2CH_2—. In other cases, as with vinyl acetate, light of certain frequencies favors the production of radicals and causes the substance to polymerize at ordinary temperatures.[2] Polymerization can also be induced by the introduction of free radicals into a monomer; hydrogen atoms and methyl radicals, for example, bring about the polymerization of vinyl acetate.[3] Substances such as oxygen and peroxides are also found to catalyze polymerization, and are known as sensitizers; peroxides, for example, readily produce radicals by breaking the O—O bond. In such cases the propagation and termination steps are of the same character, and a general scheme of reactions will be considered, without the nature of the initiating reaction being at first specified.

[1] Cf. J. Bevington, "Radical Polymerization," Academic Press Inc., New York, 1961.

[2] H. W. Melville, *J. Chem. Soc.*, 274 (1947).

[3] T. T. Jones and H. W. Melville, *Proc. Roy. Soc.* (*London*), **A187,** 19 (1946); see also G. V. Schultz and G. Wittig. *Naturwissenschaften,* **27,** 387, 659 (1939).

The type of propagation reaction that is involved is the addition of a radical to a double bond:

$$\mathrm{R + R'CH{=}CH_2 \rightarrow R'CH{-}CH_2R}$$

This produces another radical, which in turn can add on to a double bond. This process can continue with the formation of large radicals, which finally react with another radical to give a molecule.

The general reaction scheme for this type of polymerization reaction can be represented as follows:

(1)	$? \rightarrow \mathrm{R_1}$	Initiation
(2)	$\mathrm{R_1 + M \rightarrow R_2}$	Chain propagation
(3)	$\mathrm{R_2 + M \rightarrow R_3}$	
	$\cdots\cdots\cdots$	
(4)	$\mathrm{R_{n-1} + M \rightarrow R_n}$	
(5)	$\mathrm{R_n + R_m \rightarrow M_{n+m}}$	Termination

Here M represents a monomer molecule, $\mathrm{R_1}$ a free radical produced in the initiation step, and $\mathrm{R_n}$ a radical consisting of $\mathrm{R_1}$ added to a chain of $(n-1)$ monomer molecules. The rate of the initial formation of $\mathrm{R_1}$ will be written as v_i, and the rate constants for the propagation reactions, all assumed to be the same, will be written as k_p. Termination can involve any two radicals (including identical ones), and the rate constant for termination will be written as k_t.

Application of the steady-state treatment leads to a set of equations. The first of these, applying to $\mathrm{R_1}$, is

$$v_i - k_p[\mathrm{R_1}][\mathrm{M}] - k_t[\mathrm{R_1}]([\mathrm{R_1}] + [\mathrm{R_2}] + \cdots) = 0$$

The final term is for the removal of radical $\mathrm{R_1}$ by reaction with $\mathrm{R_1}$, $\mathrm{R_2}$, $\mathrm{R_3}$, etc.; the equation may be written as

$$v_i - k_p[\mathrm{R_1}][\mathrm{M}] - k_t[\mathrm{R_1}] \sum_{n=1}^{\infty} [\mathrm{R_n}] = 0 \tag{116}$$

Similarly for $\mathrm{R_2}$,

$$k_p[\mathrm{R_1}][\mathrm{M}] - k_p[\mathrm{R_2}][\mathrm{M}] - k_t[\mathrm{R_2}] \sum_{n=1}^{\infty} [\mathrm{R_n}] = 0 \tag{117}$$

In general, for $\mathrm{R_n}$,

$$k_p[\mathrm{R_{n-1}}][\mathrm{M}] - k_p[\mathrm{R_n}][\mathrm{M}] - k_t[\mathrm{R_n}] \sum_{n=1}^{\infty} [\mathrm{R_n}] = 0 \tag{118}$$

There is an infinite number of such equations, and the sum of all of them is[1]

$$v_i - k_t \left(\sum_{n=1}^{\infty} [\mathrm{R}_n] \right)^2 = 0 \tag{119}$$

whence

$$\sum_{n=1}^{\infty} [\mathrm{R}_n] = \left(\frac{v_i}{k_t} \right)^{1/2} \tag{120}$$

The rate of disappearance of monomer is

$$-\frac{d[\mathrm{M}]}{dt} = k_p[\mathrm{M}] \sum_{n=1}^{\infty} [\mathrm{R}_n] \tag{121}$$

$$= k_p \left(\frac{v_i}{k_t} \right)^{1/2} [\mathrm{M}] \tag{122}$$

Various special cases of this equation, corresponding to different mechanisms of initiation, will now be considered and discussed with reference to the experimental data.

In a purely *thermal* polymerization the initiation process may be a second-order reaction between monomer molecules; in this case

$$v_i = k_i[\mathrm{M}]^2 \tag{123}$$

Equation (122) therefore becomes

$$-\frac{d[\mathrm{M}]}{dt} = k_p \left(\frac{k_i}{k_t} \right)^{1/2} [\mathrm{M}]^2 \tag{124}$$

so that the overall order is the second. This law is obeyed in the polymerization of styrene in the gas phase[2] and in various solvents.[3]

If initiation involves a second-order reaction between a catalyst C and the monomer, the rate of initiation is

$$v_i = k_i[\mathrm{C}][\mathrm{M}] \tag{125}$$

Introduction of this into Eq. (122) gives for the rate of disappearance of the monomer,

$$-\frac{d[\mathrm{M}]}{dt} = k_p \left(\frac{k_i}{k_t} \right)^{1/2} [\mathrm{M}]^{3/2}[\mathrm{C}]^{1/2} \tag{126}$$

[1] It should be noted that this equation simply states that the rate of initiation is equal to the sum of the rates of all the termination processes; this must be true if steady-state conditions apply.

[2] Cf. H. M. Hulburt, R. A. Harman, A. V. Tobolsky, and H. Eyring, *Ann. N.Y. Acad. Sci.*, **44**, 371 (1943).

[3] G. V. Schultz and E. Husemann, *Z. Physik. Chem.*, **B34**, 187 (1936); **B43**, 385 (1939); H. Suess, K. Pilch, and R. Rudorfer, *ibid.*, **A179**, 361 (1937); H. Suess and A. Springer, *ibid.*, **A181**, 81 (1937); G. V. Schultz, *Z. Elektrochem.*, **47**, 265 (1941).

This law is obeyed accurately in the polymerization of styrene[1] and vinyl acetate,[2] catalyzed by benzoyl peroxide.

Another possibility with respect to a catalytic or sensitized initiation is that the initiating reaction is first order with respect to the catalyst and zero order with respect to the monomer; i.e., the initiation rate is

$$v_i = k_i[\mathrm{C}] \tag{127}$$

The rate of polymerization is then

$$-\frac{d[\mathrm{M}]}{dt} = k_p\left(\frac{k_i}{k_t}\right)^{1/2}[\mathrm{M}][\mathrm{C}]^{1/2} \tag{128}$$

This law is accurately followed by the polymerization of *d-sec*-butyl α-chloroacrylate, sensitized by benzoyl peroxide.[3]

In *photochemical* initiation the rate of the initiating step is given by

$$v_i = I \tag{129}$$

where I is the intensity of light absorbed in mole-quanta per second. The rate of polymerization is then

$$-\frac{d[\mathrm{M}]}{dt} = k_p\left(\frac{I}{k_i}\right)^{1/2}[\mathrm{M}] \tag{130}$$

Such a law is obeyed in the polymerization of ethylene induced by wavelengths of about 1,860 A.[4]

Rates of the Elementary Reactions.[5] It is of great importance for an understanding of the mechanisms of polymerizations to have knowledge of the rate constants of the various elementary processes. This presents little difficulty as far as the initiation reaction is concerned, the procedure being somewhat similar to that used by Bodenstein (p. 359) for the hydrogen-bromine reaction. The quantities that have to be measured are the rate of the overall process and the value of the kinetic chain length, γ, which, as previously, is defined as the ratio of the overall rate to the rate of the initial step,

$$\gamma = \frac{-d[\mathrm{M}]/dt}{v_i} \tag{131}$$

The kinetic chain length can, for the above mechanism, be identified with the number of repeating units in the polymer chain, a quantity that can be

[1] Schultz and Husemann, *Z. Physik. Chem.*, **B43**, 385 (1939); W. Simpson and R. N. Haward, *Trans. Faraday Soc.*, **47**, 226 (1951).

[2] A. C. Cuthbertson, G. Gee, and E. K. Rideal, *Proc. Roy. Soc.* (*London*), **A170**, 300 (1939).

[3] C. C. Price and R. W. Kell, *J. Am. Chem. Soc.*, **63**, 2798 (1941).

[4] H. S. Taylor and H. J. Emeléus, *ibid.*, **53**, 562, 3370 (1931); R. D. McDonald and R. G. W. Norrish, *Proc. Roy. Soc.* (*London*), **A157**, 480 (1936).

[5] For a review see G. M. Burnett, *Quart. Rev.* (*London*), **4**, 292 (1950).

determined in various ways. The rate v_i of the initiating reaction, and hence its rate constant, can therefore be obtained using the above equation.

This procedure has been applied to some examples, and the results are of interest. The benzoyl peroxide–catalyzed polymerization of styrene has been seen to obey the law

$$-\frac{d[\mathrm{M}]}{dt} = k[\mathrm{M}]^{3/2}[\mathrm{C}]^{1/2} \tag{132}$$

the overall frequency factor being about 10^{11}, and the activation energy between 23 and 25 kcal. The overall constant k is equal to $k_p(k_i/k_t)^{1/2}$, and the chain length is therefore equal to

$$\gamma = \frac{k_p}{(k_i k_t)^{1/2}} \frac{[\mathrm{M}]^{1/2}}{[\mathrm{C}]^{1/2}} \tag{133}$$

These relations lead to

$$\frac{1}{\gamma}\frac{d[\mathrm{M}]}{dt} = k_i[\mathrm{M}][\mathrm{C}] = v_i \tag{134}$$

The frequency factor corresponding to k_i is found to be 10^{12}, and the activation energy to be about 29 kcal;[1] similar results have been found by an alternative method, employing benzoquinone as inhibitor.[2] The frequency factor obtained is seen to be of the order usually associated with a bimolecular reaction.

Application of the same procedure to the data of Schultz and Husemann,[3] and of Foord,[4] on the uncatalyzed polymerization of styrene gives the result that the activation energy is 23 to 28 kcal, and the frequency factor between 10^4 and 10^6. This would imply that in the catalyzed reaction the catalyst has acted not by altering the energy of activation, which has remained practically constant, but by raising the frequency factor from an abnormally low value to a normal value. On the other hand, Bamford and Dewar[5] obtained an activation energy of 37 kcal, and a frequency factor of 1.23×10^{10} for the initiation process; this frequency factor is not abnormally small, and the peroxide catalyst would be concluded to act by reducing the activation energy and not by increasing the frequency factor.

The assignment of values to the rates of propagation and termination is considerably more difficult; some progress has, however, been made in this direction by following a procedure devised by Melville.[6] The overall

[1] Hulburt, Harman, Tobolsky, and Eyring, *loc. cit.*
[2] S. G. Foord, *J. Chem. Soc.*, 48 (1940).
[3] Schultz and Husemann, *loc. cit.*
[4] Foord, *loc. cit.*
[5] C. H. Bamford and M. J. S. Dewar, *Proc. Roy. Soc. (London)*, **A192**, 309 (1948).
[6] Melville, *loc. cit.;* G. M. Burnett and H. W. Melville, *Nature*, **156**, 661 (1945).

rate constant of a polymerization has been seen to be equal to $k_p(k_i/k_t)^{1/2}$; the evaluation of k_i, described previously, therefore gives the value of $k_p/k_t^{1/2}$ but does not allow a separation of the constants. Melville pointed out that a further relationship can be obtained if a measurement could be made of the total stationary concentration of the free radicals R_n which are concerned in the chain-propagating steps; thus the overall rate of reaction is [cf. Eq. (121)]

$$-\frac{d[\mathrm{M}]}{dt} = k_p[\mathrm{M}] \sum_{n=1}^{\infty} [\mathrm{R}_n] \tag{135}$$

so that, if $\sum_{n=1}^{\infty} [\mathrm{R}_n]$ is known, k_p can be determined at once from the overall rate. The method used for determining this concentration was to measure the mean lifetime τ of the active radicals. The stationary-state expression for active radicals is

$$\text{Rate of formation of radicals} = \text{rate of removal of radicals}$$

$$= \sum_{n=1}^{\infty} \frac{[\mathrm{R}_n]}{\tau} \tag{136}$$

so that if τ and the rate of formation of radicals are known, the concentration $\sum_{n=1}^{\infty} [\mathrm{R}_n]$ can be calculated. The rate of formation of radicals can be determined in various ways; one involves the use of inhibitors, and the rate can also be determined from the number of quanta absorbed in photochemical polymerizations, assuming that each absorbed photon starts a chain. The mean life τ was measured using the sector method, described in Chap. 4.

This procedure has been applied, for example, to the polymerization of vinyl acetate by Burnett and Melville[1] and by Bartlett and Swain;[2] unfortunately the results are somewhat in disagreement. By making measurements at a number of temperatures, the activation energy of the propagating reactions was found to be about 4 kcal, and the frequency factor to be about 10^5; this again indicates that there is a restriction to reaction. The rate constant of the termination reaction was found from k_i, k_p, and the overall rate; an activation energy of zero was found, and a frequency factor of approximately 10^9. This value is about what would be expected, on entropy grounds, for a reaction between molecules of some complexity. It was also possible to show, by changing the experi-

[1] *Ibid.*

[2] P. D. Bartlett and C. G. Swain, *J. Am. Chem. Soc.*, **67**, 2273 (1945); **68**, 2381 (1946).

mental conditions so as to alter the chain length, that the rate constant for propagation is practically independent of the mean chain length, and therefore is independent of the size of the reacting molecules and radicals.

PROBLEMS

1. Using Eq. (2) and the following values for the activation energies:

$$E_1 = 45.2 \text{ kcal} \qquad E_2 = 17.6 \text{ kcal} \qquad E_3 = 1.2 \text{ kcal}$$
$$E_4 = 1.2 \text{ kcal} \qquad E_5 = 0 \text{ kcal}$$

calculate the activation energy of the hydrogen-bromine reaction (**a**) at the beginning of the reaction, (**b**) in the presence of a large excess of hydrogen bromide.

2. On the basis of Quinn's mechanism for the ethane pyrolysis (Table 55, p. 402) obtain an expression for the first-order rate constant in terms of the individual rate constants.

3. Confirm that the mechanism given on page 404 leads to Eq. (80) for the overall rate of pyrolysis of ethane, maximally inhibited by nitric oxide.

4. Derive Eq. (83) for the acetaldehyde pyrolysis on the basis of the Rice-Herzfeld mechanism (p. 409), including the decomposition of the radical CHO.

5. Confirm that the mechanism given on page 411 for the pyrolysis of dimethyl ether leads to Eq. (84).

6. Confirm that the scheme on page 412 for the decomposition of dimethyl ether, inhibited by nitric oxide, leads to Eq. (86). (*Note:* The breakdown of CH_2NOH, which is slow, should be ignored.)

7. The photochemical chlorination of chloroform, $CHCl_3 + Cl_2 \rightarrow CCl_4 + HCl$, follows the rate equation

$$\frac{d[CCl_4]}{dt} = kI^{1/2}[Cl_2]^{1/2}[CHCl_3]$$

where I is the intensity of light absorbed. Devise a reaction mechanism that is consistent with this result.

8. A very instructive problem in connection with reaction mechanisms. and one that may be repeated an indefinite number of times, is the following:

Select, from the journals published within the last year, a paper dealing with a complex reaction in the gas phase. Care should be taken to choose a paper that is not of a routine character and that leads to significant conclusions.

Prepare a critical review of the paper, in which you outline the object of the work, the results obtained, and the relationship to other work in the field. Comment on the methods employed and on the expected errors in the results obtained. If a specific mechanism has been proposed, check its consistency, and comment on its uniqueness; see if any alternative mechanism seems to be preferable.

Suggest any further investigations that might profitably be carried out on the same problem.

chapter

Homogeneous Catalysis 9

By THE EARLY part of the last century there had been discovered a number of reactions whose rates were influenced by the presence of a substance that remained unchanged at the end of the process. These reactions include the conversion of starch into sugars, the rate of which was influenced by acids; the decomposition of alcohols and of hydrogen peroxide, influenced by metallic surfaces; and the formation of ammonia in the presence of spongy platinum. Such reactions were classified by Berzelius[1] in 1836 under the collective title of *catalyzed processes* and were regarded by him as taking place under the influence of a *catalytic force.* The idea of a catalytic force has not proved fruitful, but the term *catalysis* is still employed to describe the influence on reactions of substances that emerge from the process unchanged. Substances that decrease the rate of reaction are usually referred to as *negative catalysts,* or as *inhibitors.*[2]

[1] J. J. Berzelius, *Jahresber. Chem.*, **15**, 237 (1836).

[2] For a general account of catalysis and inhibition see P. G. Ashmore, "Catalysis and Inhibition of Chemical Reactions," Butterworth & Co. (Publishers), Ltd., London, 1963.

It is convenient to classify catalyzed reactions according to whether they occur homogeneously (in a single phase) or heterogeneously (at an interface between two phases). An important group of heterogeneous reactions, those catalyzed by solid surfaces, has been considered in Chap. 6. This chapter is concerned with some of the general principles of catalysis, and deals in particular with homogeneous reactions, both in the gas phase and in solution.

In view of the large number of processes that have been described as "catalyzed," it is appropriate to consider the various definitions of catalysis that have been proposed from time to time. An early definition due to Ostwald[1] was that a catalyst is "any substance that alters the velocity of a chemical reaction without modification of the energy factors of the reaction." Later he proposed an alternative definition[2] which has been widely quoted: "A catalyst is any substance that alters the velocity of a chemical reaction without appearing in the end product of the reaction." A slightly different way of saying the same thing is to say that "a catalyst alters the velocity of a chemical reaction and is both a reactant and a product of the reaction." A definition due to Bell[3] is very similar: "A substance is said to be a catalyst for a reaction when its concentration occurs in the velocity expression to a higher power than it does in the stoichiometric equation." All these definitions were intended to exclude from the category of catalysts substances that accelerated the rate of a reaction by entering into reaction and in this way disturbing the position of equilibrium; such substances are reactants in the ordinary sense. It is to be noted that in the definitions of catalysis there is no reference to the fact that a small amount of a catalyst has a large effect on the rate; this is frequently the case, but is not an essential characteristic of a catalyst.

Although by definition the amount of catalyst should be unchanged at the end of the reaction, it does not follow that the catalyst does not enter into chemical reaction as the reaction proceeds. Indeed, as knowledge of catalytic processes has developed, it has become clear that during the process the catalyst invariably enters into chemical union; in the case of one reacting substance, a complex may be formed between this (known as the substrate) and the catalyst, whereas in the case of more than one substrate the complex may involve one or more molecules of the substrate combined with the catalyst. These complexes are formed as intermediates only and decompose to give the products of the reaction, with the regeneration of the catalyst molecule. When, for example, a reaction is catalyzed by hydrogen ions, an intermediate complex, involv-

[1] W. Ostwald, *Chem. Betrachtungen*, *Aula* No. 1, 1895.

[2] W. Ostwald, *Physik. Z.*, **3**, 313 (1902).

[3] R. P. Bell, "Acid-Base Catalysis," Clarendon Press, Oxford, 1941.

ing the substrate and a hydrogen ion, is formed, and this later reacts further (e.g., with the solvent) with the liberation of the ion and the formation of the products of the reaction.

Since the catalyst is unchanged at the end of the reaction, it gives no energy to the system; according to thermodynamics it can therefore have no influence on the position of equilibrium. It follows from this that since the equilibrium constant K is the ratio of the rate constants in the forward and reverse directions, i.e., $K = k_1/k_{-1}$, a catalyst must influence the forward and reverse rates in the same proportion. This conclusion has been verified experimentally in a number of instances.[1]

It is frequently found that an extremely small amount of a catalyst will cause a considerable increase in the rate of a reaction; thus colloidal palladium at a concentration of 1 gram atom in 10^8 liters will cause hydrogen peroxide to decompose at a measurable rate. An idea of the effectiveness of a catalyst is sometimes given by expressing its turnover number, which is the number of molecules of substrate decomposed per minute by one molecule of the catalyst; for example the enzyme catalase has, under certain conditions, a turnover number of 5,000,000 for the decomposition of hydrogen peroxide. The turnover number generally varies with the temperature and with the concentration of substrate, so that it is not a particularly useful quantity in kinetic work, in which the appropriate rate coefficient is used.

Very often, especially when the reaction does not involve chains, the rate of a catalyzed reaction is directly proportional to the concentration of the catalyst; i.e.,

$$v = F[C] \tag{1}$$

where $[C]$ represents the concentration of the catalyst, and F is a function of the concentration of the substrate. It has been seen in Chap. 6 that this law is usually obeyed in reactions on surfaces, the rate being directly proportional to the surface area, i.e., to the concentration of surface sites in the system. If Eq. (1) were obeyed exactly, the rate of reaction in the absence of the catalyst would be zero. Many examples are known for which it is necessary to introduce an additional term which is independent of the catalyst concentration, viz.,

$$v = F[C] + F' \tag{2}$$

so that at zero concentration of the catalyst the reaction occurs with the velocity F'.

[1] See, for example, J. H. van't Hoff, "Vorlesungen über theoretische und physikalische Chemie," vol. I, "Die chemische Dynamik," Brunswick, 1898 [English translation by R. A. Lehrfeld, pp. 204, 214, Edward Arnold (Publishers) Ltd., London]; S. H. Maron and V. K. La Mer, *J. Am. Chem. Soc.*, **61**, 2018 (1939); R. A. Alberty, *Advan. Enzymol.*, **17**, 1 (1955); R. A. Alberty and R. M. Bock, *J. Am. Chem. Soc.*, **75**, 1921 (1953).

MECHANISMS OF CATALYSIS

A number of reaction schemes for catalyzed reactions have been worked out in individual cases. The main feature of such schemes is that an intermediate complex is formed between the catalyst and at least one of the substrate molecules, and that this complex undergoes subsequent reactions. In the simplest type of catalyzed reaction, involving only one substrate, the substrate and the catalyst form a complex, which subsequently decomposes with the formation of the products and the regeneration of the catalyst, this decomposition taking place in a single stage; many surface reactions are of this type, the complex being the adsorbed reactant molecule. In other cases, also exemplified by certain surface reactions, the complex involves the catalyst and two substrate molecules. In more complicated types of catalysis, the catalyst may act in a different way, by giving rise to free radicals which initiate chain processes; some examples are given at the end of this chapter.

The case of a nonchain mechanism involving a single substrate will be considered first. A kinetic scheme to account for the phenomena associated with this type of catalysis was put forward by Herzfeld;[1] a slightly more general mechanism, which appears to apply to most types of catalysis involving only one substrate and not involving chain reactions, is as follows:[2]

$$\text{(1)} \qquad \mathrm{C + S \underset{k_{-1}}{\overset{k_1}{\rightleftharpoons}} X + Y}$$

$$\text{(2)} \qquad \mathrm{X + W \xrightarrow{k_2} P + Z}$$

Here C represents the catalyst, and S the substrate; X is the intermediate complex, and Y some substance which is formed in addition to it. W is a molecule which reacts with the complex to give the product or products P with elimination of a molecule Z. It is assumed that the reaction products are at such a low free-energy level that the reverse reaction $\mathrm{P + Z \rightarrow X + W}$ may be neglected. The treatment to be given will apply only to initial rates of reaction; otherwise very clumsy kinetic expressions are obtained, and it is difficult to analyze the experimental data with respect to them.

In surface catalysis, X is an adsorption complex, and Y and W are nonexistent; k_{-1} and k_2 are in this case first-order rate constants, while k_1 is a second-order constant. The species Y and Z are also probably nonexistent in most cases of enzyme catalysis involving only one substrate. The substances Y and W do, however, play roles in acidic and

[1] K. F. Herzfeld, *Z. Physik. Chem.*, **98**, 151 (1921).

[2] K. J. Laidler and I. M. Socquet, *J. Phys. Colloid Chem.*, **54**, 519 (1950).

basic catalysis in solution; thus, if C is an acid, reaction (1) involves the transfer of a proton to S, so that Y is the base conjugate to C. Similarly, in basic catalysis, Y is the acid conjugate to the base C. In acid catalysis W is a basic or amphoteric substance which accepts a proton from X and is sometimes a solvent molecule; it may also, however, be identical with Y. In basic catalysis W transfers a proton to X and may be the solvent or another acidic substance present in the system.

Two possibilities exist with regard to the stability of the intermediate complex X, and the kinetic laws obtained depend in an important manner upon what is assumed in this connection. In the first place, the complex may be one that is reconverted into the catalyst and the substrate at a rate that is significantly greater than the rate with which it undergoes reaction (2) and gives the final products. The overall rate of reaction can then be calculated by obtaining the concentration of X from the equilibrium (1) alone and multiplying this by $k_2[W]$, this procedure being equivalent to what was done with surface reactions. Since this case corresponds to Arrhenius's concept of a chemical reaction as involving equilibrium between the reactants and the activated complex, the complexes relevant to this type of catalysis are frequently known as *Arrhenius complexes.*

The second possibility is that the intermediate complex is a much less stable species, so that the rate of its reaction (2) to give the final products is not small compared with the reverse rate of reaction (1). It is then not permissible to calculate the concentration of X by making use of the equilibrium (1), since the rate of (2) cannot be neglected. However, since the concentration of X in this case is low, it is permissible to make use of the steady-state treatment. A complex of this type is frequently known as a *van't Hoff complex.* Rate expressions for these two cases will now be obtained.

Equilibrium Treatment. If the rate of reaction (2) can be neglected in calculating the concentration of the complex X, the concentrations of X, Y, C, and S are related by

$$\frac{[X][Y]}{[C][S]} = \frac{k_1}{k_{-1}} = K \tag{3}$$

where K is the equilibrium constant. This expression allows the concentration of X to be calculated in terms of the concentrations [Y], [C], and [S], but the latter two concentrations do not correspond to the initial concentrations, since by hypothesis appreciable amounts of C and S have become combined in the intermediate complex X. If $[C]_0$ and $[S]_0$ are the initial concentrations of C and S, it follows that

$$[C] = [C]_0 - [X] \tag{4}$$

$$[S] = [S]_0 - [X] \tag{5}$$

Equation (3) therefore becomes

$$\frac{[X][Y]}{([C]_0 - [X])([S]_0 - [X])} = K \tag{6}$$

This is a quadratic in [X] and can be solved for [X]; an expression for the rate can then be written down, since the rate is equal to k_2[X][W]. However, it is more convenient to consider two special cases.

Case 1. If the initial concentration of the substrate is much greater than that of the catalyst, i.e., if $[S]_0 \gg [C]_0$, it follows that $[S]_0 - [X]$ is very close to $[S]_0$, since [X] cannot exceed $[C]_0$; Eq. (6) therefore approximates to

$$\frac{[X][Y]}{([C]_0 - [X])[S]_0} = K \tag{7}$$

whence

$$[X] = \frac{K[C]_0[S]_0}{K[S]_0 + [Y]} \tag{8}$$

The rate of reaction, equal to k_2[X][W], is therefore

$$-\frac{d[S]}{dt} = \frac{k_2K[C]_0[S_0][W]}{K[S]_0 + [Y]} \tag{9}$$

This rate equation corresponds to a variation in rate of the type represented in Fig. 80; when $K[S]_0 \ll [Y]$, the rate varies linearly with $[S]_0$,

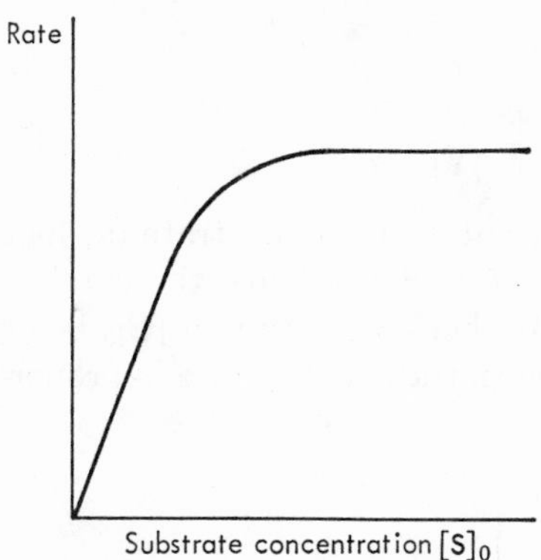

Fig. 80. The rate of reaction as a function of concentration, for a catalyzed reaction obeying Eq. (9).

whereas at higher substrate concentrations, when $K(S)_0 \gg [Y]$, the rate is independent of $[S]_0$. As long as the condition $[S]_0 \gg [C]_0$ holds, however, the rate varies linearly with $[C]_0$. It will be seen later, on the other hand, that if $[C]_0$ is increased so that the condition $[S]_0 \gg [C]_0$ no longer holds, the rate becomes independent of $[C]_0$.

This type of behavior is characteristic of reactions on surfaces and of enzyme reactions; for both of these, the species Y and W are nonexistent, and the rate law becomes

$$-\frac{d[S]}{dt} = \frac{k_2K[C]_0[S]_0}{K[S]_0 + 1} \tag{10}$$

For surface reactions this is equivalent to Eq. (29) on page 267 and corresponds to first-order kinetics at low concentrations and zero-order kinetics at higher ones. Equation (10) is also equivalent to the Michaelis-Menten law for enzyme systems (cf. p. 476); this law is usually expressed as

$$-\frac{d[S]}{dt} = \frac{k_2[C]_0[S]_0}{[S]_0 + K_m} \tag{11}$$

where K_m, the Michaelis constant, is equal to $1/K$ in the above treatment. This law has been shown to be obeyed by a variety of enzyme-catalyzed reactions.

In acid- and base-catalyzed reactions, it is found that, owing to the peculiar nature of the equilibria established in the solutions, the condition $K[S]_0 \ll [Y]$ always holds; the rate is therefore always exactly proportional to the first power of the substrate concentration.

Case 2. If on the other hand the initial concentration of the catalyst is much greater than that of the substrate, i.e., if $[C]_0 \gg [S]_0$, $[C]_0$ can be set equal to $[C]_0 - [X]$ in Eq. (6), which then becomes

$$\frac{[X][Y]}{[C]_0([S]_0 - [X])} = K \tag{12}$$

The rate of reaction is in this case

$$-\frac{d[S]}{dt} = \frac{k_2K[C]_0[S]_0[W]}{k[C]_0 + [Y]} \tag{13}$$

The rate now varies linearly with the concentration of substrate (as long as the condition $[C]_0 \gg [S]_0$ holds), but the variation with the catalyst concentration is nonlinear, the relationship between rate and $[C]_0$ being indicated in Fig. 81. At low catalyst concentrations the rate is propor-

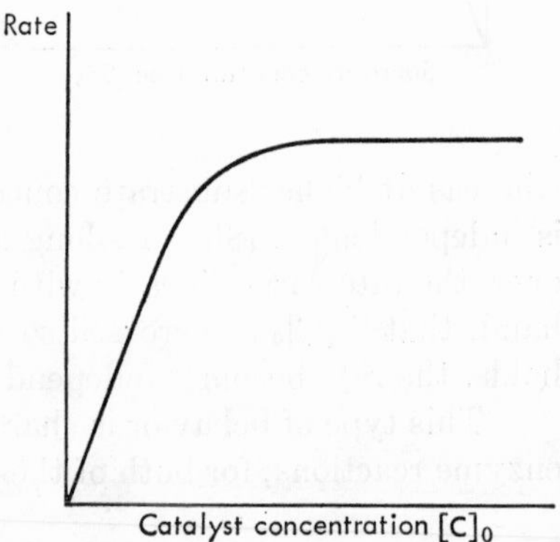

Fig. 81. The rate of a reaction as a function of the catalyst concentration, for a reaction obeying Eq. (13).

tional to the catalyst concentration, while at higher ones the rate is independent of $[C]_0$.

This type of variation of the reaction rate with the catalyst concentration has been observed experimentally, but not many investigations have been carried out in which the condition $[C]_0 \gg [S]_0$ holds. In surface reactions the rate is usually found to vary linearly with the amount of surface, but at very high catalyst concentrations the attainment of a limiting rate has occasionally been reported.[1] In acid catalysis an example of the attainment of a limiting rate with increasing acid concentration has been found by von Euler and Olander[2] in the hydrolysis of acetamide; this will be considered later after the rate equations have been developed for the case of acid and base catalysis.

Steady-state Treatment. If reaction (2) occurs sufficiently rapidly, the concentration of [X] is small, and the steady-state treatment can therefore be applied. The steady-state expression for [X] is

$$\frac{d[X]}{dt} = k_1[C][S] - k_{-1}[X][Y] - k_2[X][W] = 0 \tag{14}$$

Substitution of $[C]_0 - [X]$ for [C] and of $[S]_0 - [X]$ for [S] gives

$$k_1([C]_0 - [X])([S]_0 - [X]) - k_{-1}[X][Y] - k_2[X][W] = 0 \tag{15}$$

Since [X] is small, the term in $[X]^2$ can be neglected; with this approximation Eq. (15) gives rise to

$$[X] = \frac{k_1[C]_0[S]_0}{k_1[C]_0 + k_1[S]_0 + k_{-1}[Y] + k_2[W]} \tag{16}$$

The rate of reaction is therefore

$$-\frac{d[S]}{dt} = \frac{k_1k_2[C]_0[S]_0[W]}{k_1([C]_0 + [S]_0) + k_{-1}[Y] + k_2[W]} \tag{17}$$

This equation again indicates that at low concentrations of catalyst and of substrate the rate varies linearly with the concentration of each of these, and that at higher concentrations of either, the rate will become independent of that concentration.

In catalysis by surfaces and by enzymes, W and Y are usually nonexistent, and the rate law then becomes

$$-\frac{d[S]}{dt} = \frac{k_1k_2[C]_0[S]_0}{k_1([C]_0 + [S]_0) + k_{-1} + k_2} \tag{18}$$

An equation somewhat similar to this, but lacking the (usually small) $k_1[C]_0$ term in the denominator, was first derived by Briggs and Haldane[3] with reference to enzyme-catalyzed reactions. Equation (18) predicts

[1] Cf. W. F. Seyer and C. W. Yip, *Ind. Eng. Chem.*, **41**, 378 (1949).
[2] H. von Euler and A. Olander, *Z. Physik. Chem.*, **131**, 107 (1927).
[3] G. E. Briggs and J. B. S. Haldane, *Biochem. J.*, **19**, 338 (1925).

the same type of variation of the rate with the substrate concentration as does Eq. (10), which is based on the equilibrium treatment, and in fact becomes equivalent to Eq. (10) if $k_2 \ll k_{-1}$. If $[C]_0$ is small compared with $[S]_0$, the Michaelis constant K_m [cf. Eq. (11)] is given by

$$K_m = \frac{k_{-1} + k_2}{k_1} \tag{19}$$

The kinetic laws derived above will later be applied in some detail to acid-base-catalyzed and enzyme-catalyzed reactions. General catalytic mechanisms for chain reactions, with examples, are considered at the end of the chapter.

Activation Energies of Catalyzed Reactions. Depending upon the system and the conditions, there are a number of different relationships between the overall activation energy of a catalyzed reaction and the activation energies of the individual steps. Consider, for example, a reaction to which Eq. (10) applies; this is an equation for an Arrhenius complex which is at equilibrium with the reactants. At low substrate concentrations the rate is equal to $k_2K[C]_0[S]_0$, and since $K = k_1/k_{-1}$, the rate constant is k_1k_2/k_{-1}. The overall activation energy is therefore given by

$$E_{\text{low}} = E_1 + E_2 - E_{-1} \tag{20}$$

At high substrate concentrations, on the other hand, the rate given by Eq. (10) reduces to $k_2[C]_0$, and the activation energy is then simply

$$E_{\text{high}} = E_2 \tag{21}$$

These two relationships are equivalent to those discussed on page 269 and represented[1] in Figs. 59 and 82*b*.

In the case of a van't Hoff intermediate, with $[C]_0$ negligible compared with $[S]_0$, it follows from Eq. (18) that at high substrate concentrations the activation energy is again equal to E_2. At low substrate concentrations the rate is given by

$$v_{\text{low}} = \frac{k_1k_2}{k_{-1} + k_2} [C]_0[S]_0 \tag{22}$$

This equation in general does not correspond to the applicability of the Arrhenius law to the reaction. Two special cases, to which the law applies, may however be distinguished. If $k_2 \gg k_{-1}$, Eq. (22) reduces to

$$v_{\text{low}} = k_1[C]_0[S]_0 \tag{23}$$

and the activation energy is given by

$$E_{\text{low}} = E_1 \tag{24}$$

[1] E in Fig. 59 is equivalent to E_2, and λ to $E_{-1} - E_1$.

If on the other hand $k_1 \gg k_2$, Eq. (22) becomes

$$v_{\text{low}} = \frac{k_1 k_2}{k_{-1}} [\text{C}]_0[\text{S}]_0 \tag{25}$$

and E_{low} is again given by Eq. (20). This case is, in fact, the case of the Arrhenius complex; the steady-state treatment is the general one, and reduces to the equilibrium (Arrhenius) treatment in the case that $k_{-1} \gg k_2$.

These activation-energy relationships are illustrated schematically in Fig. 82, in terms of potential-energy diagrams.

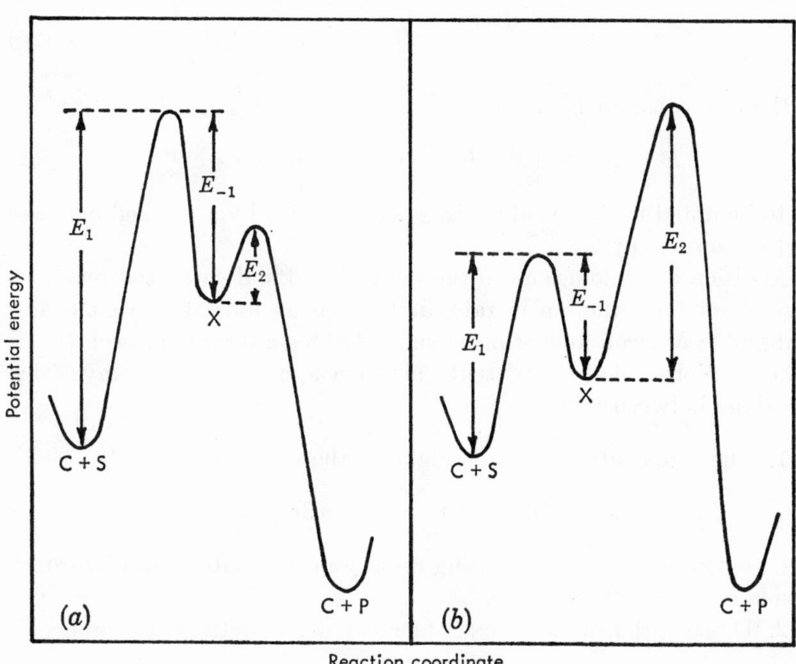

Fig. 82. Potential-energy diagrams for catalyzed reactions. Case (*a*) corresponds to $k_2 \gg k_{-1}$; the complex X is here a van't Hoff complex, and the rate-controlling step is the passage over the first barrier. Case (*b*), which resembles that shown in Fig. 59, is for an Arrhenius complex ($k_{-1} \gg k_2$); the surmounting of the second barrier now controls the rate.

Catalysis in Nonchain Gas Reactions. There are known a considerable number of homogeneously catalyzed gas reactions, many of which occur without the participation of chains. Each reaction must be treated as a separate problem, since except for very simple cases there are no general mechanisms.

A very simple type of catalysis has been observed in the thermal decomposition of *tert*-butyl alcohol,

$$(CH_3)_3COH \rightarrow (CH_3)_2C{=}CH_2 + H_2O$$

The uncatalyzed reaction does not occur at an appreciable rate below 450°C, whereas in the presence of hydrogen bromide the reaction occurs readily at some 200° lower. The uncatalyzed reaction is a first-order reaction, the rate constant of which can be represented[1] by

$$k = 4.8 \times 10^{14} e^{-65,500/RT} \qquad \text{sec}^{-1}$$

In the presence of hydrogen bromide the rate equation is[2]

$$-\frac{d[\textit{tert}\text{-BuOH}]}{dt} = k'[\textit{tert}\text{-BuOH}][\text{HBr}] \tag{26}$$

and the rate constant k' is given by

$$k' = 9.2 \times 10^{12} e^{-30,400/RT} \qquad \text{cc mole}^{-1}\ \text{sec}^{-1}$$

It is to be noted that the catalysis is accompanied by a marked decrease in activation energy.

Addition of cyclohexene to the uncatalyzed and catalyzed reactions brings about no reduction in rate, and this is an indication that chains are absent. Maccoll and Stimson suggest three alternative mechanisms for the reaction, and at the present time there appears to be no way of distinguishing between them:

1. The rate-controlling step might be the reaction

$$\textit{tert}\text{-BuOH} + \text{HBr} \rightarrow \textit{tert}\text{-BuBr} + H_2O$$

the *tert*-butyl bromide decomposing rapidly into isobutene and hydrogen bromide in a subsequent stage.

2. Direct formation of the six-membered-ring activated complex

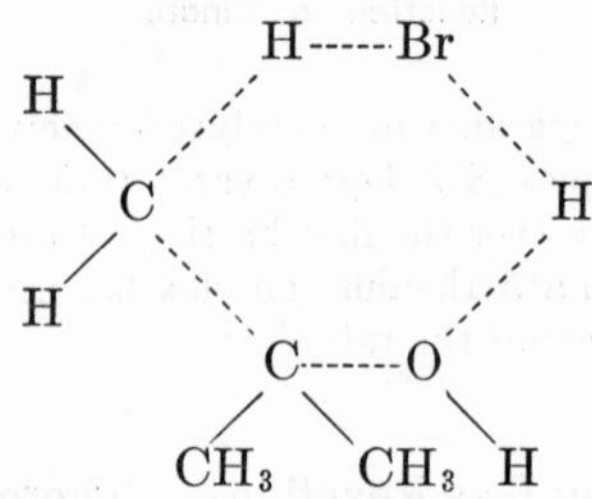

Such a complex is considered to be more likely, on steric grounds, than

[1] R. F. Schultz and G. B. Kistiakowsky, *J. Am. Chem. Soc.*, **56**, 395 (1934).
[2] A. Maccoll and V. R. Stimson, *J. Chem. Soc.*, 2836 (1960).

the four-membered-ring complex

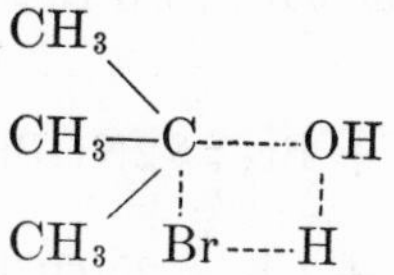

$$\begin{array}{l} CH_3 \\ \quad\diagdown \\ CH_3\text{—}C\text{-------}OH \\ \quad\diagup\ \vdots \qquad \vdots \\ CH_3 \quad Br\text{----}H \end{array}$$

3. Protonation at the oxygen atom of *tert*-butyl alcohol by the hydrogen bromide, accompanied by ion-pair formation,

$$(CH_3)_3C\text{—}OH + HBr \rightarrow (CH_3)_3C\text{—}O^+H_2Br^-$$

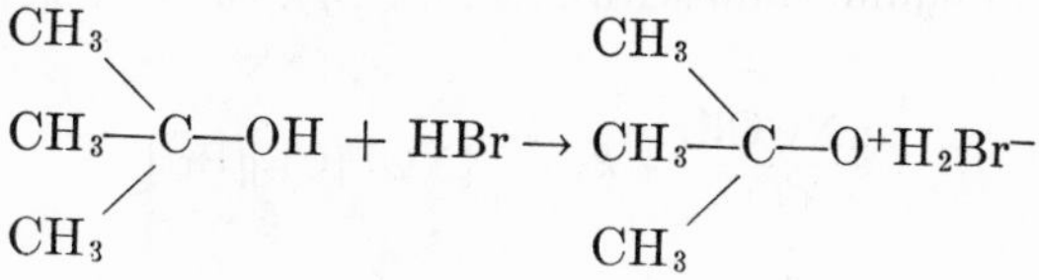

Such heterolytic mechanisms, accompanied by ion-pair formation, have been proposed for the unimolecular decompositions of alkyl halides.[1]

When a bimolecular reaction of the type

$$A + B \rightarrow P$$

is catalyzed by a substance C, a very simple mechanism involves the initial reaction of one of the reactants with C,

$$A + C \rightarrow X$$

followed by reaction of the intermediate with the other reactant,

$$X + B \rightarrow P + C$$

Either of these could be the rate-controlling step. A termolecular reaction occurring by a similar mechanism is the combination of nitric oxide and chlorine catalyzed by bromine. The uncatalyzed reaction follows the stoichiometric equation

$$2NO + Cl_2 = 2NOCl$$

and its mechanism has been considered in Chap. 4. The rate equation in the presence of bromine is[2]

$$\frac{d[NOCl]}{dt} = k[NO]^2[Cl_2] + k'[NO]^2[Cl_2][Br_2] \tag{27}$$

[1] A. Maccoll and P. J. Thomas, *Nature*, **176**, 392 (1955); Maccoll, in "Theoretical Organic Chemistry," papers presented to the Kekulé Symposium, p. 230, Butterworth Scientific Publications, London, 1959; C. K. Ingold, *Proc. Chem. Soc.*, 279 (1957).

[2] A. von Kiss, *Rec. Trav. Chim.*, **42**, 112 (1923); **43**, 68 (1924).

The first term represents the uncatalyzed reaction. The mechanism suggested by von Kiss for the catalyzed reaction is

$$2NO + Br_2 \underset{k_{-1}}{\overset{k_1}{\rightleftharpoons}} 2NOBr$$
$$2NOBr + Cl_2 \xrightarrow{k_2} 2NOCl + Br_2$$

With the assumption that the second process is rate controlling (i.e., that NOBr is in equilibrium with NO and Br), the rate is readily shown to be

$$\frac{d[NOCl]}{dt} = k_2 \frac{k_1}{k_{-1}} [NO]^2[Cl_2][Br_2] \tag{28}$$

in agreement with the experimental results. The reaction is also catalyzed by nitrogen dioxide, and the mechanism is now suggested to be

$$2NO_2 + Cl_2 \rightleftharpoons 2NO_2Cl$$
$$2NO_2Cl + 2NO \rightarrow 2NOCl + 2NO_2$$

The latter reaction undoubtedly occurs in stages.

Some catalyzed chain reactions in the gas phase are considered at the end of the chapter.

CATALYSIS BY ELECTRON AND GROUP TRANSFER IN SOLUTION

There has recently been considerable interest in the mechanisms of reactions in which the overall process is the transfer of an electron from one ion to another; such reactions may be represented in general by the stoichiometric equation

$$A^{z_A} + B^{z_B} = A^{z_A+1} + B^{z_B-1}$$

Examples are

$$V^{3+} + Fe^{3+} = V^{4+} + Fe^{2+}$$

and

$$Fe^{3+} + Fe^{2+} = Fe^{2+} + Fe^{3+}$$

The rate of the latter reaction can be measured by labeling one of the species. The reactions of analytical chemistry are frequently of this type.

At present it is not certain in particular cases whether reactions of this type occur by the direct transfer of an electron from one ion to the other, or by an indirect mechanism involving the transfer of an atom or radical. One type of indirect mechanism may be represented as follows:

$$A^{2+}OH_2 + H_2OB^+ \xrightarrow{1} \left[A^{2+}O\begin{smallmatrix} H & & H \\ & & \\ H & & H \end{smallmatrix}OB^+ \right] \xrightarrow{2}$$

$$\begin{array}{ccc} A^{2+}O{-}H\ (H) & + & H{-}OB^+ \\ \downarrow 3 & & \downarrow 3' \ + H^+ \\ A^+OH_2 + H^+ & & H_2OB^{2+} \end{array}$$

The process essentially involves a hydrogen-atom transfer from one of the water molecules of hydration to another. This transfer takes place in stage 2; stage 3 involves proton transfers, and the overall process is simply an electron transfer.

Another matter about which there is still uncertainty is whether there is ever, in an elementary step, the transfer of more than one electron at a time. In many cases the evidence is that the reaction occurs in stages, each involving the transfer of one electron. Thus the rate law[1] for the process

$$2Fe^{2+} + Tl^{3+} = 2Fe^{3+} + Tl^+$$

is

$$v = \frac{k_1k_2[Fe^{2+}][Tl^{3+}]}{k_{-1}[Fe^{3+}] + k_2[Fe^{2+}]} \tag{29}$$

This is easily explained in terms of the mechanism

$$Fe^{2+} + Tl^{3+} \underset{k_{-1}}{\overset{k_1}{\rightleftharpoons}} Fe^{3+} + Tl^{2+}$$

$$Tl^{2+} + Fe^{2+} \xrightarrow{k_2} Fe^{3+} + Tl^+$$

In other cases, however, the kinetic law is simple, and there may then be a doubt as to the mechanism; in any case, however, it seems clear that one-electron transfers occur more readily than two-electron ones.

In any overall process where two electrons are transferred, it is often possible for catalysis to be brought about by a species having two valence states differing by unity; examples are Cu^+-Cu^{2+} and Ag^+-Ag^{2+}. The reaction

$$V^{3+} + Fe^{3+} = V^{4+} + Fe^{2+}$$

is, for example, catalyzed by either Cu^+ or Cu^{2+} ions, the rate being proportional to the concentrations of V^{3+} and Cu^{2+} but not of Fe^{3+}. This

[1] K. G. Ashurst and W. C. E. Higginson, *J. Chem. Soc.*, 3044 (1953).

can be explained in terms of the mechanism

$$V^{3+} + Cu^{2+} \rightarrow V^{4+} + Cu^{+} \qquad \text{(slow)}$$
$$Cu^{+} + Fe^{3+} \rightarrow Cu^{2+} + Fe^{2+} \qquad \text{(fast)}$$

the first reaction being the rate-determining one. This type of mechanism is conveniently represented as follows:

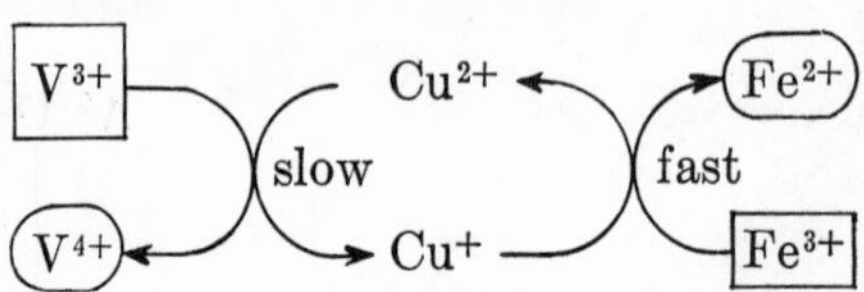

The reactants are in squares, and the products circled.

Similarly, the reaction

$$Tl^{+} + 2Ce^{4+} = Tl^{3+} + 2Ce^{3+}$$

is catalyzed by silver ions,[1] and the mechanism suggested is

$$Ce^{4+} + Ag^{+} \rightleftharpoons Ce^{3+} + Ag^{2+} \qquad \text{(fast)}$$
$$Ag^{2+} + Tl^{+} \rightarrow Tl^{2+} + Ag^{+} \qquad \text{(slow)}$$
$$Tl^{2+} + Ce^{4+} \rightarrow Tl^{3+} + Ce^{3+} \qquad \text{(fast)}$$

This scheme of reactions is conveniently represented by the following diagram:

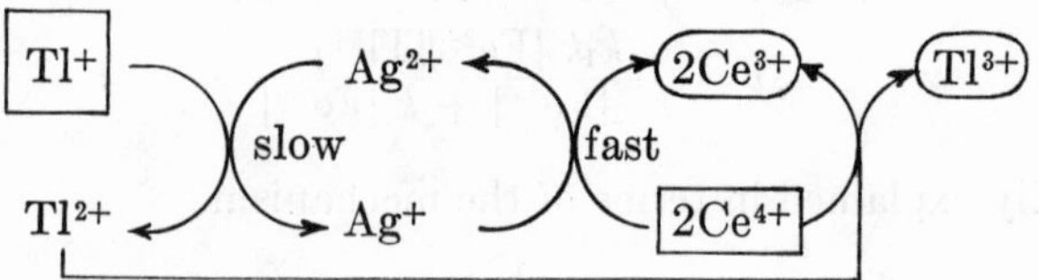

An interesting group of solution reactions involves molecular hydrogen. It appears that molecular hydrogen can bring about reductions in solutions in two different ways, by a homolytic split and a heterolytic split. The homolytic dissociation of hydrogen,

$$H_2 \rightarrow 2H$$

is endothermic by about 103 kcal per mole. The heterolytic split is much more endothermic, but in aqueous solution the ions are hydrated, and the endothermicity is then only about 33 kcal per mole:

$$H_2 \rightarrow H_{aq}^{+} + H_{aq}^{-} - 33 \text{ kcal per mole}$$

The homolytic dissociation of hydrogen is catalyzed by metal surfaces, which are therefore good catalysts for reactions between hydrogen and other substances.

[1] W. C. E. Higginson, D. R. Rosseinsky, J. B. Stead, and A. G. Sykes, *Discussions Faraday Soc.*, **29**, 49 (1960).

In 1938 Calvin[1] showed that cuprous ions catalyze certain reductions, including the reduction of benzoquinone by hydrogen in pyridine solution, and a number of similar processes have since been studied.[2] It is usually found that the rates of such reactions are independent of the substrate concentration, and are functions of the hydrogen pressure, the catalyst concentration, and often of the pH. This indicates that the rate-controlling step is the reaction between the catalyst and the hydrogen, and it is customary to say that the catalyst brings about the "activation of hydrogen."

As an example of this kind of reaction may be mentioned the reduction of dichromate ions by hydrogen in the presence of silver ions (Ag^+) as catalysts. The rate equation for this system has been found[3] to be

$$v = k[H_2][Ag^+]^2 + \frac{k'[H_2][Ag^+]^2}{[H^+] + k''[Ag^+]} \tag{30}$$

The first term is attributed to the homolytic splitting of hydrogen, perhaps occurring as

$$2Ag^+ + H_2 \rightarrow 2AgH^+$$

and possibly occurring in two stages. This process would be followed by the rapid reduction of the dichromate ion by AgH^+, a process that is undoubtedly complex. The second term is attributed to an initial heterolytic splitting of hydrogen, occurring as follows:

$$Ag^+ + H_2 \underset{k_{-1}}{\overset{k_1}{\rightleftharpoons}} AgH + H^+$$

$$AgH + Ag^+ \xrightarrow{k_2} 2Ag + H^+ \text{ or } AgH^+ + Ag$$

Either Ag or AgH^+ then reacts rapidly with the dichromate ion. The steady-state equation for the intermediate AgH is

$$k_1[Ag^+][H_2] - k_{-1}[AgH][H^+] - k_2[AgH][Ag^+] = 0 \tag{31}$$

whence

$$[AgH] = \frac{k_1[Ag^+][H_2]}{k_{-1}[H^+] + k_2[Ag^+]} \tag{32}$$

and

$$v = k_2[AgH][Ag^+] \tag{33}$$

$$= \frac{k_1k_2[Ag^+]^2[H_2]}{k_{-1}[H^+] + k_2[Ag^+]} \tag{34}$$

This accounts for the second term in the empirical rate equation (30). Evidence for the occurrence of the reactions $Ag^+ + H_2 \rightleftharpoons AgH + H^+$ is

[1] M. Calvin, *Trans. Faraday Soc.*, **34,** 1181 (1938).

[2] For reviews see J. Halpern, *Quart. Rev.* (*London*), **10,** 463 (1956); *Advan. Catalysis*, **11,** 301 (1959).

[3] A. H. Webster and J. Halpern, *J. Phys. Chem.*, **60,** 280 (1956); **61,** 1239, 1245 (1957).

that HD is formed when the process is carried out in water enriched with D_2O (in which D^+ ions will be present).

ACID-BASE CATALYSIS

The study of catalysis by acids and bases has played a very important part in the development of chemical kinetics, since many of the reactions studied in the early days of the subject were of this type. Reference has already been made to the work of Kirchhoff on the hydrolysis of starch by dilute acids, and to Thénard's study of the decomposition of hydrogen peroxide catalyzed by alkalies. The first quantitative study of a chemical reaction has been seen to have been Wilhelmy's investigation of the inversion of cane sugar catalyzed by acids.

The early investigations of the kinetics of reactions catalyzed by acids and bases were carried out at the same time that the electrolytic dissociation theory was being developed, and the kinetic studies contributed considerably to the development of that theory. The reactions considered from this point of view were chiefly the inversion of cane sugar and the hydrolysis of esters. It was first realized by Ostwald[1] and Arrhenius[2] that the ability of an acid to catalyze these reactions is independent of the nature of the anion but is approximately proportional to its electrical conductivity. According to them, the conductivity of an acid is a measure of its strength, i.e., of the concentration of hydrogen ions, and the hydrogen ions were assumed to be the sole effective acid catalysts. It was similarly shown[3] that for catalysis by alkalies the rate is proportional to the concentration of the alkali but independent of the nature of the cation, indicating that the active species is the hydroxide ion.

The idea that the only catalyzing species in reactions of this type are the hydrogen and hydroxide ions was a very useful one, but has been found to require modification in a number of instances, as will be discussed later. Many reactions do exist, however, for which only these two ions are effective catalysts, so that it is of interest first to discuss the kinetic laws that are obeyed in such cases. These considerations will be applicable, for example, to the hydrolysis of esters, which have not been shown to be catalyzed by anything except these two ions (apart from enzymes).

If such a reaction is carried out in a sufficiently strongly acid solution, the concentration of hydroxide ions may be reduced to such an extent that these ions do not have any appreciable catalytic action; the hydrogen ions are then the only effective catalysts, and the rate of reaction (at least

[1] W. Ostwald, *J. Prakt. Chem.*, **30**, 39 (1884).

[2] S. Arrhenius, *Z. Physik. Chem.*, **2**, 495 (1888); **4**, 244 (1889); **28**, 317 (1899).

[3] L. T. Reicher, *Ann.*, **228**, 257 (1885).

at concentrations of catalyst and substrate that are not too high) would be given by an expression of the type

$$v = k_{H^+}[H^+][S] \tag{35}$$

where k_{H^+} is the rate constant for the hydrogen-ion-catalyzed reaction. Such a reaction would be of the second overall order with respect to concentration but of the first order with respect to time (cf. p. 16), since in a given run the hydrogen-ion concentration remains constant. The first-order law that is obtained in a measurement of the amount of reaction as a function of time may be expressed by the equation

$$v = k'_{H^+}[S] \tag{36}$$

The first-order constant is related to the second-order constant by

$$k'_{H^+} = k_{H^+}[H^+] \tag{37}$$

Similarly, for catalysis by hydroxide ions the first-order constant is given by

$$k'_{OH^-} = k_{OH^-}[OH^-] \tag{38}$$

If catalysis is effected simultaneously by hydrogen and hydroxide ions and reaction may also occur spontaneously, i.e., without a catalyst, the rate of reaction may be written as

$$v = k_0[S] + k_{H^+}[H^+][S] + k_{OH^-}[OH^-][S] \tag{39}$$

The first-order rate constant is therefore given by

$$k = k_0 + k_{H^+}[H^+] + k_{OH^-}[OH^-] \tag{40}$$

In these equations k_0 is the rate constant of the spontaneous reaction, and k_{H^+} and k_{OH^-} are known as the catalytic constants for H^+ and OH^-, respectively.

The rate equation may be expressed in more convenient form by making use of the fact that $[H^+][OH^-] = K_w$, where K_w is the ionic product of water. Elimination of $[OH^-]$ gives

$$k = k_0 + k_{H^+}[H^+] + \frac{k_{OH^-}K_w}{[H^+]} \tag{41}$$

while elimination of $[H^+]$ gives

$$k = k_0 + \frac{k_{H^+}K_w}{[OH^-]} + k_{OH^-}[OH^-] \tag{42}$$

In many cases one of these terms containing concentration is negligibly small compared with the other. If work is carried out with 0.1 *N* hydrochloric acid, for example, the second term in Eq. (41) is $k_{H^+} \times 10^{-1}$ while the third term is $k_{OH^-} \times 10^{-13}$ (since $K_w = 10^{-14}$); consequently, unless

k_{OH^-} is at least 10^9 greater than k_{H^+}, the third term will be negligible compared with the second, so that at this acid concentration catalysis by hydroxide ions will be negligible compared with that by hydrogen ions. Similarly, in 0.1 N sodium hydroxide solution catalysis by hydrogen ions will usually be unimportant compared with that by hydroxide ions. In general, there will be an upper range of hydrogen-ion concentrations at which catalysis by hydroxide ions will be unimportant, and a lower range at which catalysis by hydroxide ions will predominate and catalysis by hydrogen ions will be unimportant. Within these ranges the rate will be a linear function of $[H^+]$ and of $[OH^-]$, respectively. In the former range the value of the catalytic constant k_{H^+} can readily be determined from the experimental data; in the lower range k_{OH^-} can be so determined. The constants for the hydrolysis of ethyl acetate were measured in this manner by Wijs,[1] who also obtained a value for K_w. This he did by making use of the fact that the velocity is a minimum when the second and third terms in Eqs. (41) and (42) are equal; this gives rise to

$$[H^+]_{\min} = \left(\frac{k_{OH^-}K_w}{k_{H^+}}\right)^{1/2} \tag{43}$$

so that from the values of $[H^+]_{\min}$, k_{H^+}, and k_{OH^-}, the ionic product K_w can be obtained.

The various possibilities that may arise in reactions of this type have been classified by Skrabal,[2] who plotted the logarithm of the rate constant against the pH of the solution (cf. Fig. 83). The most general type of behavior is represented in curve a, which shows regions of catalysis by hydrogen and hydroxide ions, separated by a region in which the amount of catalysis is unimportant in comparison with the spontaneous reaction. When the catalysis is largely by hydrogen ions, $k = k_{H^+}[H^+]$, so that

$$\log k = \log k_{H^+} + \log [H^+] \tag{44}$$

or

$$\log k = \log k_{H^+} - \text{pH} \tag{45}$$

The slope is therefore -1, which is the slope of the left-hand limb. The slope of the right-hand limb is similarly $+1$, and the velocity in the intermediate region is equal to $k_0[S]$, so that k_0 can be determined directly from the rate in this region.[3] A curve of type a is given by the mutarotation of glucose.

If the rate of the spontaneous reaction is sufficiently small [the exact condition is $k_0 \ll (K_w k_{H^+} k_{OH^-})^{1/2}$], the horizontal part of the curve is not found, the two limbs intersecting fairly sharply (curve b). This type of

[1] J. J. A. Wijs, *Z. Physik. Chem.*, **11**, 492 (1893); **12**, 415 (1893).

[2] A. Skrabal, *Z. Elektrochem.*, **33**, 322 (1927).

[3] The straight lines do not, of course, meet sharply; it is easy to show from the equations that there is a rounding off at the points of intersection, the curves being 0.3 unit above the intersection points.

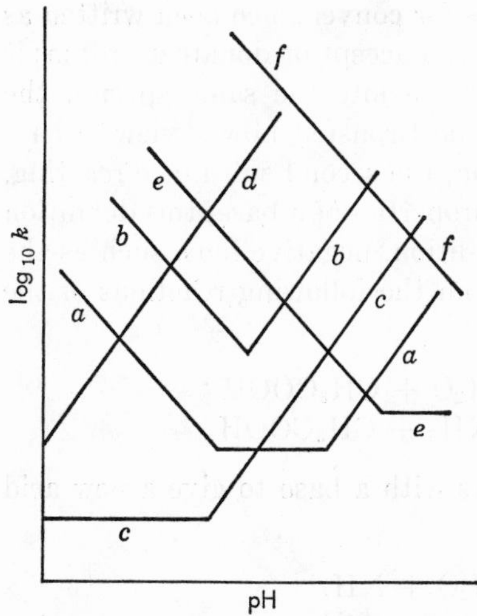

Fig. 83. The variation of the rates of acid-base-catalyzed reactions with the pH of the solution; the various cases are considered in the text. (*After Skrabal.*)

behavior is found with the halogenation of acetone and with the hydrolysis of amides, γ-lactones, and carboxylic esters. If either k_{H^+} or k_{OH^-} is negligibly small, the corresponding sloping limb of the curve is not found. If in the former case the spontaneous reaction is important, curve *c* is obtained, but if it is absent, curve *d* is obtained, the plot being a single straight line. Similarly, if k_{OH^-} is negligibly small, curves *e* and *f* may be obtained. Examples of each of these cases are known.

General Acid-Base Catalysis. According to modern views, which were developed largely by Brønsted,[1] Lowry,[2] and Lewis,[3] the properties of the hydrogen and hydroxide ions which cause them to catalyze certain types of reactions are also shown by other substances, which it is therefore convenient to classify as acids and bases. The definition of an acid[4] that was proposed independently by Brønsted and Lowry is that it is a species having a tendency to lose a proton, while a base is a species that tends to accept a proton.

This definition includes such species as the ammonium ion, which loses a proton in processes such as the following:

$$NH_4^+ + H_2O \rightarrow NH_3 + H_3O^+$$
$$NH_4^+ + OH^- \rightarrow NH_3 + H_2O$$

[1] J. N. Brønsted, *Rec. Trav. Chim.*, **42,** 718 (1923).

[2] T. M. Lowry, *Chem. Ind. (London)*, **42,** 43 (1923).

[3] G. N. Lewis, "Valency and the Structure of Atoms and Molecules," Reinhold Publishing Corporation, New York, 1923; *J. Franklin Inst.*, **226,** 293 (1938); cf. W. F. Luder and S. Zuffanti, "The Electronic Theory of Acids and Bases," John Wiley & Sons, Inc., New York, 1946.

[4] For a review see R. P. Bell, "The Proton in Chemistry," Cornell University Press, Ithaca, N.Y., 1959.

In these equations the hydrogen ion has for convenience been written as H_3O^+, to emphasize the fact that water can accept or donate a proton; it is to be understood that H^+ and H_3O^+ denote the same species, the hydrated proton. Since, according to the Brønsted-Lowry view, a base is a species that tends to accept a proton, the second substance reacting, in the examples quoted above, has the properties of a base; this definition therefore covers H_2O and OH^-. In addition, negative ions, such as the anions of acids, are bases, as is seen from the following reactions of the acetate ion:

$$H_3O^+ + CH_3COO^- \rightarrow H_2O + CH_3COOH$$
$$NH_4^+ + CH_3COO^- \rightarrow NH_3 + CH_3COOH$$

In all these processes an acid reacts with a base to give a new acid and a new base, e.g.,

$$\underset{\text{Acid}}{H_3O^+} + \underset{\text{Base}}{NH_3} \rightarrow \underset{\text{Base}}{H_2O} + \underset{\text{Acid}}{NH_4^+}$$

A particular case is the equilibrium between an acid and a water molecule to give a hydrogen ion and a base,

$$HA + H_2O \rightleftharpoons H_3O^+ + A^-$$

The base A^- is then said to be the corresponding, or conjugate, base to the acid HA. The equilibrium constant for this reaction,

$$K_a = \frac{[H^+][A^-]}{[HA]} \tag{46}$$

is known as the acid constant of HA. Similarly, the basic constant of the base A^- is defined with respect to the equilibrium

$$H_2O + A^- \rightleftharpoons OH^- + HA$$

and is given by

$$K_b = \frac{[OH^-][HA]}{[A^-]} \tag{47}$$

From Eqs. (46) and (47)

$$K_aK_b = [H^+][OH^-] = K_w \tag{48}$$

G. N. Lewis's definition of acids and bases is more general than that given above; according to him acids are substances that accept, and bases those that donate, electron pairs with the formation of covalent bonds. This definition has the advantage of including as acids substances such as aluminum chloride which do not contain protons but which exhibit typical acidic properties. For most cases in aqueous solution, however, the two definitions are equivalent, and the Brønsted-Lowry one will be employed here.

Since, as will be discussed in more detail later, acid and base catalysis involves the transfer of a proton to or from the substrate molecule, it is to be expected that catalysis may be effected by acids and bases other than H^+ and OH^-. This has been found to be the case in a number of instances, and general acid-base catalysis is then said to occur. In other instances catalysis by species other than H^+ and OH^- has not been detected experimentally, and the catalysis is then said to be *specific* with respect to these two ions.

The idea that species other than the hydrogen and hydroxide ions may be effective catalysts was first put forward in a concrete form by H. S. Taylor[1] and by Dawson and Powis.[2] There seemed to be evidence that when certain reactions were occurring in the presence of weak acids, catalysis was effected by the undissociated acid as well as the H^+ ions produced by the dissociation of the acid; for this reason the hypothesis became known as the *dual theory*. Unfortunately, much of the evidence adduced by the early workers in the field now requires modification, because at the time information about the degree of dissociation of acids was not reliable.[3] In particular, it was then thought that the degree of dissociation of strong acids can be calculated directly from the conductivity, whereas it is now known that such acids are almost completely dissociated. Some of the evidence obtained by Dawson and Powis[4] on the reaction between acetone and iodine remains valid, however, and will now be discussed.

The rate of this reaction is proportional to the acetone concentration; on the basis of this and other evidence (cf. p. 514) the slow step is concluded to be the enolization of the acetone,

$$CH_3COCH_3 \rightarrow CH_3C(OH){:}CH_2$$

This process is followed by the rapid addition of iodine. The enolization is catalyzed by acids, and the overall reaction itself increases the acidity of the solution; consequently the reaction is studied by measuring initial rates. Some results obtained using monochloroacetic acid at a series of concentrations are shown in Table 56. The concentration of acid is shown in the first column, and the corresponding first-order rate constant in column two. The acid is sufficiently weak for the ratio of the conductivity at a given concentration to that at infinite dilution to give a

[1] H. S. Taylor, *Medd. Vetenskapsakad. Nobelinst.*, **2**, nos. 34–37 (1913); *Z. Elektrochem.*, **20**, 201 (1914); *J. Am. Chem. Soc.*, **37**, 551 (1915).

[2] H. M. Dawson and F. Powis, *J. Chem. Soc.*, **113**, 2135 (1913).

[3] For a detailed discussion of the early evidence, see R. P. Bell, "Acid-Base Catalysis," p. 48, Clarendon Press, Oxford, 1941.

[4] Dawson and Powis, *loc. cit.*

Table 56 IODINATION OF ACETONE CATALYZED BY MONOCHLOROACETIC ACID

$[CH_3COCH_3] = 0.273$ mole per liter; $K_{CH_2ClCOOH} = 1.55 \times 10^{-3}$

Acid concentration	$k \times 10^6$, min^{-1}	$\alpha = \frac{\Lambda}{\Lambda_0}$	$\frac{k \times 10^6}{[H^+]}$, liters mole^{-1} min^{-1}
0.05	4.6	0.161	571
0.10	7.6	0.117	650
0.20	11.9	0.0842	708
0.50	23.8	0.0542	878
1.00	40.1	0.0386	1,039

fairly accurate value for the degree of dissociation, from which the value of $[H^+]$ can be calculated. If the hydrogen ion were the only catalyst, the ratio of the rate to its concentration, i.e., $k/[H^+]$, would be constant, but the figures in the last column show that the ratio increases as the acid concentration is increased. This rise is attributed to the fact that the concentration of the undissociated acid increases as the total concentration increases, and the catalytic constant for the undissociated acid can be calculated from the figures by plotting $k/[H^+]$ against $[\text{acid}]/[H^+]$. The catalytic constant for H^+ can, moreover, be calculated by extrapolating k back to zero concentration, when the acid is completely dissociated. The values obtained in this way were

$$k_{H^+} = 4.48 \times 10^{-4} \text{ liter mole}^{-1} \text{ min}^{-1}$$

and

$$k_{CH_2ClCOOH} = 2.37 \times 10^{-5} \text{ liter mole}^{-1} \text{ min}^{-1}$$

so that the first-order rate constant of the overall process can be written as

$$k = k_{H^+}[H^+] + k_{CH_2ClCOOH}[CH_2ClCOOH] \text{ min}^{-1} \quad (49)$$

$$= 4.48 \times 10^{-4}[H^+] + 2.37 \times 10^{-5}[CH_2ClCOOH] \text{ min}^{-1} \quad (50)$$

A similar treatment was applied by Dawson to a number of other acids, but the values obtained in some cases need revision, and the evidence for catalysis by the undissociated acid is then less strong.

If general acid-base catalysis is occurring in a system containing an acid HA, the overall reaction rate is given by an equation of the form

$$v = k_0[S] + k_{H^+}[H^+][S] + k_{OH^-}[OH^-][S] + k_{HA}[HA][S] + k_{A^-}[A^-][S] \quad (51)$$

The first term represents the spontaneous reaction. The first-order rate constant of the process is similarly

$$k = k_0 + k_{H^+}[H^+] + k_{OH^-}[OH^-] + k_{HA}[HA] + k_{A^-}[A^-] \qquad (52)$$

In an experimental study of such a system there are therefore five constants to be evaluated, and this requires judicious planning of the investigation. The problem is simplified if there is a range of pH values over which the reaction is not appreciably catalyzed by free hydrogen or hydroxide ions, as in curve *a* of Fig. 83. When this is the case, it is possible, by the use of buffers, to maintain the pH constant within this range, and to evaluate the constant for one constituent of the buffer by varying its concentration. Thus if an acetic acid–acetate buffer is used, the constant for the acid can be obtained by working with buffers having various acid concentrations but constant acetate-ion concentrations, all the buffers corresponding to pH values within the range of negligible catalysis by H^+ and OH^-. When there is no such range for the reaction, a similar procedure is used in a region in which there is catalysis by H^+ and OH^- ions, and a correction is made for the catalysis by these ions.

Mechanisms of Acid-Base Catalysis. The idea that one step in a reaction catalyzed by an acid or a base is always the transfer of a proton between the substrate and the catalyst has already been mentioned. In a previous section the mechanism of catalysis was considered with reference to the scheme

$$C + S \underset{k_{-1}}{\overset{k_1}{\rightleftharpoons}} X + Y$$

$$X + W \xrightarrow{k_2} P + Z$$

and it may be seen that if C is an acidic catalyst, which transfers a proton to the substrate, Y is the base conjugate to C. Similarly, if C is a base, Y is its conjugate acid. The species W may be either the solvent or a solute, and the kinetics are, in general, different, according to which plays the dominant role. In the former case, i.e., if W is the solvent, Z is the lyonium ion when C is acidic (e.g., Z is H^+ if water is the solvent). On the other hand, Z is the lyate ion (e.g., OH^- if water is the solvent) when C is a basic catalyst. The species W may also be a basic substance present in solution, if C is acidic, or an acidic solute if C is basic; in the former case Y is the acid conjugate to C; in the latter case the base conjugate to C. These various possibilities are summarized in Table 57, in which HA represents an acidic solute and B a basic one; the solvent, taken here to be water, may act as either an acid or a base. A valid mechanism corresponds to taking any pair of C and Y and combining that pair with any pair of W and Z, subject to the condition that if C is

Table 57 NATURE OF REACTING SPECIES IN ACID-BASE CATALYSIS

Type of catalysis	C	Y	W	Z
Acid	HA	A^-	H_2O	H_3O^+
Acid	H_2O	OH^-	B	BH^+
Base	B	BH^+	H_2O	OH^-
Base	H_2O	H_3O^+	HA	A^-

acting as an acid, W must act as a base, and vice versa; the former will be referred to as acid catalysis, and the latter, when C is basic and W acidic, as basic catalysis. It is seen that eight different possibilities exist, and the theoretical treatment is further complicated by the fact that the intermediate X may be either a stable or an unstable complex.

No attempt is made here to give a detailed treatment of the various mechanisms, or to discuss all the possible cases.[1] Acid catalysis only will be treated explicitly; the rate equations for basic catalysis can be obtained using the same methods, and the main results are later summarized in a table.

As has been seen, the first stage in an acid-catalyzed reaction is a proton transfer to the substrate S, and the second a proton transfer from the protonated substrate SH^+. In aqueous solution the initial proton transfer can be from a hydrogen ion H^+ or from some other acidic species present in solution; this species will be represented as BH^+. The proton transfer from SH^+ may be to a water molecule or to some basic species B present in the solution. It will be seen that the species that transfers the proton to the substrate in the initial stage does not have an important effect on the kinetic behavior. The species to which BH^+ transfers the proton in the second stage is, however, a matter of importance. If the transfer is to a solvent molecule, i.e., if the process is

$$SH^+ + H_2O \rightarrow S + H_3O^+$$

the mechanism is said to be a *protolytic* one. If on the other hand, the proton transfer in the second stage is to a solute molecule,

$$SH^+ + B \rightarrow S + BH^+$$

the mechanism is said to be a *prototropic* one. It will be seen later that in the latter case there is general catalysis. In a protolytic mecha-

[1] For a more detailed treatment, including a discussion of some rather special cases, see R. P. Bell, "The Proton in Chemistry," chap. 9, Cornell University Press, Ithaca, N.Y., 1959.

nism, however, the catalysis may be specific or general, according to circumstances.

The protolytic mechanisms will be considered first. The processes are

$$S + BH^+ \underset{k_{-1}}{\overset{k_1}{\rightleftharpoons}} SH^+ + B$$

and

$$SH^+ + H_2O \xrightarrow{k_2} P + H_3O^+$$

where P represents the product or products of reaction. One must also consider the equilibrium for the ionization of the acidic species BH^+,

$$BH^+ + H_2O \rightleftharpoons B + H_3O^+$$

The equilibrium constant for this reaction will be written as K. Application of the steady-state treatment to the species SH^+ gives

$$k_1[S][BH^+] - k_{-1}[SH^+][B] - k_2[SH^+] = 0 \tag{53}$$

the concentration of water being assumed to be incorporated in the rate constant k_2. To simplify the treatment, it will first be assumed that the concentrations of substrate and catalyst are both sufficiently small that little of either of them is incorporated in the intermediate SH^+; that is, the amounts of S and BH^+ that are free are assumed to be equal to the total amounts introduced into the solution. The concentration of SH^+ is

$$[SH^+] = \frac{k_1[S]_0[BH^+]_0}{k_{-1}[B] + k_2} \tag{54}$$

where $[S]_0$ and $[BH^+]_0$ represent initial concentrations. The rate of formation of products is therefore

$$v = k_2[SH^+] = \frac{k_1k_2[S]_0[BH^+]_0}{k_{-1}[B] + k_2} \tag{55}$$

Two special cases of this equation must now be considered, depending upon the relative magnitudes of $k_{-1}[B]$ and k_2. If $k_{-1}[B]$ is much greater than k_2, the species SH^+ is essentially at equilibrium (it is an Arrhenius complex). In this case Eq. (55) reduces to

$$v = \frac{k_1k_2}{k_{-1}} \frac{[S]_0[BH^+]_0}{[B]} \tag{56}$$

The acid dissociation constant K is, however, given by

$$K = \frac{[B][H^+]}{[BH^+]_0} \tag{57}$$

and this with Eq. (56) gives

$$v = \frac{k_1k_2}{k_{-1}K} [S]_0[H^+] \tag{58}$$

This mechanism therefore leads to specific catalysis, in spite of the fact that the initial transfer was from the solute species BH^+.

If, on the other hand, k_2 is much greater than $k_{-1}[B]$, which means that the complex is a van't Hoff complex,[1] the rate equation (56) becomes

$$v = k_1[S]_0[BH^+]_0 \tag{59}$$

The rate-controlling step is now the formation of the intermediate BH^+. There will be a term of this kind for each acidic species present in solution, so that catalysis by various species may be detected, and the catalysis is of the general type.

The prototropic mechanism, in which the proton transfer from SH^+ is to a basic species B present in solution, may be written as

$$S + BH^+ \underset{k_{-1}}{\overset{k_1}{\rightleftharpoons}} SH^+ + B$$

$$SH^+ + B \xrightarrow{k_2} P + H_3O^+$$

Again the equilibrium

$$BH^+ + H_2O \rightleftharpoons B + H_3O^+$$

must be considered. The steady-state equation is

$$k_1[S][BH^+] - k_{-1}[SH^+][B] - k_2[SH^+][B] = 0 \tag{60}$$

whence, with $[S] \approx [S]_0$ and $[BH^+] \approx [BH^+]_0$,

$$[SH^+] = \frac{k_1[S]_0[BH^+]_0}{(k_{-1} + k_2)[B]} \tag{61}$$

The rate is now

$$v = k_2[SH^+][B] = \frac{k_1k_2[S]_0[BH^+]_0}{k_{-1} + k_2} \tag{62}$$

There is now general acid catalysis, irrespective of whether the complex is an Arrhenius or a van't Hoff complex.

The equations that have just been derived are only valid provided that the concentrations of both catalyst and substrate are sufficiently low; otherwise, significant fractions of either the catalyst or the substrate will be converted into the intermediate SH^+, and the concentrations of BH^+ and of S cannot be regarded as equal to the total concentrations. Of particular interest is the situation that arises when the catalyst is present in excess, and equations that cover this situation will now be considered.

The *protolytic* case will be dealt with first; the relevant steady-state equation is Eq. (53). Since the catalyst is in excess, the initial concen-

[1] The possibility that acid-base catalysis may involve van't Hoff complexes was first considered by J. N. Brønsted, *Chem. Rev.*, **5**, 321 (1928).

tration of free substrate must be written as

$$[S] = [S]_0 - [SH^+] \tag{63}$$

where $[S]_0$ is the total concentration of substrate; this equation simply states that the substrate either is free or is present as SH^+. Since the catalyst is in excess, there is no need to employ a similar equation for it. Equation (53) becomes

$$k_1([S]_0 - [SH^+])[BH^+]_0 - k_{-1}[SH^+][B] - k_2[SH^+] = 0 \tag{64}$$

whence

$$[SH^+] = \frac{k_1[S]_0[BH^+]_0}{k_{-1}[B] + k_2 + k_1[BH^+]_0} \tag{65}$$

The two cases are now:

1. Arrhenius complex, with k_2 small; the rate equation is

$$v = \frac{k_1k_2[S]_0[BH^+]_0}{k_{-1}[B] + k_1[BH^+]_0} \tag{66}$$

Together with the equilibrium equation (57), this gives

$$v = \frac{k_1k_2[S]_0[H^+]}{k_{-1}K + k_1[H^+]} \tag{67}$$

There is thus *specific hydrogen-ion catalysis*, and the rate *reaches a limiting value* at high hydrogen-ion concentrations.

2. van't Hoff complex, with k_2 large; the rate is now

$$v = k_1[S]_0[BH^+]_0 \tag{68}$$

There is general catalysis, with no limiting rate at high acid concentrations.

When the mechanism is a *prototropic* one, the rate equation is (60), and this with (63) gives

$$k_1([S]_0 - [SH^+])[BH^+]_0 - (k_{-1} + k_2)[SH^+][B] = 0 \tag{69}$$

The steady-state concentration of SH^+ is thus

$$[SH^+] = \frac{k_1[S]_0[BH^+]_0}{(k_{-1} + k_2)[B] + k_1[BH^+]_0} \tag{70}$$

The rate, equal to $k_2[SH^+][B]$, is

$$v = \frac{k_1k_2[S]_0[BH^+]_0}{k_{-1} + k_2 + k_1[BH^+]_0/[B]} \tag{71}$$

Irrespective of the relative magnitudes of k_{-1} and k_2, there is thus general acid catalysis. There is no attainment of a limiting rate, since at high acid concentrations the rate is proportional to [B], which continues to rise as the total acid concentration rises.[1]

The conclusions that have been reached are summarized in Table 58.

Table 58 MECHANISMS OF ACID CATALYSIS

Mechanism	Arrhenius complex	van't Hoff complex
Protolytic mechanism:		
$S + BH^+ \rightleftharpoons SH^+ + B$ $SH^+ + H_2O \rightarrow P + H_3O^+$	Specific Limiting rate	General No limiting rate
Prototropic mechanism:		
$S + BH^+ \rightleftharpoons SH^+ + B$ $SH^+ + B \rightarrow P + BH^+$	General No limiting rate	General No limiting rate

S = substrate
BH^+ = acid catalyst
B = conjugate base

It is to be noticed in particular that a limiting rate is found only in the case of the protolytic mechanism with an Arrhenius complex. When there is a limiting rate it is therefore correct to conclude that this case applies, and that there is specific catalysis. It is to be emphasized that failure to detect general catalysis does not necessarily mean that it does not occur; as will be seen in the next section, the relationship between catalytic ability and acid strength may be such that all other solute species are much less effective than hydrogen ions, so that their effects cannot be readily observed.

The relationships for base catalysis, which exactly parallel those for acid catalysis, are summarized in Table 59.

As an example of a reaction for which a limiting rate has been observed, the base-catalyzed hydrolysis of $C_6H_5NHCOCF_3$ may be mentioned.[2] It is concluded that this process occurs by a protolytic mechanism and that the intermediate is of the Arrhenius type. Evidence of

[1] In fact, at sufficiently high concentrations of $[BH^+]_0$, [B] is proportional to the square root of $[BH^+]_0$, so that the rate will become proportional to the square root of $[BH^+]_0$ instead of becoming independent of $[BH^+]_0$.

[2] S. S. Biechler and R. W. Taft, *J. Am. Chem. Soc.*, **79**, 4927 (1957).

Table 59 MECHANISMS OF BASE CATALYSIS

Mechanism	Arrhenius complex	van't Hoff complex
Protolytic mechanism:		
$SH + B \rightleftharpoons S^- + BH^+$ $S^- + H_2O \rightarrow P + OH^-$	Specific Limiting rate	General No limiting rate
Prototropic mechanism:		
$SH + B \rightleftharpoons S^- + BH^+$ $S^- + BH^+ \rightarrow P + B$	General No limiting rate	General No limiting rate

SH = substrate
B = base catalyst
BH^+ = conjugate acid

the same kind has been found in the acid-catalyzed hydrolysis of amides[1] (cf. p. 506).

Catalytic Activity and Acid-Base Strength. Since acid-base catalysis always involves the transfer of a proton from the acid catalyst or to the basic catalyst, it is natural to seek a correlation between the effectiveness of a catalyst and its strength as an acid or base; this strength is a measure of the ease with which the catalyst transfers a proton to or from a water molecule. The first suggestion of a connection between the catalytic constant k_a and the acid constant K_a was made in 1914 by H. S. Taylor,[2] who proposed the relationship

$$k_a = k_{H^+}K_a^{1/2} \tag{72}$$

where k_{H^+} is the catalytic coefficient of the hydrogen ion. This equation agreed only in a very approximate manner with the data, and a more satisfactory relationship, viz.,

$$k_a = G_aK_a^{\alpha} \tag{73}$$

was proposed in 1924 by Brønsted and Pederson;[3] here G_a and α are constants, the latter being less than unity. The analogous equation for basic catalysis is

$$k_b = G_bK_b^{\beta} \tag{74}$$

[1] H. von Euler, *Svensk. Vet. Akad. Forh.*, No. 4 (1899); *Z. Physik. Chem.*, **28**, 619 (1899); **32**, 384 (1900); **36**, 641 (1901); B. S. Rabinovitch and C. A. Winkler, *Can. J. Res.*, **B20**, 73 (1942); J. T. Edward, H. P. Hutchison, and S. C. R. Meacock, *J. Chem. Soc.*, 2520 (1955); J. T. Edward and S. C. R. Meacock, *ibid.*, 2000 (1957); D. Rosenthal and T. I. Taylor, *J. Am. Chem. Soc.*, **79**, 2684 (1957).

[2] H. S. Taylor, *Z. Elektrochem.*, **20**, 201 (1914).

[3] J. N. Brønsted and K. J. Pederson, *Z. Physik. Chem.*, **108**, 185 (1924).

The relationship between the catalytic constant of a base and the acid strength of the conjugate acid may similarly be expressed as

$$k_b = G_b' \left(\frac{1}{K_a}\right)^{\beta} \tag{75}$$

β is again always less than unity. These equations [(73), (74), and (75)] are commonly spoken of as *Brønsted relationships.*

The equations require a slight modification if they are to be applied to an acid which has more than one ionizable proton or to a base which can accept more than one proton. Thus if a long-chain fatty acid, $CH_3(CH_2)_nCOOH$, is compared with the dibasic acid $HOOCCH_2(CH_2)_n$-$COOH$, and if there is negligible interaction between the two carboxyl groups, the acid strength of the dicarboxylic acid will be twice that of the monocarboxylic acid, since in the former molecule the ion can be formed by the loss of either of the two protons. For the same reason the catalytic strength of the dicarboxylic acid will be twice that of the monocarboxylic acid. These two facts are, however, inconsistent with the Brønsted relationship (73) as it stands, since a ratio of 2 in the acid strengths would lead to a ratio of 2^{α} in the catalytic constants, and this is generally less than 2. This anomaly is avoided if both the acid strength and the catalytic constant are divided by the number of protons involved in the dissociation; in the example given, the modified catalytic constants of the two acids would be equal, as would be the modified acid strengths, and the relationship (73) would therefore be obeyed. This, however, is still not completely satisfactory; thus in the case of the two acids $HOOC(CH_2)_nCOOR$ and $HOOC(CH_2)_nCOO^-$, both of which have one dissociable proton, the catalytic strengths are the same; on the other hand the acid strength of the second is only one-half that of the first since the ion $^-OOC(CH_2)_nCOO^-$ into which the second dissociates has two points at which a proton may be added, whereas the ion of the first acid has only one. These results are again inconsistent with Eq. (73) and to remove the difficulty it is necessary to multiply the dissociation constant of $HOOC(CH_2)_nCOO^-$ by 2 before inserting it into the equation.

The conclusions may be generalized by means of the relationships[1]

$$\frac{k_a}{p} = G_a \left(\frac{qK_a}{p}\right)^{\alpha} \tag{76}$$

and

$$\frac{k_b}{q} = G_b \left(\frac{p}{qK_a}\right)^{\beta} \tag{77}$$

In Eq. (76) p is the number of dissociable protons bound equally strongly in the acid, while q is the number of equivalent positions in the conjugate base to which a proton may be attached; similarly, in Eq. (77) q is the

[1] J. N. Brønsted, *Chem. Rev.*, **5**, 322 (1928).

number of positions in the catalyzing base to which a proton may be attached, while p is the number of equivalent dissociable protons in the conjugate acid. It is to be noted[1] that the ratio q/p in Eq. (76) can be identified with the ratio σ_S/σ_{SH^+} of symmetry numbers, where SH^+ is the catalyzing acid, and S its conjugate base. The statistical factor p is the same as the factor employed on page 84.

Equations (76) and (77) have been applied to a large number of experimental data, particularly relating to the base-catalyzed decomposition of nitramide and the acid-base-catalyzed mutarotation of glucose. In the former case it was found that very good agreement could be obtained if the bases were classified according to the number of charges on them, different values of G_b and β being taken for each class. Some results[2] for uncharged bases are shown in Table 60 and for bases having

Table 60 DECOMPOSITION OF NITRAMIDE

$$\text{Uncharged bases: } k_b = \frac{1.70 \times 10^{-4}}{K_A{}^{0.75}}$$
$$(p = q = 1)$$

Catalyst	k_a	k_b Observed	k_b Calculated
Water	55.5	6.8×10^{-6}	8.2×10^{-6}
p-Chloroaniline	9.1×10^{-5}	0.21	0.18
Aniline	2.0×10^{-5}	0.54	0.57
p-Toluidine	7.0×10^{-6}	1.16	1.24

one negative charge in Table 61; the agreement is very satisfactory, although G_B and β are appreciably different in the two cases. For the mutarotation of glucose it is no longer advantageous to classify the catalysts, except into acids and bases. For the bases the best agreement was obtained with β equal to 0.4 while with the acids the best value of the index was 0.3.

It is easy to show that the Brønsted relationships are actually special cases of the linear free-energy relationships. Consider a reaction catalyzed by a series of homologous acids; the Hammett equation

$$\log k = \log k_0 + \sigma\rho \tag{78}$$

[1] S. W. Benson, *J. Am. Chem. Soc.*, **80**, 5151 (1958); D. M. Bishop and K. J. Laidler, *J. Chem. Phys.*, **42**, 1688 (1965).

[2] Cf. R. P. Bell, "Acid-Base Catalysis," pp. 86–87, Clarendon Press, Oxford, 1941.

Table 61 DECOMPOSITION OF NITRAMIDE

Bases with one negative charge: $k_b/q = 7.2 \times 10^{-5}\left(\frac{p}{qK_a}\right)^{0.80}$

Catalyst	p	q	K	k_b Observed	k_b Calculated
Hydroxide ion	1	2	1.1×10^{-16}	1×10^{6}	1×10^{9}
Propionate ion	1	2	9.4×10^{-6}	0.822	0.90
Acetate ion	1	2	1.3×10^{-5}	0.649	0.66
Primary phosphate ion	3	2	7.6×10^{-3}	0.0079	0.0096

may therefore be expected to apply, and the corresponding equation for the dissociation is

$$\log K = \log K_0 + \sigma\rho' \tag{79}$$

The substituent constants σ will be the same in both equations but the reaction constants ρ and ρ' will be different. Equations (78) and (79) can be written as

$$\frac{1}{\rho}\log k = \frac{1}{\rho}\log k_0 + \sigma \tag{80}$$

and

$$\frac{1}{\rho'}\log K = \frac{1}{\rho'}\log K_0 + \sigma \tag{81}$$

Subtraction leads to

$$\frac{1}{\rho}\log k - \frac{1}{\rho'}\log K = \text{const} \tag{82}$$

whence

$$\log \frac{k^{1/\rho}}{K^{1/\rho'}} = \text{const} \tag{83}$$

This may be written as

$$\log \frac{k}{K^{\rho/\rho'}} = \text{const} \tag{84}$$

or

$$k = GK^{\alpha} \tag{85}$$

where G and α are constants, the latter being equal to the ratio ρ/ρ'.

On the basis of this argument the Brønsted relationships may be expected to apply particularly satisfactorily to catalysis by a series of homologous acids or bases. They also apply, although not so exactly, to acids and bases that do not belong to homologous series.

Salt Effects in Acid-Base Catalysis. The influence of neutral salts on the rates of reactions in solution was discussed in Chap. 5. This matter is of particular importance in connection with acid-base catalysis, since in addition to its possible catalytic action a salt may exert an influence by changing the activity coefficients of other species in solution. For this reason much of the early evidence regarding catalysis by species other than hydrogen and hydroxide ions must be discounted, the apparent catalytic action being in reality a salt effect.

In the study of acid-base catalysis it is convenient to classify salt effects as *primary* and *secondary*. The primary effects arise from the fact that the rate of a bimolecular interaction in solution between A and B is given by (cf. p. 220)

$$v = k_0[\mathrm{A}][\mathrm{B}]\frac{f_\mathrm{A}f_\mathrm{B}}{f_\ddagger} \tag{86}$$

where the f's are the activity coefficients. Since salts influence the f's, they affect the velocity v and the rate constant, equal to $k_0f_\mathrm{A}f_\mathrm{B}/f_\ddagger$, in accordance with the laws discussed in Chap. 5.

The secondary salt effects are not concerned with the direct influence of a salt on the rate of reaction, but with its influence on the concentrations of the reactants. The equilibrium constant for the dissociation of a weak acid HA can be written as

$$K_a = \frac{[\mathrm{H}^+][\mathrm{A}^-]}{[\mathrm{HA}]}\frac{f_{\mathrm{H}^+}f_{\mathrm{A}^-}}{f_\mathrm{HA}} \tag{87}$$

where K_a is a true constant at a given temperature and in a given solvent. Since salts influence the activity coefficients, they also influence the concentrations of H^+, A^-, and HA, and in this way indirectly influence the rate of a reaction involving one of these species. The activity coefficient f_HA for a neutral molecule is only slightly influenced by the ionic strength, while f_{H^+} and f_{A^-} are both decreased by increasing the ionic strength u (at low ionic strengths) according to the Debye-Hückel law

$$-\log_{10} f_i = Qz_i^2u^{1/2} \tag{88}$$

The net result is therefore an increase in the degree of dissociation of HA, i.e., an increase in $[H^+]$ and $[A^-]$ and a decrease in [HA]. Salt effects of this kind are, of course, produced not only by foreign salts but also by salts which are playing a part in the reaction.

The fundamental work on both primary and secondary salt effects in chemical kinetics has been done largely by Brønsted and his coworkers.[1] Positive secondary salt effects have been observed in acid-catalyzed reac-

[1] Brønsted and Pederson, *loc. cit.;* J. N. Brønsted and C. E. Teeter, *J. Phys. Chem.*, **28**, 579 (1924); Brønsted and C. V. King, *J. Am. Chem. Soc.*, **47**, 2523 (1925); Brønsted and W. F. K. Wynne-Jones, *Trans. Faraday Soc.*, **25**, 58 (1929); cf. M. Kilpatrick, *J. Am. Chem. Soc.*, **48**, 2091 (1926).

tions involving weak uncharged acids, since salts, as has already been described, increase the degree of dissociation and hence the hydrogen-ion concentration; the effect is similar to a purely catalytic action, with which it is apt to be confused. The same type of result is found in hydroxide-ion catalysis in the presence of weak uncharged bases, the concentration of hydroxide ions being increased by the addition of the salt, Different results are found, however, if the acid or base is charged. With strong acids and bases the secondary salt effects are small, since the species are almost completely dissociated under all conditions.

Acidity Functions.[1] A certain amount of information about the mechanisms of reactions catalyzed by acids has been provided by investigations carried out in concentrated acid solutions. Unfortunately, in spite of a considerable amount of work in this field, the situation remains somewhat confused. The difficulty is basically that in arriving at conclusions about reaction mechanisms on the basis of the behavior in strongly acid solutions, one is obliged to proceed largely on the basis of analogy between different kinds of processes. As a result, the conclusions that can be drawn are by no means firm ones. Provided that this is realized, the procedure is of value, but many mistakes have been made as a result of lack of caution in employing the method.

In dilute solutions of acids the most useful measure of the acidity of a solution is the pH, which is simply a logarithmic measure of the hydrogen-ion concentration. In dilute solutions there is no difficulty about calculating or measuring hydrogen-ion concentrations, but serious problems arise in more concentrated solutions; the quantities measured (for example, by using concentration cells) are in fact the *activities* of the hydrogen ions, and there is no reliable way of calculating concentrations from activities except in very dilute solutions. Moreover, in concentrated acid solutions there is not necessarily any correlation between rate constants and either hydrogen-ion concentrations or activities.

As a result of these difficulties, the suggestion has been made that it is more useful to define certain acidity functions as a measure of acid strength, and to attempt to correlate these with rate constants. These acidity functions are obtained experimentally by making spectrophotometric measurements of the concentrations of two forms of appropriate indicators. The reason why several different acidity functions are in use is that each is related to a different type of equilibrium involving indicators; a relationship between a particular acidity function and a rate constant may be obtained if the equilibria involved are of a similar type. All the acidity functions become identical with the pH as the solution is made more dilute.

The first and best-known of the acidity functions, due to Hammett

[1] M. A. Paul and F. A. Long, *Chem. Rev.*, **57**, 1 (1957); Long and Paul, *ibid.*, 935.

and Deyrup,[1] is based on an equilibrium of the type

(1) $$B + H^+ \rightleftharpoons BH^+$$

An example of such an equilibrium is found in solutions of anilines,

(2) $$C_6H_5NH_2 + H^+ \rightleftharpoons C_6H_5NH_3^+$$

The equilibrium constant for such reactions is

$$K = \frac{[BH^+]}{[B][H^+]} \frac{f_{BH^+}}{f_B f_{H^+}} \tag{89}$$

where the f's are the activity coefficients. If BH^+ and B are species that can be distinguished spectrophotometrically, it is possible to measure $[BH^+]/[B]$, and K can also be measured in more dilute solutions. Equation (89) may be written as

$$\log K - \log \frac{[BH^+]}{[B]} = -\log a_{H^+} \frac{f_B}{f_{BH^+}} \tag{90}$$

where a_{H^+}, equal to $[H^+]f_{H^+}$, is the activity of the hydrogen ion. In Eq. (90) the quantities on the left-hand side are experimentally observable; the function on the right can therefore be measured in any acidic solution by introducing a suitable indicator and measuring the concentrations of the two species. The quantity on the right-hand side of Eq. (90) was defined as the acidity function H_0:

$$H_0 \equiv -\log a_{H^+} \frac{f_B}{f_{BH^+}} \tag{91}$$

The use of the function is that there may be a correlation with rate constants in the case of processes occurring by a mechanism in which there is a preequilibrium of the same type as reaction (1) above. Suppose, for example, that a reaction occurs by the mechanism

$$X + H^+ \rightleftharpoons XH^+ \quad \text{(rapid)}$$
$$XH^+ \rightarrow \text{products} \quad \text{(slow)}$$

If the second step is slow and rate determining, the overall rate is proportional to the *concentration* of activated complexes, $(XH^+)^\ddagger$, corresponding to this step,

$$v = k^\ddagger[(XH^+)^\ddagger] \tag{92}$$

These activated complexes are in equilibrium with the species XH^+,

$$\frac{a_\ddagger}{a_{XH^+}} = \frac{[(XH^+)^\ddagger]}{[XH^+]} \frac{f_\ddagger}{f_{XH^+}} = K_X^\ddagger \tag{93}$$

[1] L. P. Hammett and A. J. Deyrup, *J. Am. Chem. Soc.*, **54**, 2721 (1932); L. P. Hammett, "Physical Organic Chemistry," chap. 9, McGraw-Hill Book Company, New York, 1940.

where $a_‡$ and $f_‡$ have been written for the activity and activity coefficient, respectively, of the activated complex. The rate is therefore given by

$$v = k^‡K_X{}^‡[XH^+]\frac{f_{XH^+}}{f_‡} \tag{94}$$

For the preequilibrium,

$$\frac{a_{XH^+}}{a_X a_{H^+}} = \frac{[XH^+]}{[X]}\frac{f_{XH^+}}{f_X a_{H^+}} = K_X \tag{95}$$

so that the rate is

$$v = k^‡K_X{}^‡K_X\frac{f_X}{f^‡}\,a_{H^+}[X] \tag{96}$$

The first-order rate coefficient, defined by $v/[X]$, is therefore

$$k = k^‡K_X{}^‡K_X\frac{f_X}{f_‡}\,a_{H^+} \tag{97}$$

so that
$$\log k = \log\,(k^‡K_X{}^‡K_X) + \log a_{H^+}\frac{f_X}{f_‡} \tag{98}$$

Comparison of Eqs. (91) and (98) shows that the acidity function and the rate coefficient contain similar ratios, namely,

$$a_{H^+}\frac{f_B}{f_{BH^+}} \qquad \text{and} \qquad a_{H^+}\frac{f_X}{f_‡}$$

The ratios f_B/f_{BH^+} and $f_X/f_‡$ may vary in a manner somewhat similar to each other, since in both cases the species in the denominator contains one more proton than that in the numerator. A correlation between $\log k$ and H_0 might therefore be expected; a plot of one against the other might give a line of slope equal to -1. As will be seen, such relationships have been observed in a number of instances in which there is independent evidence for this type of kinetic mechanism.

An alternative type of kinetic mechanism that undoubtedly occurs in some cases is

$$Y + H^+ \rightleftharpoons YH^+ \qquad \text{(rapid)}$$
$$YH^+ + H_2O \rightarrow \text{products} \qquad \text{(slow)}$$

This mechanism differs from the previous one in that the activated complex in the slow process consists of the substrate Y to which a proton *and a water molecule* have been added; in the previous case the activated complex consisted simply of the substrate molecule X plus a proton. Application of the same treatment to this second case leads to the result

$$\log k = \log\,(k^‡K_Y{}^‡K_Y) + \log a_{H^+}a_{H_2O}\frac{f_Y}{f_‡} \tag{99}$$

This differs from Eq. (98) in containing the additional factor a_{H_2O}.

It was suggested rather tentatively by Hammett and Zucker[1] that if a reaction occurs by this type of mechanism, there might be a correlation between the logarithm of the rate constant and the pH rather than H_0; the suggestion was, in fact, that it might be possible to decide between the two mechanisms by seeing whether the logarithm of the rate constant showed a better correlation with pH or with H_0. Unfortunately this particular procedure has not proved to be very useful, partly because it has sometimes been applied in too uncritical a manner. A number of examples are now known in which the "Hammett-Zucker hypothesis" leads to conclusions that are clearly in error (cf. pp. 501–511). It is to be noted from Eq. (99) that a correlation between log k and pH is only to be expected if the quantity

$$a_{H_2O} \frac{f_{H^+}f_Y}{f_\ddagger}$$

remains essentially constant over a range of acidities, and there is no obvious reason why this should be so. As a result, correlations with H_0 are capable of a more reliable interpretation than are correlations with pH. The Hammett-Zucker hypothesis in its original form should therefore be abandoned; correlations with H_0 may be given some weight, but should still be treated with considerable reserve.

Some success has also been achieved with another acidity function defined[2] with respect to an equilibrium of the type

$$ROH + H^+ \rightleftharpoons R^+ + H_2O$$

This function is now usually written as H_R, but was formerly written as C_0 and as J_0. An example of such an equilibrium is

$$(C_6H_5)_3COH + H^+ \rightleftharpoons (C_6H_5)_3C^+ + H_2O$$

The equilibrium constant is now

$$K = \frac{a_{R^+}a_{H_2O}}{a_{ROH}a_{H^+}} = \frac{a_{H_2O}[R^+]f_{R^+}}{a_{H^+}[ROH]f_{ROH}} \tag{100}$$

Separation of measurable and unmeasurable quantities leads to

$$\log K - \log \frac{[R^+]}{[ROH]} = -\log \frac{a_{H^+}f_{ROH}}{a_{H_2O}f_{R^+}} \tag{101}$$

and H_R may therefore be defined by

$$H_R \equiv -\log \frac{a_{H^+}f_{ROH}}{a_{H_2O}f_{R^+}} \tag{102}$$

[1] L. P. Hammett and L. Zucker, *J. Am. Chem. Soc.*, **61**, 2779, 2785 (1939).
[2] N. C. Deno, J. J. Jaruzelski, and A. Schriesheim, *ibid.*, **77**, 3044 (1955).

As before, it may be measured by determining the quantities on the left-hand side of Eq. (101).

A correlation between this acidity function and the rate constant may be expected if a reaction proceeds by a mechanism of the type

$$\begin{aligned} \mathrm{ZOH + H^+ \rightleftharpoons Z^+ + H_2O} &\qquad \text{(rapid)} \\ \mathrm{Z^+ \rightarrow products} &\qquad \text{(slow)} \end{aligned}$$

In this case a water molecule is split off in the preequilibrium and the activated complex in the slow step consists of the substrate plus a proton minus a water molecule. The rate constant for the reaction is now given by

$$\log k = \log (k^{\ddagger} K_Z^{\ddagger} K_Z) + \log \frac{a_{H^+} f_{ZOH}}{a_{H_2O} f_{\ddagger}} \tag{103}$$

This differs from Eq. (98) by the inclusion of the factor a_{H_2O} in the denominator, rather than in the numerator as in Eq. (99). A comparison between Eqs. (102) and (103) shows that a correlation between log k and H_R is to be expected when the mechanism is of this type.

Table 62 CORRELATIONS OF MECHANISMS WITH ACIDITY FUNCTIONS

Mechanism	Rate depends on	Acidity function	Examples
$X + H^+ \rightleftharpoons XH^+$ (rapid) $XH^+ \rightleftharpoons P$ (slow)	$a_{H^+} \dfrac{f_X}{f_{\ddagger}}$	H_0	Hydrolysis of β-lactones Formation of γ-lactones Depolymerization of paraldehyde; H-D exchange with benzene
$Y + H^+ \rightleftharpoons YH^+$ (rapid) $YH^+ + H_2O \rightarrow P$ (slow)	$\dfrac{a_{H^+} a_{H_2O} f_Y}{f_{\ddagger}}$	(pH)	Hydrolysis of acetals Hydrolysis of γ-lactones Enolization of acetophenone
$ZOH + H^+ \rightleftharpoons Z^+ + H_2O$ (rapid) $Z^+ \rightarrow P$ (slow)	$\dfrac{a_{H^+} f_{ZOH}}{a_{H_2O} f_{\ddagger}}$	H_R	Aromatic nitration Oxidation of formic acid by HNO_2

The three types of correlations are summarized in Table 62, which includes some examples; for a discussion of individual reactions, reference should be made to a review by Taft, Deno, and Skell.[1] A few examples of satisfactory correlations may be mentioned very briefly. A correlation with the H_0 acidity function has been found[2] for the reaction between *tert*-butyl alcohol and acrylonitrile, with the formation of *N*-*tert*-butylacrylamide, in sulfuric acid solutions. The mechanism is believed to involve the initial rapid addition of a proton to the alcohol ROH,

$$ROH + H^+ \rightleftharpoons ROH_2^+$$

followed by slow reaction between ROH_2^+ and acrylonitrile. The activated complex therefore contains the same amount of water as the substrate, and the correlation with H_0 is expected.

Hydrogen-deuterium exchange reactions with benzene,[3] in sulfuric acid solutions, also show a correlation with the H_0 function. In fully deuterated benzene, for example, the initial rapid preequilibrium involves the addition of a proton,

$$C_6D_6 + H^+ \rightleftharpoons C_6D_6H^+$$

and this is followed by the slow splitting off of D^+.

Aromatic nitrations in sulfuric acid solutions follow the H_R acidity function.[4] This is consistent with other evidence (cf. p. 521) that leads to the conclusion that there is a rapid preequilibrium,

$$HNO_3 + H^+ \rightleftharpoons NO_2^+ + H_2O$$

followed by the slow reaction of the NO_2^+ ion with the aromatic compound. Since the activated complex contains one water molecule less than the reactants, a correlation with H_R is expected. A similar type of mechanism is involved in the oxidation of formic acid by nitrous acid in sulfuric acid solutions.[5] The rapid preequilibrium is now

$$HNO_2 + H^+ \rightleftharpoons NO^+ + H_2O$$

and the NO^+ reacts slowly with the formic acid. A correlation with H_R is therefore expected, and is observed.

The situation with regard to acidity functions can be summarized by saying that a good correlation of log k with H_0 or H_R (but not pH) is a useful *indication* of a particular kind of mechanism. Since the correla-

[1] R. W. Taft, N. C. Deno, and P. S. Skell, *Ann. Rev. Phys. Chem.*, **9**, 303 (1958).

[2] *Ibid.*

[3] E. L. Mackor, P. J. Smit, and J. H. van der Waals, *Trans. Faraday Soc.*, **53**, 1309 (1957).

[4] N. C. Deno and R. Stein, *J. Am. Chem. Soc.*, **78**, 578 (1956); N. C. Deno, H. J. Peterson, and E. Sacher, *J. Phys. Chem.*, **65**, 199 (1961).

[5] Deno, Jaruzelski, and Schriesheim, *loc. cit.*

tions depend upon analogies between different kinds of processes, the conclusions must always be treated with considerable caution, and attempts made to obtain other kinds of evidence.

A much more elaborate attempt to classify reaction mechanisms has recently been made by Bunnett,[1] whose procedure is to plot ($\log k + H_0$) against $\log a_{H_2O}$. The slope w of such a plot is a parameter which describes the manner in which the reaction responds to catalysis by strong mineral acids. The procedure is claimed by Bunnett to be more reliable than the simple use of acidity functions.

CATALYSIS BY ENZYMES[2]

Catalysis by enzymes, the biological catalysts, is much more specific than that by acids and bases. Some enzymes show *absolute specificity;* an example is urease, which will only catalyze the hydrolysis of urea,

$$CO(NH_2)_2 + H_2O \rightarrow CO_2 + 2NH_3$$

A lower degree of specificity is shown by such enzymes as the proteolytic enzymes, which catalyze the hydrolysis of the peptide linkage provided that certain conditions are satisfied in the neighborhood of the linkage; this is known as *group specificity.* Many enzymes exhibit *stereochemical specificity*, in that they catalyze the reactions of one stereochemical form and not the other; the proteolytic enzymes, for example, only catalyze the hydrolysis of peptides made up from amino acids in the L configuration.

Basically the enzymes are all proteins, but they may be associated with nonprotein substances (known as coenzymes or prosthetic groups) that are essential to the action of the enzyme. Some enzymes are catalytically inactive in the absence of certain metal ions. For a number of enzymes the evidence is that the catalytic activity is due to a relatively small region of the protein molecule; this region is usually referred to as the *active center*.

The study of the kinetics of enzyme-catalyzed reactions is still in its infancy, and much remains to be done before the details of the mechanisms will be fully worked out. A serious difficulty is that the exact structures of enzyme molecules are at the present time unknown; it is, in fact, necessary to draw conclusions about enzyme structures from the kinetic evidence. What has been done indicates that the mechanisms are frequently very complex; a number of elementary steps usually take

[1] J. F. Bunnett, *J. Am. Chem. Soc.*, **83**, 4956 (1961).

[2] K. J. Laidler, "The Chemical Kinetics of Enzyme Action," Clarendon Press, Oxford, 1958; for a briefer treatment see P. G. Ashmore, "Catalysis and Inhibition of Chemical Reactions," chap. 4, Butterworth & Co. (Publishers), Ltd., London, 1963.

place, each one of which involves rather complicated interactions between several groups on the enzyme and substrate molecules. In the present very general and brief account, emphasis will be placed on the kinetic effects of concentration, pH, and temperature, and on some of the types of mechanisms that appear to be involved.

Influence of Concentrations. The rates of enzyme-catalyzed reactions are usually proportional to the first power of the enzyme concentration. The dependence on substrate concentration, however, is frequently as shown in Fig. 84. The rate varies linearly with the substrate concen-

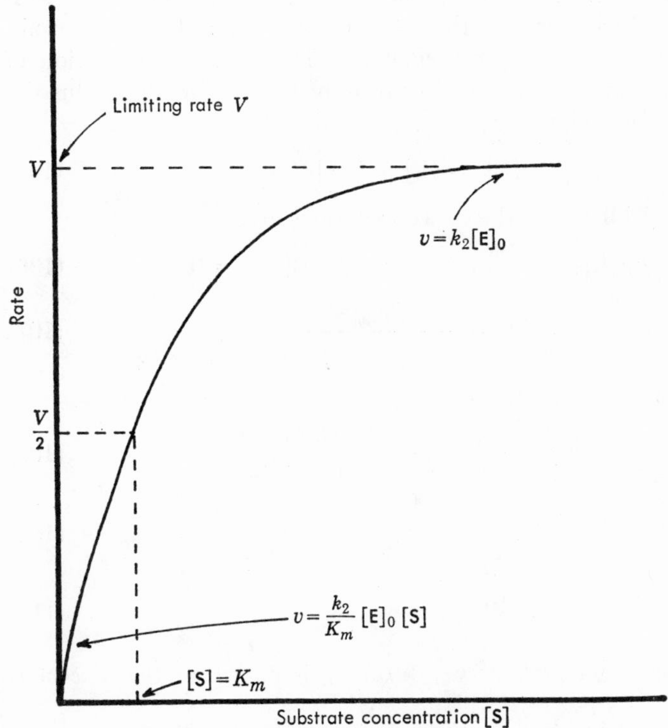

Fig. 84. The variation of rate with substrate concentration for an enzyme-catalyzed reaction obeying the Michaelis-Menten equation.

tration at low concentrations (first-order kinetics), and becomes independent of substrate concentration (zero-order kinetics) at high concentrations. This type of behavior, which is reminiscent of that found in surface reactions (p. 267), was first explained by Michaelis and Menten[1]

[1] L. Michaelis and M. L. Menten, *Biochem. Z.*, **49**, 333 (1913)

in terms of the mechanism

$$E + S \underset{k_{-1}}{\overset{k_1}{\rightleftharpoons}} ES$$

$$ES \xrightarrow{k_2} E + P$$

Here E and S are the enzyme and substrate, P is the product, and ES is an addition complex. The steady-state treatment was first applied to this mechanism by Briggs and Haldane;[1] the steady-state equation is

$$k_1[E][S] - k_{-1}[ES] - k_2[ES] = 0 \tag{104}$$

In studies of enzyme reactions the molar concentration of substrate is usually very much greater than that of the enzyme; very little of the substrate is therefore bound to the enzyme. The total concentration of enzyme, $[E]_0$, is equal to the concentration of free enzyme, [E], plus the concentration of complex, [ES],

$$[E]_0 = [E] + [ES] \tag{105}$$

Elimination of [E] between these two equations gives

$$k_1([E]_0 - [ES])[S] - (k_{-1} + k_2)[ES] = 0 \tag{106}$$

whence

$$[ES] = \frac{k_1[E]_0[S]}{k_{-1} + k_2 + k_1[S]} \tag{107}$$

The rate of reaction is therefore

$$v = k_2[ES] = \frac{k_1 k_2[E]_0[S]}{k_{-1} + k_2 + k_1[S]} \tag{108}$$

$$= \frac{k_2[E]_0[S]}{\dfrac{k_{-1} + k_2}{k_1} + [S]} \tag{109}$$

$$= \frac{k_2[E]_0[S]}{K_m + [S]} \tag{110}$$

In this equation K_m, equal to $(k_{-1} + k_2)/k_1$, is known as the *Michaelis constant.*

When [S] is sufficiently small, it may be neglected in the denominator in comparison with K_m,

$$v = \frac{k_2}{K_m}[E]_0[S] \tag{111}$$

so that the kinetics are first order in substrate concentration. When, on the other hand, $[S] \gg K_m$,

$$v = k_2[E]_0 \tag{112}$$

[1] G. E. Briggs and J. B. S. Haldane, *Biochem. J.*, **19**, 338 (1925).

and the kinetics are zero order. The behavior shown in Fig. 84 is that consistent with Eq. (110). The applicability of the equation to experimental data may be tested by putting it into a form corresponding to a linear plot. Thus the method of Lineweaver and Burk[1] involves using the equation in its reciprocal form,

$$\frac{1}{v} = \frac{K_m}{k_2[\mathrm{E}]_0[\mathrm{S}]} + \frac{1}{k_2[\mathrm{E}]_0} \tag{113}$$

and plotting $1/v$ against $1/[\mathrm{S}]$. A somewhat better procedure, due to Eadie,[2] uses the equation in the form

$$\frac{vK_m}{[\mathrm{S}]} + v = k_2[\mathrm{E}]_0 \tag{114}$$

and a plot is made of $v/[\mathrm{S}]$ against v. In either case the values of K_m and $k_2[\mathrm{E}]_0$ can be determined from the slopes and intercepts. If the molar concentration $[\mathrm{E}]_0$ of the enzyme is also known, k_2 can be calculated; k_1 and k_{-1} cannot, however, be separated and must be determined by other methods, such as by studies of the "transient phase" of the reaction, i.e., by measuring rates before the steady state is established.

Many reactions obey the Michaelis-Menten law [Eq. (110)], and a number of Michaelis constants have been determined, sometimes over a range of temperatures. The validity of the empirical law does not, however, establish the mechanism, since it is possible for a more complex mechanism to give rise to the same form of the rate equation. An example is the mechanism

$$\mathrm{E} + \mathrm{S} \underset{k_{-1}}{\overset{k_1}{\rightleftharpoons}} \mathrm{ES} \overset{k_2}{\rightarrow} \mathrm{ES'} \overset{k_3}{\rightarrow} \mathrm{E} + \mathrm{P}$$

in which an additional intermediate complex has been introduced. Application of the steady-state treatment to this mechanism leads to the equation

$$v = \frac{\dfrac{k_2k_3}{k_2 + k_3}[\mathrm{E}]_0[\mathrm{S}]}{\dfrac{k_{-1} + k_2}{k_1}\dfrac{k_3}{k_2 + k_3} + [\mathrm{S}]} \tag{115}$$

which is of exactly the same form as Eq. (110); a study of rate as a function of substrate concentration therefore cannot distinguish between the two mechanisms. Methods have been developed for the detection and estimation (usually by spectrophotometry) of intermediates in enzyme systems,[3] and such methods have contributed greatly to the understand-

[1] H. Lineweaver and D. Burk, *J. Am. Chem. Soc.*, **56**, 658 (1934).

[2] G. S. Eadie, *J. Biol. Chem.*, **146**, 85 (1942).

[3] B. Chance, *ibid.*, **151**, 553 (1943), and many later papers.

ing of reaction mechanisms. Information has also been provided by studies[1] of the transient phase, or pre-steady-state period, in enzyme reactions. The treatments have been extended to reactions between two substrates and to inhibited systems. Sometimes the rate does not attain a limiting value as the substrate concentration is reached, but passes through a maximum; this has been explained in terms of a mechanism in which a second substrate molecule can become attached to the enzyme-substrate complex,

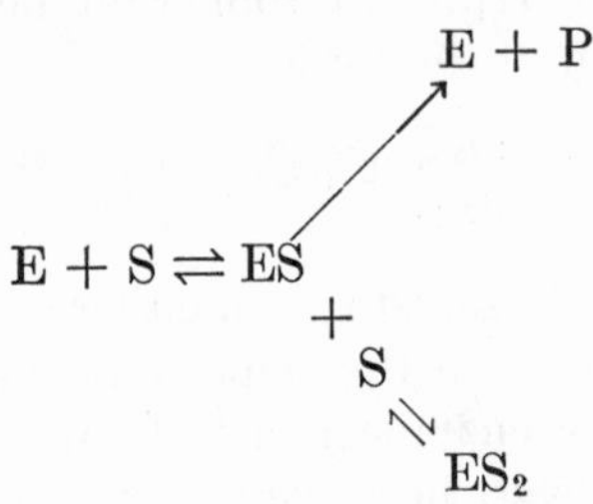

At high substrate concentrations ES_2 is formed in comparatively large amounts, and if it is unreactive, the rate will be low. Other interpretations of substrate inhibition have, however, been presented[2] with reference to the results for particular systems.

Influence of pH. When the pH is varied, the rates of enzyme-catalyzed reactions generally pass through a maximum value, as shown schematically in Fig. 85. The general explanation of this was first given by Michaelis and his coworkers,[3] but the detailed steady-state treatment has only recently been given;[4] indeed its application to more complex systems, and to the transient phase, still remains to be worked out. The basic idea is that the active center of the enzyme can exist in three states of ionization,

$$EH_2 \overset{K_b}{\rightleftharpoons} EH \overset{K_a}{\rightleftharpoons} E$$

In this scheme the form EH_2 obviously bears one more positive charge (or one less negative charge) than EH, and EH has one more positive charge than E; for simplicity the charges are omitted. The dissociation constants are represented by K_b and K_a.

[1] H. Gutfreund and J. M. Sturtevant, *Proc. Natl. Acad. Sci.*, **42,** 719 (1956); *Biochem. J.*, **63,** 656 (1956); J. A. Stewart and L. Ouellet, *Can. J. Chem.*, **37,** 751 (1959).

[2] R. M. Krupka and K. J. Laidler, *J. Am. Chem. Soc.*, **83,** 1448 (1961).

[3] L. Michaelis and H. Davidsohn, *Biochem. Z.*, **35,** 386 (1911); L. Michaelis and M. Rothstein, *ibid.*, **110,** 217 (1920); cf. H. von Euler, K. Josephson, and K. Myrbäck, *Z. Physiol. Chem.*, **134,** 39 (1924).

[4] K. J. Laidler, *Trans. Faraday Soc.*, **51,** 528 (1955); "The Chemical Kinetics of Enzyme Action," chap. 5, Clarendon Press, Oxford, 1958.

Each of the three forms of the enzyme can interact with the substrate (assumed, for simplicity, not to ionize), and the resulting enzyme-substrate complex can also exist in three different states of ionization,

$$EH_2S \overset{K_b'}{\rightleftharpoons} EHS \overset{K_a'}{\rightleftharpoons} ES$$

If it is postulated that EHS is the only form that can give rise to products, the reaction scheme is then

$$\begin{array}{ccccc} EH_2 & \overset{K_b}{\rightleftharpoons} & EH & \overset{K_a}{\rightleftharpoons} & E \\ \Downarrow\!\Uparrow & & {\scriptstyle k_1}\Downarrow\!\Uparrow{\scriptstyle k_{-1}} & & \Downarrow\!\Uparrow \\ EH_2S & \overset{K_b'}{\rightleftharpoons} & EHS & \overset{K_a'}{\rightleftharpoons} & ES \\ & & \downarrow{\scriptstyle k_2} & & \\ & & EH + P & & \end{array}$$

Application of the steady-state treatment to this reaction scheme[1] leads to a rate equation of a very complex form, and it is difficult to apply it to the experimental data. It is easy to see, however, that the scheme is qualitatively consistent with the behavior shown in Fig. 85. In acid

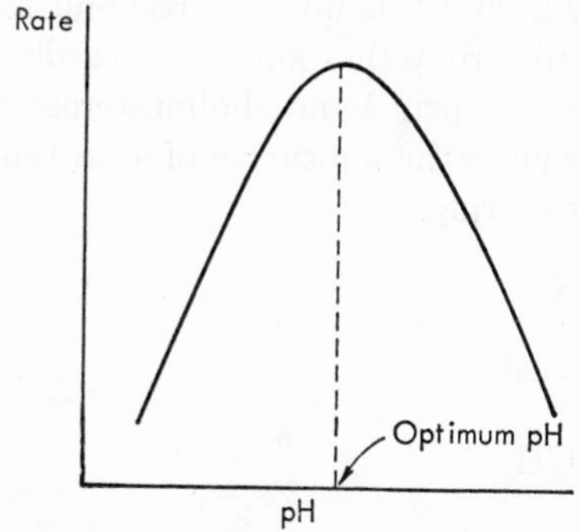

Fig. 85. The variation of the rate of an enzyme-catalyzed reaction with the pH of the solution.

solution, for example, the equilibria all lie over to the left, the enzyme existing largely as EH_2 and the complex as EH_2S; since EHS is the reactive form, the rate will be low. Similarly, in basic solution the forms E and ES will predominate, and the rate will again be low. At some intermediate pH, the *optimum pH*, the concentration of EHS and the rate will have their maximum values.

Considerable simplification in the form of the rate equation is

[1] K. J. Laidler, *Trans. Faraday Soc.*, **51**, 528 (1955).

obtained if one applies the steady-state treatment to the scheme[1]

$$\begin{array}{ccccc} EH_2 & \overset{K_b}{\rightleftharpoons} & EH & \overset{K_a}{\rightleftharpoons} & E \\ & & k_1 \downarrow \uparrow k_{-1} & & \\ EH_2S & \overset{K_b'}{\rightleftharpoons} & EHS & \overset{K_a'}{\rightleftharpoons} & ES \\ & & \downarrow k_2 & & \\ & & EH + P & & \end{array}$$

This differs from the previous scheme in that the processes $EH_2 + S \rightleftharpoons EH_2S$ and $E + S \rightleftharpoons ES$ are assumed to be unimportant. The constants K_a, K_b, K_a', and K_b' are the acid dissociation constants for the processes shown. Application of the steady-state treatment to this scheme leads to the rate equation

$$v = \frac{k_2[E]_0[S]}{(1 + K_a/[H^+] + [H^+]/K_b)K_m + (1 + K_a'/[H^+] + [H^+]/K_b')[S]} \tag{116}$$

By measuring rates over a range of substrate concentrations and of pH values it is possible to determine the values of k_2, K_m, K_a, K_b, K_a', and K_b'.

The values of K_a and K_b, relating to the free enzyme, are of great value in leading to conclusions about the nature of the ionizing groups that are concerned with the reaction, i.e., that are at the active center. Pepsin, for example, has a pK_b value of 2.2, and this must correspond to the carbonyl group, which is the only organic group that ionizes so readily. Several enzymes, including trypsin,[2] chymotrypsin,[3] and cholinesterase,[4] have a pK value of about 7.2, and this suggests the ionization of a proton attached to a nitrogen atom in an imidazole ring,

```
        CH=N
       /    |
    HN      |
       \    |
        C==CH
        |
```

The values of K_a' and K_b', in comparison with those of K_a and K_b, have provided valuable information with regard to the way in which the ionizing groups at the active center interact with the substrate.[5] Unfortunately even the rather complex reaction scheme given above is probably

[1] von Euler, Josephson, and Myrbäck, *loc. cit.*; K. Myrbäck, *Z. Physiol. Chem.*, **158**, 160 (1926); S. G. Waley, *Biochem. Biophys. Acta*, **10**, 27 (1953).

[2] J. A. Stewart and L. Ouellet, *Can. J. Chem.*, **37**, 751 (1959).

[3] K. J. Laidler and M. L. Barnard, *Trans. Faraday Soc.*, **52**, 497 (1956).

[4] R. M. Krupka and K. J. Laidler, *ibid.*, **56**, 1477 (1960).

[5] Cf. Laidler, "The Chemical Kinetics of Enzyme Action," chap. 5.

too simple for most enzyme mechanisms, and more elaborate schemes must be proposed.[1]

Influence of Temperature. Information about mechanisms has been provided by studies of the influence of temperature on rates. Account must be taken of the fact that the enzymes themselves undergo a deactivation process which has a very high activation energy and also a very high frequency factor; at temperatures of 35° or higher (depending on the particular enzyme), the enzyme may undergo very rapid deactivation during the course of a kinetic experiment, and a low rate of reaction will then be observed. As a result, the rates of enzyme-catalyzed reactions frequently pass through a maximum as the temperature is raised; the temperature at which the rate is a maximum is often referred to as the *optimum temperature*, its value depending upon the conditions of the experiment. The process of enzyme inactivation, which is due to the denaturation of the protein, has been investigated kinetically in some detail.

By working at sufficiently low temperatures, at which no appreciable inactivation occurs, or by making a correction for the inactivation, it is possible to determine the effect of temperature on the enzyme-catalyzed reaction itself. The analysis of the results must take account of the fact that the rate law may be of the form

$$v = \frac{k_2[\mathrm{E}]_0[\mathrm{S}]}{K_m + [\mathrm{S}]} \tag{117}$$

so that a simple dependence of the rate on the temperature is not to be expected. However, at sufficiently high substrate concentrations,

$$v = k_2[\mathrm{E}]_0 \tag{118}$$

so that, since k_2 is expected to vary with temperature according to the Arrhenius law, exactly the same temperature dependence will be found for v provided that one works at constant enzyme concentration. Under these conditions a plot of $\log_{10} v$ against $1/T$ should therefore give a straight line, and this has been found to be the case for a number of enzyme systems.

At sufficiently low enzyme concentrations the rate equation becomes

$$v = \frac{k_2}{K_m}[\mathrm{E}]_0[\mathrm{S}] \tag{119}$$

Since $K_m = (k_{-1} + k_2)/k_1$, this becomes

$$v = \frac{k_1 k_2}{k_{-1} + k_2}[\mathrm{E}]_0[\mathrm{S}] \tag{120}$$

[1] See, for example, Krupka and Laidler, *Trans. Faraday Soc.*, **56**, 1467 (1960); *J. Am. Chem. Soc.*, **83**, 1445, 1448, 1454, 1458 (1961).

In general, a simple dependence of rate on temperature is not to be expected under these conditions of low substrate concentrations. In the special case that k_2 is much greater than k_{-1}, Eq. (120) becomes

$$v = k_1[\mathrm{E}]_0[\mathrm{S}] \tag{121}$$

A plot of log v against $1/T$ should then be a straight line, and the activation energy calculated from its slope will correspond to k_1; it will therefore apply to the reaction between enzyme and substrate with the formation of the enzyme-substrate complex. If, on the other hand, k_{-1} is much greater than k_2, the rate equation becomes

$$v = \frac{k_1 k_2}{k_{-1}} [\mathrm{E}]_0[\mathrm{S}] \tag{122}$$

The activation energy that is obtained from a plot of log v against $1/T$ will now be equal to $E_1 + E_2 - E_{-1}$, where these are the activation energies corresponding to the three elementary reactions.

Table 63 gives values of rate constants, activation energies, and frequency factors for three enzyme-catalyzed reactions, and for comparison the values for other catalysts are included. It is to be particularly noted that the enzymes are, molecule for molecule, very much more effective

Table 63 COMPARISON OF KINETIC PARAMETERS FOR CATALYZED REACTIONS*

Reaction	Catalyst	T, °C	k	A	E, kcal per mole
			liters mole^{-1} sec^{-1}		
Hydrolysis of urea	H_3O^+	62.0	7.4×10^{-7}	1.8×10^{10}	24.6
Hydrolysis of urea	Urease	20.8	5.0×10^{6}	1.7×10^{13}	6.8
Hydrolysis of adenosine triphosphate	H_3O^+	40.0	4.7×10^{-6}	2.4×10^{9}	21.2
Hydrolysis of adenosine triphosphate	Myosin	25.0	8.2×10^{6}	1.6×10^{22}	21.1
Decomposition of hydrogen peroxide	None	22.0	10^{-7}	10^{6}	17–18
	Fe^{2+}	22.0	56.0	1.8×10^{9}	10.1
Decomposition of hydrogen peroxide	Catalase	22.0	3.5×10^{7}	6.4×10^{8}	1.7

* For references see K. J. Laidler, "The Chemical Kinetics of Enzyme Action," Clarendon Press, Oxford, 1958.

catalysts than are the nonbiological catalysts. In urease and catalase this higher effectiveness is related to a very much smaller activation energy, and this is so for a number of other enzyme systems. The enzymes evidently exert their action by allowing the process to occur by a very much more favorable reaction path. The exact manner by which they do this is by no means understood. In Chap. 10 the detailed mechanisms of some enzyme-catalyzed reactions are considered.

CATALYSIS IN CHAIN REACTIONS

A number of catalyzed reactions, particularly those occurring in the gas phase, involve chain mechanisms, the function of the catalyst often being to initiate chains by producing free radicals. No general principles are involved with regard to these reactions; each has to be treated separately. Examples of free-radical mechanisms in catalyzed reactions will now be considered briefly.

Decomposition of Ozone Catalyzed by Chlorine. Chlorine has a marked influence on the homogeneous thermal decomposition of ozone, the rate following the law[1]

$$-\frac{d[O_3]}{dt} = k[O_3]^{3/2}[Cl_2]^{1/2} \tag{123}$$

This has been interpreted in terms of the mechanism

(1) $$Cl_2 + O_3 \rightarrow ClO + ClO_2$$
(2) $$ClO_2 + O_3 \rightarrow ClO_3 + O_2$$
(3) $$ClO_3 + O_3 \rightarrow ClO_2 + 2O_2$$
(4) $$ClO_3 + ClO_3 \rightarrow Cl_2 + 3O_2$$

In this scheme ClO_2 and ClO_3 are chain carriers, the ClO decomposing into the elements without initiating chains. The steady-state expression for ClO_3 is

$$k_2[ClO_2][O_3] - k_3[ClO_3][O_3] - k_4[ClO_3]^2 = 0 \tag{124}$$

and that for ClO_2 is

$$k_1[Cl_2][O_3] + k_3[ClO_3][O_3] - k_2[ClO_2][O_3] = 0 \tag{125}$$

Addition of these expressions gives

$$k_1[Cl_2][O_3] - k_4[ClO_3]^2 = 0 \tag{126}$$

whence

$$[ClO_3] = \left(\frac{k_1[Cl_2][O_3]}{k_4}\right)^{1/2} \tag{127}$$

Also

$$[ClO_2] = \frac{k_3(k_1[Cl_2][O_3]/k_4)^{1/2}}{k_2} + \frac{k_1[Cl_2]}{k_2} \tag{128}$$

[1] M. Bodenstein, E. Padelt, and H. J. Schumacher, *Z. Physik. Chem.*, **B5**, 209 (1929); A. Hamann and H. J. Schumacher, *ibid.*, **B17**, 293 (1932).

The overall rate of decomposition is given by

$$-\frac{d[O_3]}{dt} = k_1[Cl_2][O_3] + k_2[ClO_2][O_3] + k_3[ClO_3][O_3] \quad (129)$$

Introduction of Eqs. (127) and (128) gives

$$-\frac{d[O_3]}{dt} = 2k_3\left(\frac{k_1}{k_4}\right)^{1/2}[Cl_2]^{1/2}[O_3]^{3/2} + 2k_1[Cl_2][O_3] \quad (130)$$

If reaction (1) can be assumed to be unimportant, i.e., if the chains are long, this equation reduces to

$$-\frac{d[O_3]}{dt} = 2k_3\left(\frac{k_1}{k_4}\right)^{1/2}[O_3]^{3/2}[Cl_2]^{1/2} \quad (131)$$

in agreement with the experimental law.

Decomposition of Acetaldehyde Catalyzed by Iodine. The decompositions of many organic substances, such as acetaldehyde, propionaldehyde, ethyl ether, and methyl alcohol, are catalyzed by molecular iodine. The effectiveness of iodine as a catalyst is related to the ease of dissociation of the molecule into atoms, which attack the organic molecule. The proposed mechanism[1] in acetaldehyde decomposition is, for example,

$$I_2 \underset{k_{-1}}{\overset{k_1}{\rightleftharpoons}} 2I$$

$$I + CH_3CHO \xrightarrow{k_2} HI + CH_3CO$$

$$CH_3CO \xrightarrow{k_3} CH_3 + CO$$

$$CH_3 + I_2 \xrightarrow{k_4} CH_3I + I$$

$$CH_3 + HI \xrightarrow{k_5} CH_4 + I$$

$$CH_3I + HI \xrightarrow{k_6} CH_4 + I_2$$

The iodine is eventually regenerated, and the overall process is the formation of methane and carbon monoxide, as in the uncatalyzed reaction. Application of the steady-state treatment to this mechanism leads to the result that the rate is given by

$$v = k_2\left(\frac{k_1}{k_{-1}}\right)^{1/2}[I_2]^{1/2}[CH_3CHO] \quad (132)$$

The activation energy for the catalyzed reaction, about 32.5 kcal, is significantly lower than that for the uncatalyzed reaction, about 48 kcal.

Catalysis of Organic Decompositions by Nitric Oxide. The effect of nitric oxide on organic decompositions has been discussed in the previous chapter, where it was seen that at low concentrations of nitric oxide there is generally inhibition, and that at higher concentrations there is catalysis.

[1] G. K. Rollefson and R. F. Faull, *J. Am. Chem. Soc.*, **59**, 625 (1937).

All the mechanisms proposed in the previous chapter for the effect of nitric oxide lead to the result that at sufficiently high nitric oxide concentrations the rate is given by

$$v = 2k_1[\mathrm{M}][\mathrm{NO}] \tag{133}$$

where [M] is the concentration of the reacting substance, and k_1 is the rate constant for the initiating reaction, which is the abstraction of a hydrogen atom by a nitric oxide molecule:

$$\mathrm{RH + NO \xrightarrow{k_1} R + HNO}$$

In agreement with this hypothesis, the activation energies at high nitric oxide concentrations are frequently very close to the calculated endothermicities for this initiation process.

Catalyzed Decomposition of Hydrogen Peroxide. The decomposition of hydrogen peroxide in aqueous solution in glass vessels is partly heterogeneous, occurring to some extent on the surface of the vessel and also on particles of dust liberated from the glass walls.[1] In quartz vessels the reaction is largely homogeneous,[2] but is catalyzed markedly by ferrous and other ions. The catalysis of the reaction by ferrous ions was studied kinetically by Haber and Weiss,[3] who proposed a chain mechanism for the process. Their mechanism requires modification on the basis of more recent work by Barb, Baxendale, George, and Hargrave,[4] who propose the scheme

$$\begin{aligned} \mathrm{Fe^{2+} + HOOH} &\rightarrow \mathrm{Fe^{3+} + OH^- + OH} \\ \mathrm{Fe^{2+} + OH} &\rightarrow \mathrm{Fe^{3+} + OH^-} \\ \mathrm{OH + HOOH} &\rightarrow \mathrm{H_2O + HOO} \\ \mathrm{Fe^{2+} + HOO} &\rightarrow \mathrm{Fe^{3+} + HOO^-} \\ \mathrm{Fe^{3+} + HOO} &\rightarrow \mathrm{Fe^{2+} + O_2 + H^+} \end{aligned}$$

They have shown that this mechanism is consistent with all the experimental results and have determined some of the individual rate constants. They find, for example, that the rate constant for the first reaction can be expressed as

$$k = 4.45 \times 10^8 e^{-9,400/RT} \qquad \text{liter mole}^{-1}\ \text{sec}^{-1}$$

The small value of the frequency factor is no doubt due to the separation of opposite charges in the activated state.

[1] F. O. Rice, *ibid.*, **48**, 2099 (1926); *J. Phys. Chem.*, **31**, 1507 (1927).

[2] A. C. Robertson, *J. Am. Chem. Soc.*, **53**, 382 (1931).

[3] F. Haber and K. Weiss, *Proc. Roy. Soc.* (*London*), **A147**, 333 (1934); cf. F. Haber and R. Willstätter, *Ber.*, **64**, 2844 (1931).

[4] W. G. Barb, J. H. Baxendale, P. George, and K. R. Hargrave, *Trans. Faraday Soc.*, **47**, 462 (1951).

PROBLEMS

1. The hydrolysis of a substance is specifically catalyzed by hydrogen ions, the rate constant being given by

$$k = 4.7 \times 10^{-2}[H^+] \text{ sec}^{-1}$$

When the substance was dissolved in a 10^{-3} M solution of an acid HA, the rate constant was found to be 3.2×10^{-5} sec^{-1}. Calculate the dissociation constant of the acid HA.

2. The mechanism of certain azo-coupling reactions is believed to be

$$RN_2^+ + R'\text{—}H \rightleftharpoons R\text{—}N\text{=}N\text{—}R'^+\text{—}H$$
$$R\text{—}N\text{=}N\text{—}R'^+\text{—}H + B \rightarrow R\text{—}N\text{=}N\text{—}R' + HB^+$$

Obtain an expression which relates the second-order rate constant to the concentration of the basic catalyst B.

3. The following are some acid dissociation constants and catalytic constants for the decomposition of nitramide, for a number of basic ions:

Ion	K_a	k, min^{-1}
Hydroxide	1.1×10^{-16}	1×10^{6}
Trimethylacetate	9.4×10^{-6}	0.822
Propionate	1.3×10^{-5}	0.649
Acetate	1.8×10^{-5}	0.504
Phenyl acetate	5.3×10^{-5}	0.232
Benzoate	6.5×10^{-5}	0.189
Formate	2.1×10^{-4}	0.082
Monochloroacetate	1.4×10^{-3}	0.016
o-Nitrobenzoate	7.3×10^{-3}	0.0042
Dichloroacetate	5.0×10^{-2}	0.0007

Plot the data in a way that demonstrates the applicability of the Brønsted relationship, and determine the constants of the equation.

4. A solution is 0.2 M with respect to acetic acid and 0.1 M with respect to sodium acetate. If the dissociation constant of acetic acid is 1.8×10^{-5}, and the exponent α in the Brønsted equation is 0.8 for a given acid-catalyzed reaction, calculate the percentage reaction due to hydrogen ions, acetic acid, and water.

5. The first-order rate constant for an enzyme-catalyzed reaction is 3.0×10^{-4} sec^{-1}. If the enzyme concentration is 4.5×10^{-3} g per liter, and the molecular weight of the enzyme is 350,000, calculate the second-order rate constant for the reaction.

6. Verify Eq. (115) for an enzyme-catalyzed reaction involving two intermediates.

7. Obtain an expression for the rate of an enzyme-catalyzed reaction involving inhibition by substrate, on the basis of the mechanism given on page 478.

8. Derive Eq. (116) on the basis of the mechanism given.

chapter

Some Reaction Mechanisms in Solution 10

THIS CHAPTER WILL describe a small number of reactions in solution which occur by complex mechanisms. This subject is a very vast one, and it is impossible to do more than select a few reactions that seem to be of particular interest from the kinetic point of view. For further information, and for more comprehensive treatments, the reader is referred to the many books and review articles[1] that deal with both organic and inorganic reactions.

Kinetic studies provide very valuable information about reaction mechanisms, especially when work has been done over a wide range of conditions. Measurements can, for example, be carried out at various concentrations, temperatures, and hydrostatic pressures, and can be

[1] See, for example, A A. Frost and R. G. Pearson, "Kinetics and Mechanism," 2d ed., John Wiley & Sons, Inc., New York, 1961, especially chap. 12; J. Hine, "Physical Organic Chemistry," McGraw-Hill Book Company, New York, 1962; E. S. Gould, "Mechanism and Structure in Organic Chemistry," Holt, Rinehart and Winston, Inc., New York, 1963; E. S. Gould, "Inorganic Reactions and Structure," Holt, Rinehart and Winston, Inc., New York, 1955.

made in a variety of solvents. It is also important, in an attempt to elucidate a reaction mechanism, to obtain as much information as possible from nonkinetic sources; stereochemical studies, for example, have frequently proved to be very valuable.

It must be emphasized that it is never possible to arrive at a firm conclusion about a reaction mechanism. If evidence points toward a particular mechanism, it is always possible to devise a *more complicated* mechanism that is equally consistent with the facts. In view of this, one must always apply the principle of Occam's razor,[1] and accept the simplest mechanism that is consistent with all of the evidence that is available at a given time.

ORGANIC SUBSTITUTION REACTIONS[2]

Many organic reactions belong to the class known as substitutions, being of the type

$$X + Y—Z \rightarrow X—Y + Z$$

In solution such reactions generally occur by a heterolytic type of mechanism, the bond being broken with a separation of charges. In some cases X is a negative ion or the negative end of a dipolar molecule. When it attacks the molecule Y—Z, it induces a shift of electron density from Y to Z, and at the same time electron density is shifted to Y. If X is a neutral molecule, the activated complex can be represented as

$$X^{\delta+}\text{----}Y\text{----}Z^{\delta-}$$

whereas if it is a negative ion, the complex will be

$$X^{\delta-}\text{----}Y\text{----}Z^{\delta-}$$

In both cases the charge residing on Y will be small, and may be either positive or negative. The products of reaction are the negative ion Z^- and the species X—Y. A simple example of this type of reaction is the hydrolysis of an alkyl chloride by hydroxide ions,

$$OH^- + R—Cl \rightarrow ROH + Cl^-$$

Reactions of this type are known as *nucleophilic substitutions*, since the substituting species is seeking out a positive center toward which it can push electrons. An *electrophilic* reagent, on the other hand, is one that seeks out a negative center, and withdraws electrons from it. There are two different ways in which a nucleophilic substitution reaction can occur, and these are referred to as S_N1 and S_N2 mechanisms. The S_N1

[1] Entia non sunt multiplicanda praeter necessitatem.

[2] C. K. Ingold, "Structure and Mechanism in Organic Chemistry," chap. 7, Cornell University Press, Ithaca, N.Y., 1953.

(substitution, nucleophilic, unimolecular) mechanism involves an initial slow ionization of Y—Z,

$$\text{Y—Z} \xrightarrow{\text{slow}} \text{Y}^+ + \text{Z}^-$$

followed by a rapid reaction of the positive ion Y^+ with the nucleophilic reagent; if this is a negative ion X^-, the process is

$$\text{Y}^+ + \text{X}^- \xrightarrow{\text{fast}} \text{Y—X}$$

The first process is rate determining, and the rate is therefore proportional to the concentration of YZ and not to that of X; the kinetics are first order. The initial ionization is usually referred to as unimolecular, but solvent molecules may also play an important role.

The second mechanism, referred to as S_N2 (substitution, nucleophilic, bimolecular), involves an attack by X on the species YZ, the reaction now going in one stage. In this case the rate is proportional to the concentrations of X and of YZ, so that the rate-determining step is bimolecular. If, however, X is a solvent molecule, the reaction will be kinetically of the first order since the concentration of X is constant. Additional evidence is therefore necessary to distinguish between the two mechanisms in such cases.

It is important to recognize that there is no sharp distinction between the S_N1 and S_N2 mechanisms; it is, in fact, convenient to regard the S_N1 mechanism as the extreme case of the S_N2 mechanism in which X is making a vanishingly small contribution toward the breaking of the Y—Z bond. The activated complex for the reaction may be represented as

$$\text{X}^{+a} \cdots\cdots \text{Y}^{+b} \cdots\cdots \text{Z}^{-(a+b)}$$

where a and b designate the *changes* in the effective charges on X and Y. In the S_N1 mechanism $a = 0$, whereas if $a \neq 0$, the mechanism has some S_N2 character. If a is close to zero, the behavior is close to the S_N1 behavior; it is convenient[1] to refer to it as $S_N2(1)$. If a is not small, the mechanism can be called $S_N2(2)$. Kohnstam[2] in particular has studied the intermediate regions between S_N1 and S_N2 behavior.

One way of distinguishing between the mechanisms is based on the products of reaction in the two cases. Consider, for example, the hydrolysis of the alkyl halide

```
R1
  \
R2—C—X
  /
R3
```

[1] K. J. Laidler, *Suomen Kemistilehti*, **A33**, 44 (1960).
[2] G. Kohnstam, *Chem. Soc. (London) Spec. Publ.* **16**, 179 (1962).

in which the halide X and three different groups are attached to the carbon atom. If reaction occurs by the S_N1 mechanism, the ion $CR_1R_2R_3^+$ will be formed, and this will tend to have a planar configuration. When this ion reacts with a water molecule or a hydroxide ion there will be an approximately equal chance of the hydroxyl group becoming attached to each side, and the resulting alcohol $R_1R_2R_3COH$ will be a racemic mixture. Racemization may not be quite complete, since the environment may not be the same on the two sides of the ion; the halide ion, for example, may be held by electrostatic attraction to the front side. The result of the reaction may therefore be that there is preferential formation of one stereoisomer.

If reaction proceeds by an S_N2 mechanism, on the other hand, the attack by the nucleophilic agent is at the face of the carbon tetrahedron that is opposite to the halogen atom; the result is therefore inversion of stereochemical configuration. Such an inversion is often known as a Walden inversion, and may be represented schematically as follows:

$$HO^- + R_2{-}\overset{R_1\diagdown}{\underset{R_3\diagup}{C}}{-}X \rightarrow HO^{\delta-}\cdots\cdots\overset{R_1\;\;R_2}{\underset{R_3}{C}}\cdots\cdots X^{\delta-} \rightarrow HO\overset{\diagup R_1}{\underset{\diagdown R_3}{C}}{-}R_2 + X^-$$

It is also possible to arrive at a conclusion as to mechanism from the effects of substituents on the rates of reactions. As discussed, in the molecule YZ the influence of a substituent on the ease of ionization of the Y—Z bond will be the opposite to its effect on the ease of approach of the reagent X. The effect of a substituent will therefore provide valuable information as to whether the reaction is controlled by the ionization (S_N1) or the attack of the reagent (S_N2).

A distinction between the two mechanisms can also be made by studying the effect of changing the dielectric constant of the solvent.[1] Ionizing solvents, for example, will strongly favor reaction by the S_N1 mechanism, and will have a much smaller effect on reaction by the S_N2 mechanism. The method does, however, involve some difficulties of interpretation, since specific solvation effects are sometimes important. The method is nevertheless of value when used with other methods.

Studies at high pressure are also valuable in distinguishing between reaction mechanisms, including the S_N1 and S_N2 mechanisms; this method has been used in particular by Whalley.[2] The S_N1 mechanism will generally be associated with a large volume decrease, owing to the

[1] Laidler, *loc. cit.*

[2] E. Whalley, *Trans. Faraday Soc.*, **55**, 798 (1959), and later papers; for a review see E. Whalley, in V. Gold (ed.), "Advances in Physical Organic Chemistry," vol. 2, p. 93, Academic Press Inc., New York, 1964.

production of charges in the activated state. The S_N2 mechanism, on the other hand, will not lead to as large a volume decrease. Similarly, the magnitude of the entropy of activation provides information, but it is not as clear-cut as that provided by the volume of activation.

Hydrolysis of Alkyl Halides. The hydrolyses of alkyl halides, RX, represent the simplest group of organic substitution reactions. Hydrolysis may occur by reaction with a water molecule or a hydroxide ion, both of which are nucleophilic reagents; there is therefore the possibility of both S_N1 and S_N2 reactions.

The S_N1 reactions occur by the mechanism

$$R\text{—}X \xrightarrow{\text{slow}} R^+ + X^-$$

$$R^+ + OH^- \xrightarrow{\text{fast}} ROH$$

or

$$R^+ + H_2O \xrightarrow{\text{fast}} ROH + H^+$$

The ion R^+ produced in the initial step is known as a *carbonium* ion. The rate of the ionization, and therefore of the overall reaction, is increased by the introduction of an electron-releasing (+I) substituent, such as a methyl group. The rate will be independent of whether the subsequent reaction involves OH^- or H_2O, and will be the same for other reactants such as Cl^-.

If, however, the mechanism is of the S_N2 type, the rate is determined by the ease with which the RX can accept electrons from the nucleophilic reagent; the rate will therefore increase with the nucleophilicity, and will decrease if an electron-releasing substituent is introduced into R.

The mechanism may change in a series in which substituents are progressively introduced. An interesting case of this, first pointed out by Gleave, Hughes, and Ingold,[1] is found in the hydrolysis of the alkyl iodides. For the series

CH_3I	$CH_3\text{—}CH_2I$	$(CH_3)_2CHI$	$CH_3\text{—}CI(CH_3)_2$
Methyl iodide	Ethyl iodide	Isopropyl iodide	*tert*-Butyl iodide

in which methyl groups are added to the carbon atom, the rates are as shown in Fig. 86. The addition of a methyl group decreases the rate of the S_N2 reaction and increases the rate of the S_N1 reaction; the reaction will occur mainly by the mechanism having the higher rate. The reaction occurs largely by an S_N2 mechanism for the methyl and ethyl iodides, but largely by the S_N1 mechanism for the isopropyl and *tert*-butyl iodides. The S_N1 mechanism becomes gradually more important than the S_N2 one

[1] J. L. Gleave, E. D. Hughes, and E. K. Ingold, *J. Chem. Soc.*, 236 (1935).

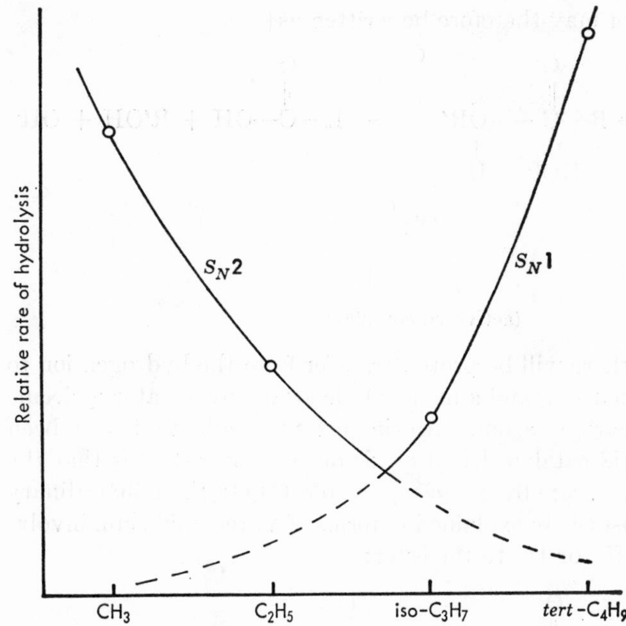

Fig. 86. The variation in rate of hydrolysis as methyl groups are introduced into aliphatic iodides.

as the methyl groups are substituted. If the nucleophilic reagent is varied, becoming gradually less nucleophilic, the S_N2 mechanism becomes gradually less important, until finally the S_N1 mechanism takes over when the nucleophilic reagent is too weak to contribute toward the breaking of the bond.

HYDROLYSIS OF ESTERS

The hydrolyses of ordinary esters are catalyzed by a number of agents, such as acids, bases, and enzymes. The acid and base catalysis in aqueous solution is largely of the specific type, being brought about by hydrogen and hydroxide ions. The enzymes are very much more effective catalysts than the H^+ and OH^- ions, and the mechanism of their action is discussed later.

Catalysis by Acids and Bases. In both the acid-catalyzed and base-catalyzed hydrolyses of esters in aqueous solution, there is generally a nucleophilic attack on the carbonyl carbon atom and an electrophilic attack on the alcoholic oxygen atom. If the hydrolysis is in alkaline solution, the nucleophilic attack is brought about by the hydroxide ion, and the electrophilic attack (actually a proton transfer) by a water molecule; the mechanism may therefore be written as

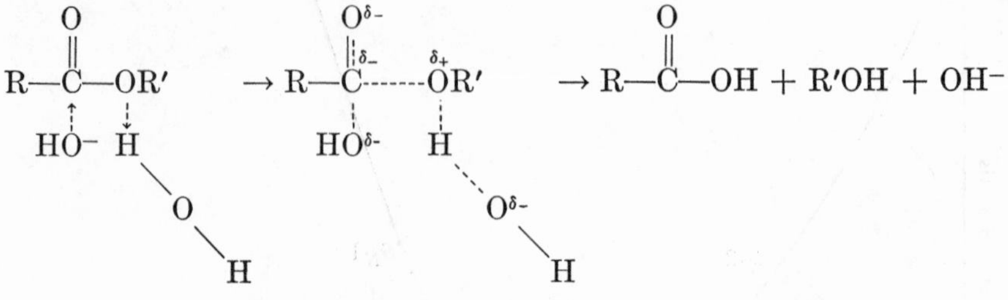

$$\begin{array}{c} \mathrm{O} \\ \| \\ \mathrm{R{-}C{-}OR'} \\ \uparrow \quad \downarrow \\ \mathrm{HO^- \; H} \\ \diagdown \\ \mathrm{O} \\ \diagdown \\ \mathrm{H} \end{array} \rightarrow \begin{array}{c} \mathrm{O^{\delta-}} \\ \|\vdots^{\delta-} \quad \delta_+ \\ \mathrm{R{-}C\cdots\cdots OR'} \\ \vdots \qquad \vdots \\ \mathrm{HO^{\delta-} \quad H} \\ \ddots \\ \mathrm{O^{\delta-}} \\ \diagdown \\ \mathrm{H} \end{array} \rightarrow \begin{array}{c} \mathrm{O} \\ \| \\ \mathrm{R{-}C{-}OH} \end{array} + \mathrm{R'OH} + \mathrm{OH^-}$$

(activated complex)

In acid hydrolysis there will be proton transfer from the hydrogen ion to the alcoholic oxygen atom, and a nucleophilic attack by a water molecule on the carbonyl carbon atom. An important result that has been obtained for the acid-catalyzed hydrolysis of ordinary esters is that the reactions occur more rapidly in heavy water (D_2O) than in ordinary water.[1] This is most easily explained in terms of a preequilibrium involving the transfer of H^+ or D^+ to the ester:

$$(1) \qquad \mathrm{H_3O^+} + \begin{array}{c} \mathrm{O} \\ \| \\ \mathrm{R{-}C{-}O{-}R'} \end{array} \rightleftharpoons \begin{array}{c} \mathrm{O} \\ \| \\ \mathrm{R{-}C{-}O^+{-}R'} \\ \qquad | \\ \qquad \mathrm{H} \end{array} + \mathrm{H_2O}$$

or

$$(2) \qquad \mathrm{D_3O^+} + \begin{array}{c} \mathrm{O} \\ \| \\ \mathrm{R{-}C{-}O{-}R'} \end{array} \rightleftharpoons \begin{array}{c} \mathrm{O} \\ \| \\ \mathrm{R{-}C{-}O^+{-}R'} \\ \qquad | \\ \qquad \mathrm{D} \end{array} + \mathrm{D_2O}$$

The equilibrium

$$\mathrm{D_3O^+ + H_2O \rightleftharpoons H_2DO^+ + D_2O}$$

lies over to the right, which means that D_3O^+ gives up D^+ more readily than H_2DO^+ (or H_3O^+) gives up H^+; this may be expressed in terms of dissociation energies as follows:

$$D(\mathrm{D_2O{-}D^+}) < D(\mathrm{H_2O{-}D^+})$$

There is a general principle, shown in Fig. 87, that the *heavy atom favors the strong bond;* the conclusion is therefore that equilibrium (2) lies further to the right than does equilibrium (1). The occurrence of these reactions as preequilibria thus explains why reaction with D_3O^+ is faster than that with H_3O^+.

The mechanism suggested for the acid-catalyzed hydrolysis of an

[1] W. E. Nelson and J. A. V. Butler, *ibid.*, 957 (1938); J. C. Hornel and Butler, *ibid.*, 1361 (1936); K. Schwartz, *Z. Elektrochem.*, **40**, 474 (1936).

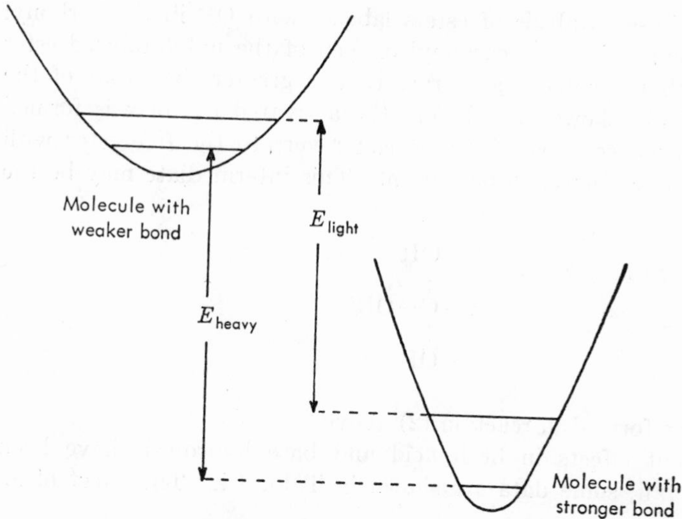

Fig. 87. Illustration of the general principle that, in an equilibrium, the *heavy atom favors the strong bond.* The difference between the zero-point levels is greater for the molecule with the stronger bond: i.e., E_{heavy} is greater than E_{light}.

ordinary ester is therefore

$$\text{(1)}\quad H_3O^+ + R\text{—}\overset{\overset{\displaystyle O}{\|}}{C}\text{—}OR' \underset{}{\overset{\text{fast}}{\rightleftharpoons}} R\text{—}\overset{\overset{\displaystyle O}{\|}}{C}\text{—}\underset{\underset{\displaystyle H}{|}}{O^+}\text{—}R' + H_2O$$

$$\text{(2)}\quad H_2O + R\text{—}\overset{\overset{\displaystyle O}{\|}}{C}\text{—}\overset{+}{O}\genfrac{}{}{0pt}{}{\diagup H}{\diagdown R'} \xrightarrow{\text{slow}} R\text{—}\underset{\underset{\displaystyle H\diagup\ \diagdown H}{\displaystyle O^+}}{\overset{\overset{\displaystyle O^-}{|}}{C}}\text{—}\overset{+}{O}\genfrac{}{}{0pt}{}{\diagup H}{\diagdown R'} \xrightarrow{\text{slow}} R\text{—}\overset{\overset{\displaystyle O}{\|}}{C}\text{—}O^+H_2 + R'OH$$

$$\text{(3)}\quad R\text{—}\overset{\overset{\displaystyle O}{\|}}{C}\text{—}O^+H_2 + H_2O \xrightarrow{\text{fast}} R\text{—}\overset{\overset{\displaystyle O}{\|}}{C}\text{—}OH + H_3O^+$$

The distinction between the stages is not necessarily as clear-cut as represented above.

A valuable piece of evidence was obtained by Bender,[1] who studied

[1] M. L. Bender, *J. Am. Chem. Soc.*, **73,** 1626 (1951); M. L. Bender, R. D. Ginger, and J. P. Unik, *ibid.*, **80,** 1044 (1958).

the acid and base catalysis of esters labeled with O^{18} in the carbonyl group. He found that the carbonyl oxygen of the unhydrolyzed ester exchanges with the solvent at a rate that is greater than that of the hydrolysis. This shows that before the activated complex is formed there is produced some species that can revert to the free ester with exchange of the carbonyl carbon atom. This intermediate may be the ester hydrate

$$\begin{array}{c} \text{OH} \\ | \\ \text{R—C—OR}' \\ | \\ \text{OH} \end{array}$$

or the complex formed in reaction (2) above.

Substituent effects in both acid and base hydrolysis have been studied in detail; some data are shown in Table 64. The effect of an

Table 64 SUBSTITUENT EFFECTS IN ESTER HYDROLYSIS
Solvent: acetone/water (40 volumes of water diluted with acetone to 100 volumes)

Ester	Rate constant	Frequency factor	Activation energy, kcal per mole
	liters mole^{-1} sec^{-1}		
Acid hydrolysis† *at 100°C:*			
Ethyl benzoate	9.33×10^{-5}	6.9×10^{7}	20.3
Ethyl *p*-nitrobenzoate	1.15×10^{-4}	3.7×10^{7}	19.7
Ethyl *p*-toluate	8.13×10^{-5}	7.6×10^{7}	20.4
Alkaline hydrolysis§ *at 25°C:*			
Ethyl benzoate	2.87×10^{-3}	1.5×10^{8}	14.6
Ethyl *p*-nitrobenzoate	2.44×10^{-1}	3.6×10^{8}	12.4
Ethyl *p*-toluate	1.16×10^{-3}	1.6×10^{8}	15.2

† E. W. Timm and C. N. Hinshelwood, *J. Chem. Soc.*, 862 (1938).
§ E. Tommila and C. N. Hinshelwood, *ibid.*, 1801.

electron-attracting substituent (e.g., NO_2) in the acidic (i.e., R) group of the ester is to decrease the activation energy and to increase the rate, for both acid and base hydrolysis. This is attributed to the fact that such a substituent makes it easier for the nucleophilic agent to attack the carbonyl carbon atom; this effect appears to be the predominant one in both cases. In acid hydrolysis the neutral water molecule makes the nucleophilic attack [reaction (2) above], whereas in basic hydrolysis the negatively charged hydroxide ion does so; this explains why the substituent effect is greater in basic hydrolysis. The rates are considerably greater, and the activation energies less by 5 to 7 kcal, in basic hydrolysis; this is due to the fact that the nucleophilic attack will be much easier for the negatively charged ion.

The entropies of activation for ester hydrolyses are strongly negative, ranging from -20 to -30 cal deg^{-1} mole^{-1}. No completely satisfactory quantitative explanation for these low values has been given, but an important effect is undoubtedly the partial immobilization of water molecules in the activated state, brought about as a result of the distribution of charges on the activated complex. In the acid hydrolysis occurring by the mechanism given above the overall entropy of activation is the sum of the entropy change ΔS_1 for the preequilibrium (1) and the entropy of activation $\Delta S_2^\ddagger$ for the slow process (2). The entropy change in process (1) is probably very small, but $\Delta S_2^\ddagger$ will have a strong negative value owing to the distribution of charges in the activated state. These will cause a considerable electrostriction of water molecules.

These mechanisms appear to apply to the ordinary aliphatic esters, but they are not the only possible mechanisms for ester hydrolysis. Day and Ingold[1] listed eight mechanisms for ester hydrolysis and suggested the following notation:

A	acid hydrolysis	*B*	base hydrolysis
1	unimolecular reaction	2	bimolecular reaction
′	acyl-oxygen scission	″	alkyl-oxygen scission

The eight possible combinations give rise to the following mechanisms, in which the slow steps are indicated:

A′1

$$\mathrm{R{-}\overset{\overset{\large O}{\|}}{C}{-}OR' + H_3O^+ \rightleftharpoons R{-}\overset{\overset{\large O}{\|}}{C}{-}\overset{+}{O}\begin{matrix}\diagup R'\\ \diagdown H\end{matrix} + H_2O}$$

$$\Big\downarrow \text{slow}$$

$$\mathrm{R{-}C^+{=}O + R'OH}$$

$$\Big\downarrow +\mathrm{H_2O}$$

$$\mathrm{RCOOH + H^+}$$

[1] J. N. E. Day and C. K. Ingold, *Trans. Faraday Soc.*, **37**, 686 (1941).

*A′*2
$$\mathrm{R{-}\overset{\overset{O}{\|}}{C}{-}OR' + H_3O^+ \rightleftharpoons R{-}\overset{\overset{O}{\|}}{C}{-}O^+{<}^{R'}_{H} + H_2O}$$

$$\mathrm{R{-}\overset{\overset{O}{\|}}{C}{-}O^+{<}^{R'}_{H} + H_2O \xrightarrow{slow} R{-}\overset{\overset{O}{\|}}{C}{-}O^+{<}^{H}_{H} + R'OH}$$

$$\mathrm{R{-}\overset{\overset{O}{\|}}{C}{-}O^+{<}^{H}_{H} \xrightarrow{+H_2O} RCOOH + H_3O^+}$$

*A″*1
$$\mathrm{R{-}\overset{\overset{O}{\|}}{C}{-}OR' + H_3O^+ \rightleftharpoons R{-}\overset{\overset{O}{\|}}{C}{-}O^+{<}^{R'}_{H} + H_2O}$$

$$\mathrm{R{-}\overset{\overset{O}{\|}}{C}{-}O^+{<}^{R'}_{H} \xrightarrow{slow} R{-}\overset{\overset{O}{\|}}{C}{-}OH + R'^+}$$

*A″*2
$$\mathrm{R{-}\overset{\overset{O}{\|}}{C}{-}OR' + H_3O^+ \rightleftharpoons R{-}\overset{\overset{O}{\|}}{C}{-}O^+{<}^{R'}_{H} + H_2O}$$

$$\mathrm{R{-}\overset{\overset{O}{\|}}{C}{-}O^+{<}^{R'}_{H} + H_2O \xrightarrow{slow} R{-}\overset{\overset{O}{\|}}{C}{-}OH + R'{-}O^+H_2}$$

*B′*1
$$\mathrm{R{-}\overset{\overset{O}{\|}}{C}{-}OR' \xrightarrow{slow} R{-}\overset{\overset{O}{\|}}{C}{}^+ + R'O^-}$$

$$\mathrm{R{-}\overset{\overset{O}{\|}}{C}{}^+ + 2H_2O \rightarrow R{-}\overset{\overset{O}{\|}}{C}{-}OH + H_3O^+}$$

$$\mathrm{R'O^- + H_2O \rightarrow R'OH + OH^-}$$

*B′*2
$$\mathrm{OH^- + R{-}\overset{\overset{O}{\|}}{C}{-}OR' \xrightarrow{slow} R{-}\overset{\overset{O}{\|}}{C}{-}OH + OR'^-}$$

$$\mathrm{H_2O + OR'^- \rightarrow R'OH + OH^-}$$

*B″*1
$$\mathrm{R{-}\overset{\overset{O}{\|}}{C}{-}OR' \xrightarrow{slow} R{-}\overset{\overset{O}{\|}}{C}{-}O^- + R'^+}$$

$$R'^{+} + 2H_2O \rightarrow R'OH + H_3O^{+}$$

$B''2$

$$R{-}\overset{\overset{\large O}{\|}}{C}{-}OR' + H_2O \xrightarrow{\text{slow}} R{-}\overset{\overset{\large O}{\|}}{C}{-}O^{-} + R'OH_2^{+}$$

$$R'OH_2^{+} + H_2O \rightarrow R'OH + H_3O^{+}$$

Of these mechanisms, $A'2$ and $B'2$ are the ones discussed above; they apply to many simple esters under ordinary conditions. Mechanisms $B'1$ and $A''2$ have not yet been observed. Some of the characteristics of these eight mechanisms are given in Table 65, which shows the order of

Table 65 MECHANISMS FOR ESTER HYDROLYSIS

Mechanism	Configuration of R′	Substituent effect		Steric hindrance
		R	R′	
$A'1$	Retention	0	+	No
$A'2$	Retention	0	0	Yes
$A''1$	Racemization	+	0	No
$A''2$	Inversion	+	0	Yes
$B'1$	Retention	0	−	No
$B'2$	Retention	−	−	Yes
$B''1$	Racemization	+	−	No
$B''2$	Inversion	0	−	Yes

reaction, and indicates whether there will be retention or inversion of configuration, or racemization, in the case of an asymmetric alkyl group R′. The table also shows whether an electron-repelling group in R and R′ will increase (+) or decrease (−) the rate of reaction, and whether the bulkiness of R or R′ will cause steric hindrance to reaction.

It is difficult to make a decision as to mechanism, since the effects are not so clear-cut as implied by Table 65. The evidence for one particular reaction, the acid hydrolysis of methyl acetate, is as follows. Acid hydrolysis is involved and the mechanism must be $A'1$, $A'2$, $A''1$, or $A''2$. The two latter possibilities, involving alkyl-oxygen scission, are eliminated for reactions of this type by the observation[1] that the acid

[1] Investigations of this kind have been carried out for a number of esters, for both acid and alkaline hydrolysis; for example, S. C. Datta, J. N. E. Day, and C. K. Ingold [*J. Chem. Soc.*, 838 (1939)] studied the acid hydrolysis of methyl hydrogen succinate in this way.

hydrolysis of ordinary esters in water containing an excess of O^{18} gives rise to

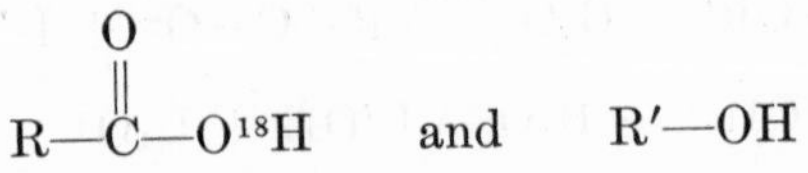

$$R{-}\overset{\overset{\textstyle O}{\|}}{C}{-}O^{18}H \qquad \text{and} \qquad R'{-}OH$$

The labeled atom is found in the acid and not in the alcohol, so that the bond broken must be that between the carbonyl carbon atom and the alcoholic oxygen atom.

The mechanism must therefore be $A'1$ or $A'2$. In both of these there is the same preequilibrium, involving the transfer of a proton to the ester; in the $A'1$ mechanism the second step is unimolecular,

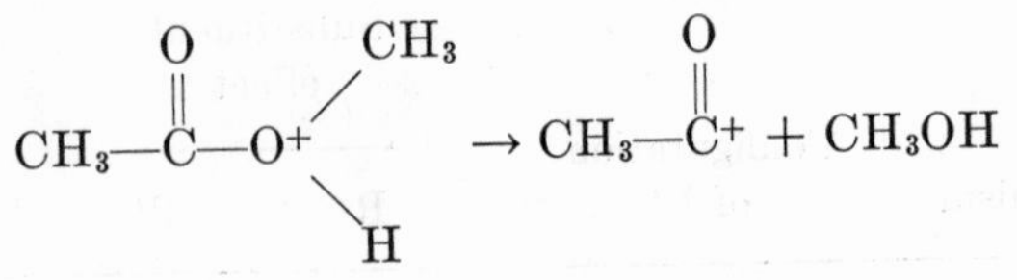

$$CH_3{-}\overset{\overset{\textstyle O}{\|}}{C}{-}\overset{+}{O}\begin{matrix}\diagup CH_3\\ \diagdown H\end{matrix} \rightarrow CH_3{-}\overset{\overset{\textstyle O}{\|}}{C^+} + CH_3OH$$

while in the $A'2$ mechanism the second step involves a water molecule,

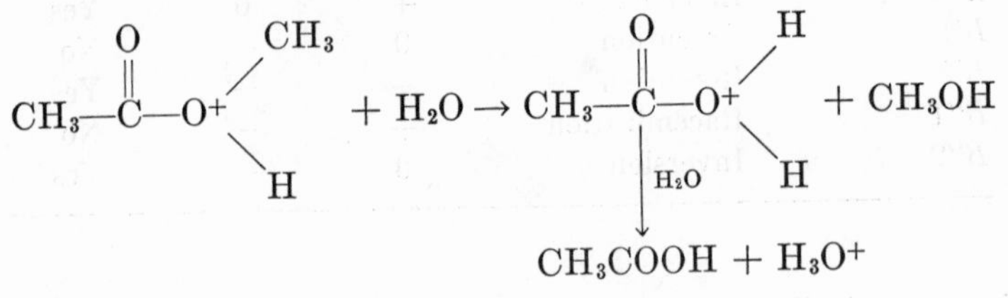

$$CH_3{-}\overset{\overset{\textstyle O}{\|}}{C}{-}\overset{+}{O}\begin{matrix}\diagup CH_3\\ \diagdown H\end{matrix} + H_2O \rightarrow CH_3{-}\underset{\underset{\textstyle H_2O}{|}}{\overset{\overset{\textstyle O}{\|}}{C}}{-}\overset{+}{O}\begin{matrix}\diagup H\\ \diagdown H\end{matrix} + CH_3OH$$

$$\downarrow$$

$$CH_3COOH + H_3O^+$$

In the $A'1$ case the activated complex differs from the initial state mainly in having an elongated carbon-oxygen bond; it will have a slightly higher entropy and volume than the initial state. In the $A'2$ case, on the other hand, a water molecule has been incorporated, and this will lead to a decrease in entropy and volume. In addition there may be an increase in polar character in the activated complex; this will lead to a further loss of entropy and volume.

A number of different lines of evidence have indicated that the $A'2$ mechanism is the one that applies to the acid catalysis of methyl acetate and of other similar esters. These pieces of evidence are in brief as follows:

1. *Substituent Effects.* It was seen above that in ethyl benzoate and its derivatives the direction of the substituent effects in acid catalysis is that predicted on the basis of the approach of a water molecule to the

protonated ester. This indicates that the $A'2$ mechanism applies to the benzoates, which are similar in kinetic behavior to the aliphatic esters.

2. *Steric Effects.* The rate is reduced by bulky substituents near the reaction site,[1] the effect being in addition to the normal inductive and resonance effects of the substituents.

3. *Influence of Solvent.* The reaction is accelerated by increasing the dielectric constant of the solvent.[2] This implies a somewhat polar activated complex, as in the $A'2$ mechanism.

4. *Entropy of Activation.* The entropy of activation[3] is -21.2 cal deg^{-1} $mole^{-1}$. This value is the sum of the entropy ΔS for the initial proton transfer and the entropy of activation $\Delta S_2^\ddagger$ for the slow step. The value of ΔS is expected to be small and slightly positive; $\Delta S_2^\ddagger$ must therefore be strongly negative. As discussed above, this result is only consistent with the $A'2$ mechanism.

5. *Influence of Pressure.* The volume of activation for the hydrolysis of methyl acetate calculated from the effect of hydrostatic pressure on the rate,[4] is -9.1 cc per mole. The volume change in the preequilibrium is expected to be small, so that the slow step probably involves a negative volume of activation. This result is consistent with the $A'2$ mechanism, but not with the $A'1$ mechanism, which would give a small positive or zero volume of activation.

6. *Acidity Functions.* It has been found by Tal'vik and Pal'm[5] that in concentrated acid solutions the rate of the hydrolysis of *ethyl* acetate shows a correlation with Hammett's acidity function H_0. As seen in Chap. 9, the straightforward conclusion from this is that a water molecule is not incorporated in the activated complex, which means that the $A'1$ mechanism applies. This conclusion, however, is out of line with all the other evidence; this is therefore apparently a case in which the evidence from acidity functions is unreliable.

Enzyme Catalysis. Much work has been done on the enzyme-catalyzed hydrolysis of esters, but the details are still by no means understood. As usual with enzyme-catalyzed reactions the rates pass through a maximum as the pH is varied, and this is attributed to the fact that the active center of the enzyme contains both an acidic (—A—H)

[1] C. K. Ingold, "Structure and Mechanism in Organic Chemistry," p. 335, Cornell University Press, Ithaca, N.Y., 1953.

[2] K. J. Laidler and P. A. Landskroener, *Trans. Faraday Soc.*, **52**, 200 (1956); for an alternative interpretation, see E. Tommila and M. L. Murto, *Acta Chem. Scand.*, **17**, 1947 (1963).

[3] A. Lamble and W. C. McC. Lewis, *Trans. Chem. Soc.*, 2330 (1914).

[4] A. R. Osborn and E. Whalley, *Can. J. Chem.*, **39**, 1094 (1961); cf. also A. Bogojawlensky and G. Tammann, *Z. Physik. Chem.*, **23**, 13 (1897).

[5] A. L. Tal'vik and V. A. Pal'm, *Zh. Fiz. Khim.*, **33**, 1214 (1959).

and a basic (—B) site; the enzyme can therefore be represented schematically as

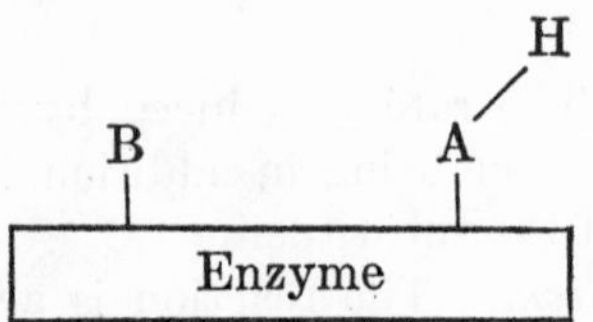

Since in some of the mechanisms for both acid and base catalysis there is a nucleophilic attack on the carbonyl carbon atom, and a proton transfer to the alcoholic oxygen atom, it is natural to suspect that in enzymatic catalysis there is a simultaneous nucleophilic attack by the basic group B and a proton transfer by the acidic group —A—H. Such a "push-pull" mechanism might well lead to very efficient catalysis, and this may be the explanation for the very high effectiveness of enzymes.

Such mechanisms may be considered in further detail with special reference to one ester hydrolysis that has been investigated very carefully, namely, the hydrolysis of acetylcholine,

$$CH_3\overset{\overset{\displaystyle O}{\|}}{C}—OCH_2CH_2N^+(CH_3)_3 + H_2O \rightarrow CH_3COOH + HOCH_2CH_2N^+(CH_3)_3$$

catalyzed by the enzyme acetylcholinesterase.[1] This enzyme, which plays a very important role in nerve conduction, has a molecular weight of about 3,000,000, and it appears that there are about 100 active centers per molecule. Studies of the variation of rate with pH have indicated[2] that there are two pH-sensitive groups at each active center, having pK values of 6.5 and 9.3. The first of these probably corresponds to an imidazole group which is active in its nonprotonated form; the latter probably corresponds to a phenolic group, active in its neutral form. It has also been concluded from work with certain inhibitors that a serine hydroxyl group plays an important role at each active center.

Another conclusion of great significance is that this enzyme possesses, some 7 A from the other groups in the active center, an *anionic* site. The evidence for this[3] is based on studies with inhibitors containing cationic centers, such as quaternary ammonium salts. This anionic site undoubtedly interacts with the positive nitrogen atom when the substrate undergoes reactions. There is also chemical evidence that a serine residue is close to the esteratic and anionic sites.

[1] For reviews see I. B. Wilson, *Discussions Faraday Soc.*, **20,** 119 (1955); K. J. Laidler, "The Chemical Kinetics of Enzyme Action," chap. 10, Clarendon Press, Oxford, 1958.

[2] R. M. Krupka and K. J. Laidler, *Trans. Faraday Soc.*, **56,** 1467, 1477 (1960).

[3] F. Bergmann, I. B. Wilson, and D. Nachmansohn, *J. Biol. Chem.*, **186,** 693 (1950).

The picture that thus emerges for the active center of the enzyme is represented in Fig. 88.

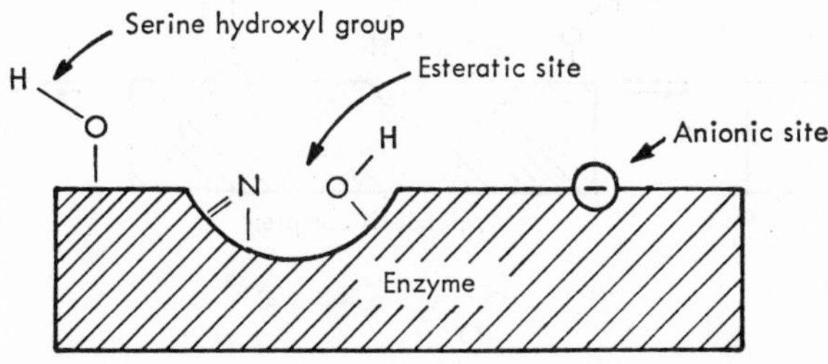

Fig. 88. Schematic representation of the active center of the cholinesterase molecule, as revealed by kinetic studies.

Studies of the overall kinetics of the enzyme-catalyzed hydrolysis of acetylcholine have shown that with increasing substrate concentration the rate first increases and then decreases. This indicates that a Michaelis-Menten addition complex is formed, and also an inactive complex in which an additional substrate molecule has become attached to the enzyme. Wilson and Calib[1] have studied the temperature dependence of the rate over a range of substrate concentrations, and have concluded that subsequent to the addition complex there is formed an acetylated enzyme, which later is hydrolyzed into the enzyme and acetic acid.

Kinetic studies of the reaction with various substrates and inhibitors and over a range of pH values[2] have led to the conclusion that in the Michaelis-Menten addition complex the acid and basic groups of pK 6.5 and 9.3 are interacting with the enzyme, but that in the acyl enzyme they are free again. The simplest explanation of this is that the acylation is on the serine hydroxyl group. The reaction sequence that is arrived at on the basis of this evidence is shown schematically in Fig. 89. Krupka and Laidler[3] have drawn further conclusions concerning the detailed interactions that occur at each stage of the reactions. The essential idea is that each step occur by a concerted mechanism, in which some groups are pushing electrons, and others are pulling them. The high efficiency of the enzymes as catalysts may well be explained in this manner.

HYDROLYSIS OF OTHER COMPOUNDS

The kinetics of the hydrolysis of a number of other types of substances have also been investigated, and offer interesting similarities and

[1] I. B. Wilson and E. Calib, *J. Am. Chem. Soc.*, **78**, 202 (1956).
[2] Krupka and Laidler, *loc. cit.; J. Am. Chem. Soc.*, **83**, 1445, 1448, 1454 (1961).
[3] *Ibid.*, 1458.

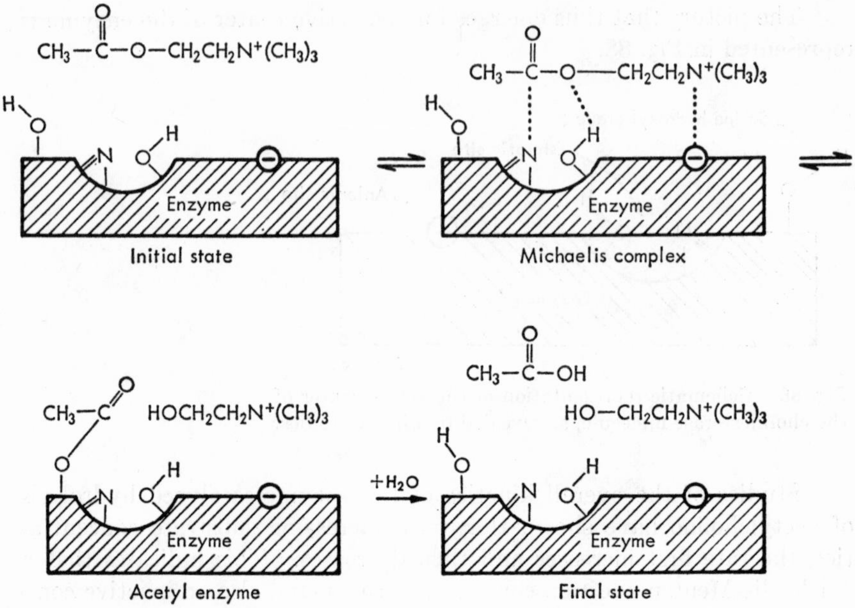

Fig. 89. Schematic mechanism for the hydrolysis of acetylcholine, catalyzed by the enzyme acetylcholinesterase.

contrasts with the hydrolysis of esters. Only a brief account is given here, attention being confined to the acid hydrolysis of acetals, amides, epoxides, ethers, and γ-lactones.

Hydrolysis of Acetals. The acetals are formed by the combination of aldehydes and alcohols, and have the general structure

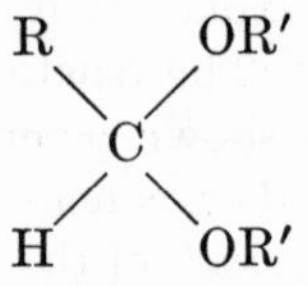

$$\begin{array}{ccc} R & & OR' \\ & \diagdown\ \diagup & \\ & C & \\ & \diagup\ \diagdown & \\ H & & OR' \end{array}$$

A well-known member of the series, usually known simply as *acetal*, is

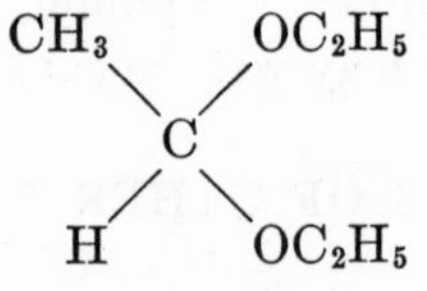

$$\begin{array}{ccc} CH_3 & & OC_2H_5 \\ & \diagdown\ \diagup & \\ & C & \\ & \diagup\ \diagdown & \\ H & & OC_2H_5 \end{array}$$

The hydrolysis of this compound has not been studied as carefully as has the hydrolysis of esters, but a number of points have been established.[1]

[1] Cf. R. P. Bell, "Acid-Base Catalysis," p. 76, Clarendon Press, Oxford, 1941; F. A. Long and M. A. Paul, *Chem. Rev.*, **57**, 925 (1957).

In aqueous solution the hydrolysis undergoes specific hydrogen-ion catalysis, and the rate is greater in D_2O than in H_2O. This suggests that there is an initial preequilibrium involving a proton transfer from the H_3O^+ ion,

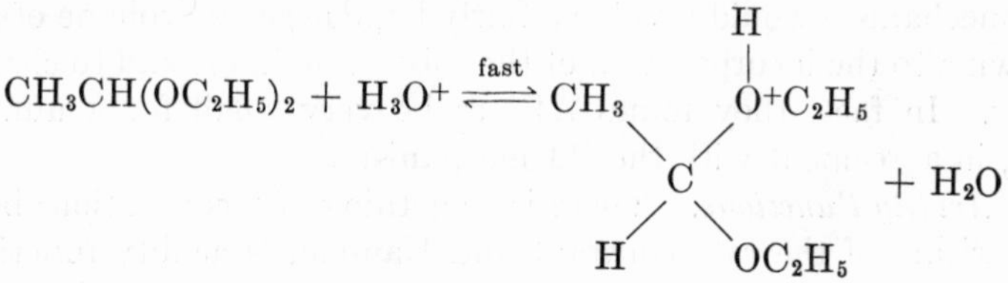

$$CH_3CH(OC_2H_5)_2 + H_3O^+ \overset{\text{fast}}{\rightleftharpoons} \begin{array}{ccc} CH_3 & & \overset{\displaystyle H}{|}\!\!\!\;\;O^+C_2H_5 \\ & \diagdown\;\diagup & \\ & C & \\ & \diagup\;\diagdown & \\ H & & OC_2H_5 \end{array} + H_2O$$

The slow step in the reaction is believed to be

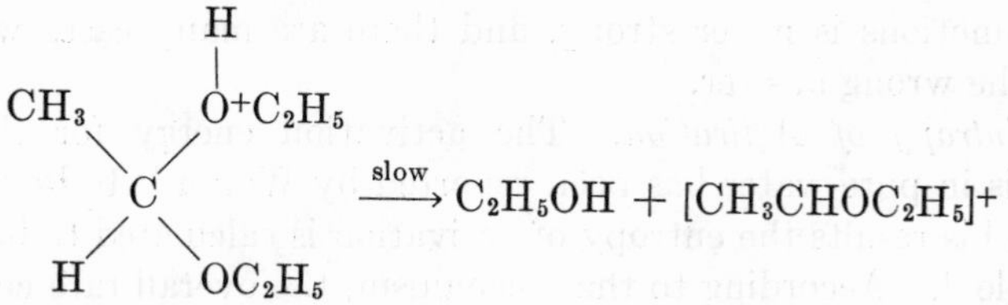

$$\begin{array}{ccc} CH_3 & & \overset{\displaystyle H}{|}\!\!\!\;\;O^+C_2H_5 \\ & \diagdown\;\diagup & \\ & C & \\ & \diagup\;\diagdown & \\ H & & OC_2H_5 \end{array} \xrightarrow{\text{slow}} C_2H_5OH + [CH_3CHOC_2H_5]^+$$

followed by

$$[CH_3CHOC_2H_5]^+ + H_2O \xrightarrow{\text{fast}} CH_3CHO + C_2H_5OH + H^+$$

The species $[CH_3CHOC_2H_2]^+$ is to be regarded as existing in a resonance state involving the structures

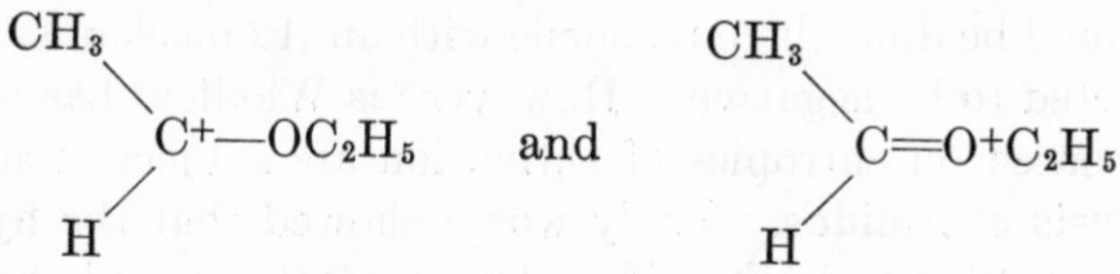

$$\begin{array}{l} CH_3 \\ \quad\diagdown \\ \quad\;\; C^+\!\!-\!OC_2H_5 \\ \quad\diagup \\ H \end{array} \quad \text{and} \quad \begin{array}{l} CH_3 \\ \quad\diagdown \\ \quad\;\; C\!=\!O^+C_2H_5 \\ \quad\diagup \\ H \end{array}$$

This mechanism is of the $A1$ type,[1] in contrast with the $A2$ mechanism which applies to the hydrolysis of ordinary esters. Some of the evidence in favor of the $A1$ mechanism is as follows:

1. *Substituent Effects.* Ingold[2] has pointed out that the substituent effects in the reaction are strong enough to require the $A1$ mechanism. Thus the rate increases greatly in the series

Formal:acetal:ketal

[1] Since there is no carbonyl group in the compound, there is only one mode of scission, and there is no need to discriminate between the A' and A'' mechanisms.

[2] Ingold, *op. cit.*

and this is in the direction expected if the slow step is simply a unimolecular breakdown of the protonated substrate.

2. *Pressure Effects.* Whalley and Koskikallio[1] have argued that if the mechanism is $A1$, the volume of activation should be small, whereas an $A2$ mechanism would involve a fairly large negative volume of activation, owing to the incorporation of the solvent molecule and to changes in polarity. In fact, they found $\Delta V^\ddagger$ to be very small for a number of acetals, in agreement with the $A1$ mechanism.

3. *Acidity Functions.* There is something of a correlation[2] between the logarithm of the rate constant and Hammett's acidity function H_0. This result is consistent with the conclusion that a water molecule is not incorporated into the activated state, and therefore supports the $A1$ mechanism. However, as has been emphasized, the evidence from acidity functions is never strong, and there are many cases where one obtains the wrong answer.

4. *Entropy of Activation.* The activation energy for the acetal hydrolysis in pure water has been reported by Wolford[3] to be 22.4 kcal, and from his results the entropy of activation is calculated to be 15.3 cal deg^{-1} mole^{-1}. According to the mechanism, the overall rate constant is equal to k_2K, where K is the equilibrium constant for reaction (1), and k_2 is the rate constant for reaction (2), which is the slow step. The entropy of activation is therefore equal to $\Delta S_1 + \Delta S_2^\ddagger$, where ΔS_1 is the overall entropy change for the preequilibrium, and $\Delta S_2^\ddagger$ is the entropy of activation for reaction (2). There is some uncertainty in the value to be expected for ΔS_1, but it is not likely to be very positive. The value of 15.3 eu for the overall entropy of activation thus suggests that $\Delta S_2^\ddagger$ is fairly large and positive. This result is consistent with an $A1$ mechanism, but would be difficult to reconcile with an $A2$ mechanism, for which $\Delta S_2^\ddagger$ is expected to be negative. However, as Whalley[4] has emphasized, conclusions based on entropies of activation are subject to uncertainty.

Hydrolysis of Amides. Early work[5] showed that the hydrolysis of amides is susceptible to both acid and base catalysis, and that the reactions are second order in dilute solution. At sufficiently low concentrations of acid there is a good correlation between the logarithm of the rate constant and the pH, and the Hammett-Zucker hypothesis would lead

[1] E. Whalley, *Trans. Faraday Soc.*, **55**, 798 (1959); J. Koskikallio and E. Whalley, *ibid.*, 809.

[2] P. Salomaa, *Acta Chem. Scand.*, **11**, 461 (1957); R. K. Wolford, *J. Phys. Chem.*, **67**, 632 (1963).

[3] Wolford, *loc. cit.*

[4] Whalley, *loc. cit.*

[5] W. Ostwald, *J. Prakt. Chem.*, **27**, 1 (1883); E. E. Reid, *Am. Chem. J.*, **21**, 284 (1899); **24**, 397 (1900); J. C. Crocker, *J. Chem. Soc.*, 593 (1907); H. von Euler and A. Olander, *Z. Physik. Chem.*, **131**, 107 (1927).

to the conclusion that the mechanism is of the $A'2$ type, as follows:

$$H_3O^+ + RCONH_2 \overset{\text{fast}}{\rightleftharpoons} RCONH_3^+ + H_2O$$

$$H_2O + RCONH_3^+ \xrightarrow{\text{slow}} RCO{-}O^+\!\begin{matrix} H \\ H \end{matrix} + NH_3$$

$$\downarrow H_2O$$

$$RCOOH + H_3O^+$$

A complication exists, however, in that the rate ceases to be linear in [H+] at higher acid concentrations, and actually reaches a maximum value at an acid concentration that is usually between 2 and $5M$.[1] This result was at one time explained in terms of the hypothesis that at high acid concentrations the protonated amide combined with the anion of the acid, forming an unhydrolyzable complex. This, however, was shown to be incorrect by the fact that the position of the maximum rate was independent of the amide concentration. It was then suggested[2] that the falling off of the rate at high acid concentrations is due to the decreased activity of the water. This hypothesis has been found[3] to provide a satisfactory quantitative treatment of amide hydrolysis in acid solution. It is to be noted that the hypothesis is only consistent with an $A'2$ mechanism.

The situation may be formulated as follows, in terms of the general $A'2$ mechanism:

$$H_3O^+ + S \overset{K_1}{\rightleftharpoons} SH^+ + H_2O$$

$$SH^+ + H_2O \overset{K_2}{\rightleftharpoons} X^\ddagger \overset{k}{\rightarrow} \text{products}$$

Application of the steady-state treatment leads to the result that the rate is

$$v = kK_2[SH^+][H_2O]\frac{f_{SH^+}f_{H_2O}}{f_{X^\ddagger}} \tag{1}$$

$$= kK_1K_2[S][H^+]\frac{f_Sf_{H^+}}{f_{X^\ddagger}} \tag{2}$$

[1] A. Benrath, Z. *Anorg. Chem.*, **151,** 53 (1926); T. W. J. Taylor, *J. Chem. Soc.*, 2741 (1930); O. Reitz, *Z. Elektrochem.*, **44,** 693 (1938); V. K. Krieble and K. A. Holst, *J. Am. Chem. Soc.*, **60,** 2976 (1938); B. S. Rabinovitch and C. A. Winkler, *Can. J. Res.*, **B20,** 73 (1942); J. T. Edward, H. P. Hutchison, and S. C. R. Meacock, *J. Chem. Soc.*, 2520 (1955).

[2] Krieble and Holst, *loc. cit.*

[3] J. T. Edward and S. C. R. Meacock, *J. Chem. Soc.*, 2000 (1957).

The quantity $f_S f_{H_3O^+}/f_{X^\ddagger}$ is believed to be fairly constant, so that the rate can be written as

$$v = k'[S][H^+] \tag{3}$$

where k' is a second-order rate constant for the reaction. The experimentally determined first-order rate constant k^1, which expresses the variation in rate with acid concentration, is given in terms of the sum of the concentrations of S and SH^+,

$$v = k^1([S] + [SH^+]) \tag{4}$$

Hammett's acidity function h_0 is defined by[1]

$$h_0 = K_{SH^+} \frac{[SH^+]}{[S]} \tag{5}$$

Elimination of [S] and $[SH^+]$ from Eqs. (3), (4), and (5) then leads to

$$k^1 = \frac{k' K_{SH^+}[H^+]}{K_{SH^+} + h_0} \tag{6}$$

This relationship was first given by Edward and Meacock.[2]

The following special cases of this equation are of interest:

1. If the acid concentration is sufficiently small, $h_0 \ll K_{SH^+}$, so that the rate constant is given by

$$k^1 = k' K_{SH^+}[H^+] \tag{7}$$

This is the situation with amides at low acid concentrations. Equation (7) is also obeyed in ester hydrolysis at all acid concentrations that have been investigated; the reason for the difference is considered below.

2. At sufficiently high acid concentrations, $h_0 \gg K_{SH^+}$, so that

$$k^1 = \frac{k' K_{SH^+}[H^+]}{h_0} \tag{8}$$

At concentrations greater than about $2M$, h_0 increases much more rapidly than $[H^+]$, with the result that k^1 decreases with increasing acid concentration.

The reason why the esters do not show the kind of behavior represented by Eq. (8) is that they are very weak bases, so that K_{SH^+} is large; the inequality $h_0 \ll K_{SH^+}$ therefore always applies, and it is not possible to reach such high concentrations of acid that h_0 is comparable with K_{SH^+}.

The Edward-Meacock treatment provides a satisfactory interpretation of the main results obtained in amide hydrolysis, but Edward and

[1] This is an alternative acidity function to H_0, defined in Eq. (91) on page 469; $H_0 = -\log_{10} h_0$.

[2] Edward and Meacock, *loc. cit.*

Campbell[1] have recently discussed the results in terms of Bunnett's alternative treatment (p. 474) of the behavior at high acid concentrations. This treatment, which is considerably more complicated, appears to provide a slightly better quantitative interpretation.

Hydrolysis of Epoxides. Several kinetic studies have been made of the hydrolysis of epoxides, the simplest example of which is

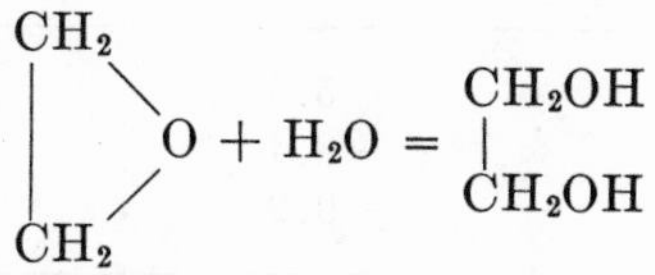

$$\begin{matrix} CH_2 \\ | \quad \diagdown \\ | \quad\quad O \\ | \quad \diagup \\ CH_2 \end{matrix} + H_2O = \begin{matrix} CH_2OH \\ | \\ CH_2OH \end{matrix}$$

The reactions are first order in both epoxide and acid, and show the general characteristics of specific acid catalysis.[2] There is undoubtedly an initial proton transfer,

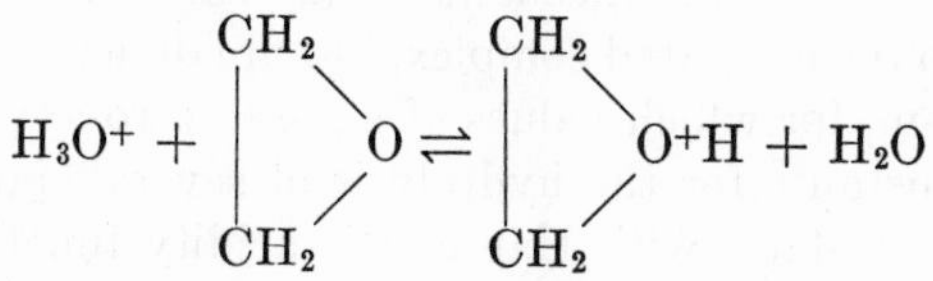

$$H_3O^+ + \begin{matrix} CH_2 \\ | \quad \diagdown \\ | \quad\quad O \\ | \quad \diagup \\ CH_2 \end{matrix} \rightleftharpoons \begin{matrix} CH_2 \\ | \quad \diagdown \\ | \quad\quad O^+H \\ | \quad \diagup \\ CH_2 \end{matrix} + H_2O$$

The second step may correspond to either an *A*1 or an *A*2 mechanism. In the former case

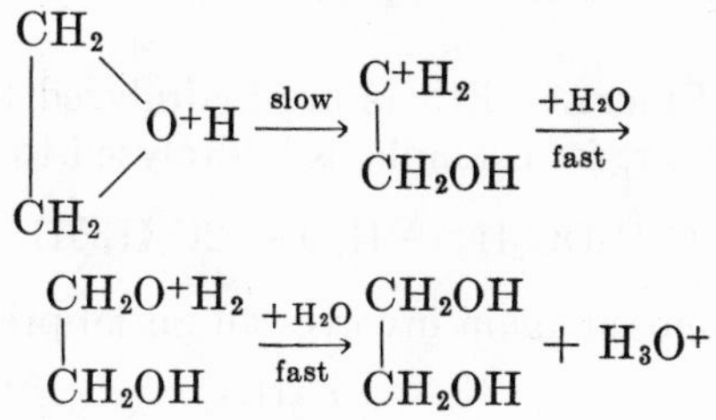

$$\begin{matrix} CH_2 \\ | \quad \diagdown \\ | \quad\quad O^+H \\ | \quad \diagup \\ CH_2 \end{matrix} \xrightarrow{\text{slow}} \begin{matrix} C^+H_2 \\ | \\ CH_2OH \end{matrix} \xrightarrow[\text{fast}]{+H_2O}$$

$$\begin{matrix} CH_2O^+H_2 \\ | \\ CH_2OH \end{matrix} \xrightarrow[\text{fast}]{+H_2O} \begin{matrix} CH_2OH \\ | \\ CH_2OH \end{matrix} + H_3O^+$$

In the *A*2 case

$$H_2O + \begin{matrix} CH_2 \\ | \quad \diagdown \\ | \quad\quad O^+H \\ | \quad \diagup \\ CH_2 \end{matrix} \xrightarrow{\text{slow}} \begin{matrix} CH_2O^+H_2 \\ | \\ CH_2OH \end{matrix} \xrightarrow[\text{fast}]{+H_2O} \begin{matrix} CH_2OH \\ | \\ CH_2OH \end{matrix} + H_3O^+$$

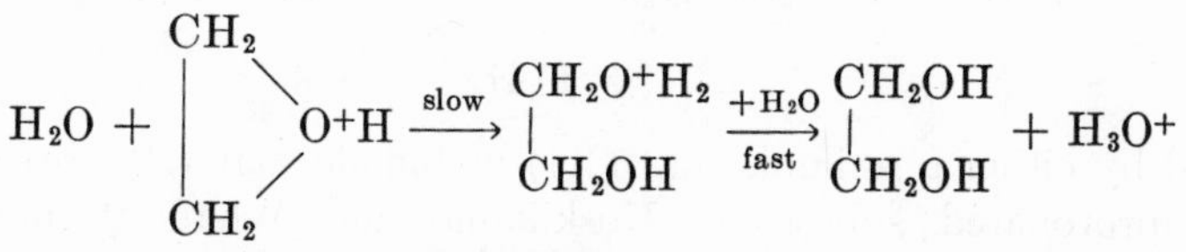

That the *A*2 mechanism is in fact the correct one is shown by the values, listed in Table 66, of the volumes of activation[3] and of the

[1] J. T. Edward and H. J. Campbell, to be published; cf. Campbell's Ph.D. Thesis, McGill University, 1961.

[2] J. N. Brønsted, M. Kilpatrick, and M. L. Kilpatrick, *J. Am. Chem. Soc.*, **51,** 428 (1929); A. M. Eastham and G. A. Latremouille, *Can. J. Chem.*, **30,** 169 (1952); F. A. Long and J. G. Pritchard, *J. Am. Chem. Soc.*, **78,** 2663 (1956); Pritchard and Long, *ibid.*, 2667, 6008.

[3] Koskikallio and Whalley, *Trans. Faraday Soc.*, **55,** 815 (1959).

Table 66 VOLUMES AND ENTROPIES OF ACTIVATION FOR THE HYDROLYSIS OF EPOXIDES

Epoxide	$\Delta V^{\ddagger}$, cc per mole (at 0°C)	$\Delta S^{\ddagger}$, cal deg^{-1} mole^{-1} (at 20°C)
Ethylene	−5.9	−6.1
Propylene	−8.4	−4.3
Isobutylene	−9.2	−4

entropies of activation.[1] The negative values for both these quantities are consistent with the $A2$ mechanism, in which a water molecule is incorporated into the activated complex, but are difficult to reconcile with the $A1$ mechanism, for which values of close to zero are expected.

The rate constants for the hydrolysis of several epoxides, including ethylene oxide, correlate[2] with Hammett's acidity function H_0, but not with [H$^+$]. On the basis of the Hammett-Zucker hypothesis the conclusion would be that the mechanism is $A1$. This is at variance with the other evidence, and it therefore appears that the hypothesis fails for this reaction.

Hydrolysis of Ethers.[3] Ethers are hydrolyzed to alcohols by acid catalysis; diethyl ether, for example, is hydrolyzed to ethanol,

$$C_2H_5OC_2H_5 + H_2O \rightarrow 2C_2H_5OH$$

The mechanism proposed again involves an initial proton transfer,

$$H_3O^+ + C_2H_5OC_2H_5 \rightleftharpoons (C_2H_5)_2O^+\text{—}H + H_2O$$

followed by either a unimolecular ($A1$) or bimolecular ($A2$) breakdown of the protonated substrate. Koskikallio and Whalley[4] found the entropy of activation of the diethyl ether hydrolysis to be −9.0 cal deg^{-1} mole^{-1}, and the volume of activation to be −8.5 cc per mole. These negative values provide strong evidence in favor of the bimolecular ($A2$) mechanism.

[1] F. A. Long, J. G. Pritchard, and F. E. Stafford, *J. Am. Chem. Soc.*, **79**, 2362 (1957).

[2] Pritchard and Long, *loc. cit.*

[3] Cf. R. L. Burwell, *Chem. Rev.*, **54**, 615 (1954).

[4] J. Koskikallio and G. Whalley, *Can. J. Chem.*, **37**, 788 (1959).

For this reaction there is a correlation with the H_0 acidity function, which would, on the basis of the Hammett-Zucker hypothesis, suggest the *A*1 mechanism. The hypothesis is again inconsistent with the other evidence.

Hydrolysis of γ-Lactones. γ-Butyrolactone has an unstrained five-membered ring, and its hydrolysis to γ-hydroxybutyric acid,

```
        CH2                          CH2
       /   \                        /   \
   CH2       C=O + H2O → CH2              COOH
       \     |                      \
        CH2—O                        CH2OH
```

is catalyzed by acids and bases; there is no detectable hydrolysis by water. It was shown by Long and Friedman,[1] using water labeled with O^{18}, that the scission occurs at the acyl oxygen atom in both acid and base catalysis. Only the acid-catalyzed reaction will be considered here.

By analogy with the acid-catalyzed hydrolyses of similar compounds, such as esters, it is supposed that there is an initial proton transfer to the acyl-oxygen atom of the lactone:

```
                                              CH2
                  CH2                        /   \
                 /   \         fast         /     \
H3O+ + CH2            C=O  ⇌  CH2                  C=O + H2O
                 \    |                     \     /
                  CH2—O                      CH2—O+
                                                 |
                                                 H
```

The slow process may be a unimolecular breakdown of the protonated lactone (the *A*′1 mechanism),

```
            CH2                     CH2
           /   \                   /   \
          /     C=O → CH2               C+=O
   CH2   /      |                  \    |
         \      O+                  CH2+ OH
          \    /  \
           CH2     H
```

or an attack by a water molecule (the *A*′2 mechanism),

```
      CH2
     /   \                          CH2
    /     \                        /   \
CH2        C=O + H2O → CH2              C=O   + H+
    \     /                        \      \
     CH2—O+                         CH2OH  OH
          \
           H
```

[1] F. A. Long and L. Friedman, *J. Am. Chem. Soc.*, **72**, 3692 (1950).

A decision between the two possibilities has been arrived at by Osborn and Whalley[1] on the basis of a study of the effect of pressure on the rate. The volume of activation was found to be −8.4 cc per mole, and this negative value is consistent with the $A'2$ mechanism but cannot be reconciled with the $A'1$ mechanism, which would lead to a value close to zero. Osborn and Whalley conclude that the negative value can be explained entirely in terms of the formation of a partial bond between the oxygen atom of the water molecule and the carbonyl carbon atom, and that there appears to be little electrostriction. This means that the activated complex, which has the structure

```
                    H
                    | δ+
         CH2        O—H
        /   \      .
     CH2      C
     |        :  \\
     |        :    O
     CH2——————O δ+
              |
              H
```

is not highly polar.

The conclusion that the $A'2$ mechanism applies is supported by the fact that the entropy of activation[2] for the reaction is −20.9 cal deg^{-1} mole^{-1}. This large negative value, which is similar to that for ester hydrolysis, is also only consistent with an $A'2$ mechanism. The entropy of activation tends, however, to suggest a fairly polar activated state, since it is hard to explain such a low value in terms of structural changes alone.

For the hydrolysis of γ-butyrolactone there is a correlation[3] between the logarithm of the rate constant and the pH of the solution. The Hammett-Zucker hypothesis leads to the conclusion that the activated complex contains a water molecule, i.e., that the $A'2$ mechanism applies. In this case, therefore, the hypothesis is consistent with the other evidence.

It may be noted that the β-lactones, such as β-propiolactone, behave quite differently; Osborn and Whalley have compared and contrasted them with the γ-lactones.

HYDRATION OF ACETALDEHYDE

Acetaldehyde is hydrated to the extent of about 60 percent in water at room temperature, the rate of hydration being too great to be measured

[1] A. R. Osborn and E. Whalley, *Trans. Faraday Soc.*, **58**, 2144 (1962).

[2] F. D. Coffin and F. A. Long, *J. Am. Chem. Soc.*, **74**, 5767 (1952).

[3] F. A. Long, W. F. McDevit, and F. B. Dunkle, *J. Phys. Colloid Chem.*, **55**, 813, 829 (1951).

by conventional methods. Bell and Darwent[1] studied the kinetics of the reaction at 0°C, using a dilatometric method, and showed that the reaction exhibits general acid-base catalysis. Later Bell and Clunie[2] developed a more satisfactory technique for studying this and other fast reactions; it is known as the *thermal maximum method* and involves measuring the maximum temperature rise that is developed during the reaction.

Using this method Bell, Rand, and Wynne-Jones[3] carried out an extensive investigation of the hydration of acetaldehyde, using a number of buffer systems, and determined the various catalytic constants. At 25°C they found that the first-order catalytic constant can be represented by the equation

$$k = 0.0079 + 930[\mathrm{H^+}] + 8 \times 10^4[\mathrm{OH^-}] + k_{\mathrm{HA}}[\mathrm{HA}] + k_{\mathrm{B}}[\mathrm{B}]\ \mathrm{sec^{-1}} \quad (9)$$

where [HA] and [B] are the concentrations of the acidic and basic species in the buffer, and k_{HA} and k_{B} are the corresponding catalytic constants. It was found that the k_{HA} values showed a satisfactory correlation with the dissociation constants, in accordance with the Brønsted relationship, when the appropriate statistical factors were taken into account. The k_{B} values, on the other hand, bore no simple relationship to the base strengths, and it was concluded that steric factors were having an important effect.

A significant conclusion that can be drawn[4] from the results on this reaction is that the catalytic constants contain no term involving the product [HA][B]. It has been suggested from time to time[5] that some acid-base catalyzed reactions proceed by a *concerted mechanism*,[6] in which the activated complex contains both the acidic and the basic species. The absence of a term in [HA][B] means that there is no evidence for such a mechanism for this particular reaction.

The mechanism proposed[7] for catalysis by the acid species BH^+ is

[1] R. P. Bell and B. de B. Darwent, *Trans. Faraday Soc.*, **46**, 34 (1950).

[2] R. P. Bell and J. C. Clunie, *Proc. Roy. Soc.* (*London*), **A212**, 16, 33 (1952); Bell, V. Gold, J. Hilton, and M. H. Rand, *Discussions Faraday Soc.*, **17**, 151 (1954).

[3] R. P. Bell, M. H. Rand, and K. M. A. Wynne-Jones, *Trans. Faraday Soc.*, **52**, 1093 (1956).

[4] R. P. Bell, "The Proton in Chemistry," p. 151, Cornell University Press, Ithaca, N.Y., 1959.

[5] See, for example, C. G. Swain, *J. Am. Chem. Soc.*, **72**, 4578 (1950); for a discussion see R. P. Bell, *op. cit.*, pp. 147–154.

[6] Various other names have been given to the mechanism, including *ternary*, *synchronous*, *push-pull*, and *bimolecular* (the latter referring to the number of catalyst molecules).

[7] R. P. Bell and W. C. E. Higginson, *Proc. Roy. Soc.* (*London*), **A197**, 141 (1949); Bell and Darwent, *loc. cit.*

$$\text{(1)} \qquad CH_3CHO + H_2O + BH^+ \rightarrow CH_3CH\begin{matrix} OH \\ O^+H_2 \end{matrix} + B$$

$$\text{(2)} \qquad CH_3CH\begin{matrix} OH \\ O^+H_2 \end{matrix} + B \rightleftharpoons CH_3CH(OH)_2 + BH^+$$

in which reaction (1) is rate determining. Similarly for base catalysis the rate-determining step is postulated to be

$$\text{(1)} \qquad CH_3CHO + H_2O + B \rightarrow CH_3CH\begin{matrix} OH \\ O^- \end{matrix} + BH^+$$

followed by the rapid equilibrium

$$\text{(2)} \qquad CH_3CH\begin{matrix} OH \\ O^- \end{matrix} + BH^+ \rightleftharpoons CH_3CH\begin{matrix} OH \\ OH \end{matrix} + B$$

These mechanisms are clearly consistent with general acid-base catalysis.

HALOGENATION OF ACETONE

The reaction between acetone and a halogen occurs according to the following stoichiometric equation:

$$CH_3COCH_3 + X_2 \rightarrow CH_3COCH_2X + HX$$

The reaction has been studied[1] using chlorine, bromine, and iodine, and it was found that at sufficiently high concentrations of halogen the rate is independent of the halogen concentration. Also, under these conditions the rate of halogenation is independent of which halogen is used. It follows that under these circumstances the rate-controlling step is the enolization of the acetone,

$$CH_3COCH_3 \rightarrow CH_3\overset{\overset{OH}{|}}{C}{=}CH_2$$

[1] R. P. Bell and K. Yates, *J. Chem. Soc.*, 1927 (1962).

and that this is followed by addition of the halogen and the elimination of a molecule of hydrogen halide,

$$CH_3\overset{\overset{\displaystyle OH}{|}}{C}{=}CH_2 + X_2 \rightarrow CH_3\underset{\underset{\displaystyle X}{|}}{\overset{\overset{\displaystyle OH}{|}}{C}}{-}CH_2X \rightarrow CH_3COCH_2X + HX$$

At low halogen concentrations the addition of halogen becomes rate determining,[1] the rate then being proportional to the halogen concentration.

It was noted in the previous chapter that iodination of acetone was the first reaction for which it was firmly established that general acid-base catalysis was involved. A number of acidic and basic species have been investigated, and their catalytic constants determined.[2] Table 67 shows

Table 67 CATALYTIC CONSTANTS FOR THE IODINATION OF ACETONE†

Catalyst	K_a	$k_a \times 10^6$, liters mole^{-1} sec^{-1} Observed	Calculated
Dichloroacetic acid	5.7×10^{-2}	220	270
α-β-Dibromopropionic acid	6.7×10^{-3}	63	54
Monochloroacetic acid	1.41×10^{-3}	34	32
Glycolic acid	1.54×10^{-4}	8.4	7.9
β-Chloropropionic acid	1.01×10^{-4}	5.9	6.2
Acetic acid	1.75×10^{-5}	2.4	2.2
Propionic acid	1.34×10^{-5}	1.7	1.8
Trimethylacetic acid	9.1×10^{-6}	1.9	1.5

† The values in this table are from various sources; for a review see R. P. Bell, "Acid-Base Catalysis," Clarendon Press, Oxford, 1941; "Acids and Bases," Methuen & Co., Ltd., London, 1952.

some catalytic constants for this reaction, together with the acid dissociation constants of the catalysts. The Brønsted equation relating the catalytic constants to the dissociation constants is

$$k_a = 7.90 \times 10^{-4} K_a^{0.62} \qquad \text{sec}^{-1}$$

[1] *Ibid.* K. Yates and W. V. Wright, *Can. J. Chem.*, **41,** 2882 (1963).

[2] H. M. Dawson and F. Powis, *J. Chem. Soc.*, **103,** 2135 (1913), and many subsequent papers by Dawson; J. N. Brønsted, *Trans. Faraday Soc.*, **24,** 728 (1928); O. M. Lidwell and R. P. Bell, *Proc. Roy. Soc. (London)*, **A176,** 88 (1940).

Table 67 shows the values that are calculated using this relationship; the agreement with the experimental values is satisfactory. The catalysts listed are all uncharged acids for which p and q (cf. p. 464) are equal to unity; when charged acids having different values of p and q are considered, a different equation must be used to obtain the best agreement.

The mechanism proposed for acid catalysis is that in the initial step the acetone accepts a proton from the acid,

$$BH^+ + CH_3COCH_3 \underset{k_{-1}}{\overset{k_1}{\rightleftharpoons}} CH_3\overset{\overset{O^+H}{\|}}{C}CH_3 + B$$

and that the protonated substrate gives up its proton to a solute base B, at the same time changing over to the enol form:

$$CH_3\overset{\overset{O^+H}{\|}}{C}CH_3 + B \xrightarrow{k_2} CH_3\overset{\overset{OH}{|}}{C}{=}CH_2 + BH^+$$

This is a prototropic mechanism, the general equations for which were given on page 460. Application of the steady-state treatment to the concentration of the intermediate gives rise to

$$\frac{d[\text{enol}]}{dt} = \frac{k_1 k_2 [BH^+][CH_3COCH_3]}{k_{-1} + k_2} \tag{10}$$

At sufficiently high halogen concentrations the rate of halogenation will be equal to this rate of enolization. In an optically active ketone the rate of racemization should also be equal to the rate of halogenation, and the rate of exchange of heavy hydrogen should also be the same. These rates are in fact equal,[1] and this supports the mechanism proposed.

The rate equation (10) is consistent with the occurrence of general acid catalysis, since any acidic solute species can play the role of BH^+. The rate equation also implies that the reaction is a prototropic one, the second step involving the solute base B rather than a solvent molecule; otherwise, with an Arrhenius complex, specific hydrogen-ion catalysis would have been found (cf. Table 59, p. 463). The mechanism suggested is also supported by some additional lines of evidence, and is now well established.

At low concentrations of halogen the rate of enolization is no longer rate controlling, and the kinetics under these circumstances may be

[1] C. K. Ingold and C. L. Wilson, *J. Chem. Soc.*, 773 (1934); P. D. Bartlett and C. H. Stauffer, *J. Am. Chem. Soc.*, **57**, 2580 (1935); O. Reitz, *Z. Physik. Chem.*, **179**, 119 (1937).

formulated in terms of the mechanism

$$\text{(1)}\quad BH^+ + CH_3COCH_3 \underset{k_{-1}}{\overset{k_1}{\rightleftharpoons}} CH_3\overset{\overset{\displaystyle O^+H}{\|}}{C}CH_3 + B$$

$$\text{(2)}\quad CH_3\overset{\overset{\displaystyle O^+H}{\|}}{C}CH_3 + B \underset{k_{-2}}{\overset{k_2}{\rightleftharpoons}} CH_3\overset{\overset{\displaystyle OH}{|}}{C}{=}CH_2 + BH^+$$

$$\text{(3)}\quad CH_3\overset{\overset{\displaystyle OH}{|}}{C}{=}CH_2 + X_2 \overset{k_3}{\rightarrow} CH_3\underset{\underset{\displaystyle X}{|}}{\overset{\overset{\displaystyle OH}{|}}{C}}{-}CH_2X \xrightarrow{\text{fast}} CH_3COCH_2X + HX$$

Application of the steady-state treatment to this scheme gives

$$v = \frac{k_1k_2k_3[BH^+][CH_3COCH_3][X_2]}{k_{-1}\,k_{-2}[BH^+] + (k_{-1} + k_2)k_3[X_2]} \tag{11}$$

When $[X_2]$ is sufficiently large, the rate is independent of $[X_2]$, but at low concentrations the rate becomes

$$v = \frac{k_1k_2k_3}{k_{-1}\,k_{-2}}[CH_3COCH_3][X_2] \tag{12}$$

The rate is then predicted to be proportional to the halogen concentration and independent of the acid concentration, in agreement with experiment.

In the base-catalyzed reaction the ketone is believed to react with the base B to form a negative ion, to which two alternative structures can be assigned:

$$CH_3COCH_3 + B \rightleftharpoons \left\{\begin{matrix} CH_3COCH_2^- \\ CH_3\underset{\underset{\displaystyle O^-}{|}}{C}{=}CH_2 \end{matrix}\right\} + BH^+$$

The negative ion thus formed is then supposed to react with the halogen,

$$CH_3\underset{\underset{\displaystyle O^-}{|}}{C}{=}CH_2 + I_2 \rightarrow CH_3\underset{\underset{\displaystyle O^-}{|}}{\overset{\overset{\displaystyle I}{|}}{C}}{-}CH_2I$$

$$CH_3\underset{\underset{\displaystyle O^-}{|}}{\overset{\overset{\displaystyle I}{|}}{C}}{-}CH_2I + HA \rightarrow CH_3COCH_2I + HI + A^-$$

The reaction of the halogen with the negative ion is more likely than that with the uncharged enol, owing to the strong electron-attracting character of the halogen.

THE ALDOL CONDENSATION

Under the action of basic catalysts two molecules of acetaldehyde condense together with the formation of aldol,

$$CH_3\overset{\overset{\displaystyle O}{\|}}{C}—H + CH_3\overset{\overset{\displaystyle O}{\|}}{C}—H \rightarrow CH_3\underset{\underset{\displaystyle H}{|}}{\overset{\overset{\displaystyle OH}{|}}{C}}—CH_2\overset{\overset{\displaystyle O}{\|}}{C}—H$$

The mechanism proposed for this aldol condensation involves an initial transfer of a proton from an acetaldehyde molecule to the basic catalyst,

$$\text{(1)} \qquad B + CH_3\overset{\overset{\displaystyle O}{\|}}{C}—H \underset{k_{-1}}{\overset{k_1}{\rightleftharpoons}} BH^+ + {}^-CH_2\overset{\overset{\displaystyle O}{\|}}{C}—H$$

The carbanion produced, which will exist in a resonance state between

$${}^-CH_2\overset{\overset{\displaystyle O}{\|}}{C}—H \quad \text{and} \quad CH_2{=}\overset{\overset{\displaystyle O^-}{|}}{C}—H$$

can either accept a proton again from BH^+ [the reverse of reaction (1)], or add on to a second acetaldehyde molecule,

$$\text{(2)} \qquad CH_3\underset{\underset{\displaystyle H}{|}}{\overset{\overset{\displaystyle O}{\|}}{C}} + {}^-CH_2\overset{\overset{\displaystyle O}{\|}}{C}—H \overset{k_2}{\rightarrow} CH_3\underset{\underset{\displaystyle H}{|}}{\overset{\overset{\displaystyle O^-}{|}}{C}}—CH_2\overset{\overset{\displaystyle O}{\|}}{C}—H$$

Finally the ion produced accepts a proton in a very rapid reaction, to form the aldol molecule.

Application of the steady-state treatment to this scheme gives rise to

$$[H—\overset{\overset{\displaystyle O}{\|}}{C}—CH_2^-] = \frac{k_1[CH_3CHO][B]}{k_2[CH_3CHO] + k_{-1}[BH^+]} \tag{13}$$

If more than one base is simultaneously effective, $k_1[B]$ and $k_{-1}[BH^+]$ must be replaced by summations. The rate of formation of product is given by

$$\frac{d[\text{aldol}]}{dt} = \frac{k_1k_2[CH_3CHO]^2[B]}{k_2[CH_3CHO] + k_{-1}[BH^+]} \tag{14}$$

Two limiting cases of this are important. In the first one $k_2[CH_3CHO] \gg k_{-1}[BH^+]$, when

$$\frac{d[\text{aldol}]}{dt} = k_1[CH_3CHO][B] \tag{15}$$

In the second case $k_{-1}[BH^+] \gg k_2[CH_3CHO]$, when

$$\frac{d[\text{aldol}]}{dt} = \frac{k_1k_2}{k_{-1}} \frac{[CH_3CHO]^2[B]}{[BH^+]} \tag{16}$$

If K_b is the basic ionization constant of B, corresponding to the reaction

$$B + H_2O \rightleftharpoons BH^+ + OH^-$$

K_b is given by

$$K_b = \frac{[BH^+][OH^-]}{[B]} \tag{17}$$

Equation (16) may therefore be written as

$$\frac{d[\text{aldol}]}{dt} = \frac{k_1k_2}{k_{-1}K_b} [CH_3CHO]^2[OH^-] \tag{18}$$

This equation corresponds to specific catalysis by the hydroxide ion, in contrast to Eq. (15) which corresponds to general basic catalysis that may be brought about by any species B present in the solution. Which of the rate equations, (15) or (18), is obeyed depends upon the relative magnitudes of $k_2[CH_3CHO]$ and $k_{-1}[BH^+]$, and therefore on whether the carbanion $HCOCH_2^-$ reacts more rapidly with acetaldehyde or with BH^+; this depends upon the relative rate constants and on the concentrations.

The kinetics of the aldol condensation have been studied by Bell and his coworkers,[1] using sodium hydroxide and other basic catalysts. Certain complications exist; thus some polymer is produced in addition to aldol, and in water the acetaldehyde is present as a hydrate from which it is liberated fairly slowly. At 25°C the rate of formation of aldol in solutions of sodium hydroxide was found to be

$$v = (2.6 \times 10^{-14} + 0.111[OH^-])[CH_3CHO] \tag{19}$$

At very low concentrations of alkali the first term disappeared, and the rate went to zero at zero concentration of sodium hydroxide. Acetate ions were found to have no detectable catalytic effect. In spite of this, however, the reaction was concluded to follow the rate equation (15), in view of the fact that the reaction was first order, and not second order, in acetaldehyde.

Support for this conclusion is provided by some results of Bonhoeffer and Walters,[2] who studied the aldol condensation in the presence of heavy water. They found that there was no deuterium uptake in the aldol except in its hydroxyl group. This implies that the carbanion $HCOCH_2^-$

[1] R. P. Bell, *J. Chem. Soc.*, 1637 (1937); R. P. Bell and W. C. E. Higginson, *Proc. Roy. Soc.* (*London*), **A197**, 141 (1949); R. P. Bell and J. C. Clunie, *Trans. Faraday Soc.*, **48**, 439 (1952).

[2] K. F. Bonhoeffer and W. D. Walters, *Z. Physik. Chem.*, **A181**, 441 (1938); cf. also R. P. Bell and M. J. Smith, *J. Chem. Soc.*, 1691 (1958).

reacts with an acetaldehyde molecule more rapidly than with water, for if reaction with water were significant the reaction

$$HCOCH_2^- + D_2O \rightleftharpoons HCOCH_2D + OH^-$$

would occur in heavy water and would give rise to deuterated aldol. A number of kinetic studies on aldol condensations have been carried out with other aldehydes, and the results have confirmed the mechanism proposed above.

The equilibrium in the aldol condensation involving acetaldehyde lies well over to the right. A similar type of reaction occurs with ketones, such as acetone,

$$CH_3\overset{\overset{\displaystyle O}{\|}}{C}CH_3 + CH_3\overset{\overset{\displaystyle O}{\|}}{C}CH_3 \rightleftharpoons CH_3\underset{\underset{\displaystyle OH}{|}}{\overset{\overset{\displaystyle CH_3}{|}}{C}}\text{—}CH_2\overset{\overset{\displaystyle O}{\|}}{C}CH_3$$

In this case the equilibrium lies very much over to the left, and the reaction can only be studied conveniently from the diacetone alcohol side. A considerable amount of kinetic work has been done on the cleavage reaction also,[1] and the results lead to the conclusion that the mechanism is the reverse of that discussed above for the aldol condensation.

AROMATIC SUBSTITUTION

The kinetics and mechanisms of reactions in which benzene and other aromatic compounds undergo substitution have been studied for a considerable number of years. The most detailed work in this field has been done on the nitration of aromatic compounds, and the present account will deal largely with this type of reaction.[2]

The manner in which substituents on the aromatic ring influence the rate and nature of the nitration process may be considered first. The rate of nitration is increased by groups, such as the methyl group, that have a positive inductive effect, i.e., that push electrons into the aromatic ring. Groups like the nitro group, which withdraw electrons, cause a decrease in the rate of nitration. These results suggest that the nitration

[1] C. C. French, *J. Am. Chem. Soc.*, **51,** 3215 (1929); G. M. Murphy, *ibid.*, **53,** 977 (1931); V. K. LaMer and M. L. Miller, *ibid.*, **57,** 2674 (1935).

[2] For reviews see R. J. Gillespie and D. J. Millen, *Quart. Rev.* (*London*), **2,** 277 (1948); E. D. Hughes, in "Theoretical Organic Chemistry," papers presented to the Kekulé Symposium, p. 209, Butterworth Scientific Publications, London, 1959; A. A. Frost and R. G. Pearson, "Kinetics and Mechanism," 2d ed., pp. 351–363, John Wiley & Sons, Inc., New York, 1961; P. B. D. de la Mare and J. H. Ridd, "Aromatic Substitution, Nitration and Halogenation," Butterworth & Co. (Publishers), Ltd., London, 1959.

is brought about by an electrophilic species (now known to be NO_2^+), which reacts most rapidly at a carbon atom that has the highest electron density.[1] The substituent effects on aromatic substitution are discussed in detail in many books on physical organic chemistry, and will not be considered here.

Early studies of the kinetics of nitration led to a rather complicated dependence of rate on concentrations and other conditions. The behavior is, however, much simpler when concentrated sulfuric acid is used as solvent.[2] The nitration of nitrobenzene, for example, is first order in nitric acid and first order in nitrobenzene. In organic solvents such as dioxane, with nitric acid in excess, the nitration is zero order in benzene, toluene, and ethylbenzene, and the rates are the same, under the same conditions, for all three compounds.[3] For aromatic compounds of lower reactivity, such as chlorobenzene, the rate depends on the concentration of the chlorobenzene, the order being between zero and one. With the still less reactive compound nitrobenzene the order is unity with respect to the nitrobenzene concentration.[4]

The conclusion from these results is that nitration occurs in two stages: in the first the nitric acid reacts with the solvent to form a reactive intermediate, and in the second reaction this intermediate reacts directly with the aromatic compound. There is a considerable amount of evidence that this intermediate is the NO_2^+ ion, which in concentrated acid solutions is formed by the reaction

$$(1) \qquad HNO_3 + HA \rightleftharpoons NO_2^+ + H_2O + A^-$$

In concentrated sulfuric acid, for example, the reaction is

$$HNO_3 + H_2SO_4 \rightleftharpoons NO_2^+ + H_2O + HSO_4^-$$

The second reaction is the nucleophilic attack of the NO_2^+ ion on a carbon atom in the aromatic nucleus, with the elimination of a proton:

$$(2) \qquad NO_2^+ + Ar\text{—}H \rightarrow Ar\text{—}NO_2 + H^+$$

Either of these two reactions may be the slow and rate-determining step. For the more reactive aromatic compounds, such as benzene and toluene, the second step is faster, and the first is slower and rate determining; the rate therefore does not depend on the concentration of the aromatic compound, and is independent of the nature of the compound provided that reaction (1) remains rate determining. For less reactive aromatic

[1] The exact criterion is that reaction will occur mainly at the position that will give rise to an activated complex of lowest free energy. Usually, but not quite always, this means attack at the atom of highest electron density.

[2] H. Martinsen, *Z. Physik. Chem.*, **50**, 385 (1905); **59**, 605 (1907).

[3] G. A. Benford and C. K. Ingold, *J. Chem. Soc.*, 929 (1938).

[4] E. D. Hughes, C. K. Ingold, and R. I. Reed, *Nature*, **158**, 448 (1946)

compounds the second step is rate determining, and the rate becomes proportional to the first power of the concentration. Chlorobenzene represents an intermediate case, neither process being completely rate determining.

The role of HA in reaction (1) may be played by a second molecule of HNO_3, in which case reaction (1) is

$$HNO_3 + HNO_3 \rightleftharpoons NO_2^+ + NO_3^- + H_2O \tag{1'}$$

The occurrence of this equilibrium explains why there is inhibition by nitrate ions, which repress the formation of NO_2^+. The fact that the formation of NO_2^+ occurs in this way is supported by the result that the overall rate constants for nitration reactions correlate with the H_R acidity function.[1] However, as has been emphasized, conclusions from acidity functions must be treated with considerable caution.

Reaction (2) occurs by an initial addition of NO_2^+ to the aromatic molecule,

$$NO_2^+ + Ar\text{—}H \rightarrow ArNO_2H^+ \tag{2'}$$

followed by a proton transfer to any base A^- that is present in solution,

$$ArNO_2H^+ + A^- \rightarrow ArNO_2 + HA \tag{2''}$$

Reaction (2″) is fast, and (2′) is slow and rate determining. Support for the fact that reaction (2″) is fast and does not influence the overall rate is provided by the result that if the hydrogen in the aromatic ring is replaced by tritium (the radioactive isotope of hydrogen, of mass 3), there is no effect on the rate. The removal of the tritium ion is known to occur less rapidly than that of the proton, so that there would have been a reduction in rate if reaction (2″) had had a significant effect on the overall rate.

POLYMERIZATION IN SOLUTION

In Chap. 8 two important mechanisms of polymerization were discussed; they were the *addition* and the *free-radical* mechanisms. Both these mechanisms are very common in the gas phase, but they are also frequently found in solution; several of the examples referred to in Chap. 8 were in fact reactions in solution.

Polymerizations in the liquid phase and in solution also frequently occur by mechanisms that do not take place readily in the gas phase. These are the ionic mechanisms, in which the propagation steps involve ions rather than free radicals. The evidence for the occurrence of such

[1] N. C. Deno and R. Stein, *J. Am. Chem. Soc.*, **78**, 578 (1956); N. C. Deno, H. J. Peterson, and E. Sacher, *J. Phys. Chem.*, **65**, 199 (1961).

mechanisms is that the reactions are catalyzed not by free radicals but by substances that are either acidic or basic, in the general Lewis sense. Also, the rates of such reactions vary with the dielectric constant of the solvent in the manner expected of ionic processes.

The ionic mechanisms of polymerization may be classified as *cationic* or *anionic*, according as the catalysis is brought about by cationic or anionic species. The kinetics and mechanisms of ionic polymerization[1] will now be considered briefly, after which something will be said about the mechanism of polymerization in emulsions.

Cationic Polymerization. A great many acidic substances have been found to be effective catalysts for the polymerization of unsaturated substances such as isobutene: they include

1. Hydrogen acids such as HCl, H_2SO_4, and H_3PO_4
2. Lewis acids, such as $AlCl_3$ and BF_3
3. Cation-forming substances such as I_2 and $AgClO_4$

All these substances are electron acceptors, and are therefore acids in Lewis's generalized sense.

In order to account for polymerizations brought about by such catalysts, Price[2] proposed the following *polar-bond* mechanism, the acidic catalyst being represented as MX:

Initiation:

(1) $MX + CH_2{=}CHR \rightleftharpoons X{-}M^-{-}CH_2{-}C^+HR$

(2) $X{-}M^-{-}CH_2{-}C^+HR + CH_2{=}CHR \rightarrow X{-}M^-{-}CH_2{-}CHR{-}CH_2{-}C^+HR$

Propagation:

(3) $X{-}M^-{-}CH_2{-}CHR{-}CH_2{-}C^+HR + CH_2{=}CHR \rightarrow X{-}M^-{-}CH_2{-}CHR{-}CH_2{-}CHR{-}CH_2{-}C^+HR$

. . . .

(4) $X{-}M^-{-}(CH_2{-}CHR)_n{-}CH_2{-}C^+HR + CH_2{=}CHR \rightarrow X{-}M^-{-}(CH_2{-}CHR)_{n+1}{-}CH_2{-}C^+HR$

Termination:

(5) $X{-}M^-{-}(CH_2{-}CHR)_n{-}CH_2{-}C^+HR \rightarrow M{-}(CH_2{-}CHR)_n{-}CH{-}CR + HX$

Reactions (1) and (2) may be regarded as constituting the initiation step; they are written in this way to avoid postulating a third-order reaction, but the two processes are equivalent to a third-order initiation if the initial equilibrium (1) is rapid. The rate of initiation is

$$v_i = k_2[X{-}M^-{-}CH_2{-}C^+HR][CH_2{=}CHR] \tag{20}$$

$$= k_2K_1[MX][CH_2{=}CHR]^2 \tag{21}$$

[1] For a review see D. C. Pepper, *Quart. Rev.* (*London*), **8,** 88 (1954); G. M. Burnett, "Mechanism of Polymer Reactions," chap. 11, Interscience Publishers, New York, 1954; P. H. Plesch (ed.), "Cationic Polymerization and Related Complexes," W. Heffer & Sons, Ltd., Cambridge, England, 1953.

[2] C. C. Price, *Ann. N.Y. Acad. Sci.*, **44,** 351 (1943); "Reactions at Carbon-Carbon Double Bonds," Interscience Publishers, New York, 1946.

where K_1 is the equilibrium constant for reaction (1), and k_2 the rate constant for reaction (2).

A series of steady-state equations can now be written; the first is

$$k_i[MX][CH_2{=}CHR]^2 - k_p[X{-}M^-{-}CH_2{-}CHR{-}CH_2{-}C^+HR][CH_2{=}CHR] - k_t[X{-}M^-{-}CH_2{-}CHR{-}CH_2{-}C^+HR] = 0 \quad (22)$$

Here k_i has been written for k_2K_i, and k_p is the rate constant for the chain-propagating step (3); all these steps are assumed to have the same rate constant. The general steady-state equation is

$$k_p[X{-}M^-{-}(CH_2{-}CHR)_n{-}CH_2{-}C^+HR][CH_2{=}CHR] - k_p[X{-}M^-{-}(CH_2{-}CHR)_{n+1}{-}CH_2{-}C^+HR][CH_2{=}CHR] - k_t[X{-}M^-{-}(CH_2{-}CHR)_{n+1}{-}CH_2{-}C^+HR] = 0 \quad (23)$$

The sum of all the equations is

$$k_i[MX][CH_2{=}CHR]^2 - k_t \sum_{n=1}^{\infty} [X{-}M^-{-}(CH_2{-}CHR)_n{-}CH_2{-}C^+HR] = 0 \quad (24)$$

whence

$$\sum_{n=1}^{\infty} [X{-}M^-{-}(CH_2{-}CHR)_n{-}CH_2{-}C^+HR] = \frac{k_i}{k_t}[MX][CH_2{=}CHR]^2 \quad (25)$$

The rate of disappearance of monomer is

$$-\frac{d[CH_2{=}CHR]}{dt} = k_p[CH_2{=}CHR] \sum_{n=1}^{\infty} [X{-}M^-{-}(CH_2{-}CHR)_n{-}CH_2{-}C^+HR] \quad (26)$$

$$= \frac{k_ik_p}{k_t}[MX][CH_2{=}CHR]^3 \quad (27)$$

This rate law is in agreement with experiment for a number of ionic polymerizations.

It would appear that this polar-bond mechanism is applicable to certain polymerizations, such as the polymerization of styrene catalyzed by aluminum chloride in carbon tetrachloride solution.[1] This type of mechanism cannot, however, be the correct one in a number of cases of cation polymerization. An objection to it as a general mechanism is that

[1] D. M. Clark, in "Cationic Polymerization and Related Complexes," *op. cit.*, p. 99; D. O. Jordan and A. R. Mathieson, *ibid.*, p. 90; *J. Chem. Soc.*, 2354, 2358, 2363 (1952).

the zwitterions postulated as the chain carriers are of low stability when the charges are separated by a long saturated chain.

In a considerable number of cases of cationic polymerization it is found that a *co-catalyst* must be present in addition to the acidic catalyst. Thus the polymerization of isobutene catalyzed by boron trifluoride will only occur in the presence of a small amount of water, which is believed to act as a co-catalyst.[1] The polar-bond mechanism provides no interpretation of the necessity of a co-catalyst. To explain this type of behavior Evans and Polanyi[2] suggested that the acidic catalyst reacts with the co-catalyst to form ions, and that the cation adds on to the monomer to form a carbonium ion. In catalysis by BF_3 in the presence of moisture, for example, the ions are believed to be formed by the process

$$BF_3 + H_2O \rightleftharpoons HOBF_3^- + H^+ \tag{1}$$

and to remain together as an ion pair $HOBF_3^-H^+$; this is followed by addition of the proton to the monomer; in isobutene polymerization, for example,

$$HOBF_3^-H^+ + CH_2{=}C(CH_3)_2 \xrightarrow{k_i} C(CH_3)_3^+ + HOBF_3^- \tag{2}$$

In isobutene polymerization this is followed by a series of propagation reactions in which a carbonium ion is added to the monomer:

$$(CH_3)_3C^+ + CH_2{=}C(CH_3)_2 \xrightarrow{k_p} (CH_3)_3CCH_2\overset{+}{C}\begin{matrix}\diagup CH_3\\ \diagdown CH_3\end{matrix} \tag{3}$$

$$(CH_3)_3CCH_2\overset{+}{C}\begin{matrix}\diagup CH_3\\ \diagdown CH_3\end{matrix} + CH_2{=}C(CH_3)_2 \xrightarrow{k_p} (CH_3)_3CCH_2\underset{CH_3}{\overset{CH_3}{\overset{|}{\underset{|}{C}}}}{-}CH_2\overset{+}{C}\begin{matrix}\diagup CH_3\\ \diagdown CH_3\end{matrix} \tag{4}$$

and so on. Termination occurs by one of the polymer cations splitting off a hydrogen atom,

$$\sim CH_2\overset{+}{C}\begin{matrix}\diagup CH_3\\ \diagdown CH_3\end{matrix} \xrightarrow{k_t} \sim CH{=}C(CH_3)_2 + H^+ \tag{5}$$

[1] A. G. Evans and G. W. Meadows, *Trans. Faraday Soc.*, **46**, 327 (1950).
[2] A. G. Evans and M. Polanyi, *J. Chem. Soc.*, 252 (1947).

A number of different kinetic equations can arise from this mechanism, according to the assumption made about the rate-determining initiation step. Suppose, for example, that the equilibrium (1) is rapid and that the slow initiation process is (2); the concentration of ion pairs is given by

$$[HOBF_3^-H^+] = K[BF_3][H_2O] \tag{28}$$

where K is the equilibrium constant. The rate of initiation is therefore

$$v_i = k_iK[BF_3][H_2O][\text{monomer}] \tag{29}$$

In the steady state this is equal to the sum of the rates of all the termination steps:

$$k_iK[BF_3][H_2O][\text{monomer}] = k_t \sum_{n=1}^{\infty} [P_n^+] \tag{30}$$

where P_n^+ is the carbonium ion containing n molecules of monomer. It follows that

$$\sum_{n=1}^{\infty} [P_n^+] = \frac{k_i}{k_t} K[BF_3][H_2O][\text{monomer}] \tag{31}$$

and the overall rate of polymerization is

$$v = \frac{k_ik_p}{k_t} K[BF_3][H_2O][\text{monomer}]^2 \tag{32}$$

In many cases either the catalyst or the co-catalyst is present in excess, so that its concentration does not appear explicitly. A number of systems have been found to conform to this type of kinetic equation. It is of interest to note that if the individual ion $HOBF_3^-$, rather than the ion pair, were to react with the monomer in reaction (2), the rate equation would involve the catalyst and co-catalyst concentrations to their *half* powers. Square-root laws would also be found if termination involved two ions. Square-root laws have never been observed, so that it appears that the ion pairs are the reactive species, and that termination involves the elimination of an ion in a unimolecular reaction.

Anionic Polymerization. The polymerization of olefins can also be brought about by basic catalysts such as aqueous alkalis, the alkali metals, sodamide, and the metal alkyls. A kinetic study by Higginson and Wooding[1] of the polymerization of styrene catalyzed by potassamide in liquid ammonia showed that the rate was given by

$$v = k[NH_2^-][\text{styrene}]^2 \tag{33}$$

[1] W. C. E. Higginson and N. S. Wooding, *ibid.*, 760, 778, 1178 (1952).

These results were explained in terms of the following mechanism:

Initiation

$$NH_2^- + CH_2{=}CHC_6H_5 \rightarrow NH_2{-}CH_2C^-HC_6H_5$$

Propagation

$$NH_2{-}CH_2{-}[CHC_6H_5{-}CH_2]_nC^-HC_6H_5 + CH_2CHC_6H_5 \rightarrow NH_2{-}CH_2{-}[CHC_6H_5{-}CH_2]_{n+1}C^-HC_6H_5$$

Termination

$$\sim\!\sim C^-HC_6H_5 + NH_3 \rightarrow \sim\!\sim CH_2C_6H_5 + NH_2^-$$

In weaker bases, such as the metal alkyls, it appears[1] that these frequently do not act as true catalysts but are incorporated into the polymer. The polymerization of butadiene in the presence of a metal alkyl MR, for example, is believed to occur by the mechanism

$$MR + C_4H_6 \rightarrow R{-}C_4H_6{-}M$$
$$R{-}C_4H_6{-}M + C_4H_6 \rightarrow R{-}[C_4H_6]_2M \qquad \text{etc.}$$

Such polymerizations are kinetically analogous to those occurring by a condensation mechanism. The chains are terminated by certain impurities which act as "interceptors."

Emulsion Polymerization.[2] During recent years there has been considerable interest in the kinetics and mechanisms of polymerizations occurring in emulsions. The substituted ethylenes, for example, are conveniently caused to polymerize in aqueous emulsions. A typical procedure that has been used with monomers like methyl methacrylate,

$$\begin{array}{ccc} H & & CH_3 \\ & \diagdown \; \diagup & \\ & C{=}C & \\ & \diagup \; \diagdown & \\ H & & COOCH_3 \end{array}$$

is to form an aqueous emulsion with the monomer, using an emulsifying agent such as cetyltrimethylammonium bromide. Addition of Fenton's reagent (ferrous ions and hydrogen peroxide) may then be used to initiate polymerization; this reagent generates radicals, and the polymerization occurs by a free-radical mechanism. The practical advantage of emulsion polymerization is that the reactions proceed much more rapidly than in bulk systems.

Only a very brief account will be given here of the kinetics of emulsion polymerizations. Emulsions formed by soaps have been shown by

[1] K. Ziegler, *Ann. Chem.*, **567**, 43 (1950).

[2] Cf. Burnett, *op cit.*, chap. 9.

McBain[1] and Harkins[2] to contain *micelles* consisting of layers of oriented soap molecules. When monomers such as methyl methacrylate are added to such a soap solution, they are *solubilized*, which means that some of the monomer penetrates the micelles. The remainder of the monomer exists in the form of suspended droplets in the aqueous phase.

It was suggested by Harkins[3] that in emulsion systems there are two principal loci where polymerization takes place. Initially, when there is not much polymer present, the micelles largely consist of monomer. The radii of the micelles are much smaller than those of the droplets, and the micelles present a much larger interfacial area; as a result, most of the polymerization takes place in the micelles. The free radicals generated by the initiating medium (e.g., Fenton's reagent) in the aqueous phase are captured by the micelles, and at the same time monomer is transferred from the droplets to the micelles, where they react with the radicals. The micelles grow larger and soon consist mainly of polymer particles with soap adsorbed on them. After 2 to 3 percent of the monomer has been converted into polymer, the micelles have in fact largely turned into polymer particles. From this point on, the polymerization takes place mainly in the polymer particles.

A quantitative formulation of this theory was put forward by Smith and Ewart.[4] Its application to the second phase of the polymerization, when the polymerization is occurring mainly in the polymer particles, is in brief as follows. The number of polymer particles remains approximately constant, and varies very little from one system to another; on the average there are about 10^{14} particles per cc. Suppose that the initiator concentration is such that about 10^{13} free radicals are produced per cc per sec. If all these enter the polymer particles, a particle will on the average acquire a radical once in about every 10 sec. Once a radical has entered a particle it adds on to monomer units at a rate equal to $k_p[\mathrm{M}]$, where k_p is the rate constant for the propagation process, and [M] is the concentration of monomer in the particles.

If a radical enters a particle that already contains a radical, it will at once combine with it, and from this it follows that at any time one-half of the polymer particles will contain one radical and the other half no radical. The rate of polymerization is therefore equal to

$$v = \tfrac{1}{2}k_p[\mathrm{M}]N \tag{34}$$

when N is the total number of polymer particles. This relationship has

[1] J. W. McBain, *Advan. Colloid Chem.*, **1**, 124 (1942).

[2] W. D. Harkins, *J. Chem. Phys.*, **13**, 381 (1945); W. D. Harkins and R. S. Stearns, *ibid.*, **14**, 215 (1946).

[3] W. D. Harkins, *J. Am. Chem. Soc.*, **69**, 1428 (1947).

[4] W. V. Smith and R. H. Ewart, *J. Chem. Phys.*, **16**, 592 (1948).

been confirmed for a number of systems,[1] and the k_p values derived are in reasonable agreement with those obtained in other ways. Relationships between the number of particles N and the concentrations of emulsifier and initiator have been derived by Smith and Ewart[2] and by Medvedev,[3] whose model is a little different from that outlined above.

ELECTRON-TRANSFER REACTIONS[4]

Reference was made in the previous chapter to a class of reactions in which there is a transfer of an electron from one ion in solution to another; examples are

$$Fe^{3+} + Fe^{2+} \rightarrow Fe^{2+} + Fe^{3+}$$

and

$$Fe^{3+} + Cr^{2+} \rightarrow Fe^{2+} + Cr^{3+}$$

The kinetics of the first reaction can be studied by isotopic labeling of one of the ions. An important question that arises in connection with such reactions is whether the electron is transferred directly from one ion to the other, or whether the process occurs in stages.

Two distinct types of activated complexes for such reactions have been proposed. One is the *bridged* activated complex; in this the two ions are connected by a common solvent molecule, which belongs to the coordination spheres of both reactant ions. Such a complex may be represented as follows for the ferric-chromous system:

$$Fe^{3+}\text{----}H_2O\text{----}Cr^{2+}$$

The second form for the activated complex is the *outer sphere* type, in which there has been no interpenetration of the hydration shells of the ions; in this case, when the electron is transferred, there is no change in the number or nature of the groups attached to each of the ions. It is also possible that the electron is transferred first to the solvent and then from the solvent to an ion; this may occur in liquid ammonia but is unlikely in water.

Examples of some reactions which probably involve bridged activated complexes are as follows. Electron transfers between ferrous and

[1] W. V. Smith, *J. Am. Chem. Soc.*, **70**, 3695 (1948); **71**, 4077 (1949); M. Morton, P. P. Sanatiello, and H. Landfield, *J. Polymer Sci.*, **8**, 111, 215, 279 (1952); J. G. Brodyan, J. A. Cala, T. Konen, and E. L. Kelley, *J. Colloid Sci.*, **18**, 73 (1963); K. G. McCurdy and K. J. Laidler, *Can. J. Chem.*, **42**, 825 (1964).

[2] Smith and Ewart, *loc. cit.*

[3] S. S. Medvedev, "International Symposium on Macromolecular Chemistry," p. 174, Pergamon Press, New York, 1959.

[4] For reviews of various aspects of these reactions see F. S. Dainton, *Chem. Soc. (London) Spec. Publ.*, **1**, 18 (1954); H. Taube, *Can. J. Chem.*, **37**, 129 (1959); J. Halpern, *Quart. Rev. (London)*, **15**, 207 (1961); R. T. M. Fraser, *Rev. Pure Appl. Chem.*, **11**, 64 (1961); N. Sutin, *Ann. Rev. Nucl. Sci.*, **12**, 285 (1962).

ferric ions are accelerated by sulfuric acid, and it has been suggested[1] that an HSO_4^- ion becomes attached to the ferrous ion,

$$[(H_2O)_5Fe^{II}OSO_3H]^+$$

and an SO_4^{2-} ion to the ferric ion,

$$[(H_2O)_5Fe^{III}OSO_3]^+$$

When these ions come together, it is suggested that there is formed an activated complex in which the proton forms a bridge between the two ions; the transfer of this proton is equivalent to an electron transfer in the same direction,

$$[(H_2O)_5Fe^{II}OSO_3H]^+ + [(H_2O)_5Fe^{III}OSO_3]^+ \rightarrow$$
$$[(H_2O)_5Fe^{II}OSO_3\text{----}H\text{----}O_3SOFe^{III}(H_2O)_5]^{2+} \rightarrow$$
$$\text{(activated complex)}$$
$$[(H_2O)_5Fe^{III}OSO_3]^+ + [(H_2O)_5Fe^{II}OSO_3H]^+$$

There is, however, no conclusive evidence for this mechanism.

Evidence for a bridged complex has also been obtained[2] for the reaction

$$[(NH_3)_5Co^{III}Cl]^{2+} + Cr^{2+} \rightarrow Co^{2+} + Cr^{III}Cl^{2+} + 5NH_3$$

the ammonia forming the ammonium ion in acid solution. It can be shown that the $CrCl^{2+}$ ion cannot be formed by reaction between Cr^{3+} and Cl^-, since when radioactive Cl^- is added to the solution, no radioactivity is found in the $CrCl^{2+}$. The oxidant $[(NH_3)_5CoCl]^{2+}$ is only substituted with great difficulty. It follows from these facts that the Co—Cl bond must exist in the activated complex, which means that the complex is of the bridged type.

Similar evidence has led to the conclusion[3] that electron transfer by bridging occurs with such ligands as the halide ions, CN^-, SO_4^{2-}, PO_4^{3-}, and water. The rates increase in the series F < Cl < Br < I, and this supports the view that electron transfer takes place through the ligand rather than directly between the metal atoms.

Examples of reactions occurring by outer-sphere complexes[4] are

$$MnO_4^{2-} + MnO_4^- \rightarrow MnO_4^- + MnO_4^{2-}$$

and

$$Fe(CN)_6^{4-} + Fe(CN)_6^{3-} \rightarrow Fe(CN)_6^{3-} + Fe(CN)_6^{4-}$$

[1] K. H. Lieser and H. Schroeder, *J. Inorg. Nucl. Chem.*, **14,** 98 (1960); cf. also W. L. Reynolds and S. Fakushina, *Inorg. Chem.*, **2,** 176 (1963); R. L. S. Willix, *Trans. Faraday Soc.*, **59,** 1315 (1963).

[2] H. Taube, H. Myers, and R. L. Rich, *J. Am. Chem. Soc.*, **75,** 4118 (1953).

[3] Taube, *loc. cit.*

[4] A. C. Wahl, *Z. Elektrochem.*, **64,** 47 (1960); cf. also L. Gjertsen and A. C. Wahl, *J. Am. Chem. Soc.*, **81,** 1572 (1959).

Reactions of this type are studied using isotopes, or by the use of nuclear or electron-spin resonance techniques. The former reaction has been found to be accelerated by cesium ions, and this indicates that a bridged activated complex is formed; it may be represented as

$$[MnO_4\text{----}Cs\text{----}MnO_4]^{2-}$$

The positive cesium ion reduces coulombic repulsion. The rate constant for the MnO_4^{2-}-MnO_4^- reaction in the absence of Cs^+ is 4×10^4 liters mole^{-1} sec^{-1}; this is much greater than for the reactions occurring by bridged activated complexes, in agreement with the fact that the necessity for solvent rearrangement is much less for the outer-sphere complexes.

Theories of Electron Transfer.[1] Although the transfer of an electron from one species to another is in some respects a simple process, its theoretical treatment presents considerable difficulty. Various suggestions have been made concerning the manner in which the transfer occurs, and it is still not possible to decide among the different possibilities.

It has been seen that a process such as

$$Fe^{3+} + Fe^{2+} \rightarrow Fe^{2+} + Fe^{3+}$$

may not occur as a simple electron-transfer process at all; the anions that are inevitably present may play an important role. Even if they do not, the process may involve the transfer of a hydrogen atom from a water molecule in the hydration shell of one of the ions to a water molecule in the hydration shell of the other. Thus for the Fe^{2+}-Fe^{3+} reaction Dodson and Davidson[2] have formulated the mechanism as follows:

$$Fe^{2+}O\begin{matrix}\diagup H\\ \diagdown H\end{matrix} \quad + \quad \begin{matrix}H\diagdown\\ H\diagup\end{matrix}OFe^{3+} \rightarrow \left[Fe^{2+}O\begin{matrix}\diagup H & H\diagdown\\ \diagdown H\nearrow & H\diagup\end{matrix}OFe^{3+} \right] \rightarrow$$

$$\begin{matrix} Fe^{2+}O\text{—}H & + & H\text{—}O(H_2)Fe^{3+} \\ \downarrow & & \downarrow \\ Fe^{3+} + OH^- & & H_3O^+ + Fe^{2+} \end{matrix}$$

Objections to this mechanism have, however, been raised by Halpern[3] on

[1] Cf. E. Sacher and K. J. Laidler, in J. O'M. Bockris and B. E. Conway (eds.), "Recent Advances in Electrochemistry," vol. 3, Academic Press Inc., New York, and Butterworth & Co. (Publishers), Ltd., London, 1964.

[2] R. W. Dodson and N. Davidson, *J. Phys. Chem.*, **56**, 866 (1952).

[3] Halpern, *loc. cit.*

energetic grounds; the endothermicity of a reaction involving a hydrogen atom transfer is considered to be too large to be consistent with the activation energies observed.

It seems reasonable to suppose that some reactions of this type do occur by a direct electron transfer, and a number of workers have developed theories of such processes. Calculations have, for example, been made, on the basis of various models, of the free energy of activation for the Fe^{2+}-Fe^{3+} system, on the hypothesis that there is a direct transfer. The experimental value[1] at 25°C is 16.8 kcal per mole, and this can be taken as a lower limit for the value corresponding to direct transfer; if in fact another mechanism predominates, the value for direct transfer must be greater than 16.8 kcal. Calculations that have been made indicate that direct electron transfer can probably occur with a free energy of approximately this amount, so that it appears that the direct process plays a significant role.

A complete treatment is beyond the scope of this book. A number of factors have to be taken into consideration, and the following are the most important aspects of the theoretical treatments:

1. *Approach of the Ions.* A significant contribution to the free energy of activation is made by the free energy required to bring the ions together. This matter was considered briefly on page 224, and Fig. 52 shows the change in free energy with separation, for the Fe^{2+}-Fe^{3+} system. The treatment[2] shows that dielectric saturation has a significant effect at the distances of interest.

2. *Solvent Reorganization.* The process of electron transfer proceeds by a more economical path if a certain amount of reorganization of the hydration shells of the ions *precedes* the transfer. In the Fe^{2+}-Fe^{3+} system the overall reaction may be represented as

$$Fe^{2+}_{II} + Fe^{3+}_{III} \rightarrow Fe^{3+}_{III} + Fe^{2+}_{II} \tag{1}$$

where Fe^{2+}_{II} denotes a ferrous ion surrounded by its normal hydration shell, and Fe^{3+}_{III} denotes a ferric ion surrounded by its normal hydration shell. Suppose that the electron transfer were to occur without prior solvent reorganization; then, since the transfer is much more rapid than the reorganization, the process would initially be

$$Fe^{2+}_{II} + Fe^{3+}_{III} \rightarrow Fe^{3+}_{II} + Fe^{2+}_{III} \tag{2}$$

the products formed in this stage being the ions having hydration shells

[1] J. Silverman and R. W. Dodson, *J. Phys. Chem.*, **56**, 846 (1952).

[2] K. J. Laidler, *Can. J. Chem.*, **37**, 138 (1959); E. Sacher and K. J. Laidler, *Trans. Faraday Soc.*, **59**, 396 (1963).

of the wrong type. It is estimated that the processes

$$Fe^{2+}_{II} \rightarrow Fe^{2+}_{III}$$

and

$$Fe^{3+}_{III} \rightarrow Fe^{3+}_{II}$$

are endothermic by about 30 and 54 kcal per mole, respectively, so that reaction (2) is endothermic by about 84 kcal. The reaction therefore does not occur by this mechanism, which would have much too high an activation energy.

The alternative is for the solvent shells to undergo partial reorganization *prior* to the electron transfer; the electron only moves after the stage has been set by the suitable movement of the water molecules. The water molecules in Fe^{3+}_{III} are held somewhat closer to the ions than in Fe^{2+}_{II}, and the solvent reorganization therefore involves a slight swelling of the hydration shell about the ferric ion, and a slight contraction of that about the ferrous ion. These movements must occur to an extent that causes the solvent atmosphere to become essentially the same about each ion, and calculation indicates[1] that about 6.5 kcal per mole is required for this reorganization. The process may be represented as

$$Fe^{2+}_{II} + Fe^{3+}_{III} \rightarrow Fe^{2+}_{*} + Fe^{3+}_{*} - 6.5 \text{ kcal}$$

the asterisks representing the reorganized hydration shells. The overall process may thus be represented as

$$Fe^{2+}_{II} + Fe^{3+}_{III} \xrightarrow[\text{and reorganization}]{\text{approach of ions}} Fe^{2+}_{*}\text{-}Fe^{3+}_{*} \xrightarrow[\text{transfer}]{\text{electron}}$$

$$Fe^{3+}_{*}\text{-}Fe^{2+}_{*} \xrightarrow[\text{and reorganization}]{\text{separation of ions}} Fe^{3+}_{III} + Fe^{2+}_{II}$$

3. *The Actual Electron Transfer.* Some theories have treated the electron transfer process as an *adiabatic* process, others as a *nonadiabatic* one. In the *adiabatic* theories the system passes smoothly through an activated state into the final state. The electron is not considered as a discrete particle; instead the system passes through a series of intermediate states which in the case of the ferrous-ferric system are of the type

$$Fe^{x+}\text{-}Fe^{(5-x)+}$$

with x varying continuously from 2 to 3. Hush[2] in particular has given a detailed theory of this type, based largely on an electrostatic model but with a correction made for crystal-field effects. His theory agrees very satisfactorily with the experimental results.

[1] Sacher and Laidler, *loc. cit.*

[2] N. S. Hush, *Trans. Faraday Soc.*, **57**, 557 (1961); cf. also R. A. Marcus, *J. Chem. Phys.*, **24**, 966 (1956); **26**, 867, 872 (1957); *Trans. N.Y. Acad. Sci.*, **19**, 423 (1957); *Can. J. Chem.*, **37**, 155 (1959); *Discussions Faraday Soc.*, **29**, 21 (1960).

In the *nonadiabatic* theories the electron is treated as a discrete particle, and consideration is given to the potential-energy changes that occur when the electron travels from one ion to the other. When this is done, it is found that the energy barrier is very high; Fig. 90 shows the

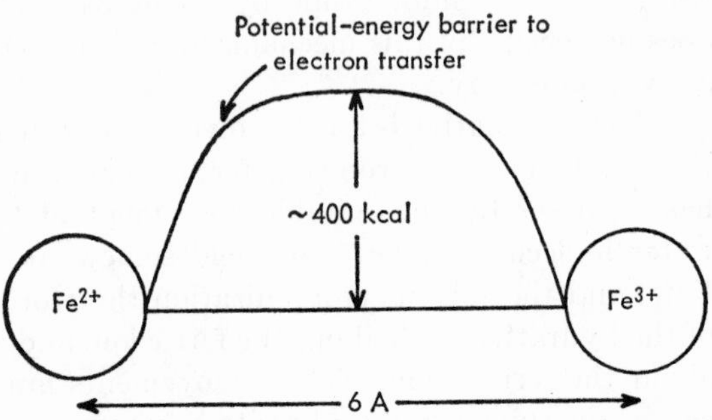

Fig. 90. The potential-energy barrier to electron transfer when Fe^{2+} and Fe^{3+} are 6 A apart in aqueous solution. The electron must tunnel through the barrier, the transmission coefficient for which is about 5×10^{-7}.

situation for the ferrous and ferric ions separated by a distance of 6 A. The barrier becomes lower as the ions are brought together, but this requires energy, and a compromise must be reached. In any case the barrier is always much too high for the electron to be able to surmount it at the required speed; instead the electron passes through the barrier by quantum-mechanical tunneling, which it can do very much more rapidly.

The calculations for the Fe^{2+}-Fe^{3+} system, based on the nonadiabatic model, indicate that the reaction occurs most effectively when the ions are separated by about 4.2 A. A free energy of about 4.5 kcal is required to bring the ions together to this distance, and the transmission coefficient for tunneling corresponds to about 5 kcal per mole. Together with about 6.5 kcal for reorganization, this leads to a calculated free energy of activation of about 16 kcal, in reasonable agreement with the experimental value.

The general conclusion is that both the adiabatic and nonadiabatic theories are capable of giving a satisfactory interpretation of the experimental results. A decision between the two mechanisms therefore cannot be made; possibly the reactions occur in part by both mechanisms, and probably processes of indirect transfer play a role in addition.

RAPID PROTON-TRANSFER REACTIONS

Brief consideration will finally be given to a group of rapid reactions in which there is a simple transfer of a proton from one solute species to another. Rate constants for a number of such reactions have been measured by Eigen,[1] who used relaxation techniques; the theory of these was outlined in Chap. 1, and the experimental methods were explained briefly in Chap. 2.

An example of a reaction of this type is

$$H_3O^+ + OH^- \rightarrow 2H_2O$$

Using the dissociation field version of the relaxation technique, Eigen and De Maeyer[2] found the rate constant of this reaction to be 1.4×10^{11} liters mole^{-1} sec^{-1}. A number of other processes of a similar type have been found to have rate constants that are almost as large as this, but no case of a higher rate has yet been found. Some values are collected in Table 68.

[1] For reviews see M. Eigen, *Suomen Kemistilehti,* **A34,** 25 (1961); M. Eigen and L. De Maeyer, in. A. Weissberger (ed.), "Techniques of Organic Chemistry," vol. 8, part 2, Interscience Publishers, New York, 1963; M. Eigen and K. Kustin, *ICSU Rev.,* **5,** 97 (1963).

[2] M. Eigen and L. De Maeyer, *Z. Elektrochem.,* **59,** 986 (1955).

Table 68 RATE CONSTANTS FOR PROTON-TRANSFER REACTIONS

Reaction	*Rate constant, liters mole^{-1} sec^{-1}*
$H_3O^+ + OH^- \rightarrow 2H_2O$	1.4×10^{11}
$H_3O^+ + F^- \rightarrow H_2O + HF$	1×10^{11}
$H_3O^+ + SO_4^{2-} \rightarrow H_2O + HSO_4^-$	1×10^{11}
$H_3O^+ + CH_3COO^- \rightarrow H_2O + CH_3COOH$	4.5×10^{10}
H_3O^+ + imidazole† $\rightarrow H_2O$ + imidazolium$^+$ ion	1.5×10^{10}
$H_3O^+ + (CH_3)_3N \rightarrow H_2O + (CH_3)_3NH^+$	2.5×10^{10}
$OH^- + NH_4^+ \rightarrow H_2O + NH_3$	3.3×10^{10}
$OH^- + CH_3NH_3^+ \rightarrow H_2O + CH_3NH_2$	3.7×10^{10}
$OH^- + (CH_3)_3NH^+ \rightarrow H_2O + (CH_3)_3N$	1.0×10^{10}
OH^- + imidazolium$^+ \rightarrow H_2O$ + imidazole	2.3×10^{10}

† Imidazole is HC(=N)–CH; the imidazolium ion is HC(=N$^+$H)–CH. (Ring structures: N / HC CH / HN——CH and H / N$^+$ / HC CH. / HN——CH)

These reactions are good examples of *diffusion-controlled* reactions, the rate-determining step being not the proton-transfer process but the approach of the reactants to one another. The theory of diffusion-controlled reactions has been reviewed,[1] and only a very brief account will here be given. For a reaction between two ions of charges $z_A e$ and $z_B e$, and diffusion constants D_A and D_B, it was deduced by Debye[2] that the rate constant in liters mole^{-1} sec^{-1} is given by

$$k \approx \frac{4\pi N z_A z_B e^2 (D_A + D_B)}{10^3 \epsilon \mathbf{k} T \left[\exp \left(\dfrac{z_A z_B e^2}{\epsilon \mathbf{k} T \sigma} \right) - 1 \right]} \tag{35}$$

Here ϵ is the dielectric constant, and σ the average separation at which the proton transfer occurs. The derivation of this equation is based on Stokes' law for the viscous drag on a spherical particle. Eigen and De Maeyer[3] have shown that for most ionic recombinations in very dilute aqueous solution the reaction distance σ is approximately 7.5 A. Insertion of this value into Eq. (35), together with the appropriate values for an aqueous solution, leads to the result that

$$k \approx 8.8 \times 10^{14} (D_A + D_B) \tag{36}$$

Use of the diffusion constants for H_3O^+ and OH^- (9.28×10^5 and 5.08×10^5 cm^2 per sec, respectively) leads to the value of 1.3×10^{11} liters mole^{-1} sec^{-1}, in satisfactory agreement with the experimental value of 1.4×10^{11} liters mole^{-1} sec^{-1}. Similarly, for the reaction

$$H_3O^+ + F^- \rightarrow HF + H_2O$$

the calculated value is 9.4×10^{10} liters mole^{-1} sec^{-1}, to be compared with the experimental[4] value of 1.0×10^{11} liters mole^{-1} sec^{-1}. In both these cases it therefore seems certain that the reactions are diffusion controlled.

When an ion-recombination reaction involves more complicated ions, as in some of the cases in Table 68, steric factors reduce the rate constants somewhat. If one of the species is neutral, the rate is again reduced, since there is no longer any electrostatic attraction. In the reaction

$$C_6H_4(OH)CO_2^- + OH^- \rightarrow C_6H_4(O^-)CO_2^- + H_2O$$

[1] R. M. Noyes, in G. Porter (ed.), "Progress in Reaction Kinetics," vol. 1, p. 129, Pergamon Press, Oxford, 1961.

[2] P. Debye, *Trans. Electrochem. Soc.*, **82**, 265 (1942).

[3] M. Eigen and L. De Maeyer, *Proc. Roy. Soc. (London)*, **A247**, 505 (1958).

[4] M. Eigen and K. Kustin, *J. Am. Chem. Soc.*, **82**, 5952 (1960).

the rate constant is about 10^7 liters $mole^{-1}$ sec^{-1}. This can be explained in terms of the electrostatic repulsion, and of hydrogen bonding between the hydroxyl group and an oxygen atom on the carboxylate ion.

Particular interest attaches to the results with imidazole, in view of the fact that the imidazole ring appears to exist at the active center of many enzymes. It is seen from Table 68 that the transfer of a proton from H_3O^+ to imidazole is a rapid diffusion-controlled reaction, as is the transfer of a proton from the imidazolium ion to a hydroxide ion. Eigen[1] has pointed out that in reactions of the type

$$\text{Imidazole} + \text{hydrogen donor} \rightleftharpoons \text{imidazolium ion} + \text{hydrogen acceptor}$$

the rate is always diffusion controlled (with k equal to 10^9 to 10^{10} liters $mole^{-1}$ sec^{-1}) in one of the two directions, and that it is always fairly rapid in the other direction. The direction in which the reaction is rapid is that in which there is an overall decrease in energy; in the reverse direction there is necessarily an activation energy. Imidazole appears to be unique as far as the speed of its reactions in both directions is concerned, and it is able to operate readily in both directions at pH values around 7. It seems certain that these results with imidazole provide an important clue to the elucidation of the problem of the high efficiencies of enzymes as catalysts.

[1] M. Eigen and K. Kustin, *J. Am. Chem. Soc.*, **82,** 5952 (1960).

appendix

A

Determination of Rate Constants by Numerical Methods[1]

THE NUMERICAL calculation of chemical rate constants, in terms of observed concentrations of reactants, plotted as functions of time, is a special case of the following general problem.

Given a system

$$\dot{y} = \phi(y,t,\alpha_K) \tag{1}$$

of ordinary differential equations, together with initial conditions $y(0) = \beta$ and observed values $y_1, \ldots, y_n$ which are assumed to be a sample of some particular solution of (1), corresponding to specific but unknown values of the parameters α and (possibly) β at given times $t_1, \ldots, t_n$; to determine the values of α and β which characterize this solution.

This problem admits numerous variants, according as some, or all, of the initial concentrations β are known, and according as the concentra-

[1] This appendix was written by J. L. Howland, Department of Mathematics, University of Ottawa.

tions of some, or all, of the various reactants, whose concentrations are represented by the components of the solution vector y, may be observed. In any case, the total number of observations should be greater than, or equal to, the number of parameters α, β to be determined; ordinarily many more observations than parameters are available.

This problem is a generalization of the problem which is encountered in measuring most of the familiar chemical and physical constants; in the more elementary cases, in which analytic solutions of (1) in terms of exponential or harmonic functions are available, simple graphical or elementary least-squares techniques may be applied. In more complicated cases, such as the analysis of radioactive decay data, or the harmonic analysis of periodic—e.g., tidal—data, special techniques and, indeed, special mechanical devices are employed. In its more recent contexts, this problem occurs in the determination of the orbit parameters of artificial satellites in terms of tracking data, and the most modern high-speed digital computing machines have been employed in its solution.[1]

The method of differential corrections may be employed in the most general case. This method consists in the repeated application of the following steps:[1–3]

1. Obtain estimates $\alpha^{(0)}$, $\beta^{(0)}$ of the unknown parameters in (1) by any means available—e.g., analogy with previous results, steady-state solutions, simple graphical procedures.

2. Form the equations of variation associated with the system (1) by differentiating (1), in turn, with respect to the unknown parameters and interchanging the order of differentiations with respect to the parameters and with respect to time. Thus, if $u_K = \partial y / \partial \alpha_K$,

$$\dot{u}_K = \frac{\partial \phi}{\partial y} u_K + \frac{\partial \phi}{\partial \alpha_K}; \qquad u_K(0) = 0 \tag{2}$$

[1] S. D. Conte, The Computation of Satellite Orbit Trajectories, in Franz L. Alt and Morris Rubinoff (eds.), "Advances in Computers," vol. 3, pp. 1–76, Academic Press Inc., New York, 1962. (Pages 48–66 contain a discussion of various methods of parameter estimation, but particularly of differential corrections, as described above. The results of practical experience are discussed, and statistical procedures described. Various references are given.)

[2] G. W. Booth and T. I. Peterson, "Non-linear Estimation," M and A No. 3, Mathematics and Applications Department, IBM, 590 Madison Avenue, New York, N.Y., 10022. (Contains a description of method of differential corrections plus statistical methods and a detailed description of a computer program. References for statistical techniques are given.)

[3] J. L. Howland and R. Vaillancourt, A Generalized Curve-fitting Procedure, *J. Soc. Ind. Appl. Math.*, **9** (2), 165–168 (1961). (Contains a description of the use of variational equations in conjunction with differential corrections, complements previous reference. Gives example of kinetic problem.)

and, if $v_K = \partial y/\partial\beta_K$

$$(3) \qquad \dot{v}_K = \frac{\partial\phi}{\partial y} v_K; \qquad \left.\frac{\partial y_i}{\partial\beta_K}\right|_{\pm=0} = \partial_{iK}$$

where $\partial\phi/\partial y$ is a Jacobian whose elements are the partial derivatives $\partial\phi_i/\partial y_j$.

3. Using the estimated parameter values, integrate (1), (2), and (3) numerically, obtaining, in particular, values of y, u_K, v_K at the observed times $t_1, \ldots, t_n$.

4. Formulate the system of equations

$$(4) \quad y(t,\alpha,\beta) = y(t,\alpha^{(0)},\beta^{(0)}) + \sum_K u_K(\alpha_K - \alpha_K{}^{(0)}) + \sum_K v_K(\beta_K - \beta_K{}^{(0)})$$

and, for each value $t_1, \ldots, t_n$ of t, substitute the observed data on the left-hand side and the values computed in step 3 above on the right-hand side.

5. Solve the linear system thus derived from (4) by conventional least-squares techniques, to obtain values of $\alpha_K - \alpha_K{}^{(0)}$ and $\beta_K - \beta_K{}^{(0)}$, from which new estimates $\alpha_K{}^{(1)}$ and $\beta_K{}^{(1)}$ of the parameters are obtained by addition.

6. If the changes in parameter estimates are significant, take the new values and return to step 1 above.

There are no general mathematical results which guarantee the convergence of this procedure from any particular choice $\alpha^{(0)},\beta^{(0)}$ of initial estimates, nor, indeed, which guarantee that the results obtained are the best possible, when convergence is obtained. Recent research has led to the development of elaborate statistical procedures to assess the accuracy of the final results in the case of convergence.[1] These have been applied as a basis for assessing the relative merits of several proposed kinetic models for a given reaction.

[1] T. I. Peterson, Reaction Kinetics Optimization Using Non-linear Estimation, *Chem. Eng. Progr. Symp. Ser.*, **56,** no. 31. (Nonlinear estimation methods are used as a basis for selecting appropriate kinetic models.)

appendix

Numerical Values[1] B

$\mathbf{k} = 1.381 \times 10^{-16}$ erg per deg
$\mathbf{h} = 6.626 \times 10^{-27}$ erg sec
$N = 6.023 \times 10^{23}$ mole^{-1}
$R = 1.986$ cal deg^{-1} mole^{-1}
$\pi = 3.1416$
$e = 2.718$ (base of natural logarithms)
$e = 4.803 \times 10^{-10}$ abs. esu (electronic charge)
$\mathbf{k}/\mathbf{h} = 2.084 \times 10^{10}$ sec^{-1} deg^{-1}
$\mathbf{k}T/\mathbf{h} = 5.692 \times 10^{12}$ sec^{-1} at 0°C
$= 6.213 \times 10^{12}$ sec^{-1} at 25°C
$= 7.775 \times 10^{12}$ sec^{-1} at 100°C
$= 16.11 \times 10^{12}$ sec^{-1} at 500°C
$e\mathbf{k}/\mathbf{h} = 5.663 \times 10^{10}$ sec^{-1} deg^{-1}
$e^2\mathbf{k}/\mathbf{h} = 1.539 \times 10^{11}$ sec^{-1} deg^{-1}
$8\pi\mathbf{k} = 3.470 \times 10^{-15}$ erg deg^{-1}
$8\pi\mathbf{k}T = 9.478 \times 10^{-13}$ erg at 0°C
$= 10.35 \times 10^{-13}$ erg at 25°C
$= 12.95 \times 10^{-13}$ erg at 100°C
$= 26.83 \times 10^{-13}$ erg at 500°C

[1] *Natl. Bur. Std. Tech. News Bull.*, October, 1963.

BIBLIOGRAPHY

Full references to the literature have been given in the text, but it has been thought worth while to list the monographs and review articles pertaining to the various phases of chemical kinetics.

For general treatments of the subject see:

HINSHELWOOD, C. N., "Kinetics of Chemical Change," Clarendon Press, Oxford, 1940.

LAIDLER, K. J., "Reaction Kinetics," vols. 1 and 2, Pergamon Press, Oxford, 1963.

FROST, A. A., and R. G. PEARSON, "Kinetics and Mechanism," 2d ed., John Wiley & Sons, Inc., New York, 1961.

BENSON, S. W., "Foundations of Chemical Kinetics," McGraw-Hill Book Company, New York, 1960.

FRIESS, S. L., and A. WEISSBERGER (eds.), "Investigations of Rates and Mechanisms of Reactions," vols. 1 and 2 (vol. 8, parts 1 and 2, of "Technique of Organic Chemistry"), Interscience Publishers, New York, 1953 and 1963.

The following are more particularly concerned with gas reactions:

TROTMAN-DICKENSON, A. F., "Gas Kinetics," Butterworth & Co. (Publishers), Ltd., London, 1955.

SZABÓ, Z. G., "Fortschritte der Kinetik der homogenen Gasreaktionen," Steinkopff, Darmstadt, 1961.

CREMER, E., and M. PAHL, "Kinetik der Gasreaktionen," Gruyter, Berlin, 1961.

SEMENOFF, N. N., "Some Problems in Chemical Kinetics and Reactivity," Moscow, 1954 (two English translations are available: one by M. Boudart, Princeton University Press, Princeton, N.J., 1958; one by J. E. S. Bradley, Pergamon Press, London, 1958).

KASSEL, L. S., "Kinetics of Homogeneous Gas Reactions," Reinhold Publishing Corporation, New York, 1932.

DANIELS, F., "Chemical Kinetics," Cornell University Press, Ithaca, N.Y., 1938.

KONDRATIEV, V. N., "Kinetics of Chemical Gas Reactions," Academy of Sciences, Moscow, 1958 (an English translation, in two volumes, has been issued by the U.S. Atomic Energy Commission; a second translation, edited by N. B. Slater, has been published by the Pergamon Press, Oxford, 1964).

Students wishing to keep abreast of recent advances in the field are recommended to refer to recent issues of *Chemical Reviews*, *Quarterly Reviews* (*London*), *Annual Review of Physical Chemistry*, and *Annual Reports of the Chemical Society*, and to G. Porter (ed.), "Progress in Reaction Kinetics," Pergamon Press, Oxford. Numerical data are to be found in

Tables of Chemical Kinetics, *Natl. Bur. Std.* Circ. **510** (1951); supplement published in 1956.

The following books and review articles pertain to special topics arranged according to the chapters of the present book:

1. *The Analysis of Kinetic Results*

LAIDLER, K. J., *op. cit.*, vol. 2, chap. 1.

MELLOR, J. W., "Chemical Statics and Dynamics," Longmans & Co., Ltd., London, 1904.

SKRABAL, A., "Homogenkinetik," Theodor Steinkopff, Dresden and Leipzig, 1941

SZABÓ, Z. G., *op. cit.*, chap. 1.

FROST, A. A., and R. G. PEARSON, *op. cit.*, chap. 8.

LETORT, M., Thesis, University of Paris, 1937.

HOUGEN, O. A., and K. M. WATSON, "Chemical Process Principles," vol. 3, John Wiley & Sons, Inc., New York, 1947.

CALDIN, E. F., "Fast Reactions in Solution," Blackwell Scientific Publications. Ltd., Oxford, 1964.

2. *The Measurement of Reaction Rates*

H. W. MELVILLE and B. G. GOWENLOCK, "Experimental Methods in Gas Reactions," Macmillan & Co., Ltd., London, 1964.

NOYES, W. A., and P. A. LEIGHTON, "The Photochemistry of Gases," Reinhold Publishing Corporation, New York, 1941.

Discussions Faraday Soc., **17** (1954).

EIGEN, M., and K. KUSTIN, "The Study of Very Rapid Reactions in Solution by Relaxation Spectrometry," *ICSU Rev.*, **5**, 97 (1963).

PRICHARD, H. O., Shock Waves, *Quart. Rev. (London)*, **14**, 46 (1960).

BRADLEY, J. N., "Shock Waves in Chemistry and Physics," Methuen & Co., Ltd., London, 1962.

GAYDON, A. G., and I. R. HURLE, "The Shock Tube in High Temperature Chemical Physics," Reinhold Publishing Corporation, New York, 1963.

SIMPSON, C. J. S. M., *Ann. Rept. Chem. Soc.*, **43**, 46 (1961).

HERSCHBACH, D. R., Chemical Reactions in Crossed Molecular Beams, *Vortex*, **22**, no. 8 (1961).

3. *The Mechanisms of Elementary Processes*

HINSHELWOOD, C. N., *op. cit.*, especially chaps. 1 to 4.

FOWLER, R. H., and E. A. GUGGENHEIM, "Statistical Thermodynamics," chap. 12, Cambridge University Press, New York, 1939.

GLASSTONE, S., K. J. LAIDLER, and H. EYRING, "The Theory of Rate Processes," McGraw-Hill Book Company, 1941, especially chaps. 3 and 4.

KASSEL, L. S., *op. cit.*

MELANDER, L., "Isotope Effects on Reaction Rates," The Ronald Press Company, New York, 1960.

BIGELEISEN, J., and M. WOLFSBERG, Theoretical and Experimental Aspects of Isotope Effects in Chemical Kinetics, *Advan. Chem. Phys.*, **1**, 15 (1958).

JOHNSTON, H. S., Large Tunnelling Corrections in Chemical Reaction Rates, *ibid.*, **3**, 131 (1960).

MONTROLL, E. W., and K. E. SHULER, The Application of the Theory of Stochastic Processes to Chemical Kinetics, *ibid.*, **1**, 361 (1958).

The Transition State, *Chem. Soc. (London) Spec. Publ.*, **16** (1962).

LAIDLER, K. J., and J. C. POLANYI, Theories of the Kinetics of Bimolecular Reaction, in G. Porter (ed.), "Progress in Reaction Kinetics," vol. 3, Pergamon Press, Oxford, 1965.

4. *Elementary Gas-Phase Reactions*

STEACIE, E. W. R., "Atomic and Free Radical Reactions," Reinhold Publishing Corporation, New York, 1954.

KUTSCHKE, K. O., and E. W. R. STEACIE, The Chemistry of Free Radicals in the Gas Phase, in "Vistas in Free Radical Chemistry," Pergamon Press, Oxford, 1959.

HINSHELWOOD, C. N., *op. cit.*, especially chaps. 1 to 4.

KASSEL, L. S., *op. cit.*

SEMENOFF, N. N., *op. cit.*

SCHUMACHER, H. J., "Chemische Gasreaktionen," Theodor Steinkopff, Dresden and Leipzig, 1938.

KAUFMAN, F., Reactions of Oxygen Atoms, in G. Porter (ed.) "Progress in Reaction Kinetics," vol. 1, Pergamon Press, Oxford, 1961.

TROTMAN-DICKENSON, A. F., *op. cit.*

TROTMAN-DICKENSON, A. F., *Ann. Rept. Chem. Soc.*, 36 (1959).

SLATER, N. B., "Theory of Unimolecular Reactions," Cornell University Press, Ithaca, N.Y., 1959.

KERR, J. A., and A. F. TROTMAN-DICKENSON, The Reactions of Alkyl Radicals, in "Progress in Reaction Kinetics," vol. 1.

LAMPE, F. W., J. L. FRANKLIN, and F. H. FIELD, Kinetics of the Reactions of Ions with Molecules, in "Progress in Reaction Kinetics," vol. 1.

5. *Elementary Reactions in Solution*

MOELWYN-HUGHES, E. A., "The Kinetics of Reactions in Solution," Clarendon Press, Oxford, 1947.

AMIS, E. S., "Kinetics of Chemical Change in Solution," The Macmillan Company, New York, 1949.

GLASSTONE, S., K. J. LAIDLER, and H. EYRING, *op. cit.*, chap. 8.

LEFFER, J. E., and E. GRUNWALD, "Rates and Equilibria of Organic Reactions," John Wiley & Sons, Inc., New York, 1963.

LAIDLER, K. J., The Influence of the Solvent on Reaction Velocity, *Suomen Kemistilehti*, **A33,** 44 (1960).

DAVIES, C. W., Salt Effects in Solution Kinetics, in "Progress in Reaction Kinetics," vol. 1.

HAMANN, S. D., "Physico-chemical Effects of Pressure," Butterworth Scientific Publications, London, 1957.

GONIKBERG, M. G., "Chemical Equilibria and Reaction Rates at High Pressures," Izdatel'stoo Academii Nauk S.S.R., Moscow, 1960 (a translation is available from the Office of Technical Services, U.S. Department of Commerce, Washington, D.C.).

NOYES, R. M., Effects of Diffusion Rates on Chemical Kinetics, in "Progress in Reaction Kinetics," vol. 1.

6. *Reactions on Surfaces and in the Solid State*

BRUNAUER, S., "Physical Adsorption," Princeton University Press, Princeton, N.J., 1943.

MILLER, A. R., "The Adsorption of Gases on Solids," Cambridge University Press, New York, 1949.

GARNER, W. E. (ed.), "Chemisorption," Butterworth & Co. (Publishers), Ltd., London, 1957.

TRAPNELL, B. M. W., "Chemisorption," Butterworth Scientific Publications, London, 1955.

LAIDLER, K. J., Chemisorption, in P. H. Emmett (ed.), "Catalysis," vol. 1, Reinhold Publishing Corporation, New York, 1954.

HINSHELWOOD, C. N., *op. cit.*, chap. 8.

GLASSTONE, S., K. J. LAIDLER, and H. EYRING, *op. cit*, chap. 7.

ASHMORE, P. G., "Catalysis and Inhibition of Chemical Reactions," part 3, Butterworth & Co. (Publishers), Ltd., London, 1963.

SCHWAB, G. M., H. S. TAYLOR, and R. SPENCE, "Catalysis," D. Van Nostrand Company, Inc., Princeton, N.J., 1937.

LAIDLER, K. J., Kinetic Laws in Surface Catalysis, and Absolute Rates of Surface Reactions, in "Catalysis," vol. 1.

SCHWAB, G. M., "Handbuch der Katalyse," Springer-Verlag OHG, Berlin, 1941 (reprinted by Edwards Brothers, Inc., Ann Arbor, Mich., 1945).

BAKER, M. McD., and G. I. JENKINS, The Electronic Factor in Heterogeneous Catalysis, *Advan. Catalysis*, **1,** 1 (1955).

REES, A. L. G., "Chemistry of the Defect Solid State," Methuen & Co., Ltd., London, 1954.

GARNER, W. E. (ed.), "Chemistry of the Solid State," Butterworth & Co. (Publishers), Ltd., 1955.

Eley, D. D., "Catalysis and the Chemical Bond," University of Notre Dame Press, Notre Dame, Ind., 1954.

Parravano, G., and M. Boudart, Chemisorption and Catalysis on Oxide Semiconductors, *Advan. Catalysis*, **1,** 47 (1955).

Heterogeneous Catalysis, *Discussions Faraday Soc.*, **8** (1950).

Fensham, P. J., Semiconductivity and Catalysis, *Quart. Rev.* (*London*), **11,** 227 (1957).

Jost, W., "Diffusion in Solids, Liquids and Gases," Academic Press Inc., New York, 1960.

de Boer, J. H. (ed.), "Reactivity of Solids," Elsevier Publishing Company, Amsterdam, 1961.

Gill, E. K., and J. A. Morrison, Kinetics of Solids, *Ann. Rev. Phys. Chem.*, **14,** 205 (1963).

Kemball, C., The Catalytic Exchange of Hydrocarbons with Deuterium, *Advan. Catalysis*, **11,** 223 (1959).

Reference should be made to the various volumes of *Advances in Catalysis,* and of "Catalysis," edited by P. H. Emmett, Reinhold Publishing Corporation, New York.

7. *Complex Reactions*

Skrabal, A., *op. cit.*

Steacie, E. W. R., *op. cit.*

Kutschke, K. O., and E. W. R. Steacie, *loc. cit.*

Frost, A. A., and R. G. Pearson, *op. cit.*, chap. 8.

Minkoff, G. J., "Frozen Free Radicals," Interscience Publishers, New York, 1960.

Trotman-Dickenson, A. F., "Gas Kinetics," Butterworth & Co. (Publishers), Ltd., London, 1955.

Trotman-Dickenson, A. F., "Free Radicals," Methuen & Co., Ltd., London, 1959.

Walling, C., "Free Radicals in Solution," John Wiley & Sons, Inc., New York, 1954.

Ingram, D. J , "Free Radicals as Studied by Electron Spin Resonance," Butterworth & Co. (Publishers), Ltd., London, 1959.

Dainton, F. S., "Chain Reactions: An Introduction," Methuen & Co., Ltd., London, 1956.

Rollefson, G. K., and M. Burton, "Photochemistry and the Mechanisms of Chemical Reactions," Prentice-Hall, Inc., Englewood Cliffs, N.J., 1939.

Noyes, W. A., and P. A. Leighton, "The Photochemistry of Gases," Reinhold Publishing Corporation, New York, 1941.

Staude, H., "Photochemie," Bibliographisches Institut AG, Mannheim, 1962.

Jennings, K. R., The Production, Detection and Estimation of Atoms in the Gaseous Phase, *Quart. Rev.* (*London*), **15,** 237 (1961).

Laidler, K. J., "The Chemical Kinetics of Excited States," Clarendon Press, Oxford, 1955.

Lind, S. C., C. J. Hochanadel, and T. A. Ghormley, "Radiation Chemistry of Gases," Reinhold Publishing Corporation, New York, 1961.

Allen, A. O., "The Radiation Chemistry of Water and Aqueous Solutions," D. Van Nostrand Company, Inc., Princeton, N.J., 1961.

Spinks, J. W. T., and R. J. Woods, "An Introduction to Radiation Chemistry," John Wiley & Sons, Inc., New York, 1964.

8. *Some Complex Reactions in the Gas Phase*

Hinshelwood, C. N., *op. cit.*, chaps. 5 and 6.

Steacie, E. W. R., *op. cit.*

SEMENOFF, N., "Chemical Kinetics and Chain Reactions," Clarendon Press, Oxford, 1935.

MINKOFF, G. J., and C. F. H. TIPPER, "Chemistry of Combustion Reactions," Butterworth & Co. (Publishers), Ltd., London, 1962.

KNOX, J. H., *Ann. Rept. Chem. Soc.*, **59,** 18 (1962).

BURNETT, G. M., "Mechanism of Polymer Reactions," Interscience Publishers, New York, 1954.

BEVINGTON, J., "Radical Polymerization," Academic Press Inc., New York, 1961.

BURNETT, G. M., Rate Constants in Radical Polymerization Reactions, *Quart. Rev.* (*London*), **4,** 292 (1950).

Reactions of Free Radicals in the Gas Phase, *Chem. Soc. Spec. Publ.* **9** (1957).

In addition, most of the references listed under Sec. 7 include treatments of overall mechanisms.

9. *Homogeneous Catalysis*

ASHMORE, P. G., *op. cit.*

SCHWAB, G. M., H. S. TAYLOR, and R. SPENCE, *op. cit.*

SCHWAB, G. M., *op. cit.*, especially vol. 2.

HALPERN, J., Homogeneous Reactions of Molecular Hydrogen in Solution, *Quart. Rev.* (*London*), **10,** 463 (1956).

HALPERN, J., The Catalytic Activation of Hydrogen in Homogeneous, Heterogeneous and Biological Systems, *Advan. Catalysis,* **11,** 301 (1959).

BELL, R. P., "Acid-Base Catalysis," Clarendon Press, Oxford, 1941.

BELL, R. P., "Acids and Bases; Their Quantitative Behaviour," Methuen & Co., Ltd., London, 1952.

BELL, R. P., "The Proton in Chemistry," Cornell University Press, Ithaca, N.Y., 1959.

PAUL, M. A., and F. A. LONG, H_0 and Related Indicator Acidity Functions, *Chem. Rev.*, **57,** 1 (1957).

LONG, F. A., and M. A. PAUL, Application of the H_0 Acidity Function to Kinetics and Mechanisms of Acid Catalysis, *Chem. Rev.*, **57,** 935 (1957).

LONG, F. A., Applications of Acidity Functions to the Mechanisms of Acid-catalyzed Reactions, *Proc. Chem. Soc.*, 220 (1957).

LAIDLER, K. J., "The Chemical Kinetics of Enzyme Action," Clarendon Press, Oxford, 1958.

See also the volumes of *Advances in Catalysis*, and of "Catalysis," edited by P. H. Emmett, Reinhold Publishing Corporation, New York.

10. *Some Reaction Mechanisms in Solution*

FROST, A. A., and R. G. PEARSON, *op. cit.*, especially chap. 12.

HINE, J., "Physical Organic Chemistry," 2d ed., McGraw-Hill Book Company, New York, 1962.

GOULD, E. S., "Mechanism and Structure in Organic Chemistry," Holt, Rinehart and Winston, Inc., New York, 1963.

GOULD, E. S., "Inorganic Reactions and Structure," Holt, Rinehart and Winston, Inc., New York, 1963.

INGOLD, C. K., "Structure and Mechanism in Organic Chemistry," Cornell University Press, Ithaca, N.Y., 1953.

"Theoretical Organic Chemistry," papers presented at the Kekulé Symposium, Butterworth Scientific Publications, London, 1959.

DE LA MARE, P. B. D., and J. H. RIDD, "Aromatic Substitution, Nitration and Halogenation," Butterworth & Co. (Publishers), Ltd., London, 1959.

BURNETT, G. M., *op. cit.*

Plesch, P. H. (ed.), "Cationic Polymerization and Related Complexes," W. Heffer & Sons, Ltd., Cambridge, England, 1953.

Pepper, D. C., Ionic Polymerization, *Quart. Rev. (London)*, **8,** 88 (1954).

Dainton, F. S., Principles and Mechanisms in Electron-transfer Reactions, *Chem. Soc. Spec. Publ.*, **1,** 18 (1954).

Taube, H., Bridging and Non-bridging Ligand Effects in Redox Reactions of Metal Ions, *Can. J. Chem.*, **37,** 129 (1959).

Halpern, J., Mechanisms of Electron Transfer and Related Processes in Solution, *Quart. Rev. (London)*, **15,** 207 (1961).

Fraser, R. T. M., Recent Advances in Electron-transfer Reactions, *Rev. Pure Appl. Chem.*, **11,** 64 (1961).

Sutin, N., Electron-exchange Reactions, *Ann. Rev. Nucl. Sci.*, **12,** 285 (1962).

Sacher, E., and K. J. Laidler, Theories of Elementary Electron-transfer Reactions, in J. O'M. Bockris and B. E. Conway (eds.), "Recent Advances in Electrochemistry," vol. 3, Butterworth & Co. (Publishers), Ltd., and Academic Press Inc., New York, 1964.

Eyring, H., and E. M. Eyring, "Modern Chemical Kinetics," chap. 6, Reinhold Publishing Corporation, New York, 1963.

Caldin, E. F., *op. cit.*

Name Index

Adams, E. P., 66, 72
Adams, N. K., 187
Alberty, R. A., 436
Allen, A. O., 346, 408
Allen, C. R., 42
Allen, P. C., 267, 276
Anderson, H. G., 413
Anet, F. A. L., 192
Arnold, E. A., 297
Arrhenius, S., 2, 51, 450
Ashmore, P. G., 125, 434
Ashurst, K. G., 447
Askey, P. J., 411
Axworthy, H. E., 163, 378
Aynoneno, P. J., 125

Back, M. H., 193, 403, 404
Back, R. A., 398, 406
Bader, R. F. W., 192
Bagdasaryan, K. S., 132
Bak, T., 109
Balandin, A. A., 302
Baldwin, R. R., 419
Bamford, C. H., 430
Bancroft, J. L., 404
Barb, W. G., 485
Bardwell, D. C., 367, 399, 406
Barker, R. S., 100
Barklay, I. M., 201
Barnard, M. L., 480
Barrer, R. M., 272
Bartlett, P. D., 431, 516
Bateman, J. B., 43
Bates, J. R., 344, 368
Bauer, E., 107
Bauer, S. H., 110
Bawn, C. E. H., 85, 86, 382, 385
Baxendale, J. H., 485
Beck, D., 48
Becker, D. A., 407
Bedworth, R. E., 318
Beeck, O., 259, 279, 304
Belchetz, L., 339, 397
Bell, G. M., 225
Bell, J. A., 397
Bell, R. P., 81, 85, 130, 199, 201, 435, 453, 455, 458, 465, 504, 513–515, 519
Bender, M. L., 495
Bender, P., 346
Benedict, W. S., 398
Benford, G. A., 124, 199, 521
Benrath, A., 507
Benson, S. W., 120, 162, 163, 378, 379, 411, 465
Benton, A. F., 278
Berger, J., 384
Bergmann, F., 502
Berkowitz, J., 173
Bernreuther, F., 365
Berthelot, M., 2
Berzelius, J. J., 434
Beutler, H., 105, 345, 381
Biechler, S. S., 462
Bigeleisen, J., 62, 94
Bjerrum, N., 219
Blackmore, D. R., 401
Blais, N. C., 102
Bock, R. M., 436
Bockris, J. O'M., 531
Bodenstein, M., 53, 116, 117, 125, 138, 273, 276, 278, 297, 326, 328, 356–358, 361, 362, 365, 368, 370, 372, 483
Bogojawlensky, A., 501
Bohnholtzer, W., 377
Bone, W. A., 278
Bonhoeffer, K. F., 284, 352, 380, 519
Bonner, W. A., 125
Bonner, W. D., 322
Born, M., 128, 217
Bosworth, R. C. L., 306
Boudart, M., 396
Bowen, E. J., 339
Boys, S. F., 100
Bradfield, A. E., 238
Bradley, J. N., 47, 165, 191
Branch, G. E. K., 238, 244
Brandsma, W. F., 68
Brennan, D., 285
Brenschade, W., 372

Brewer, A. K., 305
Briers, F., 365
Briggs, G. E., 441, 476
Briner, E., 138, 179
Brodyan, J. G., 529
Broida, H. P., 136, 332, 337
Brønsted, J. N., 33, 219, 229, 255, 453, 460, 463, 464, 467, 509, 515
Brook, A. J. W., 42
Brown, G. R., 129
Brunauer, S., 257
Bryce, G., 285
Bryce, W. A., 335
Buben, W., 284
Buchanan, J., 236
Bunger, O. L., 102, 159
Bunnett, J. F., 474
Burgess, C. H., 361
Burk, R. E., 273, 286, 292, 293, 297–299, 362, 477
Burnett, G. M., 43, 179, 408, 429, 430, 523, 527
Burris, C. T., 234, 236
Burton, M., 334, 339, 349
Burwell, R. L., 510
Busse, W. F., 372
Butironi, C., 214
Butler, J. A. V., 201, 494
Butler, J. N., 174
Bywater, S., 129

Cala, J. A., 529
Caldin, E. E., 40, 42, 81
Calib, E., 502
Calvin, M., 32), 449
Campbell, H. J., 509
Cario, G., 344
Carter, R. C., 318
Cashion, J. K., 136
Chambers, T. S., 160
Chance, B., 39, 40, 41, 42, 477
Chanmugan, J., 125
Chapman, D. L., 179, 361, 377
Charrington, T., 46, 165
Charters, P. E., 136
Chen, D. T. Y., 215, 233, 234, 236
Chesick, J. P., 162, 197
Chiltz, G., 413
Christiansen, J. A., 219, 326, 328, 364, 370
Christie, M. I., 185
Chupka, W. A., 173
Clark, D. M., 524
Clarke, H. E., 377
Clunie, J. C., 43, 513, 519
Clyne, M. A. A., 419
Coehn, A., 365
Coffin, F. D., 512
Conn, G. K. T., 280
Constable, F. H., 258, 300
Conway, B. E., 531
Cook, G. A., 368
Cooper, K. A., 245
Couper, A., 297, 306, 314
Craggs, J. D., 347
Cramer, F., 358
Cremer, E., 258, 300, 362
Crocker, J. C., 506
Crosby, H. J., 125
Current, J. H., 175
Curtiss, C. F., 108
Cuthbertson, A. C., 429
Cvetanovic, R. J., 191

Dainton, F. S., 199, 529
Dalal, V. P., 138, 139
Dalziel, H., 42
Danby, C. J., 403, 413
Daniels, F., 372, 373, 377
Darwent, B. de B., 513
Datta, S. C., 499
Datz, S., 136
Davidsohn, H., 478
Davidson, N., 46, 165, 185, 531
Davies, C. W., 220
Davis, T. W., 334, 408
Dawson, H. M., 454, 515
Day, J. N. E., 497
de Boer, J. H., 316, 318
Debye, P., 206, 229, 536
de Donder, T., 108
Dekiau, B., 165
de la Mare, P. B. D., 535, 536
Delbanco, A., 297
Dell, R. M., 315
de Maeyer, L., 44, 535, 536
Deming, W. E., 293
Deno, N. C., 471, 473, 522
Dewar, M. J. S., 239, 430
Deyrup, A. J., 469
Diamond, H., 99
Diesen, R. W., 175
Dills, D. H., 175
Dinzes, A. I., 401
Dippy, J. F., 246

Dixon, P. S., 191
Dodd, R. E., 164
Dodson, R. W., 531, 532
Dollimore, D., 318
Dollimore, J., 318
Donnelly, R. R., 278
Dooley, M. D., 397, 401
Dostal, H., 425
Dowden, D. A., 314
Drew, C. M., 190
Dunkle, F. B., 512
Dux, W., 361

Eadie, G. S., 477
Eastman, A. M., 509
Eckart, C., 81
Edlund, K. R., 43
Edward, J. T., 463, 507, 509
Edwards, J. W., 199
Eigen, M., 44, 253, 535, 536
Eley, D. D., 284, 297, 306, 314
Elias, E. A., 335
Eliason, M. A., 110
Eltenton, G. C., 335, 401
Emeléus, H. J., 429
Emmett, P. H., 257, 258, 259, 264, 272, 278, 284, 286
Engell, J., 315
Enikolopyan, N. S., 422
Essex, H., 348
Esson, W., 2, 17, 323
Eusuf, M., 187, 404, 407, 409, 410
Evans, A. G., 385, 525
Evans, D. P., 242, 238, 243
Evans, M. G., 73, 104, 132, 133, 201, 236
Evans, M. W., 224
Evering, B. L., 333, 408
Ewart, R. H., 528
Eyring, E. M., 173
Eyring, H., 59, 68, 72, 85, 89, 99, 100, 104, 110, 120, 133, 139, 173, 199, 206, 214, 215, 225, 286, 291, 296, 303, 304, 347, 365, 369, 373, 428

Fairclough, R. A., 204
Fakushina, S., 530
Farkas, A., 279, 283, 284
Farkas, L., 279, 336, 380
Faull, R. F., 484
Fendley, J. A., 81
Field, F. H., 194
Fiquet-Fayard, F., 350
Fletcher, P. C., 285
Flory, P. J., 425
Flowers, M. C., 163
Folkins, H. O., 273
Foord, S. G., 423, 430
Forst, W., 163
Fowler, R. H., 70, 147, 263
Fraenkel, G. K., 44
Franck, J., 202, 344, 345, 354, 365
Frank, H. S., 224
Frankenburg, W. G., 259
Frank-Kemenetsky, D. A., 328
Franklin, J. L., 194
Franklin, T. L., 337
Fraser, R. T. M., 529
Freeman, A. E., 338
Freeman, G. R., 413
Freiling, E. C., 125
French, C. C., 520
Freundlich, H., 264
Frey, F. E., 400
Frey, H. M., 163, 173, 174, 175, 191, 192
Friedman, L., 173, 511
Frost, A. A., 12, 215, 322, 520
Frost, A. V., 400
Frost, D. C., 350
Frumkin, A., 265

Garner, W. E., 257, 297, 312, 318
Garvin, D., 136, 382
Gaydon, A. G., 167, 330, 421
Gee, G., 429
Geib, K. H., 352
Gershinowitz, H., 72, 140
Getz, D., 372
Ghormley, T. A., 346
Giguère, P. A., 163
Gill, E. K., 159, 163, 164, 316, 350
Gillespie, R. J., 520
Gilson, Q. H., 42
Ginger, R. D., 495
Gjertsen, L., 530
Glang, R., 315
Glasebrook, A. L., 333, 397
Glasstone, S., 70, 72, 133, 199, 209, 286, 291, 296
Gleave, J. L., 492
Glick, H. S., 396
Glissman, A., 378
Goeppert-Mayer, M., 94
Gohring, R., 362

Gold, V., 491, 513
Golden, S., 107
Goldfinger, P., 101, 380, 413
Gomes, W., 316
Gordon, A. S., 190, 396
Gordon, J. J., 238
Gore, W. L., 322
Gowenlock, B. G., 33
Grant, G. H., 245
Greaves, J. C., 334
Greaves, R. H., 377
Green, T. E., 138, 321
Greene, E. F., 48, 137
Griffing, V. F., 100
Griffiths, J. G. A., 361
Grimm, H. G., 203
Groth, W., 398
Guggenheim, E. A., 14, 33, 70, 263
Guldberg, G. M., 2
Gutfreund, H., 42, 478
Gwathmey, A. T., 304
Gwyn, P. P., 382

Haber, F., 485
Haldane, J. B. S., 441, 476
Halpern, J., 449, 529
Halsey, G. D., 265, 301
Hamann, A., 483
Hamann, S. D., 231, 236
Hammett, L. P., 239, 246, 469, 471
Harbron, E., 81
Harcourt, A. V., 2, 17, 323
Hargrave, K. R., 485
Harkins, W. D., 528
Harman, R. A., 428
Harrington, R. E., 175
Hart, E. J., 347
Harteck, P., 352, 380
Hartley, H., 273
Hartridge, H., 40
Hauffe, K., 315
Haward, R. N., 429
Heath, C. E., 396
Heitler, W., 56
Hengheim, F. A., 138
Henri, V., 342
Henry, P., 20
Herschbach, D. R., 47, 48, 125, 137
Hertel, E., 367
Herzberg, G., 191, 330
Herzfeld, K. F., 139, 326, 327, 328, 385, 402, 403, 409, 437
Hibben, J. H., 373
Higginson, W. C. E., 448, 513, 519, 526
Hildebrand, J. H., 208
Hill, D. G., 344
Hill, T. L., 129
Hiller, L. A., 104
Hine, J., 239
Hinshelwood, C. N., 65, 85, 133, 138, 147, 204, 205, 238, 241, 243, 245, 266, 267, 273, 275–277, 292, 293, 298, 299, 307, 318, 321, 383, 400, 401, 403, 411, 413, 415, 418, 419, 496
Hiromi, K., 225
Hirota, K., 304
Hirschfelder, J. O., 99, 100, 104, 106, 110, 132, 347
Hirst, H. S., 372, 373
Hirt, T. J., 396
Hoare, D. E., 163
Hobbs, J. E., 401
Hochanadel, C. J., 346
Hodges, H. J., 374
Hofeditz, W., 284, 332
Hogness, T. R., 119
Hollas, J. M., 404
Holst, K. A., 507
Hood, J. J., 50
Horiuti, J., 304
Horn, E., 384
Hornel, J. C., 494
Hornig, D. F., 165
Hougen, O. A., 24, 38
Hückel, E., 229
Huffman, R. E., 165
Hughes, E. D., 245, 492, 520, 521
Hulbert, H. M., 428
Hulett, J. R., 81
Hunt, J. K., 372
Huseman, E., 428
Hush, N. S., 533
Hutchison, H. P., 463, 507
Hutchison, W. H., 277
Huybrechts, G., 413

Imai, N., 411
Ingold, C. K., 239, 243, 245, 250, 401, 485, 492, 497, 501, 505, 515, 521
Ingold, K. U., 335
Ingram, D. J. E., 334
Iredale, T., 266

Jackson, J. L., 100
Jacobs, P. W. M., 318
Jaffé, H. H., 246
Jahn, S., 377
Jain, V. S., 411
Jamieson, J. W. S., 129
Jarizelski, J. J., 471
Jenkins, G. I., 279
Jenkins, H. O., 246
Jennings, K. R., 330
Johnson, J. S., 44
Johnston, E. H., 199, 372
Johnston, H. S., 43, 62, 81, 101, 125, 129, 298, 376, 377
Johnston, W. R., 408
Jones, B., 238, 426
Jones, H. E., 377
Jones, W. H., 338
Jordan, D. O., 524
Josephson, K., 478
Jost, W., 117, 316, 322, 358, 361
Jung, G., 365

Kammer, M. L., 206
Karmilova, L. V., 422
Karplus, M., 101, 102, 104
Kasparian, M., 81
Kassel, L. S., 150, 153, 396
Kaufman, F., 330, 336
Keier, N. P., 258
Kell, R. W., 429
Kelley, E. L., 529
Kemball, C., 279, 280, 282
Kerr, J. A., 191
Kevorkian, V., 396
Khambata, B. S., 124, 199
Khodschaian, S., 364
Kilpatrick, M., 467, 509
Kimball, G. E., 100
Kimball, G. H., 167
King, C. V., 467
Kirchhoff, J., 1
Kirkwood, J. G., 226
Kistiakowsky, G. B., 47, 72, 117, 136, 160, 165, 174, 382, 397, 413, 424, 444
Klein, F. S., 62, 136
Klingelhoefer, W. C., 365
Klingler, E., 138
Knight, H. T., 165
Knox, B. E., 397
Knox, J. H., 174, 415
Koblitz, W., 170
Koch, W., 399, 406
Kohahenko, P. N., 333
Kohnstam, G., 490
Kohnstamm, P., 68
Kokowitz, J. W., 382
Kolumban, A. D., 348
Konen, T., 529
Kooij, D. M., 272, 292
Kornfeld, G., 138, 364
Koskikallio, J., 506, 510
Kostowski, H. J., 136
Kramer, W. J., 369
Kramers, H. A., 109
Krauskopf, K. B., 367
Krauss, W., 138
Krieble, V. K., 507
Krocsak, M., 384
Krupka, R. M., 478, 480, 481, 502, 503
Kubo, R., 108
Küchler, L., 400, 402
Kummer, J. T., 258, 259
Kunsman, C. H., 293, 297
Kuntz, P. J., 99
Kuppermann, A., 407
Kustin, K., 44, 535, 536
Kutschke, K. O., 129
Kwei, G. H., 48, 137
Kyvatkowskii, D. A., 401

Lacher, J. R., 72
Ladenburg, R., 383
Laidler, K. J., 3, 34, 72, 73, 85, 98, 131, 133, 159, 162–165, 167, 187, 198, 199, 206, 214, 215, 217, 223–225, 233, 234, 236, 238, 241, 242, 251, 257, 259, 264, 267, 272, 279–281, 283–286, 291, 296, 339, 345, 347, 350, 379, 395, 400, 401, 403–411, 413, 437, 465, 474, 478–482, 490, 491, 501–503, 529, 531–533
Lamar, E. S., 293
Lamble, A., 501
LaMer, V. K., 206, 436, 520
Lampe, F. W., 194
Landfield, H., 529
Landskroener, P. A., 225, 501
Langmuir, I., 258–260, 265, 266, 276, 278, 285, 295, 318, 319, 338
Larson, L., 407
Latremouille, G. A., 509
Lautsch, W., 284, 332
Lavin, G. I., 368
Leermakers, J. A., 411

Lehrfeld, R. A., 436
Leidheiser, H., 304
Leifer, A., 101
Leighton, P. A., 37, 339, 398
Lenher, S., 372
Lennard-Jones, J. E., 304
LeRoy, D. J., 81, 335, 337, 346
Letort, M., 16, 29, 390, 408
Levine, S., 225
Lewis, B., 117
Lewis, G. N., 147, 453
Lewis, W. C. McC., 63, 117, 501
Liang, S. C., 258, 300
Lidwell, O. M., 515
Liesser, K. H., 530
Lifshitz, A., 43
Light, J. C., 106
Lin, M. C., 403
Lind, S. C., 346, 356, 367, 399, 406
Lindemann, F. A. (Lord Cherwell), 144
Lineweaver, H., 477
Linhorst, E. F., 374
Linnett, J. W., 334
Lippincott, E. R., 101
Lipscomb, F. J., 136
Liu, I. D., 163
Livingston, R. S., 255
London, F., 55, 56
Long, F. A., 173, 468, 504, 509–512
Lossing, F. P., 335
Luder, W. F., 453
Lueck, R. H., 373
Lutkemeyer, H., 358

McAulay, J., 229
McBain, J. W., 528
McCluer, W. B., 400
Maccoll, A., 444, 445
Maccormac, M., 421
McCurdy, K. G., 529
McDevit, W. F., 512
McDonald, R. D., 429
McDowell, C. A., 347, 350
McGrath, W. D., 136, 379
Mackay, G. M., 338
McKenney, D. J., 379, 411, 412, 415
McKinlay, J. D., 136
Mackor, E. L., 473
MacMahon, P. S., 361
McNesby, J. R., 190, 405, 407
Magee, J. L., 99, 349, 384
Mahain, W. H., 175
Mahav, B. H., 108, 398
Mahieu, M., 108
Mains, G. J., 398
Malet, G., 138
Mandel, R., 398
Marcelin, A., 72
Marcus, R. A., 154, 533
Marek, L. F., 400
Markham, M. C., 280, 286, 296
Maron, S. H., 436
Marshall, A. L., 344, 352
Marshall, R., 185
Martens, G., 413
Martinsen, H., 521
Mason, H. S., 44
Mathieson, A. R., 524
Matsen, F. A., 100
Mayer, J. E., 118
Mazur, J., 104, 107
Meacock, S. C. R., 463, 507
Meadows, G. W., 525
Medvedev, S. S., 529
Melander, K. H., 364
Melander, L., 90
Melville, H. W., 33, 179, 272, 426, 430
Menschutkin, N., 33, 203
Menten, M. L., 475, 520
Michaelis, L., 475, 478
Michel, K. W., 165
Mignolet, J. C. P., 306
Millen, D. J., 520
Miller, A. R., 257
Miller, M. L., 68
Milliken, G. A., 41
Mills, R. L., 376
Minkoff, G. T., 337, 415
Mitchell, J. W., 138
Moelwyn-Hughes, E. A., 65, 68, 198, 205, 211, 419
Moignard, L. A., 369
Molinari, E., 315
Montroll, E. W., 108
Moore, W. J., 3
Morgan, V. G., 243
Mori, H., 108
Morikawa, K., 336, 398
Morris, J. C., 365
Morrison, J. A., 316
Mortensen, E. M., 107
Mortensen, R. A., 334
Morton, M., 529
Mott, N. F., 318
Müller, W., 357

Mund, W., 399, 406
Murphy, G. M., 520
Murto, M. L., 501
Myers, H., 530
Myrbäck, K., 478, 480

Nachmansohn, D., 502
Nakajima, S., 108
Nakayama, K., 316
Nalbandyan, A. B., 422
Nathan, W. S., 243, 246
Nelson, W. E., 494
Nemeth, E. N., 99, 102, 106
Newling, W. B. S., 238
Newton, A. S., 398
Nicholson, P., 318
Niclause, M., 390
Nixon, A. C., 238, 244
Nordberg, M. E., 374
Norris, J. A., 48, 137
Norrish, R. G. W., 47, 136, 185, 361, 369, 379, 395, 422, 423, 429
Noyes, R. M., 536
Noyes, W. A., 37, 339
Nyrop, J. E., 305

Oatley, C. W., 306
Ogg, R. A., 125, 375, 376
Ogryzlo, E. A., 335
Ohlmer, F., 276
Okabe, H., 405, 407
Okamoto, G., 304
Olander, A., 441, 506
Olsen, L. O., 345
Ootuka, H., 384
Osborn, A. R., 501, 512
Ostwald, W., 14, 17, 18, 435, 450, 506
Ouellet, L., 478, 480

Padelt, E., 483
Padoa, M., 367
Pal'm, V. A., 501
Palmer, H. B., 165, 167, 396, 397
Paneth, F. A., 258, 284, 332
Parr, C., 101
Parravano, G., 315, 316
Patat, E., 336
Paul, M. A., 468, 504
Paul, R. E., 400
Pauling, L., 307
Pearson, L., 43
Pearson, R. G., 12, 215, 322, 520
Pease, R. N., 278, 334, 364, 366, 400
Pederson, K. J., 463
Pegis, C., 223
Peiser, A. M., 107
Pelzer, H., 72
Pepper, D. C., 523
Perlmutter-Hayman, B., 43
Perman, E. P., 377
Permatjoglou, S., 274, 314
Perrin, M. W., 234
Perrine, R. L., 125, 377
Peterson, H. J., 473, 522
Pfeiffer, W., 138
Pickles, N. J. T., 204
Pietsch, E., 273
Pilch, K., 428
Pilling, N. B., 318
Pinsent, B. R. W., 43
Pitzer, K. S., 107, 125
Platzman, R. J., 347
Plaut, H., 370
Plesch, P. H., 523
Polanyi, J. C., 73, 85, 93, 98, 99, 102, 106, 129, 131, 136
Polanyi, M., 59, 73, 104, 105, 132, 133, 135, 201, 236, 326, 328, 381, 384, 525
Polly, O. L., 411
Porter, F., 47, 367
Porter, G., 73, 98, 125, 131, 185, 191, 220, 330, 536
Porter, R. N., 101, 102, 104
Potts, J. C., 367, 369
Powell, R. E., 12, 125
Powis, F., 454, 515
Pratt, G. L., 395
Present, R. D., 108
Price, C. C., 429, 523
Prichard, C. R., 273, 274, 277, 292, 293 297, 298, 299
Prigogine, I., 94, 108
Prince, R. H., 43
Pritchard, H. O., 45, 160, 171, 196
Pritchard, J. G., 509, 510
Protheroe, J. B., 163
Prout, E. G., 318
Pyzhev, V., 267, 272, 294

Quinn, C. P., 403

Rabinovitch, B. S., 154, 161, 162, 165, 175, 463
Rabinowitch, E., 184, 201, 202, 345, 354, 365, 507
Raff, L. M., 102
Raff, R., 425
Ramsay, D. A., 404
Ramsperger, H. C., 150, 374
Ramstetter, H., 125
Rand, M. H., 513
Ransil, B. J., 100
Rapp, D., 81, 85, 93, 130
Raschig, F., 40
Reed, R. I., 521
Rees, A. L. F., 309
Reicher, L. T., 450
Reid, E. E., 506
Reitz, O., 507, 516
Remick, A. E., 239
Reynolds, P. W., 314
Reynolds, W. L., 530
Ricci, J. E., 334, 408
Rice, F. O., 333, 372, 401–403, 408, 409, 411, 485
Rice, O. K., 72, 150, 154, 170, 385, 397
Rich, R. L., 530
Richardson, M., 209
Ridd, J. H., 520
Rideal, E. K., 117, 147, 259, 266, 279, 280, 284, 304, 306, 339, 373, 397, 429
Riesenfeld, E. H., 377
Rink, J. A., 165
Ritchie, M., 369
Roberts, E. R., 283
Roberts, J. K., 257–259, 285
Roberts, R., 129, 137
Robertson, A. C., 485
Robertson, A. J. B., 292, 339
Robinson, P. L., 334
Robinson, R., 239
Rodebush, W. H., 72, 330, 365
Roginsky, S. Z., 258, 304
Rollefson, G. K., 206, 339, 365, 367, 369, 484
Rosen, N., 99
Rosenbaum, E. J., 119
Roser, D., 102, 106
Roseveare, W. E., 11, 15
Ross, J., 48, 137
Rosseinsky, D. R., 448
Rossington, D. R., 297
Roth, E., 384
Rothstein, M., 478
Roughton, F. J. W., 39, 40, 42, 43
Roughton, R. W., 206
Roxburgh, H. L., 272
Rubin, R. J., 107
Rudorfer, A., 428
Ruehrwein, R. A., 396
Ruf, H., 203
Rummel, K. W., 284
Rushbrooke, G. S., 70
Russell, K. E., 185

Sacher, E., 224, 473, 522, 531–533
Sachsse, H., 336, 400
Sadek, H., 258
Sadowski, C. M., 136
Sagert, N. H., 406, 407
St. Gilles, L. P., 2
Salomaa, P., 506
Sanatiello, P. P., 529
Saracini, M., 138
Sato, S., 62, 191
Sattler, H., 384
Scatchard, G., 207, 211, 213, 219
Schay, G., 384, 385
Schecter, A., 284
Scheffer, F. E. C., 68
Schenck, P. W., 368
Schiff, H. I., 332, 335
Schissler, D. O., 400
Schlag, E. W., 85, 161, 162
Schlueter, H., 138, 139
Schmidt, O., 305
Schoieshein, A., 471
Schroeder, H., 530
Schul'tz, E., 304
Schultz, G. V., 428
Schultz, R. F., 444
Schumacher, H. J., 125, 170, 372–374, 377, 378, 483
Schwab, G. M., 258, 273, 274, 293, 297, 300, 314
Schwartz, K., 494
Schweizer, H., 361
Scott, R. L., 208
Semenoff, N. N., 132, 415, 421, 422
Setzer, D. W., 154
Seyer, W. F., 441
Shane, G., 400, 401
Shapiro, U. G., 245
Sharma, R. D., 104
Sharp, T. E., 62, 81
Shavitt, I., 63, 93, 100, 130

Shepp, A., 179
Sherman, A., 303, 304
Shoosmith, J., 191
Shuler, K. E., 108
Sickman, D. V., 170, 408
Sicre, J. E., 125
Silverman, J., 532
Simpson, C. J. S. M., 45
Simpson, J., 185
Simpson, W., 429
Singleton, J. H., 283
Sirk, H., 364
Sirs, J. A., 43
Skell, P. S., 473
Skinner, G. B., 396
Skrabal, A., 328, 452
Slater, N. B., 150, 154, 159, 160
Slygin, A., 265
Smit, P. J., 473
Smith, A. E., 304
Smith, C., 348
Smith, D. F., 147, 400
Smith, F. T., 136, 162, 382
Smith, J. A., 185
Smith, J. H., 377
Smith, M. J., 519
Smith, W. V., 284, 528, 529
Socquet, I. M., 437
Soper, F. G., 209
Sowden, R. G., 160, 171, 196
Spall, B. C., 399
Spencer, B., 238
Spencer, J., 238
Spinks, J. W. T., 347
Sponer, H., 345
Sprenger, G., 373, 374
Sprenger, H. C., 373
Springer, A., 428
Srinivasan, R., 120
Stafford, F. E., 510
Stager, R., 273, 297
Staude, H., 339
Stauffer, C. H., 516
Staveley, L. A. K., 393, 401, 411
Steacie, E. W. R., 129, 164, 190, 273, 330, 337, 345, 346, 401
Stead, J. B., 448
Stearn, A. E., 66, 206
Stearns, R. S., 528
Steel, C., 165, 167
Stefani, A. P., 191
Stein, R., 473, 522
Steiner, A. B., 398, 400
Stevenson, D. P., 99
Stewart, J. A., 478
Stewart, T. D., 43
Stimson, V. R., 444
Stock, A., 273
Stoddart, E. M., 334
Stone, F. S., 312, 315, 316
Storch, H. H., 339, 396
Stubbs, F. J., 401, 403
Sturtevant, J. M., 15, 478
Suess, H., 428
Sugden, T. M., 332
Sugiura, Y., 99
Sullivan, J. H., 120
Sun, C. E., 304
Sutin, N., 529
Sutton, L. E., 239
Swain, C. G., 431, 513
Sykes, A. G., 448
Szabó, Z. G., 132
Szwarc, M., 191

Tabbutt, F. D., 136
Taft, R. W., 249, 462, 473
Tal'vik, A. L., 501
Tamm, K., 44
Tammann, G., 318, 501
Tanford, C., 138
Taube, H., 529, 530
Taylor, E. H., 136
Taylor, H. A., 116, 138
Taylor, H. S., 258, 265, 278, 300, 336, 338, 344, 347, 352, 398, 429, 454, 463
Taylor, T. I., 463
Taylor, T. W. J., 507
Teller, E., 306
Temkin, M., 267, 272, 294
Teves, M. C., 342
Theile, H., 400, 402
Thénard, J., 1
Thiele, E., 382
Thomas, P. J., 445
Thon, N., 362
Thrush, B. A., 47, 136, 419
Tickner, A. W., 335
Tikhomirova, N. N., 132
Tiley, P. F., 315
Timm, E. W., 133, 238, 241, 243, 496
Tingley, H. C., 273
Tipper, C. F. H., 415
Tobolsky, A. V., 428
Tollefson, E. L., 335

Tolman, R. C., 72, 110, 125, 372–374
Tommila, E., 496, 501
Tompkins, F. C., 265, 318
Topley, B., 104, 120, 273, 286, 293, 369
Townend, D. T., 421
Townshend, R. E., 279, 281
Toyama, O., 279
Trapnell, B. M. W., 257, 259
Trautz, M., 63, 137–139
Trenner, N. R., 336
Trotman-Dickenson, A. F., 160, 171, 174, 191, 196
Trowse, F. W., 40
Trulio, J. G., 100
Twigg, G. H., 280, 304

Uhlenbeck, G. E., 110
Umberger, J. Q., 206
Unger, W., 362
Unik, J. P., 495

Van Artsdalen, E. R., 413
Van der Auwera, D., 192, 398
Van der Waals, J. H., 473
van't Hoff, J. H., 15, 50, 272, 273, 292, 436
Venkataraman, B., 44
Verbeke, G., 413
Voevodsky, V. V., 132
Volmer, M., 170
Voltz, S. E., 315
von Baumbach, H. H., 273, 297
von Bogdandy, S., 381
von Euler, H., 441, 463, 478, 480, 506
von Hartel, H., 382, 385
von Muffling, L., 284
Vorwerk, W., 258

Waage, P., 2
Wachenhein, L., 138
Waddington, G., 125
Wagner, C., 315, 372
Wahl, A. C., 530
Wahrhaftig, A. L., 173
Waley, S. G., 480
Wall, F. T., 102, 104
Wall, L. A., 163
Wall, M. C., 280, 286, 296
Wallenstein, M. B., 173
Walsh, J. M., 100
Walters, E., 179
Walters, W. D., 519
Wang-Chang, C. S., 110
Wansborough-Jones, O. H., 304
Warburg, E. G., 377
Warhurst, E., 382
Wassermann, A., 124, 199, 204
Waters, W. A., 239, 246
Watson, H. B., 38, 238, 242, 243, 246
Watson, K. M., 24
Weber, J., 259, 267, 283
Webster, A. H., 449
Wegschneider, R., 323
Weiss, K., 485
Weissberger, A., 535
Weller, S., 315
Wen, W. Y., 224
Weston, R. E., 55, 62, 63, 81, 85, 93, 130, 297
Weygandt, C. N., 100
Whalley, E., 237, 491, 501, 506, 510, 512
Wheeler, A., 120, 304, 369
Wheeler, R. V., 278
White, E. C., 372, 373
Wiberg, K. B., 162
Widom, B., 110
Wieder, G. M., 154
Wigner, E., 81, 92, 106
Wijnan, M. H. J., 190
Wijs, J. J. A., 452
Wilheimy, L., 1
Willbanks, E. M., 153
Williams, E. G., 238
Williams, L., 242
Williams, W. T., 348
Willix, R. L. S., 530
Willstatter, R., 485
Wilson, C. L., 516
Wilson, D. J., 125, 129
Wilson, I. B., 502, 503
Winkler, C. A., 65, 241, 463, 507
Winter, E., 272
Winter, E. R. S., 283
Wittig, G., 426
Wojciechowski, B. W., 34, 159, 162, 395, 400, 401, 403–405, 407, 411, 412
Wolff, H., 203
Wolford, R. K., 506
Wolfsberg, M., 62, 94, 173
Wood, R. W., 352
Wood, S. E., 208
Wood, W. C., 184, 199
Wooding, N. S., 526

Woods, R. J., 347
Wright, F. J., 125
Wright, W. V., 515
Wrigley, H. E., 225
Wu, T. Y., 107
Wunsch, A., 234
Wynne-Jones, K. M. A., 513
Wynne-Jones, W. F. K., 68, 72, 89, 206, 229, 467

Xhrouet, E., 108

Yamamoto, T., 108
Yamazaki, I., 44
Yasumori, I., 101
Yates, K., 514, 515
Yip, C. W., 441
Yokota, M., 108
Yost, D. M., 125
Young, C., 102, 106

Zeldowitch, J., 265
Ziegler, K., 527
Zucker, L., 296, 471
Zuffanti, S., 453
Zur Strassen, H., 279
Zwolinski, B. J., 110

Subject Index

Absolute-rate theory, 72–85
  comparison with collision theory, 85–87, 125
  gas reactions, 85–87, 121–124
  solution reactions, 206–207
  surface reactions, 286–293
  thermodynamical formulation, 88–90
  unimolecular reactions, 165
Abstraction reactions, 125–135
Accelerated flow method, 41
Acetal hydrolysis, 504–506
Acetaldehyde decomposition, 16, 408–410, 484
  hydration, 512–514
  on surfaces, 276
Acetic acid, reaction with ethanol, 2
Acetone halogenation, 455–456, 514–517
Acetylcholinesterase, 502–503
Acid-base catalysis, 450–474
  and acid-base strength, 463–466
  general, 453–457
  mechanisms of, 457–463
  salt effects, 466–468
Acidity functions, 468–474, 501, 506
Actinometry, 37–38
Activated adsorption, 258
Activated complex, 52, 56, 72, 74
Activation energy, 53–63
  calculation of, 60–63, 99–102, 130–135, 369
  of surface reactions, 269–271
Activation entropy, 68, 89, 501, 506
Activation of hydrogen, 449
Active centers, 259
Activity coefficients, 208
Acyl chlorides, alcoholysis of, 244
Added gases, influence on reactions, 170–172, 393
Adsorption, 257–265
  absolute rates, 287–290
  activated, 258
  active centers for, 259
  chemisorption, 257–265, 310–312
  competitive, 262–263
  with dissociation, 260–262
Adsorption, ideal, 260–264
  isotherm, 259–265
  nonideal, 264–265
  statistical treatment, 263–264
Alcohol decompositions, 444–445
Aldol condensation, 518–520
Alkali metals, reaction, with chlorine, 380–384
    with halides, 136–137, 384–385
Alkyl halides, hydrolysis of, 245, 492–493
Alkyl iodides, reactions with amines, 33, 65, 203, 209, 242
Amide hydrolysis, 233, 506–509
Amines, benzoylation of, 203–204
  reactions with iodides, 33, 65, 203, 209, 242
Ammonia decomposition, homogeneous, 297
  on surfaces, 271–272, 293, 297
Ammonia-deuterium exchange, 275, 282–283
Analysis of kinetic results, 1–30
Aromatic nitration, 473
Aromatic substitution, 520–522
Arrhenius complex, 438
Arrhenius law, 50–54
Atom combinations, 175–191
  on surfaces, 284–285
Atom-molecule complex mechanism, 187–191
Atoms, detection and estimation, 330–337
  production, 285–286, 337–354
  reactions, 126–135
Autocatalysis, 9, 17
Autoxidation, 415–424
Azomethane, decomposition of, 170–171

Basin at activated state, 63, 101
Benzoquinone, addition to cyclopentadiene, 204
Benzoylation of amines, 203–204
Bimolecular reactions on surfaces, 274–283, 293–296
Bjerrum ion pairs, 222

Bond-energy–bond-order method, 101
Branching chains, 415–417
  degenerate, 421
Bromine-ethylene reaction, 43
Bromine-hydrogen reaction, 325–326, 328–329, 356–360
Bromine-methane reaction, photochemical, 413–415
Bromoacetate-thiosulfate reaction, 214–215
Brønsted-Bjerrum equation, 219–220
Brønsted relationships, 464–466
Butane decomposition, 406–407
But-2-ene, isomerization of, 164–165

Cage effect, 202, 354
Carbon monoxide–oxygen reaction on surfaces, 276, 295
Catalysis, 435–485
  acid-base, 450–474
  activation energies, 442–443
  in chain reactions, 483–485
  enzyme, 215–216, 474–483, 501–504
  homogeneous, 434–485
  in non-chain gas reactions, 443–446
  of polymerization, 428–429, 523–527
  surface, 36–37, 256–316
Chain reactions, 325–329, 356–432
  catalysis in, 483–485
Chaperon, 187
Chemiluminescence, 135–136
Chemisorption, 257–265
  electronic theories, 304–312
Chlorine, reaction, with alkali metals, 380–384
    with hydrogen, 360–370
    with nitric oxide, 138, 321–322, 445–446
N-Chloroacetanilide, conversion into *p*-chloroacetanilide, 6
Cis-trans isomerizations, 164–165
Collision number, 63, 65
Collision theory, 63–68, 118, 201–202
  comparison with absolute-rate theory, 85–87, 125
Combination of atoms and radicals, 175–191
Combination-disproportionation ratios, 190–191
Compensation effect, 251–253
Competition methods, 44
Complex reactions, 321–355
  in gas phase, 356–432
  rate equations, 322–325
  (*See also* Chain reactions)
Condensation reactions, 195
Consecutive reactions, 322–325
Coulombic energy, 56–57, 60–62
Critical coordinate, 83, 154
Cyclobutane dissociation, 171
Cyclopentadiene, addition to benzoquinone, 204
  dimerization of, 124, 199–200, 203
Cyclopropane, formation of, 174
  isomerization of, 143, 159–163, 171

d character, 308
Decomposition, 386–413
Degenerate branching, 421
Degrees of freedom, 148, 188–190
Dehydrogenation, 303
Desorption, absolute rates, 290
Deuterium-ammonia exchange, 275, 282–283
Deuterium-ethylene exchange, 280–281
Deuterium-hydrogen exchange, 315
Deuterium-methane exchange, 275, 281–282
Dielectric-constant effect, 211–214, 225–228
Dielectric saturation, 222–224
Diethyl ether decomposition, 413
Differential method, 15–17
Diffusion, in solid state, 316–318
  in solution, 205–206
  to surfaces, 265
Diffusion-controlled reactions, 206, 317, 536
Dilatometry, 32–33
Dimethyl ether, decomposition of, 410–413
Dimethylanilines, reaction with methyl iodide, 242
Dinitrogen tetroxide decomposition, 46
Dipole moments, 246
Dipole reactions, 225–230
Diradical reactions, 174, 192–193
Discharge-tube methods, 352–354
Disorder zone, 225
Disproportionation of radicals, 174–191
Double-sphere model, 212

Einstein's law, 343–344
Electromeric effect, 239
Electron-spin resonance, 43–44
Electron-spin resonance spectroscopy, 334
Electron-transfer reactions, 224, 446–450, 529–534
Electronic theories, of chemisorption, 304–312
  of heterogenous catalysis, 304–316
  of reactivity, 238–241
Electronic transitions, 80
Electrostriction, 216–217
Elementary processes, mechanisms of, 49–114
Elementary reactions, 49, 115–195
Encounters, 202
Energization, 144, 147, 169
Energy of activation, 53–63
  calculation of, 60–63, 99–102, 130–135, 369
Energy flow, 153, 175
Energy transfer, 135–137, 170–172, 186–188
Entropy of activation, 68, 89, 501, 506
Enzyme catalysis, 215–216, 474–483, 501–504
  pH effects, 478–481
  temperature effects, 481–483
Epoxide hydrolysis, 509–510
Equilibrium, 70–72
  and rate, 68–69, 73–75
Ester hydrolysis, 233, 243, 493–503
Ethane, decomposition, 164, 168, 395, 400–406
  reaction, with hydrogen atoms, 129
    with methyl radicals, 129
Ethanol, dehydration, 302
  dehydrogenation, 302
  reaction with acetic acid, 2
Ether decomposition, 410–413
  hydrolysis, 510–511
Ethyl iodide, reaction, with pyridine, 242
    with triethylamine, 203
Ethyl radical decomposition, 401–404
Ethylene-deuterium exchange, 280–281
Ethylene, hydrogenation, 274, 276–277, 278–281
  reaction, with bromine, 43
    with methylene, 174
Exchange energy, 57
Experimental methods, 31–48
Explosion limits, 417–421

Fast reactions, 39–47
Flames, 381
  cool, 421–422
Flash photolysis, 47
Flow systems, 21–24, 38–43
Fluorine monoxide decomposition, 170–171
Foreign-gas effect, 170–172, 393
Formic acid decomposition on surfaces, 273–274
Franck-Rabinowitch effect, 354
Free radicals, 330–354
  combination of, 175–191
  decomposition, 175
  detection and estimation of, 330–337
  production of, 285–286, 337–354
  in solution, 354–355
Frequency factor, 53, 87–88, 125, 211, 214–217, 228–229
  abnormal, 165–170

G value, 352
Gas-phase reactions, complex, 356–432
  elementary, 115–197
Gas reactions, 33–38, 356–432
General acid-base catalysis, 453–457
Graphical methods, 11–13
Guggenheim's method, 14–15

Half-life, 12–14
Halides, hydrolysis, 245, 492–493
  reaction with alkali metals, 136–137, 384–385
Halogen-atom combinations, 184–186
Halogenation of acetone, 455–456, 514–517
Halogens, reaction, with alkali metals, 135, 380–384
    with nitric oxide, 138–143
Hammett relationship, 246–249
Hammett-Zucker hypothesis, 471, 506, 512
Heat of activation, 89
  (*See also* Activation energy)
Heterogeneity of surfaces, 299–304
Heterogeneous reactions, 36–37, 256–316
  comparison with homogeneous reactions, 296–299
  (*See also* Surface reactions)
HO_2, 420, 422, 423
Holes in *d* band, 308–309
Hot molecules, 173–175

Hydration shell, 224
Hydride ion transfer, 194–195
Hydrocarbon oxidation, 421–424
Hydrogen atoms, production of, 352–353
  reaction, with chlorine, 135–136, 367
    with ethane, 129
    with hydrogen molecules, 55–60, 93, 129, 130, 352–353
    with methane, 129
Hydrogen-bromine reaction, 325–326, 328–329, 356–360
Hydrogen-chlorine reaction, 360–370
Hydrogen-ethylene reaction, 274, 276–281
Hydrogen-iodide decomposition, 116–119
  on gold, 293, 297
  on platinum, 292–297
Hydrogen–iodine-monochloride reaction, 322
Hydrogen-iodine reaction, 119–124
Hydrogen-ion catalysis, specific, 461
Hydrogen molecules, activation of, 449
  reaction, with deuterium molecules, 315
    with hydrogen atoms, 55–60, 93, 129, 130, 352–353
    with methyl radicals, 93, 129, 131
Hydrogen–nitric-oxide reaction, 138, 321–322, 446–447
Hydrogen–nitrous-oxide reaction, 277
Hydrogen-oxygen reaction, 417, 419–421
  on surfaces, 276, 278
Hydrogen peroxide, decomposition of, 1, 163–164, 435, 436
Hydrolysis, of acetals, 504–506
  of amides, 233, 506–509
  of epoxides, 509–510
  of esters, 233, 243, 493–503
  of ethers, 510–511
  of halides, 245, 492–493
  of lactones, 511–512
γ-Hydroxybutyric acid, conversion into lactone, 20–21
Hydroxyl radicals in solution, 355

Induction period, 324
Inductive effect, 239
Inductomeric effect, 240
Inert-gas effect, 170–172, 343
Inhibition, 17
  by nitric oxide, 393–396, 404–405, 410, 412
  of surface reactions, 268–269
Initial rates, 15–16
Initiation, of oxidation, 415–424
  of polymerization, 427–429, 523–527
Integration of rate equations, 5–15
Interatomic distance in surface catalysis, 302–304
Interconversion of energy, 135–137, 170–172, 186–187
Internal pressure, 207–209
Internal rotation, 73
Iodides, reaction with amines, 33, 65, 203, 209, 242
Iodine-acetone reaction, 455–456, 514–517
Iodine-atom combination, 182–184
Iodine-hydrogen reaction, 119–124
Iodine-monochloride–hydrogen reaction, 322
Ion decompositions, 173
Ion-dipole reactions, 225–230
Ion pairs, 222
Ion yields, 348, 352
Ionic reactions, 192–195, 210–230
Ionic recombinations, 535–537
Ionic-strength effect, 219–222, 229–230
Isolation method, 17–18
Isomerization, cis-trans, 164–165
  of cyclopropane, 143, 159–163, 171
Isotope effects, 90–98, 130, 131, 494–495

Kinematics, 102–107
Kinetic isotope effects, 90–98
Kinetic results, analysis of, 1–30
Kinetic spectroscopy, 47
Kinetic theory of collisions, 63–68

Lactone hydrolysis, 511–512
Langmuir-Hinshelwood mechanism, 266, 274–276, 280–283
Langmuir isotherm, 260–262
Langmuir-Rideal mechanism, 261, 266, 276–280
Life, mean, of radicals, 178–186
Lindemann theory, 144–147
Linear free-energy relationships, 246–249
London equation, 55, 61

Manometric methods, 33–34
Mass spectrometry, 35, 47, 335
Measurement of reaction rates, 31–48

Mechanisms of elementary processes, 49–114
Menschutkin reaction, 33, 65, 203, 209, 242
Mesomeric effect, 240
Methane, decomposition, 396–400
photobromination of, 413–415
reaction with hydrogen atoms, 129
Methane-deuterium exchange, 275, 281–282
oxidation, 422–423
Methyl iodide, reaction with amines, 33, 65, 203, 209, 242
Methyl radicals, reaction, with ethane, 129
with hydrogen, 93, 129, 131
recombination, 184
Methylene radical, 173–174, 192–193
reaction with ethylene, 174
Michaelis-Menten law, 440, 475–478
Microscopic reversibility, 110–112, 329–330
Mirror-removal method, 332–334
M/N (ionic yield), 352
Molecular beams, 47–48, 136–137
Molecularity, 5, 50, 267
Multiplet hypothesis, 302

Nitramide decomposition, 465–466
Nitration, aromatic, 473
Nitric oxide, catalysis by, 484–485
inhibition by, 393–396, 404–405, 410, 412
reaction, with bromine, 138–139, 143
with chlorine, 142–143
with hydrogen, 138, 321–322, 446–447
with oxygen, 138, 141–142, 274, 294
Nitrogen pentoxide decomposition, 199–200, 372–377
Nitrous oxide decomposition, 170–171
on surfaces, 292, 297, 314–315
Nitrous oxide–hydrogen reaction, 277
Nonuniform surfaces, 299–302
Normal modes, 155–159
Nucleophilic substitution, 489–493
Numerical methods, 538–540

Opposing reactions, 19–21
Order of reaction, 4–5
determination of, 5–18

Ortho-para hydrogen conversion, 380
on surfaces, 283–284, 297
Overlap integral, 61, 62
Oxalic acid reaction with potassium permanganate, 2
Oxidation, 415–424
of carbon monoxide, 276, 295
of hydrocarbons, 421–424
of hydrogen, 276, 278, 417, 419–421
of methane, 422–423
of nitric oxide, 138, 141–142, 274, 294
Oxygen atoms, reaction with ozone, 136
Ozone decomposition, 163, 377–380
catalyzed by chlorine, 483–484

Parabolic law, 318
Paraffins, decomposition of, 396–408
Para-ortho hydrogen conversion, 380
on surfaces, 283–284, 297
Partition functions, 70–73
Permanganate, potassium, reaction with oxalic acid, 2
pH effects, 478–481
Phosgene, formation and decomposition of, 370–372
Phosphine decomposition on surfaces, 272, 292
Photobromination of methane, 413–415
Photochemical reactions, 37–38, 339–346
Photolysis, 339–344, 398, 405, 407
Photosensitization, 344–346, 398–399, 406
Pilot reaction, 128
Plug flow, 22–24
Poisoning, 159–162
Polar effect, 239
Polar substituent constant, 250–251
Polyesterification, 345–349
Polymerization, 424–432, 522–529
addition, 424
anionic, 526–527
catalysis of, 428–429, 523–527
cationic, 523–526
condensation, 345
emulsion, 527–529
free-radical, 426–429
initiation of, 427–429, 523–527
ionic, 523–527
molecular, 424–426
Potential-energy profiles, 134, 270
Potential-energy surfaces, 54–60, 99–107, 169

Powell's method, 12–13
Predissociation, 342
Pressure, influence on rates, 231–238, 501, 506, 572
  internal, 207–209
Pressure jump method, 44
Pressure measurement, 33–34
Primary recombination, 202
Probability factor, 65
Protolytic reactions, 458–463
Proton transfer, 194, 450–474, 535–537
Prototropy reactions, 458–463
Pyridine, reaction with iodides, 242
Pyrolysis, 386–413

Quantum-mechanical tunneling, 80–81, 130
Quantum yields, 344
Quaternary ammonium salts, formation of, 33, 65, 203, 209, 242

Radical combination, 175, 191
  on surfaces, 284–285
Radical-molecule complex mechanism, 187–190
Radicals in reaction systems, 330–354
  addition to double bonds, 191–192
  detection and estimation of, 330–337
  disproportionation, 174–191
  production of, 285–286, 337–351
  reactions of, 126–135
Radiolysis, 346–352, 399–400
Random walk, 109
Rate of energization, 144, 147, 169
Rate of reaction, collision theory of, 63–68, 118, 201–202
  definition of, 4
  initial, 15–16
  measurement of, 3–28
  statistical theory of, 72–85
Rate constant, definition of, 5
  determination of, 538–540
Reaction constants, 247, 249
Reaction coordinate, 81–84
Reaction mechanisms in solution, 488–534
Reaction rates, measurement of, 31–48
Reaction vessel, 35–36
Reactions, complex, 321–355
  gas-phase, complex, 356–432
    elementary, 115–197
Reactions, in solid state, 316–318
  in solution, 31–33, 198–253
    complex, 488–529
    entropy of activation of, 215–216, 501, 506
    frequency factor of, 215–216
    substituent effects, 238–253, 496, 500–501, 505–506
  on surfaces (*see* Surface reactions)
Recombination, primary, 202, 354
  secondary, 202
Relaxation methods, 44–48
Relaxation theory, 24–28
Relaxation time, 24–28
Resonance (exchange) energy, 57
Rice-Herzfeld mechanisms, 386–390

Saturation current, 347
Secondary recombination, 202
Sector method, 178–183, 431
Semiempirical method, 62
Sensitizers, 338
Shock tubes, 45–46, 165, 423–424
Single-sphere complex, 217–219
Slow reactions, 202, 235
Sodium, reaction of, with chlorine, 380–384
    with inorganic halides, 384–385
Solid-state reactions, 316–318
Solvation, influence on rates, 209–210
Solvent influence, 198–210
  reorganization, 532–533
Specific hydrogen-ion catalysis, 461
Spectrophotometry, 43
Spectroscopy, 331–332
  electron-spin resonance, 334
Spin conservation, 166–167, 374
Starch hydrolysis, 1
Static method, 33
Statistical factors, 84–85
Statistical mechanics, 70–72
  non-equilibrium, 107–108
Statistical theory of mass spectra, 173
Statistical theory of rates (*see* Absolute-rate theory)
Steady-state treatment, 145, 327–329
  in catalysis, 441–442
Steric factor, 65
Steric hindrance, 249
Sticky collisions, 139
Stirred-flow reactor, 24
Stochastic methods, 108–110

Stoichiometry, 4, 78
Stopped-flow method, 41–43
Styrene polymerization, 428, 430, 524
Substituent effects, 238–253, 496, 500–501, 505–506
  constants, 247
  and dipole moments, 246
  on energy of activation, 241–246
Substitution, nucleophilic, 489–493
Successive reactions, 322–325
Sucrose inversion, 1
Sulfur dioxide decomposition, 167
Surface heterogeneity, 299–304
Surface reactions, 36–37, 256–316
  absolute rates of, 286–293
  activation energy of, 269–271
  bimolecular, 274–283
  inhibition, 268–269
  mechanisms of, 265–286
  molecularity, 267
  on nonuniform surfaces, 299–304
  poisoning, 268–269
  unimolecular, 267–274
Symmetry, 71, 84–85

Taft equation, 249–251
Temperature jump method, 44
Termolecular reactions, 137–143
Thermodynamical formulation of rates, 88–90
Thiosulfate-bromoacetate reaction, 214–215
Third body, 80
Third-order reactions, 137–143
Titrations, gas-phase, 336
Transfer of energy, 135–137, 170–172, 186–188
Transition state, 52
Transmission coefficient, 79–80, 167
Trapping of free radicals, 337
Triarylmethyl chlorides, alcoholysis, 244
Triethylamine, reaction with iodides, 33, 203, 209, 242
Trimolecular reactions, 137–143
Trinitrobenzoic acid decomposition, 205
True order, 16
Tunneling, 80–81

Unimolecular reactions, 143–175
  on surfaces, 267–274, 290–293

van der Waals adsorption, 257
van't Hoff complex, 438
Variability of surfaces, 299–304
Vinyl acetate polymerization, 426
Volume of activation, 232–237, 501, 506, 512

Walden inversion, 491
Wood-Bonhoeffer method, 352–353

Zero-order kinetics, 7, 268, 271, 272
Zero-point levels, 91